The Key
To Modern Freemasonry

The Hidden Mysteries of
Nature and Science

Professor Charles C. Lawrence

First published in Great Britain in 2011

Copyright © 2011

Charles C. Lawrence

The right of Charles C. Lawrence to be identified as the author of this work has been asserted in accordance with sections 77 and 78 of the Copyright Designs and Patents Act 1988.

ISBN 978-0-9550352-6-5

Publishing,
Typesetting & design by
Hamilton House Publishing Ltd.

Rochester Upon Medway,
Kent.

Printed by
Graficas Cems, S.L.,
31132 Villatuerta (Navarra), Spain

Distributed by

www.lewismasonic.com

Riverdene Business Park,
Molesey Road, Hersham,
Surrey, KT12 4RG

This work is respectfully dedicated to:

The Most Worshipful, The Past Pro Grand Master,
of the
United Grand Lodge of England

The Most Honourable,
The Marquess of Northampton, *DL*

foreword

One of the pleasures of my almost forty years of involvement in Masonic research has been to meet with those who come not from a humanities background but from the sciences or technology and have a profound love for Freemasonry and Masonic research. They bring to their research the discipline and analytical mind set of their particular field combined with enormous curiosity unencumbered by formal historical training, which often leads to them giving us new insights and a different view of what are often regarded as incontrovertible truths.

I have had many fascinating conversations with Charles Lawrence during his research for this book. The early days of organised Freemasonry have been neglected for too long, largely because there is not a huge store of documents to be poured over and analysed. What Charles has done is to look at the social, political, scientific, intellectual and religious background of the period in which we believe Freemasonry was originating and developing combined with the personalities whom we know to have been involved in the early Grand Lodge days and the major figures who formed part of their circles to see what impact they had on the development of our 'gentle craft'.

We are speculative Masons and it is right that we should speculate about how and why modern Freemasonry developed. The reader will find herein a wealth of factual information together with a new and fascinating theory which deserves to be published and discussed.

John M. Hamill, *BA, ALA,*
June 2011

V

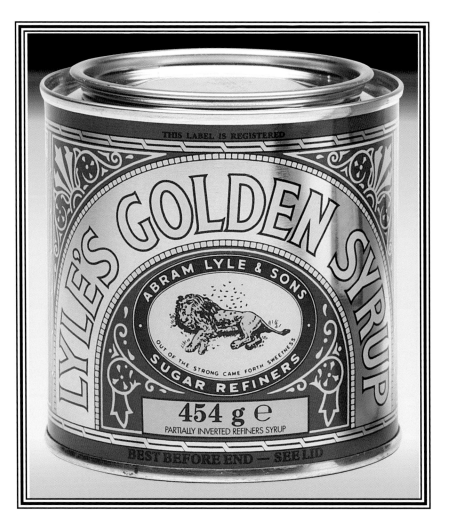

' ... Out of the Strong Came Forth Sweetness ...'

See Preface, p. xiii

The Logo on the previous page is reproduced by kind permission of Tate and Lyle Ltd.
It, as with all other such illustrative items within this work, does not imply any specific associations with the
contents or sentiments of the book itself.

Contents:

Part I
The fundamental basis of the Masonic (symbolical) science of the early 1700s with due reference to modern concepts

Abstract: This section of the work gives an insight into the level of understanding of science and technology that could have been reasonably expected of an educated man in the early 1720s; but in particular, because of their antecedents, those people known to be in an influential position within the Premier Grand Lodge at that time. At first the level is likely to appear somewhat naïve, amounting to little more than that found in schoolroom science, but on closer inspection it is realised that their grasp of the available knowledge was most profound and rounded; especially so when coupled with their remarkable understanding of geometry and mathematics, which was quite exceptional even by present day standards and certainly not that found in a modern schoolroom. The manifestations of Nature and the manner in which science could be integrated within it were central to them and their writings clearly show that it afforded them a cohesive view of the physical world and its relationship with spiritual truth. They felt that they were in a time when all was being revealed, making it possible for them to see how Nature and science were intimately related to their whole corporeal and mental faculties and in very great measure offered an explanation of their very existence and prospect of futurity.

At that time there were effectively no specialisms or implied barriers and most of those of interest here could boast a comprehensive understanding of the basic principles of all contemporary science, although even at that early stage some had clearly definable specialist interests. These basic science areas, as they would now be regarded, are considered in much the same order as they appear in the Symbolical Lecture of the Royal Arch; which by happy coincidence considers architecture first and as such is particularly appropriate given its symbolic importance to Freemasonry. It is also appropriate in that it shows clearly the contemporary move toward analysis and physical demonstration (within the public domain), rather than being dependent upon a system of knowledge transfer that was predicated upon the reclusive transfer of expertise.

Part II

The case for claiming that the ethos of early Premier Grand Lodge was influenced by predominance of Nature and Science expressed within a humanitarian context and a description of an analytical approach that demonstrates such an assertion?

Abstract: Throughout this study it is claimed that there is strong evidence to support an argument that the essential precepts of Freemasonry have remained unchanged from those enshrined in the early 1700s and to identify those individuals within the emerging Premier Grand Lodge who were responsible for it. That Premier Grand Lodge was merely one further example of the numerous clubs and societies being founded at time, but with the crucial distinction that its potential affiliates were already members of long established local societies; all of which subscribed to a basic, but highly sophisticated, ethos.

As with all the other similar enterprises at that time they had a nucleus of zealous people and as with most things related to human behaviour they were

Contents

inclined to fashion their new initiative after their own image, like interests, social disposition and association; which in the case of those with whom we are interested almost amounted to an obsession with matters scientific. Whilst a few may not have been quite so passionate there is no doubt that most of this highly influential group were heavily bound up with this emerging science and technology, with several deriving the bulk of their livelihood from it and it is therefore not surprising that it features largely in the ritual. The rate of scientific discovery during this period was astounding with each claimed as an irrefutable truth, only to then be quickly replaced by another set of equal authority. These pundits were not slow to put their thoughts on the veracity of such claims into the public domain and so it is possible from their writings, lectures and similar initiatives to obtain a clear record of contemporary thought and their particular stance within it.

Nonetheless they were in a highly political environment which obliged them to exercise some discretion which required them to perform a balancing act between the accepted religious teaching of the period and what might appear an ungodly mechanistic interpretation of some of the physical aspects of nature being promoted. Their public disposition and perceived position on these matters with respect to their feedstock (principally the existing freemasons' lodges) societies was of necessity tempered. In consequence the ritual adopted was somewhat anomalous and cautionary and what in essence was a mixture of mechanistic science and an interpretation of Newtonian/Aristotelian philosophy which ultimately accepted that all systems had their true being and origin in God's divinity and thereby acceptable to the established church. It is clearly much easier to claim such a relationship pertained than to demonstrate it, however it will be shown that by employing a technique which overlays all these otherwise disparate factors it is possible to progressively construct a model that leads to a solid basis for arriving at such an interpretation.

Part III

Influential figures well placed to have a marked effect on the evolution of the Premier Grand Lodge.

Abstract: Archival evidence clearly shows who occupied the senior offices in those formative years and there is considerable incidental evidence that indicates that there were others who were eminently capable and sufficiently well placed to also have a marked influence on the protocols and ethos of the fledgling Premier Grand Lodge. It will become clear later that it is somewhat artificial to consider these two groups as separate entities, but to avoid unnecessary complication in the first instance they will be discussed as being quite separate.

It is also evident that from the very start that whilst four men, seemingly of equal status, are recorded as 'the Founders' they were in practice far from equal, to an extent where two appear to have had little or no bearing on that which was to follow. It will be argued that one of the remaining pair is recorded throughout as occupying a range of ostensibly important positions, only to find on closer analysis, he appears to have remained passive and ineffectual; whilst the fourth was to have a massive impact and literally engineered the ultimate structure of what we would now recognise as formalised Freemasonry. This section is predicated on the proposition that formalised Freemasonry was in a state of flux until the pivotal election for Grand Master in 1723, but for completeness a brief outline of all those who occupied the important office of Grand Master and most of those who were otherwise likely to have exerted influence over the first crucial 24 years.

Contents

part IV

The lineage of the aristocratic families of the Grand Masters from 2nd Duke of Montagu, 1721, until 1st Viscount Dudley and Ward, 1742

Abstract: Given that appointment of the 2nd duke of Montagu marked the adoption of a (unwritten, but seemingly mandatory) policy that no person would be appointed to the post of Grand Master unless he could be numbered among the titled aristocracy it is of some importance to consider their lineage. This level of interest, because wherever possible, status is an important factor in the equation when trying to determine the nature and likely motivation of the people involved in the formation of the Premier Grand Lodge. In their case however, because of the complex interaction between many of them, it is of interest to study the manner in which these titles were inherited/ transferred and more particularly their comparatively modern ancestry with respect to the early 1700s. Further to observe the subtle, but surprisingly close, interrelationship between many, if not all of them, together with the other significant people who were serious players in the upper echelons of Premier Grand Lodge in those formative years.

Further it shows that in reality very few high ranking aristocracy were retained by Elizabeth I, certainly none above the rank of Baron survived (except in name only – which were later to be conferred on others not directly related). That most of the titles of interest derived from the explosion in the aristocracy followed from the ascension to the Throne of James I in 1603, thereby ensuring an extremely strong Scottish (Stuart) influence. The upheaval caused by the Civil War, under Cromwell's tolerant influence, had little impact on these families and many emerged much as they had begun and by one means or another quickly regained royal patronage. However, the greatest impact on many of those with whom we are concerned was the noble families created by the largess of Charles II towards his illegitimate offspring and these persons are interlaced in many ways with the early Grand Masters.

The associated Tables show how many of the titles afforded to these people in Masonic publications were conferred after they had already served as Grand Master and to some extent explain why, as comparatively minor aristocracy, they may have been very keen to accept the nomination of this high office.

Part V

Those factors of the sociological climate and contemporary issues that surrounded and impacted upon the instigation and subsequent structure of Premier Grand Lodge

Abstract: Good fortune with respect to the people involved and their wisdom with regard to contents, may have played a large part in the outstanding success of Formalised (Grand Lodge) Freemasonry, but that it came into existence at all was in great measure due to the favourable conditions within the social climate of the time.

The basic premise and motivation of this Part is the contention that peripheral (incidental) activities, such as Freemasonry, can only flourish if there is a buoyant economy, underpinned by general social, religious, political stability and a disposition towards any such trait. If in this instance this claim is to be substantiated then it is necessary to outline the nature of the society and the circumstances that brought it about.

When these favourable conditions prevail then it is usually accompanied by an expansion in extraneous social (leisure) activity, such as in this case: clubs, societies, coffee houses, taking tea, but of especially social interest during that period and hence of especially importance here was the public's pursuance of knowledge; notably in the form of public and private lectures and publications on scientific discovery. This was particularly sensitive then because of its potential contradiction with established religious thought, especially so with respect to the contemporary (ungodly deemed by some) upsurge of scientific/technological explanation of cause and effect. Because it is argued here that Newtonianism was of compelling (messianic belief in Newton) interest to certain of the Founders this aspect of the contemporary (thought) climate is given specific consideration.

Contents

Part VI

A consideration of the Liberal Arts and Sciences, the Hidden Mysteries of Nature and Science, their place in Freemasonry and the conclusions that may be drawn from this study

Abstract: In the preceding parts many of the facets that purport to justify or at least offer some explanation for their repeated inclusion throughout Masonic ritual were considered under discreet headings. This was deemed especially true of the above topics given the many injunctions for freemasons to study and understand them and demonstrated their importance to those who constructed the early ritual. However, the expedient of considering them as unique entities was somewhat artificial, since they are all interrelated and to correct that false impression they are here considered collectively. This is particularly true of the moral imperatives within the ritual, which the Founders considered were underpinned by the innate truths and certainties that they believed resided in Nature and science and their undoubted connection with the absolute perfection of the deity. The discussion here is to gain some further understanding of what those people believed to be the precise status of Nature and science at that time and its impact upon them.

Secondly the discussion is extended with respect to the many social factors that surrounded this new initiative and to consider the many aspects that made it so well placed to not only survive, but flourish.

Finally there is an attempt to arrive at some 'conclusions'. Whilst this work may appear to be extensive, in a work such as this it is still only a distillation of numerous aspects that should be considered more fully. The output of any person trying to research history can only be an interpretation of the facts as they see them and that in turn has usually entailed their interpretation of the interpretations of others. It is therefore hoped that these conclusions are as objective as the human disposition allows, namely that which one would intuitively expect within scientific analysis, but sadly this is rarely true of the pundits of science either and so *caveat emptor*!

Preface

Most books based upon a historical aspect of sociology open with a famous painting depicting the science, culture, architecture etc. of the period and perhaps that style should have been used here. However, because the general conclusion of this work paints a less than glamorous picture of the circumstances surrounding the individuals involved in the founding of Grand Lodge this esotericism has been replaced by a utilitarian picture that has for many years been depicted on and is now synonymous with, a tin of syrup. This choice was made because as a child it was difficult to see the physical connection of a sleeping lion with bees buzzing around it and the logo's caption of 'out of the strong came forth sweetness'. Neither is it particularly easy to understand how a society based upon the absolute epitome of humanitarian principles and that can boast tenets of the very highest integrity, could have evolved from such a strong and predatory group of individuals. Evolution could have taken it down a path of good or evil, but fortunately and despite misfortunes and the occasional presence of inevitable rouges of the type that bedevil all strands of society, it has taken the most laudable path possible, which perhaps explains its outstanding success. Why, all those years ago, Abraham Lyle chose Samson's riddle (forty-fifth Chapter of the Book of Judges) for his tins of syrup we will likely never know, but certainly out of those powerful men of the early 1720s has come forth sweetness.

General Introduction

t is estimated that throughout the World there are nearly five million men who are members of the mutually accepted 'regular' constitutions of Freemasonry. Within this Fraternity there is a passionate defence, indeed effective inviolability with respect to its basic precepts, its historic Ritual and associated protocols. This strict adherence has meant that apart from minor variations, all will have experienced intrinsically the same introduction into the Fraternity. They will have followed the same ceremonies and listened to the many thousands of words of which they are comprised. However, because of the ritual's archaic form and the fact that nowhere within it is there detailed explanation and that as a consequence, much of the meaning within these ceremonies will have escaped all but the most inquisitive. They will have been instructed to learn, to contemplate and to practice its basic precepts and to enrich their lives by a determined study of Nature and Science and indeed all avenues of learning. They will have been informed that by their own patience and industry they would, within the remit of Masonry, be rewarded with an understanding of 'the hidden mysteries' of life and by inference of futurity itself.

It was the comparatively modest objective of trying to understand the science alluded to in the Ritual that prompted this study. However, that investigation led to a greater understanding of much else and the need to address many of the unanswered questions surrounding the origins of modern Freemasonry.

Whilst the concept of Freemasonry has been the subject of much debate with respect to its antiquity, very few would dispute the contention that present day, 'regularly constituted', lodges conform to a model based upon a society, that first came to light in 1717, when certain influential (so described because they presumably had gained the backing of their respective lodges) brethren of four lodges, of the many held in the London area, formed that which is now generally known as the Premier Grand Lodge. Nonetheless, because of an innate aura, there are many freemasons who would argue intuitively and with equal force that; in essence, speculative Masonry dates from 'time immemorial'.

However, this study will show that Modern Freemasonry is a particular derivative of that 1717 initiative and that all allusion to such antiquity is essentially contrived. It will be shown that modern Freemasonry is the product of a quite modest notion: that the senior members of four, otherwise autonomous, London based lodges should meet on a quarterly basis to discuss matters of mutual benefit. Further that these lodges were typical of lodges that were the legacy of changes that had occurred over the preceding 200 years; namely the metamorphosis of the erstwhile powerful groups of operative masons' lodges into small social gatherings of the most influential members of a particular community. They had, by that time, assumed the mantle of 'speculative' freemasons, as opposed to 'operative' masons, but even as today, had managed to retain the perception within the public at large and indeed most freemasons, that there remained a strong link between the two. Further that the powerful social status that had derived from the exquisite skills and restrictive practices of the 'operative' masons had been replaced in terms of social eminence by the rank, fortune and declared altruism of its now 'speculative' counterpart.

Records of these early events are poor and how the process occurred has, for many years, been and still remains the subject of much speculation. Nonetheless it is generally accepted that these men were from an extremely influential sector of society. This amalgamation of lodges came about at a time when virtually everything that affects society and indeed the world was changing (expanding) at an incredible pace. It is not surprising therefore, that these men of influence, who were at the very centre of events, exported this aspect of their lifestyles and social patterns to Mainland Europe and more distant shores, especially the British Colonies; of which perhaps America was most significant.

In a study such as this there is a need to refer directly to matters contained in the ritual and/or constitution and so a reference model is required. Partly for historical reasons, but mainly for convenience the model chosen here is the content and phraseology of English ritual. However, there are sections where there will be a need to refer to other rituals and constitutions.

After a very modest beginning this formalised derivative of Freemasonry rapidly became a very powerful element in the upper echelons of society and it was natural that similarly influential groups, similar to those in London, would seek either to emulate it or become affiliated. Of course there were then and still remain, differences in detail within the respective constitutions, but the essential ingredients of those ceremonies has survived the geographical distances, differences in cultures and ravages of time. Indeed, to the connoisseur, ceremonies outside of the English Constitution, such as those practised in the United States and Commonwealth countries have in many instances remained more faithful to (what one might intuitively believe to be) the original forms and irrespective of constitution all rituals make constant reference to Nature and Science. Thus there is a tacit assumption that this attempt to explore the Founders' conception of 'Nature' and particularly the underlying 'Science' and its influence on the Ritual they adopted as a consequence of that understanding, will in principle be of interest to most freemasons 'where'er dispersed'.

The author's first awareness and subsequent interest in this whole subject of the 'Nature and Science' of Freemasonry occurred shortly after joining a Royal Arch Chapter, at which a visiting Provincial Grand Principal felt disposed to chastise the Chapter on a dreadful misdemeanour. The severity of the rebuke was as surprising as it was unwelcome, but was evidently consistent with his compulsion to criticize something. The target on this occasion was the placement of the Principals' Chairs, claiming that their arrangement was not 'that (the curved form) of the true Catenarian Arch' and that the Chapter should consider itself severely admonished for such an outrage. Whilst his comments contributed little towards the conviviality of the evening, they did stimulate the need to consider more closely that element of the Symbolical Lecture. Note that unless stated otherwise the term 'Symbolical Lecture' refers throughout, to the intrinsic ritual contained in: *The Ceremonies of the Holy Royal Arch* (hereafter referred to as 'Royal Arch') published in *c*.1845 – *see* Chapter Thirty-four and not the recent emaciated, now recommended, alternative version found in the English Constitution. As will become apparent he awakened interest because, his criticisms were not only harsh, but in a strictly scientific (mathematical) sense incorrect, if the accepted understanding of that architectural form was intended. However he had, albeit inadvertently, fulfilled the injunction laid upon all Masons to make 'a daily advancement in Masonic knowledge'. Furthermore, by delivering it in this unfriendly manner, he had also accomplished another of his duties, namely; to encourage that activity in another, which resulted in this particular piece of work.

The subsequent research, like most that has started from enquiry into a particular subject area, revealed as the data was gathered, evidence that further research might provide an answer to other, hitherto intractable, questions. As stated above, the original interest was simply to understand in greater detail what the Founders of modern speculative Freemasonry had intended by their admonition to all new candidates to study 'the hidden mysteries of Nature and Science'. This phrase, in one guise or another, is found throughout the present day ritual and it seemed worthy of further effort to understand the Founders' likely interpretation of that phrase and to contrast that with our own, more modern, concepts of these same phenomena.

It transpired however that there was a much deeper reason for such enquiry, because if one pursues this train of thought through to the *raison d'être* of Masonry one is struck by its complex, effectively layered, structure; which ranges from the somewhat superficial to the most profound. Thus at one end are the allegorical 'stories' woven into a colourful, highly formalised ceremony, whilst at the other end a freemason is required to take an oath that obliges him to unreservedly comply with what may be described as a determined commitment to a higher spiritual power, the ultimate in humanitarian behaviour, total compliance within the society he resides, towards his fellows creatures and disciplined self improvement through education. Whilst a competent knowledge of the wording and enactment of the perfunctory elements of the ceremonial is of considerable importance to the wellbeing of a lodge or chapter, it would be extreme to consider them imperative, whereas, to the freemason at least, the level of moral obligations and social commitment he has undertaken is of the utmost importance. At first sight the requirement to study the Liberal Arts and Science appears to fall between these two extremes until one considers more deeply the significance that this aspect of learning has played and indeed continues to play, when attempting to rationalise his conception of the higher power upon which he based his solemn commitment and appears to account for his very existence. Until this alleged importance is discussed within the general text, the assumption is made that the injunction placed upon these early freemasons to study Nature and Science was then accepted as an essential prerequisite to an understanding of the depth of their own faith and hence commitment within Freemasonry and as such it was incumbent upon them to make a determined effort. It is hoped that this rudimentary study of Nature and its associated science is nonetheless sufficiently robust to shed light on the Founders' understanding, its likely place in their thinking and be of assistance when attempting to rationalise their intentions and reconcile that with the importance of the obligations taken within Masonry both then and now.

The realisation of the profound importance of Nature and Science to Freemasonry led to a whole series of secondary considerations; such as why the Founders would have adopted this particular set of concepts and laid quite so much emphasis on science. More especially, based on the presumption that there has always been an almost obsessive desire to avoid any change, together with other indirect evidence, suggests that the essential ingredients of present day rituals have been there from the very beginning. Working on the thesis that there has been little change in the fundamental aspects of the Ritual, it might well give a strong indication of when it was compiled. Similarly, given the uniqueness of its content and format, it may also identify other important facets, such as those by whom it was conceived. Almost immediately two things became clear; first that there are in effect no actual contemporary writings relating directly to the ceremonies which would verify without doubt the content of the Ritual. Second, the very little Masonic (direct) evidence available was found to be comparatively superficial and for the most part very unreliable. This paucity of hard facts has had the same effect on most that has been written since. The unique set of contingencies that instigated the formation of Premier Grand Lodge form a closed loop and to study any particular aspect it is necessary to break open that loop, which gives rise to the question of where this is best begun. As will be explained in Chapter 1 it is for this reason that this work is divided into a number of parts. Because all rituals are insistent that Science is of great importance to Freemasons and given that it was the catalyst to this study, Part I seeks to inform the non-scientist and reawaken in the trained scientist to the importance of Nature and Science when 1) attempting to understand what the Founders believed to be the mysteries of life, or 2) their relationship to modern Freemasonry. Also why freemasons are exhorted to adhere to the original concepts (ancient landmarks) and thereby understand why it was necessary to inculcate Nature and Science into the very heart of Masonic philosophy.

Whilst enquiry of individuals has proved most helpful, it too is similarly limited and so the first part of this study is an attempt to understand the concepts, especially scientific, that the Founders most likely believed and hence wished to convey. However, unlike most previous attempts to study early Freemasonry the work is not confined to documents, artefacts etc. that are exclusively identified with Freemasonry, but rather to broaden the investigation to include such things as the social climate and prior history that led to the environment in which it was conceived and then flourished. To study the individual roles played by the Founders in their everyday activities outside of Freemasonry, within the wider community and especially their relationship to one another. Given the moral imperative for an understanding of and the repeated reference to the 'Liberal Arts and Sciences' throughout the ritual it will be shown that there is little doubt that the Founders considered them to be of considerable importance to their whole being. Nonetheless it will also become apparent that many of these contemporary concepts would have conflicted with their religious convictions and so what precisely they chose to believe and what they chose to 'reconcile' is far less certain. One of the main objectives of this work is to provide some explanation of this apparent paradox.

Again, where to begin is problematic since there is no direct evidence to suggest the exact level of understanding expected of a Freemason or precisely what he should seek to acquire. The English ritual chosen as the model for this study is particularly poor in this respect, since the first specific reference to actual scientific topics is not in Craft Freemasonry at all, but in the Symbolical Lecture of the Royal Arch. Other constitutions, such as the United States, Australia, Holland, and Belgium are somewhat better in that the Liberal Arts and Sciences are defined in greater depth in their versions of Craft ritual, whereas in Scotland for instance the Royal Arch is an integral part of Craft Freemasonry. Even so, none address the problem satisfactorily and so there is a need to correlate the level of scientific/ technological understanding, as portrayed in the various ritualistic schemes above, with (authoritative) concepts outside of Freemasonry and where these appear to show marked variation, to relate those concepts; by first defining the differences with respect to modern day understanding and from that rationalise their *raison d'être*. That procedure alone is reason for studying the subject in terms of science because much of the original scientific information of that period exists and is well documented and readily authenticated. In addition many of those characters central to this study were actively involved in that process and in a number of instances were the actual originators of those very documents.

Again within the context of English Freemasonry another potential difficulty was highlighted. In the process of preparing talks on the various aspects of the Science (essentially that found in the Symbolical Lecture) a difficulty arose, namely that because only a small percentage of freemasons are trained scientists or engineers an appropriate level of presentation had to be found. It was decided to prepare these presentations in a form that would be intelligible to the non-scientist whilst not overly offending the purist and fortunately this approach proved to be quite successful. It is with this wider audience in mind, that this same descriptive style is continued here; especially with respect to the science in Part I of this study. Whilst such an approach is certain to become a hostage to the level of 'absolute scientific rigour' that would be expected by present day specialists, it is nonetheless believed to be sufficiently consistent with current and generally accepted opinion to be valid. In any case, as will become apparent throughout, that disagreements over assumed 'facts', between so called experts were as common and as vehement during that period (early 1700s) as they are today. Whilst the science of early Freemasonry is important when attempting to understand the basic philosophy of its present counterpart it is hoped that the science discussed throughout this study will be of interest in its own right. Even so it is possible that despite the injunction to apply 'patience and industry' the scientific concepts may still prove to be sufficiently obscure to distract the non-scientific reader. In which case this should not be allowed to unduly affect the basic message or validity of the ultimate conclusion of the study, except that the scientific element will then have to be taken on trust and will still remain the subject of some 'future study'.

As stated already it is extremely difficult first to define and then understand what they actually believed, but it becomes even more difficult to answer the questions: why they did so, why in that particular form, by whom and perhaps most intriguing of all when? Clearly, to answer those questions would be most rewarding and in the process of doing so it would be likely to offer further evidence of how soon after, the formation of the original Premier Grand Lodge, Royal Arch Masonry was conceived. Freemasonry was then and remains today a ceremonially based activity and hence required a carefully structured form of ritual. Much of the continued success of Freemasonry from that time appears to have resulted from a seemingly innate sociological need for a 'cultured' person to be able to display a profound understanding of Nature, Science and Philosophy. In Part I 'Nature' is presumed to relate much more to the results of natural organic/mechanical demonstrable effects rather than being some manifestation of a God given 'created', otherwise unexplained, seemingly 'magic' or metaphysical world. The complex connotations attached to 'Nature', 'Science' and philosophy in the early 1700s and their profound effect on Premier Grand Lodge, are the *raison d'être* of the subsequent parts of this study. However, other important incidental factors emerge from this work, for instance: given that science was advancing at an incredible pace and it will be argued that the 'Science' that the Founders incorporated in the Ritual is a snapshot (frozen in time by their Masonic dictate) of the physical and natural world as they perceived it; namely the 'in vogue' version of Science which was widely accepted and likely studied if not taught in the upper echelons of academe, such as universities, academies, religious seats of learning etc in the 1720s. However, as will become apparent from Part II onwards, an equally intriguing parameter in terms of actual dating, is that their outwardly professed interpretation of 'Science' was not necessarily what they would have really believed, but to avoid complication this aspect will not be addressed in Part I.

Unfortunately, then just as now, it is difficult to know what a person acknowledges as 'truth', since it is a function of their fundamental religious and political beliefs, integrated with their worldly experiences to date, their intrinsic corporeal and mental faculties; all governed by their declared and/or inner social imperatives. However, unless that person is totally bigoted or dishonest, as the evidence accrues it forces them to accept certain physical realities, such that they would now have to accept that it is possible for a man to travel at hundreds of kilometres per hour, to fly through the air in a device or that electricity travels down a wire due to the passage of electrons, that the universe appears limitless etc. – even though at that time such concepts would have been seen by them as ludicrous or quite hostile to their current (primarily religious) beliefs. It is reasonable to suppose that those who founded Premier Grand Lodge, like most people when confronted with conflicting or disturbing implications on some contentious matter, are somehow able to readjust their thinking by mentally dismissing or conveniently rearranging some of the 'facts', thereby enabling them to sustain their intrinsic beliefs. Over the years of this study it has been necessary to conduct research in many places and look to the knowledge (or on rare occasions lack of it) of many people. However, the research has been heavily dependent on a process of iteration within and between the collective wisdom of historians, both inside, but particularly outside Freemasonry. Regrettably they are too many in number to mention in detail, but it is hoped that where direct reference has been made there are few omissions. There is a third category, such as W Bro John Hamill, erstwhile Librarian of the Grand Lodge of England, or Professor Simon Schaffer of the Historical (Scientific) Department of Cambridge University, whose knowledge is both profound and infectious. It is a humbling experience to interact with such people and/or read these learned treatises, since it is quickly realised that such work comes from many years of intense labour and profound interest. Indeed, in many cases, it requires detailed concentration by the listener/reader simply to understand the subtleties of their argument, such as, for instance, the complex sociological interactions of those times, quite apart from the task of then committing it to paper. Acknowledging the profundity of their work, the time and labour involved in any one of these topics and given the very wide remit of this study, it was clear that, after exercising due care, there was little option other than to interpolate between the writings of these widely respected authorities and to put those findings in context with the remit of this work.

Given that any study of the Freemasonry of those times is incredibly difficult because of the lack of, or conflicting, evidence the task becomes even more difficult when researching the Royal Arch, because there is in effect no evidence in written form or printed documentation whatsoever. Thus, whether or not the Science of the Symbolic Lecture is, as claimed in this study, a strong indicator of its time and surrounding circumstances and as a consequence indicates the 'Science' of Craft Freemasonry, must in the last resort be left for the reader to decide.

As this work progressed it became evident that the Science of the Symbolical Lecture could, because of the unique nature of its content, be compressed into a very tight time band, *circa* sometime in the 1720s. This because scientific concepts were changing at such a pace that if they had been incorporated in some Royal Arch Ritual later than this (say 1740 or later as suggested by most) they would have been subtly, but nonetheless significantly different – if included at all. It was decided to find out whether all the other factors, outside science and technology, were also consistent with this presumed dating. The progressive way in which these science topics and associated factors are dealt with in this study to a large degree reflects the way in which the research evolved.

Ritual is compiled and then performed by individuals and it will only last if there is a continued disposition to make it do so. The reasons for enacting ritual are many. Ceremonies such as 'Changing of the Guard', the Queen's Keys in the Tower of London, the 4th of July, Armistice, Rio de Janeiro and Easter Parades, some large, some local, such as, weddings, christenings, funerals etc., the list seems endless, but they all have the same social ingredient. In the case of Freemasonry, ceremony is the very cement that binds the structure and as such it assumes a very high profile in its activities. Whilst the reason for enacting these ceremonies may be dismissed in some simplistic way, the inner psychological reasons why each and every individual desires to take part is likely to be quite different, the trick is to make the appeal sufficiently broad and in one way or another ensure that it first attracts and then retains their participation.

When, as in this case, one is concerned with those who compiled the ritual in order to meet their own objectives and equally important to convince others to join them, the nature of the enquiry has to change. Such enquiry is obliged to speculate on who they were likely to have been and from that ask all the naturally occurring questions such as when, why, what, how etc. In the case of early-formalised Freemasonry the characters were of such note and the sociology both before and during that period so convoluted, that it becomes a most interesting and informative subject area. The subsequent parts of the work attempts to provide sufficient detail to answer many of the questions posed above and to indicate much of the social ramifications of the Premier Grand Lodge and in so doing to suggest why it took off in such spectacular fashion and a probable reason and date for the conception of the Royal Arch – namely a unifying ceremony created sometime in the early 1720s.

Acknowledgements

In a book such as this it is normal practice to include a list of acknowledgements and because of this there is a danger that its contents may be considered merely perfunctory rather than sincere. However, because this work is founded upon an integration of the knowledge/scholarship of so many others it is with sincere gratitude that I proffer thanks for their direct or indirect contribution.

From the beginning it has been necessary to make continuous references to the work and expertise of others and now it has reached the stage of publication I naturally wish to make a full acknowledgement of their place in the work and to convey my gratitude. The original study was begun some thirty years ago out of a personal interest in the subject without any view to publication and so much of the early interaction was acknowledged at the time, but unfortunately no complete record was kept of those involved. It would therefore be invidious of me to single out for special praise those of more recent acquaintance. There is some consolation in the fact that I have been able to recognise some of these contributions within the text. However I feel reasonably assured that I did thank those involved at the time and to any of those who may chance to read some part of this work, please accept my gratitude for any contribution they may have made towards it.

There is also that special category where one interacts on a personal basis such as librarians who because of their expertise are able to guide one to the appropriate text on the actual shelf saving hours of searching; especially those, who because of their depth of understanding are able to direct one to other likely text; it is difficult to express ones appreciation, especially when one chances on a gem in this way. There are those such as the Archivist of Westminster Abbey and Martin Fletcher of St Paul's who not only assist in an intellectual sense, but physically by demonstration of artefact and again that adds greatly to the way in which one perceives the subject. Of particular note within this group are those who are acknowledged experts in their field, such as John Hamill of The United Grand Lodge of England and Professor Simon Schaffer of the History Department of Cambridge University, who have been prepared to give whole chunks of their time interacting with me, which was/is a special experience. On virtually every one of the occasions cited above one comes away with a special lift, having gained a greater understanding, resolved a difficulty or recognised a need to reconsider some aspect of the work; one of course expresses one's thanks at the time, but it really goes much deeper than that.

It is proper that I should mention the *Quatuor Coronati* Lodge and its members for first approving this book and then supporting its publication and to mention certain individuals within it; in particular John Hamill, Jim Daniel, Bob Gilbert, Andy Durr, and former Lodge Secretary Peter Holland for his continued support throughout, together with their editor Peter Hamilton Currie – *see below*, however, QCCC Ltd., having been, for technical reasons, unable to undertake publication, have generously ceded all the publication rights and work they had commissioned on editing and indexing etc., in order that the book might be published with their implicit support.

Three people must be singled out: Peter Currie has to be unique in that he is not only a scholar of Freemasonry in his own right, but possesses many other talents, such as in music and a high level of competency within his chosen profession. However, not least amazing are his proof reading abilities, his use of the English language, recall of archival data and an exemplary knowledge of modern publishing methods. My thanks are due not only for the expert way in which he has conducted the work, but the delightful manner in which he has done so.

In similar vein Brent Morris is an internationally recognized Masonic scholar and mathematician as well as numbering amongst his other talents, the sleight-of-hand of an accomplished magician but in particular he is also a professional publisher and, as part of his extensive work for the *Quatuor Coronati* Lodge, he undertook the considerable task of indexing, for which, given his particular set of skills, he is peculiarly qualified. But again my thanks are not just for the sheer effort, but his friendship and support throughout this period.

Finally especial thanks must go to my wife Patricia and my daughters Sandra and Mary, who have supported and accepted the numerous hours I have taken in the research and writing, but also my wife's many hours reading through repeated drafts, checking for the inevitable errors and ensuring continuity.

The cover was evolved from the efforts of a team, but more especially Peter Currie, myself and my daughter Sandra, who also undertook the final graphics. In addition we have received help and images from many other sources and would therefore wish to acknowledge permissions from the following:

Max-Planck-Institut für Radioastronomie; The Library and Museum of Freemasonry, Freemasons' Hall, Great Queen Street, London; The National Park Service: Jefferson National Expansion Memorial, St Louis, MO, USA and The Royal Society for Newton's original telescope.

Caveat

Although I have tried extremely hard to remain objective and take a balanced view, because this study has lasted so long and ranges over so wide a field, not counting the numerous books and papers that I have omitted to read and the authorities that I have failed to consult, there are bound to be gaps or apparent ambiguities. For those I apologize and I accept full responsibility for them.

part I

An Explanation of the Masonic (Symbolical) Science of the Early 1700s with Reference to Modern Thought

Chapter One: Introduction

It is perhaps useful to reiterate that the reference model used here is that of the 'English' Constitution, but that its intrinsic content and sentiments are representative of those found in 'regular' Freemasonry throughout the World. On the very day that a candidate is initiated into Masonry he has impressed upon him the gravity of the obligation he has entered into, but further that an understanding of its true significance is only possible through education in its broadest terms. He is shortly informed that, symbolically: 'the (mason's) chisel points out to us the advantages of education, by which means alone we are rendered fit members of regularly organised society'. Education here implies an all-embracing acquisition of every aspect of learning and not the current widely held (sociological) belief that the 'arts' define culture, but that to profess an understanding of science is, in some way, Philistine and consequently infra dig. This unsympathetic perception of science must be considered as an essentially post-Second World War affectation, since, prior to this time, science was considered an absolutely essential component of any truly rounded and educated person. Indeed, in the United Kingdom a science-based subject was a compulsory part of the School Certificate of Education, which persisted even after the Second World War, until the examination system changed. It is quite clear that the Founders' views on the need for this necessary social attribute is unquestionable, since this, in its various guises is emphasised throughout the various degrees of the Ritual, for example:

'... to study more especially such of the liberal arts and sciences as may lie within the compass of your attainment and without neglecting the ordinary duties of your station to make a daily advancement in Masonic knowledge'.

'You are expected to make the liberal arts and sciences your future study ...'

'... to contemplate the intellectual faculty and trace it from its development, through the paths of heavenly science ...'.etc., etc.

However, despite these repeated references the first indication of what was actually implied by those who had quite deliberately introduced the term 'science'

1

into the English Ritual, is not found until the opening paragraphs of the 'Symbolical Lecture' in the Royal Arch. The 'Symbolical Lecture' is an interesting amalgam of what would now be considered an outmoded and for the most part inaccurate exposition of architectural, geometrical, physical factors such as light, colour, matter etc. and astronomical concepts. Only the final section of the Lecture returns to the symbolic morality, which otherwise dominates much of Craft ritual.

When this study was begun, so far as it was possible to ascertain, the Founders of modern Freemasonry appeared to have been influenced greatly by their close association with the Royal Society, aristocratic patronage and powerful social groups such as the 'Barber Surgeons' and this will be elaborated upon in Part II *et seq.* By the normal standards of those days they were exceedingly well-educated men, as for instance those freemasons considered by Clarke.[1, 2] The second important factor was that they were almost certainly of the view that it was possible for a man with sufficient zeal and perseverance to embrace virtually every aspect of what they deemed essential knowledge. Within that general concept it is reasonable to suppose that:

1) They believed that to profess knowledge of science was an essential element of the 'social graces',

2) The Nature and Science of Craft ritual and the Royal Arch as we know it today has remained essentially (in basic content at least) in the same form as that when Premier Grand Lodge was founded in the very early 1720s,

3) That the ritual was conceived by men who had received their basic education in the late 1600s or very early 1700s and there is little doubt they were strongly influenced by contemporary matters such as religion, philosophy, politics, commerce, the arts and sciences, etc., but by the 1720s they also were in a position to contribute to the dissemination of knowledge and were numbered amongst the most prominent members of that learned section of society.

4) That the acquisition of such knowledge would not have been easy, even for the privileged and effectively denied to those who were not so fortunate. This is not surprising given the social climate and the limited means of transportation and communication, coupled with the general standard of literacy and hence general availability of written knowledge. However, where such intellectual pursuits were found, they were pursued avidly. This was particularly true of the period from the middle of the 1600s leading up to, but especially during the time that Premier Grand Lodge was being formed. Often they took the form of organised lectures at the Royal

Introduction

Society; but they were also an important part of events in other public places such as in coffee houses, taverns and clubs. If the chroniclers are right they were immensely popular, with those attending paying substantial sums for the privilege. Scientific knowledge appeared also in written form, such as books, pamphlets etc.

5) They were living in times of confused and contradictory beliefs, such as alchemy and witchcraft (James's Acts pertaining to the persecution of witches were not finally repealed until 1736 and even then continued to operate in a clandestine way). Perceptions and attitudes in all aspects of life were changing at an alarming pace and it was difficult for a person to reconcile the different inflows of knowledge with some of their intrinsic and one may assume deeply held views, more particularly those likely to impinge on their fundamental religious convictions and/or social propriety.

6) Then, as now, much of the knowledge they received was very conflicting, depending on the source of the information, especially with respect to the scientific discoveries being propounded, the strength of the personalities involved and the extremes of the philosophical debate.

It therefore seems reasonable to start from the basis that they would have found some of these factors most disquieting, especially in terms of their intrinsic religious beliefs and early education. Conversely, these new concepts were most exciting and would have offered a challenge to the enquiring minds of those extremely intelligent people, who are known (one of the few verifiable facts) to have been instrumental in founding the Premier Grand Lodge.

The importance of science in the social perception of the 'educated man' during this time is perhaps best illustrated by the patronage, irrespective of background, given to those who were accepted to be highly versed in science by the otherwise 'influential' members of society. Indeed monarchs and nobility patronised talented individuals and commissioned entire projects (although sometimes this 'support' fell well short of generous) and took particular store and social acclaim through their association with these 'men of science'. Their reasons for offering such support were, in practice, rather more complex and could include: monetary gain, prestige by association, politics and, in a few cases, an actual and active interest in the subject. These reasons will be discussed in the subsequent Parts of this study. A noteworthy illustration of this interest can be found by their perception of likely commercial benefits and the virtual fortune on offer, both in the UK and abroad, for determining the precise longitude of a vessel at sea. Great commercial enterprises were being transacted, the dealings leading to the infamous South Sea Bubble being perhaps the most notable example. The favourable social persona attached to those considered to have a profound knowledge of science would help to explain why it was deemed to be an important requisite of all Masons.

Historically, this may be considered to have reached its peak in the depth of interest shown by the Victorians in all scientific discovery and technical inventions of the Industrial Revolution. Whilst this public enthusiasm for science and technology has now tapered off, it lasted up until just after the Second World War. However, since this period there has been a steady decline in the perceived importance of science in the school curriculum and it is now generally regarded in many circles as unbecoming to boast such knowledge, even to the extent of positively refuting it. Thus in order that one might understand the Founders' thinking it is necessary to repress any tendency towards this current cultural shift in society's opinion of what constitutes the 'educated man' and recognise the great importance of science to those who consolidated Craft Freemasonry and conceived the Royal Arch. In order to undertake this task it is necessary to explore the concepts of 'The Hidden Mysteries of Nature and Science'. It will be shown later that 'Nature and Science' can be and almost certainly was interpreted on several levels, but that considered in Part I is an explanation of the basic principles of 'Nature and Science' that were likely known by the rank and file freemason of that period.

It is perhaps worth restating that given the repeated exhortation within Masonic ritual for its members to constantly strive to broaden their understanding of matters scientific, it is quite surprising to find that, unlike many other constitutions, the first direct attempt to do so in the English ritual is left until nearly the end of the Royal Arch ceremony. From the perspective of English Constitution this is particularly unfortunate, since the many 'Craft' freemasons who have chosen not to progress further, remain uninformed. It is perhaps useful to explain to any such readers who have not 'completed' their Masonic journey, that the Symbolical Lecture in the Royal Arch is effectively in two halves, with only the first half ostensibly 'Scientific', but even within that context it continues to make some allusions to biblical and philosophical concepts. Indeed, as though embarrassed by association with the secular, it returns once again to further reflections on various aspects of morality in the latter part of the Lecture, albeit employing elemental scientific symbolism ('crow to take purchases' – with the implication that the listener appreciates the principle of levers). Since the work presented in Part I is concerned with the matters that were presumed by the Founders to be deemed scientific, only the first quasi scientific section of the Symbolical Lecture up to 'The Ensigns on the staves...' will be discussed in detail. Purely for convenience the topics will, except for the geometry of the greater and lesser triangles, be taken in their order of appearance.

Even today science is usually presented as a series of truisms, supported

Introduction

by 'logical (in practice the current hypothesis of the most persuasive group of experts) argument' and verified by experimentation or the more recent innovation of modelling by mathematics and computation, with at times only a sideways glance at reality. However, since most aspects of scientific dogma are usually found to be invalid in the long run, it is better to consider them as being the best hypothesis to date, whilst at the same time continuing to challenge their validity, attempting to establish from experimental and/or by mathematical analysis the degree of one's reliance upon them. Nevertheless, the Founders would, on the surface at least, appear to be much more forthright in their beliefs and in the Symbolical Lecture each piece of information is presented as an irrefutable fact.

Thus, whilst one may have doubts over their 'deep down' conviction, in terms of historical research it is most helpful, since their dogmatism has had the effect of removing ambiguity and provides the consensus of their understanding and from that the level of understanding expected of an educated man of that period. It is helpful to reiterate that it would be premature to unreservedly assume that this was indeed their belief, for as will become clear they were political animals and so what they professed to believe as opposed to what they actually believed is quite another matter. Notwithstanding the warning over the likelihood of their duality in thought and expression, for the moment it will not be pursued so that progress may be made towards an understanding of the original ceremony and from that and other clues, obtain some insight of its original (declared) content. Such consideration will however be in two parts; first to consider the Founders' publicly expressed view of 'Science', based upon contemporary conceptions held generally (or at least by large influential bodies such as universities, colleges etc.) and where appropriate put those in context with a more modern understanding of that topic. Based on that generalised perspective it is possible to hypothesise on the likely composition of the adopted Ritual and rationale behind the formation of the Royal Arch.

Herein lies a dilemma with respect to this work since it has to show clearly that science was not only an essential component in the Founders' thinking, but to the extent where it influenced their basic thoughts and actions. Further, that collectively science was not only a topic that was exciting and challenging and sufficiently so for them to include it in their leisure activities, but in fact it was an essential component of their livelihood. The difficulty is that without an understanding of the true nature of the science that preoccupied them it is difficult to appreciate its importance, but conversely, how could anyone appreciate that level of importance without some prior understanding of their immediate social environment and any individual/collective motivation? The decision to start by considering the basic science was, 1) there was no greater claim and the core subject of the work is science and 2) that any freemason reading this book would have, of necessity, been 'charged' from the moment of joining to make a study of the subject and on that basis alone may find the topic of interest in its own right. Public lectures and demonstrations and their (certain of the Founders) part in them showed that there was great public interest in the science of the day; which can be easily verified since the content of many of these lectures and papers were recorded. Because many of these lectures were given to an everyday cross-section of the educated population, they also give a strong indication of the academic level they may have been disposed to incorporate in the ritual. It is therefore useful to reflect upon and attempt to understand the concepts of (verifiable) science in the public domain at that time, remembering that these early freemasons also came from that very narrow social band who would have likely received a good education. Taking at face value the serious injunctions found in Masonic ritual there is clearly a case to understand the science of that period and explore its wider implications.

Even today where most people receive an adequate education there is still a limited number of people who have had the opportunity to study science and technology at depth, or even if they had, may have found the subject obscure or that time or lack of use, has relegated its basic concepts into the recesses of their mind, but it is equally true that few would own to a total disinterest. However, for a freemason or anyone attempting to understand the innate philosophy of Freemasonry, an understanding of science is regarded as an essential and should not be abandoned as a series of miscellaneous words in the ritual that require little attention or may even be ignored. It is salutary to note that the Founders, if the words in the ritual are taken at face value, considered such knowledge an imperative. Part I of this book is intended to address this requirement to a level (*circa* that of the contemporary public lectures, tracts etc. of the early 1720s) sufficient to give an understanding of their intent and add authority to the overall conclusions of this Study. Because science to some people is akin to 'greens' on the plate of a schoolboy, Part I is written in a palatable style that is meant to be interesting and informative rather than one of absolute scientific rigor and as such is likely to be of general interest; nonetheless, there is still a concern that it may yet prove to be a distraction or very tedious to some readers. To any who may fall within this category it is reasonable to suggest that it should not prevent their enjoyment of the other Parts of the work, which discuss many other important factors, such as the sociology and personalities, outside of science that have affected the development of early Freemasonry; except that they would now have to tacitly accept the science and its attendant ramifications, one might say imperatives, at face value.

If the number of times the Liberal Arts and Sciences, Nature, their Hidden Mysteries etc. are mentioned is an indication of the importance in terms of their allegorical and symbolical meaning, then the English Ritual, because it lacks any form of explanation, appears to be a most inappropriate model. However, irrespective of constitution, there appears to be none that are sufficiently detailed to convey the intrinsic importance of Nature and science within the philosophy of Freemasonry and if this situation is to be improved upon then there is a need to expand upon them. Unfortunately as stated above English ritual is perhaps the weakest in this respect, with specified topics left until the Symbolical Lecture of the Royal Arch, of which perhaps the most obvious is that of the innate beauty and science of architecture. In view of its obvious importance within the ethos and symbolism of Freemasonry architecture will be discussed more extensively than the other scientific elements.

Thus Part I concentrates on the physical aspects of the science and technology of the period (early 1700s) and where appropriate relates this to modern understanding. Equally important it begins to considers those aspects of science that are not included, because this too has a significant bearing on the way in which science related to the other social aspects of those individuals believed to be involved in founding Premier Grand Lodge and the formation of the Royal Arch.

Each of the subsequent Parts are concerned with and demonstrate how the many factors necessary to create and sustain such an institution were optimum at the unique moment when a successful outcome was possible. It proposes an approach that rationalises the numerous factors associated with the sociology of the period leading up to and including the foundation of Premier Grand Lodge. It shows how those involved in the comparatively narrow social activity of Freemasonry were in practice intimately and much more widely involved outside of it and how science formed the common link between these extremely influential and in some instances greatly gifted individuals. Having inter-related these erstwhile disparate factors a likely scenario is proposed for the time at which Premier Grand Lodge, United Grand Lodge as it is was later to become, was brought into being, the essential and complicated nature of the ritual used and the names of those involved.

References

1. Clarke, J., 'The medical profession and early Freemasonry', *AQC* 85 (1975), pp. 298-311.
2. Clarke, J., 'The Royal Society and early Grand Lodge', *AQC* 80 (1967), pp. 110-117.

Chapter Two: Architecture

I t has been suggested already that during the metamorphosis from 'operative' masonry to 'speculative' Freemasonry the supposed link between them became progressively more imagined than real. Irrespective of whether this assessment is accurate or not, it appears to have had little or no impact on the generally held presumption, both within and outside Freemasonry that such a link does exist and this will be alluded to throughout this work. Indeed the early ritual of speculative Freemasonry indicates that freemasons were as desperate then, as they are today, to presume a direct association with the activities, awesome skill, perfection, artistry and ethos of their operative namesakes. Whilst a few operative masons worked in other materials, such as wood (hammer beams etc) and (stained) glass, their ultimate achievement was manifest in the stonework fabric of cathedrals and great public buildings. The desire of London's speculative freemasons of the early 1700s to maintain the link was especially reinforced, as Westminster Abbey was just a mile or so away and the brand new St Paul's on their very doorstep. It is not surprising therefore that architecture is the first of the 'Sciences' to be woven into the symbolism of Craft Freemasonry and is the first element introduced into the Symbolical Lecture of the Royal Arch. The very importance of their need to maintain this cherished link is emphasised when attempting to assess their actual understanding of architecture in relation to their obsession with the other sciences. This will be approached via the model of their choice; the 'Caternarian' arch, which in their and indeed most peoples eyes, is the epitome of architectural beauty, but equally analytical science.

The derivation of the words 'Caternarian Arch' should at first sight be simply a matter of 'fact', but as with most else in this study it is dependent upon where one looks for the answer. The term 'Caternarian', is claimed by one authority as deriving from the French word for chain: *La Chaine* and in particular the natural or inherent form taken by a hanging chain or more generally a rope or cable. The Random House Dictionary claims that it comes from the Latin: caten – a chain, a trivial difference, but one that must act as the first of the many warnings in this work. That is, to 'beware of historians', not least the present one and to proceed with great care, since such 'authoritative' sources assume a gravitas that insists upon the assumption that the point at issue is an absolute fact. In this instance there is a clear conflict in 'authorities' as to whether it is of French or Latin origin. This distinction is of course of little real consequence, except that each gives their version of the derivation as an actual 'fact'. Much more significant is the underlying science behind the fact that the Catenary curve is incorporated within the design of most modern (wide span) bridges, but in reality it can be traced back to rope and vine bridges that have been used by ancient people since time immemorial.

In formal mathematics a Catenary curve is the sum of two natural (Napierian) logarithms and by definition it is possible for such a curve to pass through any three points or 'chairs' as the case may be. This may be verified by marking the arrangement of the three Principal's chairs, without any great care, on a piece of paper hanging it vertically (if the spacing is vaguely right then the paper would have to be turned upside down) and then, taking a piece of string and changing the tension in the string by moving its ends apart, to adjust its form so that the string passes through all three points. It does not have to be symmetrical to conform, as flying buttresses will confirm.

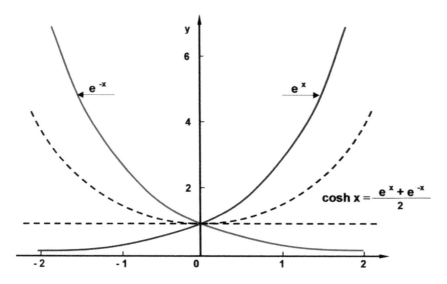

Figure 2.1. This shows the 'classic' form of a Catenary curve, the shape of which can be varied to allow it to pass through (any three points) an *ad hoc* arrangement of the Principal's chairs by changing the value of 'x' and appropriate constants.

This 'natural' form is apparent from the characteristic equation for a Catenary, inset on the graphical representation shown in Figure 2.1. It is actually the hyperbolic 'Cosh' curve, which is classically shown as the summation of two 'natural' (Napierian) logarithms. 'Natural' because it describes natural processes, such as the way in which there is a progressive slowing in the growth during the lifetime of a tree or the way in which the vibrations of a tuning fork decay and in this instance the exponential way in which the stresses are progressively disposed throughout the structure.

The resultant curve is one of, if not the most, elegant forms in architecture and perhaps is exemplified best in the modern suspension bridge, most famously the Golden Gate Bridge in San Francisco. But even where some other form of basic support mechanism is used other than cable or chain type links, such as the tie-rods or stays on the 'Queen Elizabeth II Bridge' at Dartford this basic form is retained. The Queen Elizabeth II Bridge is included because it shows that the method is so inherently sound that the actual deck or carriageway is arched according to this basic law and in this instance the stays are arranged as near as possible to this intrinsic form; technically referred to as a 'Catenary curve', *see* Figures 2.2a and 2.2b.

Figure 2.2. a)

The Golden Gate Bridge in the USA (original unknown)

Figure 2.2. b)

The Queen Elizabeth Bridge at Dartford, UK. Courtesy: Dartford River Crossing Authority

Architecture

Thus this consideration is based upon the fact that the Catenary curve is that adopted by a suspended rope or chain. It is governed by its length and the distant apart of its ends. The resulting tension in that rope or chain is a function of the combined load due to the gravitational pull on the components of its construction and the load it is designed to carry. Of course in the case of suspension bridges there are other extraneous factors such as wind load, traffic dynamics etc., but these are incidental to this basic appraisal. Whilst the Founders and hence we are concerned only with a stone structure, in order to understand the basic concepts of their argument or contention, it is helpful to first understand the basic parameters underlying the physical behaviour of a chain or rope system.

For a given length of rope the tension within it is a function of how shallow one requires the curvature to be and the object here is to show by logical steps how this may be correlated with the intrinsic crushing strength of the masonry in a stone arch or dome.

A washing line and tennis net are good everyday models to illustrate the conditions fundamental to the concepts in question. It is obvious that as one attempts to make the line approach horizontal the tension increases greatly and in the case of a heavily laden washing it is effectively impossible and the line always droops and if the line is very long it needs a clothes-prop (or several spans as in the Oakland bridge in San Francisco) or in the case of the tennis net ever increasing wire tension and stiffness of the support frames. This is why the towers on a suspension bridge, such as those shown in Figure 2.2 are made so tall, namely to allow the cable to have an appreciable amount of droop and thereby lesson the tension in the cable (or tie). The theoretical limiting factor on the span of such a bridges is the load that they are required to take, in relation to their own intrinsic strength to weight ratio, namely above a certain length it would fail under its own weight alone. Thus one could conceive of constructing a bridge from comparatively light but strong material, such carbon fibre and expect it to perform better than one made from steel. Stone on the other hand has very limited tensile strength indeed, but good crushing strength and so the architect (or master mason in earlier times) had to use it in a way that exploited its ability to withstand compressive loads.

However, what has this to do with the Founders of the Royal Arch's claim in the Symbolical Lecture that a 'Catenarian Arch is the strongest of all known architectural forms'. If the question of semantics is disregarded and by glossing over the need to justify their claim: 'the strongest known architectural form', one can readily understand the subtlety of the concept in their minds. An analogous claim would be: that the short explosive power of an Olympic 100 metres champion is somehow representative of a greater athlete than the incredible endurance of the competitor who won the Marathon, each could triumph over the other in their respective disciplines, but the answer to who is the greater, is totally subjective. Robert Hooke, an important character throughout this analysis, who assisted Christopher Wren greatly in the rebuilding of London and elsewhere, lectured upon this very subject (Catenarian form) in the middle to late 1600s, insinuating the general thesis that all such manifestations of nature were now rational in mechanical (of this world) terms. By the time that Premier Grand Lodge was formed, there was a large minority whose (Baconian/Descartian/Hobbsian type) faith in all matters scientific led to the assertion that (effectively all) natural phenomena could be explained in physical terms or by (experimental) demonstration. This mechanistic approach was the subject of lively debate amongst the general public and academe and not confined to those few in our focus. Thus this apparent convergence and explanation of the Nature with mathematical and/or scientific principles was gaining serious consideration in large sections of influential society, not least the Founders. These radical views caused considerable discomfort to the majority of those having strong religious conviction and whose central belief was that of the absolute 'creative, preservative and annihilative power of the Deity' and this may explain why they 'hurried off' in the middle of an essentially mechanistic explanation of the physical symbolism of the Lecture to the sanctuary of some spiritual connotation, albeit compromising the science somewhat. As will be suggested throughout this work, this dichotomy would appear to be all too real to the Founders and not only markedly affected their thought processes, but also those associated with them and in consequence was most likely to have had a strong influence upon the eventual form of the Ritual.

It is therefore not surprising that this natural (Catenary) and beautiful form, could, from a secular standpoint, be seen to offer the ultimate use of a material's strength, but to the faithful just as easily exemplify God's perfection and creative power and which, if one is disposed to believed it so, could be readily explained in terms of his now revealed utter scientific perfection – *see* later discussion on Newtonianism. Clearly to impart an actual model to show why this was so, would have been considered an important part of an educator's mission, a vehicle to awaken the recipient's wonderment of Nature and Science and through that provide verification of God's omnipotence. However, in attempting to do so they were obliged to employ an ad-mix of conflicting concepts. To understand the contradictions in the Founders' thinking it is helpful to consider the physics (science) of their architectural model. It also helps to explain how monastic master masons, erstwhile architects, were able to continue to enjoy their special virtuosity, by describing architecture and their practices in terms of the latest technological thinking and is another reason why the Founders were likely to have considered such an analytical explanation to be necessary and of such fundamental importance. A most revealing indication of their rationale is to examine their use of the term 'the strongest' since its phraseology

Architecture

implies that the claim is supported by the intrinsic physics of the application.

For the moment it is convenient to persist with the concept of the forces acting on a suspended chain, using the case where the curve is deep compared to its width and in the first instance consider the two bottom links - such as the centre example shown in Figure 2.3a. Clearly the middle two links have no other links below them and so they only have to carry their own weight, whereas the two above them have their own weight and the bottom two, the next above them their own and the four below them etc., etc., until the final two (one each side) links have to support the weight of half the chain. If now each link had its weight increased by some given amount, because it forms part of a bridge there is the obvious need to support the working load as well and logically the same progressive impact on each successive link would occur.

If now the chain ends are moved apart we know from the washing line analogy that the tension will increase, exponentially if the mathematical law given in Figure 2.1 is obeyed, as the separation, increases, it adds to the forces already in the links. Because of its total flexibility, those forces can only act along the axis of the (link) chain. This resulting force is therefore a combination of the uniform force of gravity pulling down (its weight and that of any superimposed load) and the force required to hold the ends of the rope/chain apart.

At any level of separation this combined force can be represented by a right angled triangle, with its shorter sides representing the two forces indicated above, both in their direction and intensity. The longest side or hypotenuse represents the combined effect or the 'resultant' force of the two. Since pulling the ends apart does not make the chain (and any superimposed load) heavier, its vertical component remains constant, but the effect of moving its ends apart have a marked impact in the horizontal direction which becomes increasingly dramatic with the separation of its ends. Much as a heavy bag of shopping becomes impossibly so if one attempts to spread ones arms outwards. Hence the force required to hold the ends apart is a function of the weight of the chain or cable, but more particularly the exponentially increasing effect on the load as its support points move apart. These factors may be listed as follows:

(a) Each link is required to take its own weight, plus any of the chain beneath it,

(b) Because it is totally flexible it hangs in a natural (most relaxed position possible - a 'Catenary') curve,

(c) Because it is totally flexible it can only take load along its length and so the forces at any one point are tangential to or lie along the centreline of the curve,

(d) At each support the fixing must take half the weight of the chain or rope (gravitational load), plus the force required to keep its ends apart, so that the load at its middle is the least or that the bottom link carries the least stress and conversely the reaction at its support its greatest,

(e) That separating force increases disproportionately (exponentially) with separation (the washing line analogy): namely in relation to the equation cited in Figure 2.1 and the forces represented at the supports are indicated in Figure 2.3b.

(f) That the forces are increased as external loads are added (washing on the line) or its own weight increases, but self weight such as chain can be quite significant, especially when the curve is inverted to form an arch and the material is stone,

(g) But most important because the rope or chain is lying in this 'natural' shape those forces, wherever they are measured, are the least necessary to support this combined applied load, for if this was not so the shape would automatically readjust until it was – a simple analogy would be the fact that a ball rolls to the bottom of a smooth trough and does not remain somewhere up its sides.

Hence the material from which it is made is stressed to the least level under these circumstances and because it is then less likely to break it may, in a convoluted way, be argued to be in its strongest possible form. However, when a specific functional and/or architectural requirement becomes the dominating priority, then other factors, such as the characteristics of the material, a particular structural form, load bearing capacity etc. will become the determining factor. Thus it is not necessarily the æsthetics, but a particular functional or say economical requirement or actual architectural form that predominates, as will be demonstrated later when Wren's construction of the dome on St Paul's Cathedral, the founder's every day model, is considered in some detail. It is not unreasonable to presume that the Founders would have believed that this innately beautiful natural form was no accident, but rather that it was symptomatic of God's greater (magical) design and hence worthy of incorporation in these most illustrious buildings. As will now be shown, it represents the most efficient use of materials when specifically applied to a dome and as such, does have high mechanically integrity, but is not necessarily '*the strongest*' structural form for all applications.

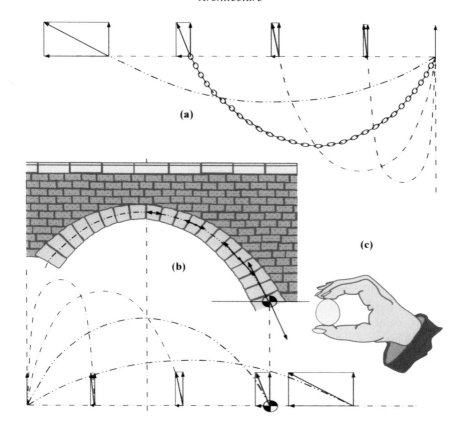

Figure 2.3 Catenarian concepts: a) Gravitational influence on a flexible rope or chain. b) Analogous form inverted as stone. c) The resistance to crushing of an egg – a natural form of dome.

The way in which the forces in a hanging rope or chain are seen to increase with separation were shown in the 'triangles of forces' shown in Figures 2.3a (tensile), we will now consider their compressive (inverted) counterpart in stone in Figure 2.3b.

Having analysed the tensile case it is now possible to consider factors relating to a stone (Catenarian) arch. In the case outlined above the only forces acting on the chain resulted from the gravitational pull. If say a short loop of washing line were made of hemp, saturated with water, allowed to freeze over night and then inverted, the arch formed by the now solid rope would, by definition, form a perfect Catenarian arch. Since the gravitational force is now acting down on the frozen arch (quasi stone links),

The Key to Modern Freemasonry

the loads would be essentially compressive. Such a rope and an equivalent schematic arch constructed in stone are shown as an extension of this concept in Figure 2.3b.

However, by extending the argument above it is clear that the very centre of the Catenarian arch so formed carries the lowest possible (compressive) force and that it is the lower parts of such an arch (its foundations and haunches) that are under the greatest thrust or compression. Thus in a Catenarian arch the 'keystone' is not, as we are later exhorted to believe, 'compressing and binding the structure', indeed the very centre of the Catenarian arch may well be a joint and as such serves to explain why the sojourners, when attempting to gain access to the Vault, were able to remove it without the ceiling collapsing. A number of Masonic historians (amongst them Clarke – *see later*) pour scorn on the 'Legend', based on the premise that the vault would have collapsed if the stones had been removed by the Sojourners, but they, like the authors of the Ritual, had failed to appreciate the nature of the structure. As will be explained later their overall scepticism was likely right and that for a whole gamut of reasons it was reasonable for them to dismiss the Legend as a mere contrivance, but the consequences of removing the centre stones could not be used as one of them.

Clearly if this Catenarian stone arch were rotated through 180 degrees it would form a Catenarian dome, the very centre of which may or may not have been solid stone, but for the purposes of the story, the Sojourners needed to find 'a compact piece of masonry, wrought in the form of a dome'. As such a Catenarian dome would be much like an igloo and if kept symmetrical would be expected to be completely stable with no top at all. Igloos are in practice built of diminishing circles of ice blocks. Because of the way ice behaves Eskimos do not necessarily support their igloo during construction, but the early masons did. Once complete the supportive 'centring' scaffolding was removed and structure was extremely sound and provided it was kept symmetrical the central masonry could be removed or never put in, as indeed many famous domes testify.

Again we can recognise this structural form in Nature as well as in classic architecture. A bird's egg is a wonderful case in point, being constructed of two connected domes. So strong is this form that even an extremely strong man (provided he applied the force uniformly) cannot cause the egg to break by compressing it as shown in Figure 2.3c. As stated above in classic architecture there are numerous examples of domes without a centre *per se*; typically St Paul's Cathedral, whose dome is a complex arrangement of three concentric hollow (forms) shapes, none of which are closed at their centre. It illustrates extremely well the subtle difference between the Founders' claim of the 'strongest of all architectural forms' with that of optimal structural strength and/or functional requirement. This because Wren required his dome to supports a lantern weighing many hundreds of tonnes and an outer dome. The outer dome was intended to be an architectural feature only and as

Architecture

such could be a comparatively light structure; it was nonetheless still very heavy and required bolstering. It also illustrates where the bulk of the loads act; namely it is at the base of the dome where in practice all the 'compressing and binding' does in fact take place. Indeed the skirt of the Dome has recently had to have its reinforcing iron band supplemented by one of stainless steel to ensure future stability. Figure 2.4 shows a greatly reduced cross-sectional drawing of the dome, which is in fact only part of a quite remarkable 'cut-away' drawing by R.B. Brookes-Greaves and Godfrey Allen. Because it is so reduced the detail is less clear and so an enlarged inset of the hole in the inner dome is given. Note that Wren has used stone instead of brick, on these upper layers for visual effect when viewed from beneath.

However, Wren may almost be considered a contemporary of the Founders and St Paul's had only recently been completed and was before their eyes on a daily basis. Moreover, he was a mathematician and like Newton would have been totally familiar (in conjunction with Robert Hooke his structural engineering colleague) with the geometry of the 'conic sections'. He also, would have fully appreciated the innate beauty of the Catenarian Arch and the potential economy of materials offered by this architectural form; but he clearly wanted the 'strongest' configuration to support his ultimate ambition of having a dome surmounted with a lantern. This was completely contrary to the wishes of the sponsors and so he mischievously nurtured his original concept of having a dome by claiming that such a design was essential to meet their requirements. He needed to conserve the hollow æsthetic nature of the design, but in order to do so it required the most efficient means of resisting the compressive loads possible: namely the forces acting directly down the (brick/stone) masonry. For this purpose he used the walls of the massive middle cone to act as the load-bearing element of this three-layered dome design.

In a discussion with respect to the physics of the construction of the dome of St Paul's, with the celebrated Masonic historian and writer Robert Gilbert, certain factors emerged: the prudence, pragmatism and form of the inner Catenarian dome, the brute functional strength of the conical middle structure and the flimsy and purely decorative beauty of the outer Dome. Gilbert, an acknowledged expert on the symbolism and allegory of Freemasonry, was struck by the innate symbolism of Wren's design. He pointed out that the inner dome may be taken to represent 'Wisdom', the centre cone 'Strength' and the outer dome 'Beauty'. This ingenious analogy illustrates perfectly the profound symbolism that may be attached to these awe-inspiring buildings or any masonic artefact. Many Masonic historians would have seized upon this quite ingenious observation and gone on to suggest that it was quite likely a part of Wren's strategy. Note: clearly they believed that for visual effect from below, Wren had used stone instead of brick on these upper layers but it is actually painted (*trompe-l'œil* – trick of the eye), to make it look so.

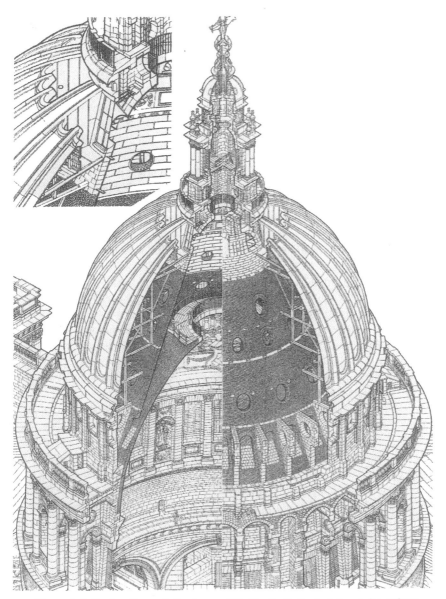

**Figure 2.4. Section through the dome of St. Paul's Cathedral. Inset shows how
Wren built with brick and faced with stone for æsthetic effect.**

Architecture

Of course it is of interest to reflect in this way and whilst it remains conjecture it remains interesting, but such reflection can after a few decades become enshrined in legend. However, Wren was a pragmatist and a mathematician and the structure was determined by the need. He may well have acknowledged that these three factors were an innate part of all such structures and his inspiration may have come from it, but whether or not it made such a dramatic influence on the design of St Paul's Dome is doubtful to say the least. Note: all three of the domes are open in the centre, indeed even right up into the very ball of the cross itself; also the tens of thousands of bricks used to construct the conical central dome and the Catenarian type inner dome, their cohesion relying upon the mutual support of their neighbours, within each hooped layer – just like the sojourner's dome. Within the central conical dome Wren employed a number of devices such as arches and windows, that lighten the structure, improve illumination and conserve materials, but in such a way that there was only notional weakening of the structure. For the outer layer he reverting to a classical ornate dome, which because it was merely decorative, he was able to adopt the classical roofing techniques used by masons of bygone days, which being constructed of comparatively light materials reduced considerably the overall load on the supporting structure. Note the way that it gained its support by loading down on to the strong the central conical form – this analysis will be extended later.

Again on the founder's doorstep was the vaulted ceiling of the Henry VII Chapel in Westminster Abbey. It beautifully illustrates the stunning technological (science) mastery of the early stonemasons, but Wren's (a fine mathematician) different, but equally stunning design shows the increasing and relentless trend over the preceding 200 years towards what would now be described as analytical science and technology; which was equally certain to have impressed the Founders greatly. They would have had seen this modern cathedral on a daily basis and unlike the certain catastrophic collapse of the Vault forecast by the Masonic historians referred to above, they would have seen that the dome clearly had no centre. After all, one of its most inspiring features is that gained from looking up into the dome from inside the Cathedral. They would have understood why this could be so and thus found no contradiction within the 'Legend' on that score, indeed might even have contrived it upon that basis. It is interesting to note that much of the outer decorative dome is in fact open to the sky at its centre, with a walkway underneath – leading to an 'interesting' drainage system.

At first sight, especially given the intellect of the Founders, it might be reasonable to suppose that the term 'strongest form' was not what they actually believed, but rather they were merely using dramatic licence to give the Ritual a particular meaning. However, as one reads Masonic and other history books one has to address the possibility that they may have been ignorant of these basic concepts and consequentially quite confused. Indeed, it is their apparent misunderstanding of the 'strongest', that is the basis of the argument put forward by Jones' in his book (and indeed other books on the subject)[1] the *History of the Royal Arch*.[2] Although the book was revised much later by Carr and Hewitt, it remains unchanged in this respect. In these books the authors attempt at some considerable length to explain the meaning of the particular 'compressing' and 'binding' terminology of the Ritual. It is of interest because in a later Masonic publication Jones was described as the greatest authority ever on the Royal Arch and if he and these other authors could get the technology wrong, then it is perhaps not unreasonable to suppose that the Founders could have done likewise.

Jones' misunderstanding was despite the fact that by the time he penned these chroniclers, two centuries had elapsed and it is certain that the general understanding of science had advanced greatly by that time and one may have expected his with it. Nonetheless he and others were strongly wedded to the notion of the inevitable collapse of the Vault, failing to make the distinction between an arch and its structurally stable derivative when rotated to form a dome.

The following section is included because 'operative' masonry is so important in the mind of the modern 'speculative' Freemasonry. Neither is its intended to be critical of their (historians') fine effort, but rather as a salutary warning to all who attempt to undertake historical analysis, to avoid converting hypothesis into fact. It illustrates not only why it was possible for this confusion over the concept of 'strongest' to be present in their minds and the Masonic historians who followed, but equally those of the Founders. Indeed in many sets of contemporary Chapter Furniture the 'dome' is represented as an arch, where the keystone and contiguous arch stones have had to be supported by a judiciously placed black painted support and which have an annoying tendency to become unstable at inappropriate times during the ceremony.

It is evident that confusion existed a long time after the early ritual was adopted, since to illustrate their argument with respect to the criticality of the arch stone and the contiguous arch stones, they (Jones *et al*) chose the fan vaulted ceiling of the Henry VII Chapel in Westminster Abbey, citing authoritative references such as reference [3]. It is of course a truly glorious example of the most advanced form of the classical late gothic style and illustrates beautifully the technical brilliance of the early operative masons and would of course been especially appreciated by the Founders. They (Jones *et al*) give a highly esoteric and symbolically justified explanation, but from the drawing in Figure 2.5, it is clear that the massive centre stones of the fans are an integral part of the mid-section of the arch and are in no sense the 'keystone'. This remarkably ingenious and stunningly beautiful design does indeed rely upon the weight of these centre pendent stones, which are major

Architecture

contributors within the arch. They do indeed 'compress and bind the structure', but clearly they and are not the 'key stone' or 'contiguous arch stones' of the actual whole arch, with the classical key stone, as normally conceived, serving as a component of the secondary smaller fans, and are off-set between the actual main arches, the centre of the actual arches are joints. These minor pendulous fans between the main arches and which form that part of the ceiling, which would otherwise be a slimmer longitudinal ridge and because are clearly very heavy would contribute massively to the already unfavourable stresses normally associated with this part of any structure.

Again the exquisite understanding of the statics and dynamics (settlement after the removal of scaffolding – centring) of these structures by these early architects is not only wonderfully illustrated by the Chapel's delicate beauty, but also their pragmatism, for these pendulous stones forming the centre of each fan, were truly massive, but even more impressive still was the fact that they were in practice stone assemblies. They were constructed such that when all the surrounding masonry was in place and the support entring was removed they would be allowed to undergo minute settlement, so that their huge weight did in fact bind it. Despite all their perfection the masons realised that some form of settling strategy would be required in order to compensate for any small, but individual 'high-spot', which might otherwise induce spurious forces that could inadvertently exceed the fracture strength of the stone. Therefore they placed thin spacers of lead on the critical faces of the joints to disperse the load hydrostatically and thereby allowed for any minor discrepancies. Clearly this strategy worked perfectly, but some scholars are of the view that early operative masons worked by custom and practice alone. Of course if they are right in this view, then this beautiful structure was not an expression of the mason's technological ability, but rather a further case of the 'luck' discussed below in the Section dealing with early masonic understanding. But as a final comment on science employed on this beautiful addition to the Abbey is to consider the flying buttresses. It has already been noted that because of the very high stresses of the pendulated ceiling and to maintain the inner slender of the columns etc. that the lateral forces would be very high indeed and the dimension of the foundations and number and solidity of the buttresses (Figure 2.5) themselves clearly show that builders knew perfectly well, from the very onset, the ultimate nature of their design and their seemingly innate flare by the beautiful adornment and tracery of the necessarily massive outer stonework.

On this same theme it is interesting to note some latter-day persons responsible for the maintenance of cathedrals were critical of the way ancient masons had left their rubble covering parts of the vaulted ceilings of cloisters and were disposed to remove it, when it was realised that the original masons had increased the gravitational (quasi hydrostatic) loading on the structure in order to increase the level of down thrust on the 'rib' and 'web' stones and thereby adding further to the stability of the vaulted ceiling. This is another example that refutes the claim of some modern historians that the ancients were rather more lucky than informed. This dismissive assessment of the level of understanding enjoyed by these early masons seems unlikely and is returned to at the end of this Section.

However, it is clear that the originators of the Ritual needed to employ the 'binding' aspect of these other architectural forms, such as Gothic, to symbolise the cohesive nature of the offices of the three Principals, but in order to do so they had either to have a misconception or use a certain amount of licence. To convey the right impression the Authors of the Ritual needed the centre stone of a Catenarian arched vault found by the sojourners be termed a 'keystone' (technically it is usually referred to as a 'boss' – but that would not have given the right impression) so that it would have the gravitas they wished to attach to it; indeed as has been shown already, the very centre of a Catenary arch may in practice have been an actual joint in the masonry.

Figure 2.5. Left: a copy of Willis' sketch of the basic structural details of the fan vaulting in the Henry VII Chapel in Westminster Abbey. Right: a cross-section of the chapel.[4]

Clearly the work of the operative mason was of paramount importance to early freemasons and indeed remains so today and so it is perhaps opportune to pause for a moment and speculate why these architectural concepts were so important to them. Quite apart from the plethora of architectural objects in lodge furniture and symbolism of the remainder, such as tracing board etc. and the need to continue the link with the past, there was also a strong sociological reason for doing so, which in modern parlance would be called 'group identity'. The following supports the view that architecture was supreme example of an 'art' and a 'science' and not, as for the

Architecture

most it had become, merely the product of building tradesmen who selective skills, but put up buildings in prescribed standard type way. It showed how technological/ scientific concepts were encapsulated in the aura of these ancient structures and why they formed the perfect model for the speculative Mason. Whilst the ethos and innate skills of the stone masonry was chosen by the Founders as the perfect model, the very science and technology that they also wished to embrace had already introduced new techniques and materials that had all but displaced the ancient craft. Further that the quite different sociological pressures were changing the functionality of buildings and which were in fact proving to be the final factor in the obsolescence of the stone mason's craft.[5] For what ever reasons the Founders chose the factors listed below for inclusion in the ritual and the merit of their choice are discussed below.

1) The precepts or building blocks of the ideal form of 'organisational' (unified) Freemasonry they envisaged had to be such as to persuade the existing influential and prestigious members of these small individual Masonic lodges to abandon their current *ad hoc* existence and unite into some grander, but regulated form. Thus bringing the disparate strands of speculative Freemasonry into a cohesive, centrally regulated and hence greater socially significant whole,

2) Whilst this new Masonic Order was to be comprised of 'speculative' Masons, the whole concept and ethos was to remain based upon the sheer perfection and outstanding beauty of religious buildings, the work of the (effectively extinct – or at least not as influential entity within society: *see* later Parts) of operative masons. To inculcate a similar ethos (fraternity) already existing within the targeted disparate Masonic lodges and retain the system of relative progression of a particular individual within them; namely that of passing through degrees of attainment and elevation by fulfilling the duties of respective offices.

3) To associate it with the exquisite craftsmanship, intrinsic understanding of materials and underlying science manifest in these buildings and relate their material perfection as the perfect model for emulation in mans quest for moral perfection.

4) These awesome and yet beautiful buildings, dwarfing all other human endeavour were devoted to and were a visible expression of their and hence mans emphatic dependence on God, but from which science, if some complimentary plausible link could not be found, would tend to lead them away.

Whilst these buildings had been constructed by masons and they could now be viewed as the personification of how technology and science had contributed to their construction, for the purposes of this emerging brand of Freemasonry they still had to be seen as being inextricable (inspired) linked with God's divinity. However, as we shall see in throughout, in the early 1700s such association could no longer be taken for granted, for they were now living through a time where, because of an increasing understanding of science, there was increasing religious uncertainty. There was a growing body of opinion, which quite unlike the earlier sporadic and ineffective individualistic attacks by those who could be labelled as scientific heretics, that was questioning the omnipotence of God in a profound way. There were now an increasing number of open public attacks, conveying the message that man may be loosened, if not freed completely, from the shackles of religious dogma. Even the cathedrals themselves, the very epitome of God's profound influence, could be analysed in a formal (Baconian type) technological way, without the need for divine inspiration and which by implication showed that it was possible for the whole of nature to be explained by similar mechanical analysis.

Because of St Paul's and all the other churches springing up around them, the Founders could at first hand relate to both Wren's and Hooke's scientific approach and appreciate how these beautiful (Baroque style) buildings had been constructed, that clearly employed a mixture of traditional and scientific/mathematical structural principles. The term 'traditional' is not used here to imply an absence of fundamental (albeit quasi scientific) thinking; for whilst it is disputed by many modern historians that the early masons did not possess a true understanding of the subtle ways in which the forces manifest themselves in the building, it is certainly not the thesis of this work. The reader may be surprised by the linking of the name Hooke with Wren when considering the reconstruction of London after the Great Fire, but in practice Hooke was extremely well skilled in architecture, technology and of particular interest here, propounded mathematical laws defining the effects of asymmetric loading on stone structures – especially that of the Catenarian arch. Indeed, the following is offered to examine and in effect challenge the imputation that these early masons were acting upon intuition only. The following is also an illustration of the complex universality of operative masons.

Some of the earliest authentic sketches available for inspection, were those made by Villard de Honnecourt (*circa* 1220-1235) of Rheims Cathedral's flying buttresses arrangement that were designed to support the sides of the Choir[6] – *see* Figure 2.6a. In Figure 2.6b a representation of Villard's actual sketch is shown as an inset. The question is how intrinsic an understanding of the forces acting upon the intended structure did Villard de Honnecourt have? An extended version of his sketch is used to illustrate, in a stylised form, the way in which the stresses (in an

Architecture

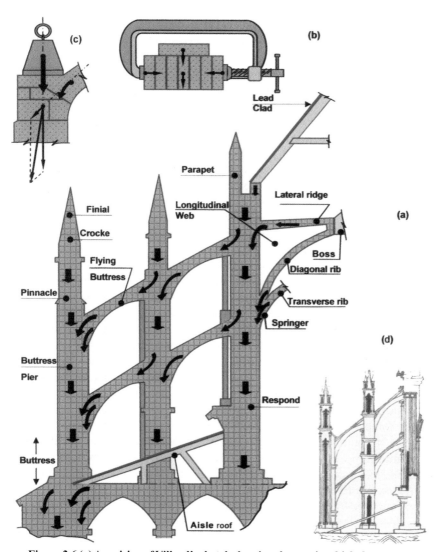

Figure 2.6 (a) A revision of Villard's sketch showing the way in which the stresses act within the structure. (b) A schematic of how un-bonded bricks may support a load if clamped together. (c) A representation of the triangle of forces that result from the use of weight (mass – quasi clamping force) of the surmounting pinnacle. (d) A reduced facsimile of Villard's original sketch.

25

analogous way to those drawn in text books to illustrate the way in which magnetic flux flows round a magnet) would manifest themselves in the structure and asks the question whether this was the way they appeared to him?

Before proceeding on we should recognise an important feature in the thinking of these early builders, for unless they had a naive belief that they would defy Nature and live forever, and assuming that they would have already been mature men to have been entrusted with such a huge task, they must have known that they would never see the outcome of their labours. This is analogous to the designers of the gardens of stately home, such as Inigo Jones or Capability Brown, who strategically planted long maturing trees such as lime, oak and chestnut in the certain knowledge that they would never see these parks as they look today. Thus when they planned the intended structure and set out and then laid the foundations they would have had needed to anticipated the intrinsic ('statics') loading of the final structure, with its thousands of tons of masonry, in the almost certain knowledge that they would never see it.

Clearly the master masons of the time, in order to express their and patron's glorification of God, wished to make the nave, aisles, transept and choir lofted structures, with beautifully ornate stone ceilings. In view of the stresses involved in order to do this, all the ribs and webs needed to be arched to some greater or lesser extent. These designs often required the lateral ridge to be almost horizontal, which if the 'washing line' analogy is used, resulted in very high sideways forces. This can be reasoned also from the triangle of forces in Figure 2.3a and 2.3b, where the curve is very shallow and as a consequence the horizontal component was certain to impose a very high lateral force. However, unlike the bridge representation in Figure 2.3b these delicate structures do not have the lateral support of say an earth bank or the solid masonry of the haunches of the bridge shown. This would therefore manifest itself as a large unsupported sideways thrust on the upper portions of a wall, which for æsthetic reasons needed to be kept slender. Before an attempt is made to interpret the sketch, there is one further factor that has to be addressed.

It is argued here that the concept shown in Figure 2.6a illustrates that the (quasi architects) master masons had an absolute understanding of and advanced thinking within their design strategy. It is virtually certain that the Founders would have appreciated this elegance of thought and execution and it would have inspired them to integrate 'operative' concepts into their Ritual. As has been stated whilst stone is strong when use in compression it has comparatively little tensile strength and so to be utilised effectively it must be used in compression. If as seen in Figure 2.6b some ordinary bricks, without any form of mortar were clamped together, they are not only be able to support (as a beam) their own weight, but depending on the clamping force, limited only by the friability of the bricks themselves, could support a large super-imposed load in addition – this is essentially the principle of pre-stressed concrete.

If this configuration is now turned through ninety degrees it can be seen that Villard used the base of the buttress as the static support face of the clamp and the gravitational force acting down through the elegant, but massive pinnacle as the clamping force. Note that in Figure 2.6a, he used as much of the outer edge as he could and on the intermediate buttress, taking advantage of their width to run the line of the outer flying buttress at a higher level. He also decided to make the outer pinnacles much more substantial, but disguises this by adding more ornate and beautifying embellishment.

It is interesting to note that although modern pollution attacks the stone work of these beautiful building at the time of their building it was effectively ageless, whereas pre-stressed concrete was always potentially prey (since its longevity was unknown) to the comparatively short-term problems of the ageing, in this case, due to the added complication of mixing materials, those of steel and concrete, it is not unusual nowadays to see the steel reinforcing rods in concrete structures exposed as a result of ageing by the weather and other effects. Of course early masons did use metal reinforcing as a strengthening device, there are many examples where the Romans used iron in this way, but it was not contingent on it being pre-stressed.

The pitch of the heavy wooden roof (lead covered) was made very steep and because of their use of stretchers, this also provided a pure 'dead-weight' downward loading on the wall of the nave. The force provided by the substantial roof was assisted further by the addition of a laced (pinnacled) parapet, which was placed at the outer edge with guttering contrived to be on the inside. As can be seen Figure 2.7 that in practice the Cathedral's two flying buttress arches as actually built, were somewhat closer together than were suggested by his earlier sketch. It could be argued that this made them look slightly less elegant, but it certainly added to their upper stability.

It is unlikely that we will ever know whether Villard could have drawn the triangle of forces suggested in Figure 2.6c and thereby actually computed the (huge) bearing load to ensure that: when combined with the sideways force being transmitted down the flying buttress it would be sufficient for it to ensure that the load would be directed down within the buttress. This level of understanding is seriously doubted by some modern historians, their argument is based on the presumption that he was incapable of actually conceiving the structure in these subtle terms and that he relied upon his intuitive judgement and an appreciable amount of luck. Given that the truth will never be known the final judgement must be left to the reader, however, it is the thesis of this study that at least the Founders understood the intrinsic (structural 'statics') technology and were anxious to communicate its elegance, combined with its stunning beauty, to the new exaltee. However, in the process of researching into the background of Villard de Honnecourt sketches it provided a most vivid illustration of the problems of relying upon the authority and hence facts, of historians.

Wilson, a Reader in the History of Architecture and thus by any reasonable standard must be considered an authority on the medieval period, writes the following in his book on gothic cathedrals:

'Unfortunately, the one extensive early 13th-century collection of architectural drawings to have survived, the so-called 'sketchbook' of Villard de Honnecourt in the bibliotheque Nationale de Paris, is not a representative sample. Villard's rendering of the eastern part of Rheims Cathedral are not merely crude but riddled with crass mistakes showing that he lacked such basic architectural skills as the ability to correlate cross sections and elevations. Equally revealing of his 'outside' status is the series of diagrams showing formulas for setting out pointed arches, Keystones and the like. Neither architects nor executant masons would have had any need of such a compilation; their procedures were enshrined in current practice and would have been transmitted orally and by example (note overtones of the early transfer of masonic ritual). But if Villard's drawings cannot be accepted as the work of a northern French architect, they do at least confirm that the main conventions of architectural drawings in use today were known by c.1230. The purpose behind Villard's 'Sketchbook' is still open to question.'[8]

Architecture

Figure 2.7. A photograph taken of the side of the Choir of Rheims Cathedral (After Harvey). Note the exceptionally severe pitch of the lead-clad roof (unusually so since lead tends to creep or sag under its own weight with time), which not only added beauty, but also provided substantial down-loading and minimised the stresses in the roof stringers (cross-ties). Note Rheims is of particular interest here and possibly to the Founders, since the same master mason was responsible for the Nave and other aspects of Westminster Abbey and the transfer of design concept is clear.

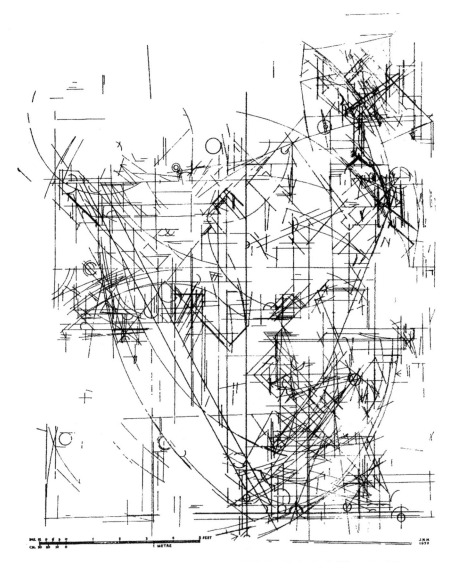

Figure 2.8. A copy of the Tracing Floor of Wells Cathedral. The actual lines are in practice quite indistinct but the image shown has been enhanced (after Colchester and Harvey).[9]

30

He later goes on to say and illustrate that there are various depictions on buildings etc. showing masons using drawing instruments dating from that very period. However, most surprising of all, given his vehemence, on the very same page as the adverse extract above, he has an actual photograph of a carving of the period depicting masons using drawing instruments. All freemasons are of course familiar with the three symbolic tracing boards, but in addition there are actual mason's floor tracings (usually scratched into a plaster screed) in places such as Wells Cathedral, which are undeniable examples of the mason's precision (within the context of stone) of that period, it is therefore difficult to see how he (Wilson) draws the distinction. Figure 2.8 is an 'enhanced' photograph of the floor in Wells Cathedral that was included and discussed by Colchester and Harvey in their writings on the architecture of that period,[10] but there are many other examples where operative masons have set out the precise nature of the stone geometry, not necessarily on the floor, typically that of the working drawings on the crypt wall of Rosslyn Chapel, Midlothian, Scotland.[11] Conversely, Harvey a well known writer on the subject of medieval architecture, in his excellent book that was essentially a section extracted from a much larger tome, written by a whole range of experts on the period, subscribes his version of Villard's contribution:

'In France, Germany, Austria, Italy and Spain there are a large number of highly finished constructional drawings and details from the thirteenth, fourteenth and fifteenth centuries, many of them of outstanding excellence. The finest quality of draughtsmanship is already noteworthy in the earliest surviving scale drawing, those of the 'Rheims Palimpset' of the middle years of the thirteenth century. These drawings, erased and cut to pieces to form pages of a book, may well have been from the hand of the Master Hugh Libergiers (died 1263), architect of the church Saint-Nicaise at Rheims, begun by him in 1229. Although none of the fragmentary drawings which survive can actually be a design for Saint-Nicaise, the style is closely similar, and there can be no doubt of the implication that small-scale drawings on parchment of the same type had been made by Libergiers in the 1220s. As we shall see, this is confirmed by the famous album of Villard de Honnecourt, certainly produced in the period 1200-35.

The finished and highly sophisticated quality of the architectural drawings produced in the first half of the thirteenth century is not merely of importance in itself; it is also compelling evidence that there must have been quite a long tradition of such draughtsmanship going back before the days of Honnecourt and Libergiers.' *et seq.*[7]

Clearly the two views appear to be completely irreconcilable. The confession here is that: for the most part, it is the basic philosophy of the latter version that appears to hold the greater truth and although an effort will be made to resist bias for the remainder of this study. The reader is now receiving information from someone that has arrived at a particular stance and must bear this in mind before forming a view on this aspect of the study. But the same questionable process will be present in all else written here and this cautionary note will be repeated at critical points throughout. Other authors have written upon this very matter and whilst accepting that he (Honnecourt) may not have been an actual architect *per se* and may have simply copied others, they are generally of the view that he was nonetheless extremely talented.

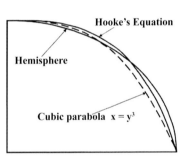

Hooke's Equation

Hemisphere

Cubic parabola $x = y^3$

Figure 2.9

A cross-section of the dome of St Paul's showing the three domes; two coventional and effectively conical (cubico-parabolical conoid) - load bearing middle dome.[13]

It is hoped that there is sufficient argument above to support the view that the Founders had a profound interest in preserving the link between the operative mason and speculative Freemasonry. That they had both appreciated and accepted the fundamental scientific achievements and brilliance of these early masons and wished to use this in their teachings. However, if Wilson's comments above are correct then there must be a lingering doubt as to whether they were themselves confused or had chosen to use poetic licence when communicating its significance in the Symbolical Lecture to the newly exalted candidate.

There is a final caveat to this Section, for as is suggested next, the Founders appeared well aware of the work of Robert Hooke, but they seem to have taken no account of the fact that he had, in the period before most of them were born, established a Law which defined the characteristic behaviour (curvature) of even an asymmetrically loaded stone arch and demonstrated his findings in much the same way as that used above to postulate the profile of the modified arch so formed. Hooke was of course an extremely prolific writer and demonstrator and consequence they may not have been aware of his findings in this instance, but this is unlikely, given their obvious interest in the subject – but it is even more doubtful that most modern engineers or architects would be *au fait* with the subtle findings of that particular piece of his work. But there is 'a twist in the tail (tale)', for although Hooke and indeed Wren were extremely talented mathematicians and Napier had published his findings on natural logarithms some hundred years earlier, the mathematics of the Catenarian form had still not been mathematically defined. That both Hooke and Wren understood the elegance of the Catenary form was made clear in a paper by Heyman.[12] He showed that Hooke realised that there was an almost perfect match between a complimentary cubic form (cubico-parabolical conoid) and that of a Catenary, *see* Figure 2.9. The interesting fact is that because Wren needed the centre to be removed, the slightly different curvature at the upper level of Hooke's inverted curve did in practice provide rather better stability from a structural point of view and that form was finally adopted in favour of the pure Catenarian or cubic revolved forms. The final mathematical solution to the Catenary form was eventually found in the early 1700s and since people like Brook Taylor and Desaguliers were extremely competent mathematicians they would have been happy with any new analytical concept of the Symbolical Lecture even though its form had been empirical up until then.

Figure 2.10a.

The 'Packhorse' Bridge at Carrbridge in the highlands of Scotland, constructed in 1717, courtesy of my wife.

Figure 2.10b.

Gateshead 'Millennium' Bridge opened 2001, courtesy of Gateshead Council, UK. Note even the much earlier bridges behind employ the same curve.

As almost pure indulgence and to illustrate the there does not have to be a 'keystone' in an arch of this type, the following photograph of the bridge at Carrbridge in the Highlands of Scotland, is given Figure 2.10a above. It was constructed to shorten the journey undertaken by funerals. The real reason for including it is not only that of its innate beauty and that lovely stretch of the River Dulnain which it spans, but because it was constructed in 1717, the same year as the first formal meeting of those who floated the concept of a Premier Grand Lodge. Figure 2.10b is a modern footbridge of very advanced design and whilst constructed almost 300 years later it still employs the same fundamental elegant form of the Catenarian arch, but again note that (a) is clearly without a defined keystone.

Conclusion

That the originators of the Symbolical Lecture were aware of the scientific/ technological concept of the forces acting within and upon structures, but that they also wished to lay emphasis on the æsthetic beauty of these buildings and to inculcate wonder and admiration and therefore employed some poetic licence in the wording of the Symbolic Lecture.

That the Catenarian Arch and indeed all other aspects of stone structures chosen by the Founders as the perfect models to illustrate consummate skill and innate link with God's perfection can, if one is disposed to do so, be analysed in 'mechanical' terms.

References

1. Shelby, L., 'Setting out the keystones of pointed arches: a note on Medieval "Baugeometric" ', in *Technology and Culture*, Vol. 10 (1965), pp. 537-548.

2. Jones, B.A., *Freemason's book of the Royal Arch* (George Harrap, London, 1969), pp. 133-137.

3. Willis, R., 'On the construction of the vaults of the Middle Ages', in *Trans. Royal Inst. of British Architects*, Vol. 1. Pt 2. (1842), pp. 1-69.

4. Willis, *ibid.*

5. Lawrence, C.C., 'A Brick-by-Brick Account of the Metamorphosis of Operative to Speculative Masonry', *AQC* 122 (2009), pp. 121-184.

6. Harvey, J., *The Master Builders* (Thames and Hudson, London, 1971). p. 52.

7. Harvey, *ibid.*

8. Wilson, C., *The Gothic Cathedral* (Thames and Hudson, London, 1996), p. 141.

9. Colchester, L. & Harvey, J., 'The Wells Tracing Floor', in *Archaeological J.,* Vol. 131 (1974), pp. 210-214.

10. Colchester & Harvey, *ibid.*

11. Shelby, L., *op. cit.,* p. 538.

12. Harvey, *op. cit.,* pp. 34-35.

13. Heyman, J., 'Hooke's cubico-parabolical conoid', in *Notes and Records of the Royal Society of London*, Vol. 52. (1998), pp. 39-50.

Chapter Three: Light – the two principal colours

ight and sight are the essence of mans being and because their very existence is dependent upon them, their significance (especially with regard to the Sun) has been built into religions and cultures in every age. It is therefore not surprising that the symbolism of light in one guise or another appears throughout Freemasonry. The object here is to establish the level of understanding of light those responsible for the early ritual had and why they adopted the version they did.

In order to gain an understanding of the prevailing science in the early 1720s, the Founders' perception of the world and the science that lay behind the technology and inherent beauty etc., of architecture and consequently Freemasonry, was discussed in Chapter Two. Taking the Symbolical Lecture as the prime indicator of the ritualists' disposition towards science it is of interest to consider their next topic: Light. However, as we shall see in Part V in the early 1700s new revelations with respect to light were of general interest, but particularly so to the group of men central to this Study. Present day ritual books contain the phrase: 'The ribbon borne by the Companions, is a sacred emblem denoting light, being composed of two of the principal colours with which the veils of the Temple were interwoven'. The ritual of Freemasonry has a tendency to verbosity (most likely true of this study also) and this seemingly throwaway statement could be taken as some fanciful remark based upon another equally arbitrary observation that these colours were often found in regal or religious settings. It is important to bear in mind that since it is not possible to know what was actually in their minds this allusion may be just fanciful, but it still poses the question of why would they, or indeed anyone, say it? As with most else in Freemasonry, extensive explanations have been proffered on this topic; such as why this or that particular colour had been selected (robes, gloves etc). In order to answer questions on colour Masonic historians have trawled the Bible and other important sources to find reasons why particular colours were first adopted into Freemasonry and remain today. However, one cannot help but conclude that most of these theses are based on their own interpretation. What is certain is that they cannot all be right, but when the scientific perceptions of the Founders are considered, it assumes a special importance because there is written proof of what several of them were prepared to proclaim as their understanding, but given all else about them, it becomes less easy to understand their choice and the purpose behind it.

However it will be reasoned here, that the phraseology and content adopted within the (then contemporary) Symbolical Lecture was based upon a still uncertain and hence compromised scientific perception of light held by those formulating the ritual. That it was most likely a compromise will be returned to in Part V, since it is almost certain that it was conceived by people especially qualified (in contemporary

Light - the two principal colours

terms) in matters scientific and that they would have at least taken a view. Their declared object, both inside and outside of Freemasonry, indicates a particular desire to communicate the importance of light to others even if they were less than certain themselves. Thus it is necessary to approach any assessment of this portion of the Ritual on the basis that it represents the Founders' publicly professed (ritualistic) understanding of the contemporary 'scientific truths'. That it was presented in this way because of their desire to inculcate 'Nature and Science' into the thinking of all fellow freemasons and that they were doing so through the then contemporary vogue of public (Symbolical in this case) lectures. Because of this uncertainty their particular explanation will be returned to later with respect to other aspects of the work, but it is introduced here to convey the scientific concepts behind that which, in view of their writings, they were likely to have believed, or at least agreed sufficiently for its inclusion in the Symbolical Lecture.

It is necessary to first understand why they chose the concept of 'the two principal colours' theory of the nature of light out of the confusing number of theories that existed at that time. Second, given the choice they made, how they rationalised/reconciled their analysis with the other strands of their scientific philosophy. The question of actually who, why and when will be considered in the later parts of this study, but it is useful to complement this somewhat by considering the scientific 'facts' available to the Founders and those authorities about them who were most likely to have influence their thinking on the concepts of light.

However, before we attempt to appraise their apparent ambiguity and to gain a proper perspective it is useful to first consider our own thinking on how we perceive and reconcile the so-called truths within modern science. This turns out to be a salutary exercise, since on an almost daily basis we are bombarded with new scientific and medical 'breakthroughs', technological innovation, staggering discoveries in space, etc. through the various media and we are forced to reconcile these new, often contradictory, concepts with respect to our current understanding. Do we interrupt our reading or hearing of a word or concept to look up or reflect on its meaning or simply continue? Some of these 'discoveries' are right others wrong, but even if we think them true and likely to affect us profoundly, we realise that it would require enormous effort to rationalise them within our present understanding and, life being rather short, we shrug our shoulders in the knowledge that it will be replaced by tomorrow's equally radical revelation – of necessity this basic dilemma of 'not being able to embrace all knowledge' will be returned to.

What then were these early (scientific) philosophies and concepts? Although we are also made aware, through the many forms of modern media, of the marvels of ancient cultures there still remains an innate belief, if not smugness, that the quasi-scientific concepts of early civilisations were quite rudimentary. However, it is quite surprising when studying their writings etc. to realise the amazing subtlety of their thinking. For instance, unless there has been a deliberate attempt to modify the writings etc., it is certain that the Egyptians knew that the surface of the Earth was (spherically) curved, but more surprising they had computed its radius to a high degree of accuracy. This insight into the true level of their thinking will require further consideration in subsequent Parts when discussing philosophy, religion and historical data, such as Solomon's Temple. Further investigation shows that the early Greek philosophers, for instance the pupils of Pythagoras, if not the great man himself, had proposed with total conviction that the World was indeed round. Aristotle, two centuries later argued that it had to be so for at least four very sophisticated reasons. In effect Aristotle's basic deduction and findings were:

1) Perfect symmetry: A sphere is the most symmetrically perfect of all objects and God only creates things that are perfect and the wonders of Nature and the earth are personified in the most perfect form: a sphere,

His experimental/observational findings:

2) Pressure: the earth's component pieces, falling naturally towards the centre, would press into a round form; precisely that which Newton and others later claimed to have discovered.

3) Shadow: in an eclipse of the moon by the Earth's shadow it is always circular: if it were a flat disc it would cast an oval (changing) shadow,

4) Star heights: even after travelling a short distance north or south, one sees a change in the elevation of the stars, which can only happen in a predictable way if one is travelling over a spherical surface.

The elegance of the deductive powers and profound writing of the ancients would have been studied by and certainly not wasted on the Founders, who would have almost certainly received a 'classics' type of education. It would have been clear that much that had been propounded (revolutionary and/or heretic concepts) by these early philosophers was by then, in essence, proving to have substance, despite the fact that there had been and still existed sustained attempts by the established church to suppress them. Thus when light was introduced into the ritual, it required them to have established in their own minds a coherent concept of light. They would have to decide the degree to which they would embrace the Ancients' philosophy, their own inner perceptions and to what extent that combination remained consistent with modern political/sociological/religious and hence permissible revelations and thinking, for it was not in their best interest to be too controversial.

Light - the two principal colours

As stated already, historically, optics and especially the study of the human eye had been deemed pre-eminent by many of the learned of virtually all advanced cultures and hence of unique importance; not least because it could be related to two of their other passions, geometry (they drew geometrical diagrams of the paths of light through the eye etc.) and music, or in their terms 'natural harmony'. This was true of the ancient world, including India and China where there were very sophisticated concepts of the way in which the eye functioned, the refraction of light caused by water and associated with that, its incidence within raindrops. Aristotle for instance had noticed that it was only possible to see a rainbow at certain times when the Sun's altitude was within a required angular range. This interest had been re-awakened in the Thirteenth Century, with many workers giving sophisticated geometric explanation of how light travelled through spheres for instance and were familiar with the possibilities of lenses made from (rather crude) pieces of glass etc. Desaguliers' portrait in Chapter Thirty-eight shows him holding a magnifying glass as an emblem of scientific sophistication. This progressive interest in light was maintained up until the period under consideration. However, by this time both telescopes and microscopes had been invented and they would have read best sellers Hooke's *Micrographia*[1] and Newton's *Optiks*[2] and certain of them would have conducted public demonstrations using lenses and prisms and as such would have had to form some opinion on the nature of light and the way in which it manifested itself.

Two things come from this: first it is important to avoid being dismissive of their comprehension of the physical world. Second, it is necessary to bear in mind that by the early 1700s they were being bombarded with profoundly differing views. In the case of light there were principally three: those of Descartes, Hooke and Newton, all at variance with each other. Although Descartes was of great importance to the science of the time, because his concepts were to some extent outside the bounds acceptable to this Group it will not be considered further. The two remaining concepts were proffered by people of extremely high intellect and repute, but for a whole gamut of reasons, personal, political and scientific, were in bitter dispute over a range of topics. Ironically nearly three hundred years later we still find that agreement over so called 'matters of fact' in science are rarely universally agreed and in consequence are hotly disputed. Their (these contemporary experts, one might fairly say geniuses) understanding of the nature of light represented an extreme example of the extent to which differing concepts can be offered as absolute truths at one and the same time, each totally dependent upon that particular individual's view. In this case they (Founders) would have almost certainly been very aware of both Newton's and Hooke's particular concepts – and if the views expressed in later Parts are correct, they would have lectured publicly upon the subject and been considered experts in their own right. Equally, they would have also been greatly influenced by and therefore reluctant to dismiss the philosophical arguments of their early education, their strongly held religious beliefs and their own, often conflicting, observations. But if now they were to include light as part of the ritual, they were no longer able to 'sit on the fence', but were now obliged to take an agreed stance.

The following discusses the nature of light, including the 'Corpuscular theories'. As an illustration of how uncertain they were likely to have been, it is helpful to consider some of the philosophy that preceded it. As will be discussed later, many of Aristotle's contemporaries considered fire to be the source of all things and especially the phenomenon of colour, whilst others considered it to be an extension of the 'four elements', with colour resulting from a combination of fire interacting with the other three elements. Aristotle believed light to be the purest form of fire and the light in the sky was unadulterated fire combined with other elements – *see* Chapters Five and Six. However, a most important factor in our appraisal is the Founders' retention of Platonism elsewhere in the Symbolical Lecture. For instance Aristotle was of the view that light was composed of two principal colours red and violet, and that all other colours were a combination (mixture) of these two unique colours.

Many ancient philosophers for instance the Greeks and the Asians (Indian) believed in the concept that all matter consisted of minute particles (Greeks – atoms) and whilst they differed over detail, believed that light was the effect of immutable sub-atoms of colour or sound. They simply extemporised on this basic theme: indeed to the extent where they believed that a dream was comprised of still smaller corpuscles and that in nightmares they were even smaller still. In practice these corpuscular concepts were to prove quite prophetic, but lacking rigour were, for the most part, forgotten.

The ascendance of Christian doctrine left no room for such irreligious speculation; it was absolutely certain to those expounding the true faith, that light, along with everything else was created by and hence attributable to God and God alone. For in Genesis God said: 'let there be light and there was light' and that this must be regarded as an indisputable fact and no alternative explanation could be tolerated. Thus apart from sporadic attempts in the eleventh, twelfth and thirteenth centuries to debunk this intransigence the acceptable fundamental (philosophical/metaphysical) perception of light was essentially that of Aristotle. Indeed, further progress had to await the arrival of more scientific astronomers and in particular Kepler in the late 1500s and of course Descartes, Hooke, Newton and others later still for a more widely agreed mechanistic explanation. During this developmental stage it was assumed that in some (rather vague and in various guises) way that light was the motion of a substance. Their allusion to 'motion' being merely the reconciliation of light's behavioural changes through objects such as fluids, lenses and prisms.

Scientific philosophers were struggling to rationalise the conflicting evidence

Light - the two principal colours

and a basic concept of light seemed to be a combination of inspired thought, conditioned by the conceptual scientific route they had travelled up to that point. Galileo had reasoned that light, like all physical effects was due to kinetic causes. For instance when he was studying sound he observed that a candle flame vibrated in sympathy with sound made close to it (analogous to the way in which light is converted to sound on the sound-track of a motion picture). Whilst he knew that the speed of light was incredibly faster than sound, he was convinced that it was nonetheless physically similar, although he appeared to have no specific view how it could be so. He had tried to measure the speed of light by exposing lanterns great distances apart on the tops of mountains, but had to conclude that light travelled in an instant (in a twinkling using his phraseology). Using his famed telescope he had observed among other things that Jupiter had four satellites that orbited the planet at regular intervals and had proposed their predictability as a means of determining time at any point on the earth. Indeed, on more than one occasion tried to use this phenomenon to establish longitude and hence claim (unsuccessfully) one of the many huge individual prizes then offered within most maritime nations, for such an achievement. It was not until the (Danish) astronomer Ole Roemer discovered that as the distance from the earth to Jupiter changed the eclipses of these satellites, were either in front or behind the predicted time by several minutes and rightly concluded that this was due to the observable effect of the speed of light over those huge, but differing, distances. Thus in the year 1676 he estimated (or rather slightly underestimated) the speed of light for the first time.

The other extreme was that light was matter and that all these effects could be explained on the basis of interaction between particles. These concepts were not restricted to Britain, but were the subject of debate in many of the centres of scholarship, but because we are concerned with the thoughts and motivations of the Founders, only those affecting the climate of opinion in Britain will be dealt with here.

During the 1600s there was a remarkable upsurge of scientific interest, not least in the phenomenon of light; resulting in the emergence in Britain of two basic schisms; centred on those of Isaac Newton and Robert Hooke. Newton is of course well known, but Hooke perhaps less so, for although a man of great genius, because of his somewhat humbler beginnings and stifled opportunity was not then, or indeed since, accorded anything like as much eminence. Unfortunately, in the field of science times have not changed and an intense rivalry (greatly influenced by the politics of the time) existed between Newton and Hooke and their disposition to take an opposite view was almost axiomatic – not least in their concepts of the nature of light, seemingly irrespective of merit. This at first may not seem to be particularly relevant, but as will be seen in Parts V and VI, they were closely associated (Hooke only through his writings) with the work of these two scientific giants and therefore

41

their views would likely have influenced the thinking of the Founders.

Further, an understanding of Hooke's and Newton's later (rather begrudging) concept on the nature of night is most important with respect to the interpretation of the words found in the Symbolical Lecture. It will also be argued that it indicates the intended (original) nature and hence timing of the Royal Arch Ritual.

Hooke's emergence into scientific reckoning could be judged to have started when he joined as an assistant to the physicist Robert Boyle and whilst grateful for the opportunity was frustrated by the level of subjugation it imposed and his entry into philosophical and experimental science in his own right was delayed for many years. He made up for this by later presenting a truly astounding number of original and quite brilliant papers on numerous aspects of science. He was appointed as the curator/experimenter to the Royal Society, of which many of the Founders were members. Indeed the same post was taken shortly after Hooke's death by Desaguliers the third Grand Master. Further, Hooke was older than Newton and shared many of the radical thoughts of Robert Boyle his erstwhile employer. Some historians argue that many of his quite breathtaking insights were just 'inspired guesses', another example that asks the question of how these various people could have been that lucky so many times? Again and at the risk of becoming boring, caution has to be exercised when relying on historians. In this instance one historian credits Hooke with the invention of the hairspring (the central component in Harrison's award winning chronometer) in a watch, whereas another credits the Dutch scientist Huygens with the same invention. Yet given the intense activity in horology during that period by single minded and highly motivated watchmakers and others, it would be more reasonable to question whether it was the invention of either scientist, but rather that it was 'appropriated', by fair means or foul, from a workaday watchmaker – on balance it would seem that Newton was not averse to borrowing in this way.

It would be inappropriate to go too deeply into certain of the various concepts of the nature of light that were in being propounded at that time, such as the concept of the æther consisting of transparent balls of varying size concentrated together by 'vortices'. From out of this muddle he (Hooke) concluded that light consisted of 've-locity' and 'matter', that it travelled instantaneously, that like sound it vibrated, but with the difference that the oscillations were transverse; unlike sound which were longitudinal. Reflection, refraction and chromatic phenomena could be accounted for by the nature of the passage of these waves across the transparent body, he was also the first to report what are now ironically referred to as Newton's rings.[3]

Consequently, Hooke felt compelled to contest the evidence being proffered by Newton, who had noted that rays of the sun on passing through a prism split into the colours of the rainbow. Substantiating his claim by showing that these rays could, with some slight, but significant exception, be reconstituted, through a series of lenses and prisms, back into whitish light, *see* Figure 3.1. Whitish, because his lenses were made of only one type of glass and as a consequence there was an inevitable degree of chromatic (dispersion) aberration. This is because in glass the level of refraction changes with colour and so the light's passage through Newton's prisms did as he predicted split into its constituent parts. However, when he used a convex lens to collect the rays together again, as by simple geometrical deduction it may have been presumed to have done, because of this aberration, failed to do so. Unfortunately for him, dispersion had already occurred and with the varying (differentially increasing) path lengths as it passed through the rest of the system only made matters worse. Because of this he came to the conclusion, quite late in his life and because of this innate tendency of light to refract differentially (dispersion in modern terms) from red through to blue, light could never be fully re-combined back into perfect white. A version of Newton's apparatus was almost certainly publicly demonstrated by the third Grand Master up to 1726, for it is well documented that he specifically lectured on Newton's *Optiks* (last published 1718)[4] and most likely by other prominent public lecturers John Senex (who became a Warden of Grand Lodge) and Robert Stukeley during the period 1715 to 1726. There were almost certainly others within this group who included some aspects of light in their lectures.

In fact, because on a number of occasions Newton received damaging doses of direct sunlight in earlier experiments, he had very poor sight and required others to conduct many of his later experiments on light, but unlikely with his degree of perception. Given this shortcoming he would not have been able to observe some of the more subtle effects present in these experiments. It is reasonable to suppose that given his thoroughness, such anomalies would have troubled him and almost certainly influenced his final conclusions. However, based on the findings reported

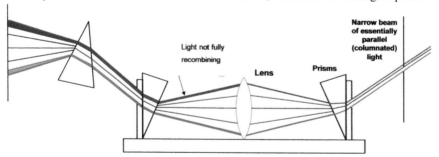

Figure 3.1. A (conveniently) modified copy of Newton's crude 2D sketch, in which he showed how white light splits into its spectral colours, was re-combined and then split again. However here because of inherent chromatic aberration the (exaggerated) separation would have worsened progressively through his relatively crude (single glass) optical system.

to him and his disposition towards 'dynamics', he considered that this behaviour could be explained by assuming that every light ray (consisting of particles) which had two faces vibrating in opposite directions, thereby explaining why close objects looked double when observed through a crystal such as Iceland Spar.

In the spectrum of the dispersed white light after passing through a prism he observed indigo at one extreme and red at the other. He argued that as the light entered the denser medium the back and front faces caused/produced a series of weak and strong impressions, the strong travelling in front and vice versa. If when they recombined on re-emerging from the prism, there was an imperceptibly small (phase lag) change, the eye would see a single strong ray, which would be red. Conversely if there were a perceptible difference then the eye would receive a blue impression. This concept was consistent with the two extremes of the rainbow. From this he concluded that the size of any (rainbow's spectrum) intermediate fundamental or primary colours were a subtle combination of these two extremes.

It is interesting to reflect on how easily it might have been for Hooke (or indeed Newton's 'extremes' concept, that he accepted late in his career) to have been persuaded to adopt a conceptual model; of there being two principle components to light, for the concept was not new. Plato considered there were 'two factors' governing the meeting of the visual fire emitted by the eye and the stream of 'corpuscles' emitted by the object. From this he concluded that: provided the particles are large enough to be split up by the visual fire then the eye would see black and conversely if the particles were small enough to split up the visual fire the eye will see white and all the colour in between are combinations of these two conditions – it had been necessary to have a solution such as this in order to explain the spectrum seen in the rainbow.

As stated earlier Aristotle's colour theory was quite different, but still rested upon the concept of 'either/or': claiming that colours result from different combinations of light and shade. A bright light and some shadow produce red; a dark shadow and weak light produce violet and again the intermediate colours follow from an intermediate combination of these two extremes.[5] By the time of Hooke all these theories were being challenged, for instance in 1674 Isaac Barrow (Newton's own tutor) still thought in terms of the early Greek black and white concept, again affirming that all other colours were a proportioned mixture of black and white. Outside of Britain the two fundamental constituents of light was propounded also, albeit in some quite bizarre guises.

At the time our Founders were at school and college Newton had not, at that early stage in his career, established himself in the all powerful position of President of the Royal Society and would not have had the power to suppress the opinions of others or blatantly peddle his own as became increasingly so when he did eventually become President. Thus the 'conventional wisdom' became that which most satisfied the rationale of an individual tutor, either personal tutors or teachers in schools and colleges. Even later, his exalted position did not protect Newton from attack on his concept of light, indeed it may have well prompted it and so his individual theories on light were under challenge all through the Founders' formative years and working life. But they were extremely committed disciples of Newton and so the wording found in the Symbolical Lecture would appear somewhat strange, unless at that stage they did not wish to digress too far from the Churches' acceptance of Aristotelian philosophy.

The problem was (if our present day theories on light are fundamentally correct) that whilst both Newton's and Hooke's versions differed they were each both right and wrong in complementary parts and equally wrong on the rest; each within their lifetimes having to concede errors in their thinking with respect to the other ideas on the subject. It would be difficult in a study such as this to go very much further into gainsaying their thoughts, but in simple terms it appears that: Newton, no doubt influenced by his beautifully conceived ideas on mechanics, believed that light was discreet particles of matter (analogous to the modern day concept of a photon: mass totally reduced to energy). Whereas Hooke believed that light propagated through the æther on curved transverse waves, rather like the ripples in a pond when a stone is thrown in, where a cork will for the most part bob up and down rather than go forward with the wave. It is not possible to know their thoughts precisely, but it is reasonable to suppose that because they were so brilliant in their thinking, they would in consequence be certain to have entertained some personal misgivings.

Indeed Newton was reported to have said, '... we cannot know whether light is a projection of bodies or merely an abstract motion'. In consequence he chose to refer to light in this speculative way, but if the section on light in the Symbolical Lecture has indeed been unaffected by the passage of time and not distorted by preceptors, scholars, historians etc. then it would appear that the Founders were at least sufficiently agreed for them to be able to instruct the newly exalted Companions on the fundamental 'concept of colour', albeit a compromise. Because it was a compromise, it required an intermediate position with respect to the differing theories above; namely that light was indeed comprised of two principal colours, from which all other colours are derived. However, because this topic is of some importance to subsequent discussion, the following is worthy of note.

Newton propounded the theory:

'Homogeneal Light has a Colour corresponding to its Degree of refrangibility, and that Colour cannot be changed by Reflexions or Refractions, (Newton's *Opticks* – Proposition II, Theory II - first published in the 1660s, although the final revision was in 1718).[6]

In effect he stated that white light was composed of a number of 'pure' colours, each with a specific degree of refrangibility (the degree to which light is refracted or bent when it enters another medium – say where a stick appears to be bent as it goes down into water). However, his Dutch contemporary Christian Huygens (who incidentally worked closely on this very topic with Hooke and Father Pardies – the epicentre of Continental science) had a rather better theory. Huygens had published his thoughts well before 1700 and so it is virtually certain that Newton was well aware of them, but preferring his own, choosing to disregard rather than debate any others.

This led Newton to several further conclusions, such as: that light was not of itself coloured, but was able to excite colour in the objects it fell upon. Again it is not possible to go into all the controversy this generated and in any case it would appear that despite his concept of the intermediate colours he writes:

'... the homogeneal light and rays which appear red, or rather make objects appear so, I call rubrifick or red-making; those which make objects appear yellow, green, blue, and violet. I call them yellow making, green-making, blue-making, violet-making and so of the rest.'

Note: his use of 'making' and not a subtle combination of 'absorption' and 'reflection'.

It was a characteristic of Newton when he could not give some precise phenomenological explanation to a particular matter, to be vague and consider it to be 'God given' and a further example of 'natural' magic. Thus he concluded after his many attempts to recombine the separated light during his experiments with prisms and lenses, that the red and blue ends of the spectrum could not (implying could never) be recombined completely.[7] This of course was later shown to be incorrect, not by a scientist, but by the optician Dolland in 1758, who made lenses from glasses of different refractive index, compensating the chromatic aberrations that Newton had experienced and could not eradicate when using individual pieces of glass fashioned out of one material.[8]

This is not meant to imply that the views of these other workers, either in Britain and especially those abroad, were of little value, for in many respects some of their concepts have proved to be more prophetic and in any case they were filtering into Britain at an increasing rate by the early 1700s. Whilst it is reasonable to suppose that this knowledge would have likely come to the attention of the few who were scientifically gifted, the most important factor was the dominance of Newton and to a lesser extent Hooke that was to influence the scientific community during this critical period in London and the other major cities of Britain. A surprisingly large number of that small band of gifted and/or privileged individuals were also members of the newly formed Premier Grand Lodge. If they were going to introduce a new innovation (the Royal Arch), it seems illogical to suppose that they would not have attempted to reconcile these differing concepts when composing the Symbolical Lecture. In this respect they clearly had sufficient common understanding to accept a consensus view on the basic concepts of 'light' for it to be included as a topic (being the source of revelation). It may have been that they did not have sufficient time or opportunity to consider at length the various scenarios which may have influenced their thinking on the subject. However, it is more likely that some of these newly emerging concepts did not fit easily into their total rationalisation of the physical and spiritual worlds and for that reason were disposed to disregard them and this very important possibility is returned to in many of the subsequent Parts.

Given the complete lack of written evidence, it has to be assumed that in those days ritual was transmitted by word of mouth only; the earliest written form of the Royal Arch Ritual in the Library of Grand Lodge is dated 1845; some one hundred and twenty years later. Given that this transference was done faithfully, then it is clear that they adopted the fundamental concept of 'the two principal colours' propounded by the near contemporary Hooke and the many others before him and for whatever reason was the one chosen by the Founders in the Symbolical Lecture.

As stated already the historical implications of the Founders' appraisal on light will be discussed in more detail later in Part V, since it appears to have a marked bearing upon the dating of the founding of the Royal Arch. To justify further this speculation as to why these concepts on light were adopted, the following points are made. Clearly well before the time of the first Chapter Meeting (1720s - 1730s) Newton's work had influenced Hooke who admitted the existence of an infinite range of colours – Hooke died in 1703. By the time that the Grand Lodge was founded, Newton had for his part deferred to Hooke's notion that light travelled as a result of vibrations, that it propagated transversely and not longitudinally and that it was the intensity of these waves that determined their colour, thus defining the extremes of red at one end and blue at the other as being in some way the determining factor. Thus from this muddled situation a third party could, if only vaguely, construct a theory which retained elements that were common to both great men. This appears to be the position adopted by the Founders when constructing the Symbolical Lecture. It implies that for some reason they accepted this compromised view and hence their stance on the fundamental nature of (colour) light.

Out of interest and again to illustrate how early the concepts of light were being questioned, it was a Frenchman called Melebranche who in 1712 stated that it was the frequency (Newton's promptitudes) that determined colour. However, that concept had to wait forty years before Euler claimed the now universally accepted concept: that it is frequency that determines colour. Euler 'inadvertently' forgot to acknowledge the work of Mclebranche, even though he was perfectly aware of it; *c'est la vie*! As will be discussed later the only nagging doubt is why, since they were likely to have known of these latest assertions, were the Founders so out of phase with this advanced thinking?

Conclusion

Thus it may be concluded that from the 1845 up to 1938 the Aldersgate version of the ritual (tacitly official) books implied that, for whatever reason, the Founders had chosen to accept the Hookean (and Platonian/Aristotelian – *see* Section on the elements) theory that there were in fact two (and only two) principal colours and in doing so relegated all other colours to some subtle combination of the two. It is safe to assume that any concept of light chosen after this time would have most likely been different.

References

1. Hooke, R., *Micrographia* (J. Martyn & J. Allestry, London, 1665 or Dover Publications Inc., Mineola, New York, 2003 [a more readable version]).

2. Newton, I., *Optiks* (Dover Publications Inc., Mineola, New York 1967 [a more readable version]).

3. Hooke, *op. cit.*

4. Newton, *op. cit.*

5. *Ibid.*

6. Taton, R., *The beginning of modern science – general history of the modern sciences (1450 – 1800)*, (Thames and Hudson, London, 1958), pp. 287-306.

7. Taton, *ibid.*

8. Bernal, J., *The Extension of Man* (Weidenfield & Nicolson, London, 1972), pp. 113-116.

Chapter four: Geometry

ypically the Symbolical Lecture found in the English Royal Arch ritual claims: 'These lights are arranged in the form of an equilateral triangle, each of the lesser [...] all equal and all equilateral', but with the difference that whilst geometry is interlaced throughout all of the preceding rituals this is the first occasion where an attempt is made to formally justify the specific nature of that geometry. However, this and all other reference to classical geometry is perhaps the most difficult of the subject areas considered within this study to place in time. As will be discussed in Part II this difficulty is due mostly to the fact that geometry, despite its classical origins, was not during the period under consideration necessarily taught in every grammar/private (now called 'public') type school. Its importance to the operative mason is patently obvious, but its esoteric connotations were by then of great importance to the speculative freemason and although they were much more subtle and the reasoning symbolic, because geometry has such absolute rigour and implicit profundity was especially so. Certainly they and we know that the triangle was the very foundation of classical (formal) geometry and it would be a necessary component in any scheme designed to emphasise the beauty of classical learning, especially if (as is believed here) they were familiar with and strongly influenced by, the basic precepts of Newtonian physics. Thus it is reasonable to suppose that it would have pleased the Founders to integrate such 'truisms' into their ritual and thereby engineer some subtle link with other physical (contemporary) concepts that they seemed most anxious to demonstrate – *see* the later Section on the origins of the Royal Arch in Part V. It is therefore well worthy of some further consideration – certainly given its specific inclusion as one of 'the seven liberal arts and sciences' designated in the explanation of the 2nd Degree Tracing Board and elsewhere. It is important to reiterate that throughout it is presumed that the Lectures were part of the Royal Arch ceremony from the very beginning.

Without the Newtonian dimension (*see* Part V) it is somehow strange that during the period that the Premier Grand Lodge and the Royal Arch were founded, when there was a frenetic interest in matters scientific, that there was such a reluctance to adopt analytical (algebraic type) mathematics, or at least within the section of scholarly society with which we are concerned. The subject of greatest interest in the numerous public lectures given at that time, were purported to explain the astronomical (gravitational) concepts propounded by Newton. Unless the content of these lectures were to be totally superficial it required the recipients to consider a concept (analysis) based on classical geometry and since time has not diminished that requirement, some explanation will be attempted below. During the period with which we are concerned this purely geometrical approach was seriously challenged by Newton's arch rival Leibnitz, who was championing his analytical version of the Calculus. Since modern Calculus is based on his (Leibnitz's) approach we know that his method had great merit and elegance which would have been sufficient in itself to annoy Newton, but it was the more threatening because of Leibnitz's Germanic origins and especially when it became most likely that he would receive a royal (now Hanoverian) invitation to visit this Country. This prospective visit merely inflamed further the already acrimonious academic conflict over who should be credited with the invention of the 'Calculus'. To Newton and many others this visit was pertinent because it was an overt expression of the newly arrived Hanoverian influence in Court Circles and which was having a large impact on society in general and our people in particular – *see* Parts II and III.

This snippet of information is introduced not as a digression, but to emphasise the importance, near (contemporary) obsession, with classical geometry and in particular the central role of the triangle in Newton's brilliant concepts on the fundamental attraction between planetary bodies and the techniques of the Calculus he used in formulating his Laws of Gravitation. So brilliant was his intellect that it is almost certain to have been able to embrace the mathematically (algebraic) analytical form, but his only public explanation was in terms of, and in places extremely obscure, (triangular/conical) geometry. The irony was that Leibnitz's method of the Calculus was infinitely more elegant and given the scientific calibre of people such as Desaguliers, Brooke-Taylor, Stukeley etc. it could have been more easily appreciated and better expressed in this form. However, this would not have satisfied the nation's obsession with the self-publicist Newton, who would in any case, have been disposed to reject it on principle, because of its source.

Even with the benefits of extremely good text books and some tuition, only a very talented person would be able to claim that to acquire a knowledge of Calculus is an easy process and only then after it has been painstakingly explained in the text (at least in the author's estimation). It is therefore the more remarkable that Newton needed, for his purposes, to actually invent (his version of) it! As has been stated already, it was the more amazing since his basic approach was via triangular geometry and very obscure conics, set out in a form that was complicated in the extreme. Indeed, Professor Richard Feynman, acknowledged as one of the World's most brilliant theoretical (mathematical) physicists of recent times and who was awarded the Nobel Prize for his mathematical modelling of atomic physics, admits to the following in a lecture he gave to his students at Cornel University.[1]

Geometry

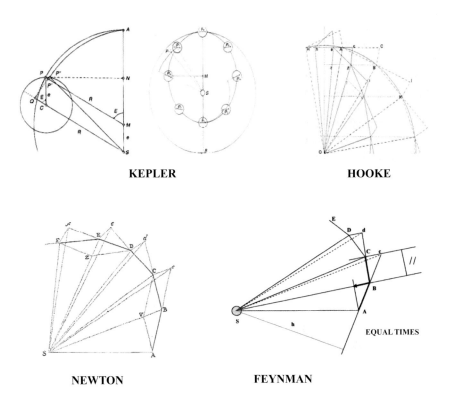

KEPLER   HOOKE

NEWTON   FEYNMAN

Figure 4.1. Various sketches of those attempting to show the influence of the Sun on planetary motion. Note the progression from Kepler's original concept. Hooke acknowledged Kepler's contribution, but Newton refuted any debt to Hooke. A representation of Feynman's 'constant angle' blackboard sketch used in his lecture[2] to undergraduate students, many others used analogous sketches, including Desaguliers – *see* Appendix 1.

'The demonstration that you have just seen is an exact copy of one in the *Principia Mathematica* by Newton, and the ingenuity and delight which you may or may not have gotten from it is that already existing in the beginning of time.

Now the remaining demonstration is not one which comes from Newton, because I found I couldn't follow it myself very well, because it involves so many properties of conic sections. So I cooked up another one.' – *see* Figure 4.1.

The comparatively recent (1990s) modifications to the Mystical lecture of the Royal Arch had begun already to relegate the importance of the triangle within the

The Key to Modern Freemasonry

(English Constitution) Ritual, but that in 2004, because of concerns over religious connotations and hence political correctness, has suppressed it even further. However, a study of early ritual books, shows that this tendency to disregard with impunity the admonition made to all incoming masters and hence effectively all the hierarchy of Masonry, 'not to make (fundamental) innovation within the Body of Masonry' seems to be a recent phenomenon, demonstrating the political expediency of this present generation rather than their predecessors' passive disregard of external criticism. It appears almost certain that they (founders) felt that there was, or had been up until their now more enlightened understanding, a strong connection between the triangle and worship in general and thus the triangle was worthy of its place in the Ritual. Since they did not seem to mind being associated with the Fraternity, but were rather proud to be a member, it would appear that they were not under pressure or at least insufficiently so, to be influenced by contemporary (parochial and political propriety) religious consideration and so, for whatever reason, their motivation to promote the triangle was quite considerable.

Thus it is reasonable to conclude that they place considerable importance on the historical, philosophical, spiritual and architectural connotations of the triangle. A probable reason for this was because it was to be found in all civilisations:

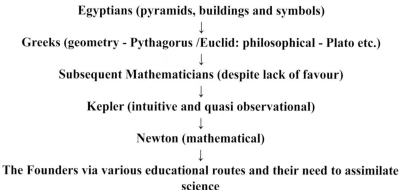

Egyptians (pyramids, buildings and symbols)
↓
Greeks (geometry - Pythagorus /Euclid: philosophical - Plato etc.)
↓
Subsequent Mathematicians (despite lack of favour)
↓
Kepler (intuitive and quasi observational)
↓
Newton (mathematical)
↓
The Founders via various educational routes and their need to assimilate science
↓
The proposed exaltee's earlier schooling, Masonic ritual and in particular the Symbolical Lecture

Geometry

However, to the Founders of Masonry there was a further important reason, namely its relevance with respect to its functionality in operative masonry and philosophy because of its mathematical rigour, thereby the imperative need to both understand and reflect upon it:

> 'These lights are placed in the form of an equilateral triangle, each of the lesser
> ... all equal all equilateral'

but it is of interest to note that in an extended (earlier) form of the Ritual were included the words:

> 'emblematical of the four points or divisions of Masonry – viz., the four levels of
> status: E. A., F. C., M. M. and H. R. A.' [this form of words was deleted from the
> published Ritual *circa* 1921].[4, 5]

However, for the moment it will be assumed that they required a vehicle to introduce the concept of greater and lesser lights (or vice versa), but for whatever reason were intrigued by the elegance surrounding the geometry of the equilateral triangle, which would likely to have been pointed out to them at school or at some early stage in their education, as a profound geometrical truism. As would have been the concept:

> 'that the sum of the interior angles of a triangle are together equal to two
> right angles'

see Figure 4.2. That the triangle may be symmetrically divided into lesser triangles will be left as essentially self-evident.

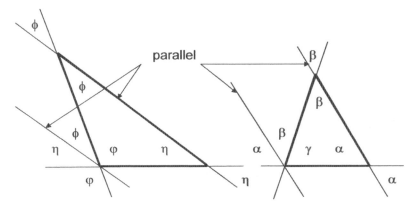

Figure 4.2. The geometrical proof: 'that the sum of the included angles of a triangle (both obtuse and acute) equal two right angles'.

Their next assertion was:

'This symbolical arrangement corresponds to the mysterious triple tau.'

This is an interesting concept because this claim is difficult to justify in terms of the classical writing of the upper or lower cases of the letter tau **T** and **τ** since the ends of the crossbar on its extremities extends (only) downwards. However, this would not have served their purpose since, to satisfy the nuances of their intended ritual, they wished to have a central '**T**' (T without the bars at its extremities) and three sub-Tees to correspond with the four triangles inside the main triangle. This would enable them to form a connection between two 'geometric truths': the first that '*the sum of the included angles of any triangle,* (in their special case an equilateral triangle), *equal two right angles*'. The second, the implications of the configuration under consideration, namely:

'the three lesser triangles at its extremities and one in the centre, all equal and all equilateral'

Thus by definition this would confirm that there were eight right angles in the enclosed angles of their highly stylised version of their so called triple Tau. The impertinent use here of 'so called' is employed because there are in fact four minor taus (at least in the current depiction) not three as can be seen in Figure 4.3. Some historians give a more elaborate biblical derivation based upon a combination of 'T' and indeed introduce the concept of an 'H'. However, the one used here is based upon the symmetry of the early jewels, which pre-date these much more recent assumptions. In any case if symmetry is to be maintained and the ritual consistent, there is a need for there to be four identical taus, but in the final analysis they may be right, for there can be no actual proof. However, it is quite clear there is a predominance throughout the whole of Royal Arch ritual of the number four, even in the very closing remarks.

As time passes it is increasingly less likely that the true intention of the authors of the Royal Arch will ever be known, but it is reasonable to speculate that the probability was that it would have been somewhat of the form outlined below. This because it was essential for them to establish a link between the triangle and the all-important 'right angle', thereby supporting the basic fundamental claim: that it was a 'true and proper thing to know a Mason by'. They would have been well aware of the important symbolic connotations of two superimposed equilateral triangles used in a number of religions (especially as this fact was stated specifically in the earlier version of the 'Mystical Lecture'), but a further recommendation for its adoption would have been its common use as an operative mason's mark.

Geometry

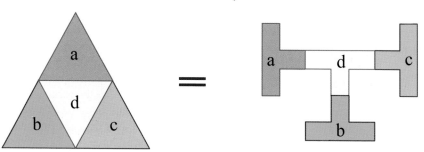

Figure 4.3. A symmetrical representation of the 'triple tau' used widely on Royal Arch summons etc., namely: 1 (equilateral) Triangle = 2 right angles = 1/4 'tau' (a stylised T).

Whether or not the Founders had been taught the importance of geometry at school, it would appear from Masonic ritual and other writings that its importance was considered to be of much greater educational significance then, than is the case today. This because all through the 17[th.] century there was a mistrust by many English scholars, of the emerging mathematical (analytical) approach being adopted by certain (foreign) academics – especially that of Leibniz cited above and discussed in Part V. It is particularly difficult to explain this aversion, because there was an upsurge in the 1500s in the concept of formal algebra in essentially the same form we know it today. Indeed, it was an Englishman: Robert Recorde who first introduced the plus (+) and minus (-) signs and more especially the equals (=) sign – *circa* 1540. However it may have been that they were simply intrigued by the angular relationships that could be attached to the triple 'Tau', deeming it appropriate because it was at once both scholarly and could be shown to be associated with the Basic Elements (*see* Chapter Six) and had obvious religious connotations. Perhaps a more significant factor is that the exaltee would be led to appreciate the important educational requirement necessary of competency in mathematics (however defined). On the presumption that without an understanding of geometry, he would be ill equipped to become a well rounded man or become fully *au fait* with the emerging (contemporary) scientific thinking; which within Freemasonry was deemed to be an essential and distinguishing characteristic.

Alternatively it may have been some other far less obvious masonic artefact they wished to illustrate, but which has been lost over the years. That classical geometry was at that time considered a most important part of any cultured person's education was without doubt and this claim will be developed immediately below. But, it must be remembered that geometry retained an important place in education until quite recent times – *circa* 1950/60s an essential part of most, if not all, Higher

School Certificate and then National (UK) Advanced Level Pure Mathematics examination papers at that time and it was in effect the only sure method of entering into a study of the 'sciences', or for that matter most subjects, at university.

As we shall see when considering 'the sphere of the Universe' by working on Tycho Brahe's extraordinary data, first as his employee and subsequently as the beneficiary of his Will, Kepler was eventually able to show that the area swept out by a planet in its orbit around the Sun was the same for any one unit of time. As planets orbit around the Sun their velocity is a function of their distance from it and the further they are away the slower they travel. This basic 'unit area to unit time' relationship is shown in the sketch in Figure 4.4b.

Nothing appertaining to science gripped the general public's imagination more than Newton's Laws of planetary motion. Whilst certain of the Founders were concerned with the excitement of Newton's mathematical concepts and the need to communicate them to a wider audience, there were some religious and appreciable technical difficulties in doing so. Certainly Newton at a personal level appeared reluctant to depart from geometric concepts and as will be seen below, his famous work *Principia* is essentially based entirely upon geometry and (impulsive) mechanics. As was pointed out above, Kepler in his work on the motion of planets had already shown that planets travel on curved trajectories and that the Sun was positioned at one of the foci of their elliptical orbits and that the area swept out by any planet in unit time was constant – *see* Figure 4.4a.

a   b

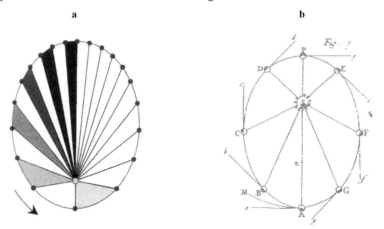

Figure 4.4 a & b). Kepler's basic concept that the area swept out by a comet or planet in unit time was constant. b) The basic concept used by Newton in postulating the laws of planetary motion (absolutely reliant on Kepler being right) as depicted by Desaguliers – *see* Apendix 1 and Figure 4.1b.

Hooke (and indeed others) had already adopted Kepler's concepts and had written to Newton on the matter, which was to become a festering sore for the rest of Hooke's life. Newton became absolutely convinced of their validity and from what followed it was clear that he was able to conceive in his mind how this could be related to some (gravitational) inter-active force of attraction between the Sun and its planets, but he needed to establish the law that governed this behaviour. Newton had already developed a most profound understanding of the laws (principles) of 'mechanics' and as these were quite fundamental, then planetary motion should by definition be totally consistent with them. If he could demonstrate such a relationship, using his Mechanics, whilst at the same time remaining consistent with Kepler's planetary behaviour, then he would have established the laws of planetary motion. Figure 4.1 includes Newton's basic diagram of the complex argument by which he was finally able to accomplish this quite remarkable feat; however before doing so it is necessary to invoke another geometric proof.

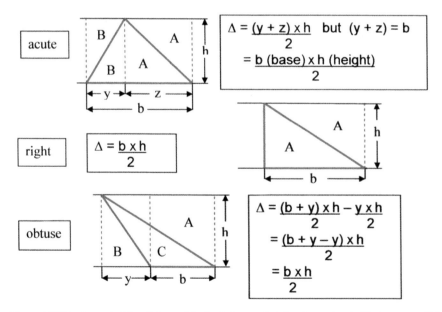

Figure 4.5 This shows that for all three of the basic forms of a triangle constructed between parallel lines its area (Δ) is half the length of its base (b) multiplied by the height (h) of separation between those lines.

Because each worker requires the concept of equal areas for triangles between parallel lines Figure 4.5 is the geometric proof that is essential in all of the various sketches in Figure 4.1, since they have to comply with Kepler's laws (especially his second Law):

1/ The orbits of planets are ellipses with the Sun in one focus.

2/ Arm from the Sun to planets sweeps out equal areas in equal times (shown to be necessary for any 'central' force).

3/ The cube of the orbit's radius divide by the square of a planet's year is the same for all planets of the solar system.

To demonstrate the basic reasoning, Newton constructed (very crude in its basic form) a series of triangular (velocity) diagrams – *see* Figure 4.1. He considered the starting point to be at the end of the line 'S' to 'B'. Each element shows how the planet would have continued on in a straight line if there had been no Sun, in this case position 'c'. He represented the modification after the Sun's gravitational attraction had pulled it off its course to position 'C' by the line 'S' to 'C'. Thus the second triangle he used to represent the (observed) position of a planet after having been deflected. Given that the position of the planet without modification would be on a line 'B' to 'c'. then 'S' to 'c' can be drawn. But to get to the observed point and to conform to Kepler's Law it would have swept out an equal area in a nominal time. If then a parallel line to 'S' to 'B' is drawn through 'C', then the line 'C' to 'c' can be drawn; because both triangles have the same height and hence area. But these are huge triangles whereas in reality the planet actually travels in a smooth curved orbit constantly shifting position and by reference to Figure 4.4 it would have been a quasi segment and not a triangle! Thus Newton's diagram would have only been representative if there had been an instantaneous change (gravity impulse) of direction for each triangle, but again simple observation shows that the planets do not jerk their way round the Sun. This is where his genius came into play, for he postulated that it could be assumed to do so if the triangles of his diagram become smaller and smaller and smaller (in the classical way of 'the Calculus') until there is no separation between them and the trajectory would then be describing a smooth path – this is precisely the technique (i.e. the 'vanishingly small' Leibniz type assumption) employed in modern analytical calculus.

For those not familiar with 'the Calculus' approach, it would reasonable to question the claim that this mathematical description of the path described by a planet was indeed continuous. A very crude demonstration of this approach can be seen every day on the television screen and the cinema, since the individual frames

Geometry

are so close together (25 × 2 frames per second) that the motion, because of the natural persistence of the eye, appears to be continuous – but if we now imagine the frame separations to be not one fiftieth of a second, but infinitely small then the motion would truly be continuous.

Although this aspect of Newton's work considerably predates the time with which we are concerned, it is important to persist with the topic in greater detail for a number of reasons, but principally two: first he did not publish it until much later and then in Latin only. Second, distributing its message through the vehicle of public lectures in the early 1700s was a major activity of several of the most important Premier Grand Lodge characters in this analysis – again *see* subsequent Parts.

The above is of course an over simplification and not a 'proof' and a better understanding of the sheer complexity of Newton's thinking and its amazing brilliance is beautifully illustrated by returning to the book by Goodstein and Goodstein.[6] The purpose of their book was in fact to expand on the elegance of the famous lecture delivered by Richard Feynman to undergraduate students at Cornell University in the USA. Within that Lecture Feynman himself expands upon the way in which Newton used Euclidean geometry:

'On the other hand, in the beginning of our science – that is, in the time of Newton – the geometrical method of analysis in the historical tradition of Euclid was very much the way to do things. And as a matter of fact, Newton's *Principia* is written in a practically completely geometrical way – all the calculus things being done by making geometric diagrams. We do it now by writing analytic symbols on the blackboard, but for your entertainment and interest I want you to ride in a buggy for its elegance, instead of a fancy automobile. So we are going to derive this fact by purely geometrical arguments – ...'.

Provided one has a reasonable understanding of basic mathematics, this book is useful in gaining an insight into the complex reasoning of Newton's work on this topic and from that to gauge the intellectual capabilities of a number of those Founders central in the creation of Premier Grand Lodge; particularly those who lectured on Newtonian physics.

In a book entitled: *Calculus Made Easy,* the author states '... that what one fool can do so can another', but most who have attempted to do so, find this trite comment to be a considerable understatement. It is hoped that the above attempt to condense Newton's brilliant geometrically based concepts into just a few brief paragraphs, has not made things worse. It is almost certainly insufficient for those arriving at the subject for the first time, to gain any profound understanding, but it is hoped sufficient to illustrate the importance of geometry. Further that it gives an impression of the scale of his revelation and why it and geometry was a pre-occupation in the minds of many in society at the time of the founding of the Royal Arch.

Having put the case to the newly exalted Companion that in order to understand the physical world he needed to have knowledge of geometry. It was reinforced immediately by proceeding to an explanation of the geometry of the jewel. In terms of the dating of events the jewel is of considerable importance since its centre motive is present in the very earliest (the likely earliest available: J.J. Rouby's jewel – 1766) versions of those made in the eighteenth century. Whatever the Founders' motivation was for introducing the geometrical concepts of the Jewel, it is interesting to study the words they employed.

'It also serves to illustrate the jewel worn by the Companions which forms by its intersections a given number of angles: these may be taken in five several combinations, and when reduced to their amount in right angles, will be found equal to the five regular platonic bodies representing the four elements and the sphere of the universe'

– the 'Platonic Bodies' being the subject of the next Chapter. It is of interest to note that the Latin inscription on the jewel *Si talia jungere possis: sit tibi scire satis*, may be reasonably translated to mean 'If thou canst understand (unite) these things: then thou knowest enough'– evidently no further pursuit warranted.

The phrase: 'It serves to illustrate the jewel worn by the Companions' cannot for several reasons be viewed in isolation, since it may be regarded as an obvious extension to the concepts surrounding the equilateral triangles of the 'Greater and Lesser Lights'. Indeed it featured so large in the Founders' estimation that they returned to it again in their consideration of the 'Regular Solids'. The common factor throughout is the symmetry of the equilateral triangle, square and the pentagon, but in the case of the jewel, just an extension of the geometrical relationships peculiar to the equilateral triangle.

A symbolic line diagram equivalent of the jewel is used in the explanation below; in essence it consists of two equilateral triangles symmetrically super-imposed upon each other, used frequently by operative masons as their individual mark. However, even on very early examples of the Jewels, the triangles are double lined and interlaced and as such are not strictly 'lines', but have pronounced width, a point of some note as will be discussed.

Most of those who have needed to commit the Symbolical Lecture to memory will admit to finding the above form of words in this particular section of the Lecture difficult to retain. This is because their message is obscure and the phraseology appears somewhat clumsy. However, if an attempt is made to try to understand the originator's geometrical reasoning, it may be regarded as being most succinct, but as usual with this study there are complications. It does however illustrate that those

Geometry

who conceived the ritual were men who clearly understood the intrinsic argument of the statement.

This aspect of the work has a further importance when it is shown to be consistent with the analysis in Part V that is concerned with the origins of the Royal Arch and the speculation over who founded the Order and why. A factor central to this aim was to establish the rationale of those responsible for the content of the ritual. If the Royal Arch was to survive they needed to make the ritual sufficiently inspiring to become an important part of the *raison d'être* for brethren to meet on a regular basis and thereby unite the Companions in a profound bond with each other. It will be claimed that this stimulation was in large part achieved through the presentation of the lectures. Clearly this may be pure conjecture and does depend to a large degree on how much, or perhaps more importantly how little, of the ritual has been deliberately or inadvertently modified since that time. It is the presumption here that the ritual has, at least in terms of its specific fundamental principles and especially the scientific content, remained unchanged.

It has been shown in the Section dealing with light, that the transfer of ritual by the written word is clearly prone to modification, since such changes are made for reasons such as grammatical, individual conception, ritualistic, political and religious correctness. Thus such modifications rely on the translator's perception of the ritual and the possible need for change and this factor will be returned to later, but a good illustration of how this may occur can be gained by reference to a book of Royal Arch Ritual dated 1921.[7, 8] Included in this book of ritual[9] is an additional, now rarely used, piece of ritual entitled 'An Explanation of the Jewel'. As one would expect this has a large section devoted to explanation of the phrase '..... its intersections forming a given number of angles: ...'. The person or persons who decided to construct this additional piece of ritual clearly had an extremely good knowledge of formal Euclidean geometry and as in the version given below, were of the view that they were in touch with the thinking of the Originals. In order that their Ritual would be taken as a convincing analysis of the jewel they needed to also relate it to the Five Regular (Platonic) Solids: as indeed will be attempted later in this analysis (no doubt with the same level of partiality, but it is hoped not with quite their absolute certainty).

In order to comply with this essential requirement of the Ritual, they had to devise a scheme which would enable them to relate the various sums of right angles derived in a sufficient number of combinations (and hence the requisite number of 'taus') to match those in the Regular Solids. Unfortunately there seems to be as many ways of demonstrating this possibility, as there have been people prepared to give the matter serious thought. However, in their case (in the seemingly 'approved' version, at least tacitly if not formally, by the Grand Chapter at that time – since this particular book of ritual gained favour) they have chosen to take a very 'convenient' version of the Jewel. In the Museum at Freemasons' Hall, London, there are many examples of very early Royal Arch Jewels and whilst there was considerable individual licence in their manufacture, it is clear that these jewels were made a long time before this supplementary ritual was written. In almost every case the two triangles are interlaced and have width (double lined) in exactly the same way as that used in all modern breast-jewels. In this instance the authors chose to ignore this fact and constructed their reasoning on a quite modified version with only one of the triangles being double lined and hence the figure is asymmetric – *see* Figure 4.5 below.

Using this configuration they were able to demonstrate a relationship between their triangles and the required number of 'Taus' etc., but in the attempt they had unfortunately modified the configuration of the Jewel itself. Since this quasi 'official' version of the Ritual Book was widely adopted by Chapters, presumably without further challenge from the establishment, this particular explanation would subsequently be regarded as the definitive explanation of the Jewel. Thus by implication any future (casual) reader could be forgiven for concluding that it represented the rationale of the Founders, but given the evidence of the earlier jewels and literature, one must merely regard it as a typical and quite modern interpretation by a Masonic ritualist/historian.

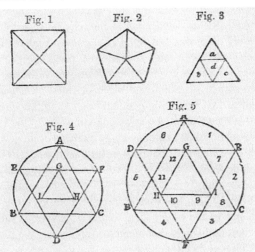

Figure 4.5. Facsimile of the sketch used by the author of the 'Explanation of the Jewel' in the Aldersgate ritual of 1931. Note that the device of introducing the additional triangle allowed them to avoid exterior lines but compromise the model.

Geometry

However, unless some ancient document comes to light there is no way of knowing what the originators actually had in mind. This position of doubt will have to remain, since as will be demonstrated below, it is possible even within the simplified single line form used here to conceive of many ways of conforming to the basic precept found in the Symbolical Lecture and there would have been very many more using double lines.

Any explanation has to obey the following: 'these may be taken in five [one for each solid presumably] several [a number units for each] combinations', and yet still remaining within the dictates of formal geometry taught at the time. Neither does it need to use a distorted interpretation of the Jewel itself and better still the technique does not need to use asymmetry or repeated forms.

Thus the Jewel may be better understood by literally doing that which they recommend; namely consider the configuration in selected symmetrical parts. However, as has been stated above, to do so it is necessary to make an assumption with respect to what they did in fact mean by a 'combination'; the validity of the following explanation has to be left to the judgement of the reader. At worse it will provide the basis, from which readers may be encouraged to attempt analysis of their own.

Not only was this configuration used by various religious sects, but also early operative mason's marks often consisted of interlaced equilateral triangles, however they were usually in a single line form. Thus for the purposes of the following analysis the illustration below consists of essentially two basic units: a central hexagon and six appended equilateral triangles and their exterior lines. The use of the angles formed by these exterior lines might at first appear to be another contrivance, but that is not so, since it has been a legitimate approach, used in formal geometry, since the ancient Greeks and especially (or indeed in most formal geometrical proofs – *see* Figure 4.2 for example) Euclidean analysis it is essential. In this case it is necessary because as we shall find, there are clearly insufficient internal angles within the figure to equate to the presumption: '... that when reduced to their amount in right angles, they will be equal to the five regular platonic solids'.

Therefore this analysis is based on the proposition that it is possible to isolate at least six quite individual (and symmetrical) combinations that will provide the basic number of right angles (and hence taus) required to construct the solid. The various unique triangular configurations used here are shown in Figure 4.6. The number contained within each figure is equivalent to the number of taus and that outside the equivalent number of right angles.

A particular set of data taken from Figure 4.6 below and is presented as Table 4.1, but it is clear one could to use many combinations of just these symmetrical subsets etc. It follows therefore that there are numerous ways of meeting the requirement specified in the Ritual. This is interesting because to the casual reader of the Ritual in question implies that there can only be one solution.

Thus it is possible to comply with the first premise contained in the ritual in a whole variety of ways, by using simple geometric axioms and without recourse to asymmetry or other devices. If one were to extend that to a configuration based on two interlaced (two line wide) triangles as these earlier authors did with just the one inner triangle, the number of possible combinations becomes very large indeed.

Elements (factors)	Solids	Number of:			combinations (suggestions)*
		faces	right angles*	taus	
Fire (lightest)	Tetrahedron	4	8	1	b to e
Air (Next lightest)	octahedron	8	16	2	b to f
Earth (most solid)	cube	6	24	3	a to g
Water (intermediate)	icosahedron	20	40	5	a to i
Sphere of the Universe	dodecahedron	12	72*	9	a,g to o, or say h,m to q etc.

* **Interior/exterior lines, corollary 32nd Problem of Euclid, etc, *see* text.**

Table 4.1. **Typical combinations that would sum to provide the equivalent taus necessary to form the Regular Solids. (Note there are the five individual examples, one for each solid, thus requiring, as they suggest, several combinations).**

Geometry

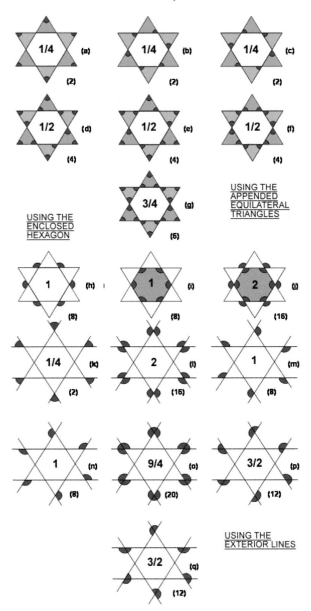

Figure 4.6 Typical combinations of included angles

65

Since the above appears to provide sufficient evidence within the framework of formal geometry it is now possible to satisfy the next requirement, whilst still remaining within the concept of the interlaced triangles. Clearly if the Founders intended to embrace the 'regular solids' within the Ritual they needed to progress to an integrated and more fundamental concept:

> '... and when reduced to their amount in right angles, will be found equal to the five regular platonic bodies, which represents the four elements and the sphere of the Universe'.

Again this is another example of how difficult it is to determine just how much of an understanding of the basic concepts of 'nature and science' was expected of the well-educated man during this narrow slot in history. The answer to this rhetorical question becomes more interesting and would be even harder and a somewhat less reassuring if the same were asked of a new exaltee today.

Conclusion

Thus it would be reasonable to categorise the status of formal geometry as follows: that in England in the early 1700s Newton's work had captured the public's (especially some very influential members who were certainly responsible for founding the Premier Grand Lodge) interest to an astonishing degree. An important factor was that Newton's great work was expressed in terms of classical geometry; essentially that of the triangle. Thus if an ordinary person and especially freemasons, because of the injunction laid upon them, were to even begin to understand the complexity of Newton's physical concepts of science and hence the natural world it was essential that they possessed an understanding of formal geometry. The writings of the time and social historians since have indicated that a good proportion would have already studied geometry to that level or would have been prepared to make the effort to do so.

That whoever he or they were who had formulated the explanation of the Jewel in the ritual and their choice of words accurately described the mechanism by which they had attempted to demonstrate it. They had created distinct sets, or building blocks, and then chose various combinations of them. Whilst it is possible to represent the five regular solids with just a single line diagram, it is clear that the double line version found in the actual breast jewel would present very many more.

References

1. Goldstein, G. & Goldstein, J., *Feynman's lost lecture* (Jonathan Cape, London, 1996).

2. Goldstein & Goldstein, *op. cit.*

3. Anon, *The perfect ceremonies of the Supreme Order of the Holy Royal Arch* (Private Publication, A. Lewis, London, 1921).

4. Anon, *op. cit.* (1953)

5. *Op. cit.* (1921)

6. Goldstein & Goldstein, *op. cit.*

7. Anon, *op. cit.* (1921)

8. *Op. cit.* (1953)

9. *Op. cit.* (1921)

Chapter Five:

'… the five regular Platonic bodies which representing the four elements and the sphere of the Universe'.

his trite half sentence from the Symbolical Lecture of the Royal Arch Ritual does in practice present some difficulty since it contains a whole gamut of quite profound concepts and so once again there is the problem of where to start. However since geometry has been discussed already and its importance in Newton's discoveries established, the formal geometric aspects of the above statement will be tackled first. Nonetheless, in order to maintain continuity the various facets will be considered in the reverse order to that found in the Symbolical Lecture and the so called four elements and the astronomical connotations attached to the fifth solid will be the subject of the two subsequent Chapters. Although the philosophy of science with respect to Freemasonry in the 1720s is deferred until Parts V and VI, it is perhaps useful to mention briefly several pertinent matters, in order to appreciate the likely 'mind set' of the Founders. First it is essential to avoid the problem of the adverse perception that most people today have of the level of scientific understanding enjoyed by the ancients before it is possible to appreciate the range of interests and sophistication enjoyed by that unique group of scientists who founded the Premier Grand Lodge in the early 1720s.

Since we are about to consider the geometry that was used by the Founders in conjunction with the Four Elements and astronomy it is important to appreciate the likely extent of understanding they had. For well over a thousand years the Church had been able to aggressively suppress philosophical and scientific debate, but prior to that period philosophers, such as those of the Greeks and Egyptian schools had propounded ideas that were surprisingly sophisticated. The popular concepts of their being 'Flat Earthers' for instance is quite wrong and has already been pointed out, the two groups cited above were certain the world was spherical and had estimated its diameter to an incredible degree of accuracy. (*see* Fig. 5) But other facets of their quite profound concepts relate directly to the remaining Sections of Part I. For instance the notion that matter consisted of indivisible particles called atoms (Democritus: *a-tomos* uncuttable and formed the essential thinking behind the branch of philosophy known as 'Atomism' – we will have recourse to return to this point when considering the elements). Undoubtedly they were aware that certain heavenly bodies (the planets) made tracks across what was essentially a fixed star pattern and that these were ascribed names and in many instances associated with particular gods. Further that this motion was within the confines of a narrow disc (the Zodiac) analogous to the way Saturn's rings rotate in a distinct disc. Plato (the

'...the five regular Platonic bodies...'

exhaltee's attention is drawn to the 'Platonic solids' during the Symbolical Lecture) was well aware of planetary motion, as was his understudy Aristotle; followed later by Ptolemy's complicated (crystal spheres) explanation of the respective orbits. To such an extent that Ptolemy's tables of planetary motion were the basis of navigation etc., for the next 1200 years. Indeed Ptolemy's concepts were referred to and illustrated in a poem by Desaguliers (third Grand Master) – *see* Part V and Appendix 1.

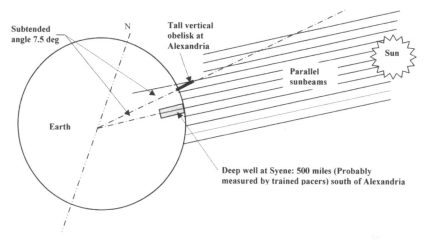

Figure 5.1. In circa 240 B.C. Eratosthenes used the above model to estimate the Earth's size. At precisely noon (no accurate clocks available and so used Sun's highest altitude) on the 22nd June the Sun's rays are reflected directly back from the water's surface of the deep well at Syene and the obelisk at Alexandria cast a shadow of 7.5 degrees. Assuming that the Sun's rays were parallel he calculated that the circa 500 miles measured was 7.5/360 of the Earth's circumference through Syene and depending on source it is suggested that his estimate he made was within 5%. He also estimated the distance of the Sun and the moon from the Earth.

Over the preceding centuries prior to the founding of the Premier Grand Lodge there had been profound challenges by a succession of philosophers on the established (accepted official doctrine – principally that of the Church) view, but mostly because of the fear of severe retribution, these never gained favour. Thus religious and political (dogma) control ensured that these concepts were not debated by the populous and this strategy was successful for a very long period. Indeed it lasted until the time when scholars such as Galileo summoned sufficient courage to make public pronouncements and by implication gave positive support for Copernicus' work. Their arguments were sufficiently cogent to plant the seeds of doubt in the populace at large, but in Britain because of the relaxed conditions following Cromwell's Commonwealth they were now becoming subject of public debate and despite the Church's continued use of spiritual and physical herbicides the seedlings began to flourish. The more noticeable because of the Church and the State's (universally) hitherto punitive suppression (often no less than death or hideous torture) enforced by earlier regime, notably that of the Spanish Inquisition, but by 1720 this was now no longer possible in Britain and Copernicus' concepts were now discussed openly. The more profound thinkers within the society fully accepted that the Earth could no longer be considered the centre of the Universe, but that in reality it was a small component of it. However, by this time many other factors, other than obscure philosophies, were affecting society. The world was beginning to open up in all aspects of human activity and whilst Copernicus and Galileo may be credited with being the principal instigators of the general acceptance of the realities of the Solar System, the change was in reality inevitable. It is perhaps of interest to reflect on the scientific chronology of this period. Figure 5.2 shows in a simplistic way some of the more influential people who would have had a strong impact in leading up to and during the time when the Premier Grand Lodge was formed and becoming established. Clearly the overall climate within English Society was such that it was possible to consolidate a number of disparate freemasons' lodges into a Masonic hierarchy (that was to emerge as the Premier Grand Lodge). As will be argued in the later Parts a principal factor in its justification and right to prosper were the intrinsic (basic precept) moral and sociological benefits of learning. This they could justify totally, by pointing to the way in which the Royal Society was then prospering, by exploiting and reflecting the high sociological benefits of scholarship – again *see* reference to Desaguliers' poem in Part V and Appendix 1.

What made their new society so special was that it would also embrace the additional attraction of high moral ethics (both religious and social) in all its many guises and of particular importance, would not exclude certain people of standing and influence. The reality was that the Royal Society and now this newly emerging organisation also contained other far less noble attributes and objectives, but this will be dealt with later.

Even if indeed, as will be claimed subsequently, the Royal Arch did in reality start sometime between 1720 and 1728, the Royal Society had by then been formed for the best part of sixty years. Certainly by that time the freedom to express a particular (anti-establishment) and hence controversial philosophy had been liberalised greatly. Mathematics, in whatever form, still remained obscure to most people and much of the scientific text existed only in Latin, such as for instance Newton's *Principia* – he even commissioned his famous work *Optiks* to be translated into Latin as late as 1704. As we have seen, Newton reliance upon the much earlier work of Tycho Brahe and Kepler, in *Principia* he had proven, to those in Britain at least, through his formal 'mechanics' approach that all the planets were part of a heliocentric system and forced by gravity to traverse the skies in elliptical orbits, with the Sun at one of its foci. It will be argued in Part V that it is almost certain that those responsible for

'...the five regular Platonic bodies...'

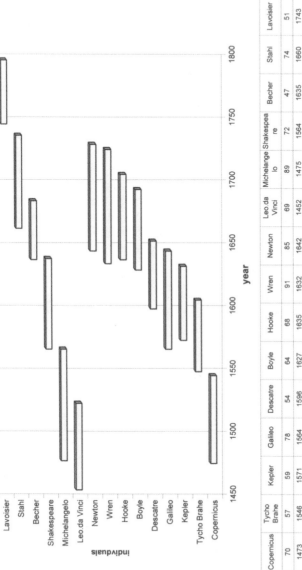

Figure 5.2 Chart of leading people in science 1450-1800.
Shakespeare and Michelangelo are included to add context

	Copernicus	Tycho Brahe	Kepler	Galileo	Descatre	Boyle	Hooke	Wren	Newton	Leo da Vinci	Michelangelo	Shakespeare	Becher	Stahl	Lavoisier
☐ lifespan	70	57	59	78	54	64	68	91	85	69	89	72	47	74	51
born	1473	1546	1571	1564	1596	1627	1635	1632	1642	1452	1475	1564	1635	1660	1743

71

the consolidated Craft ritual and Symbolical Lecture of the Royal Arch were fully aware of this concept. Given their passion and understanding of Nature and science the inclusion of the by then defunct 'regular solids' will have to be addressed – again *see* Desaguliers' poem in Appendix 1.

However, by the same token it is also clear from the basic concepts used in the Symbolical Lecture that whatever their actual understanding was at the time of compiling the Ritual, the Founders were reluctant to be quite so radical in their Lectures. The Symbolical Lecture with its scientific content appears to have been an essential component of the proposed ceremony. Our difficulty is their choice of explanation, for there was by that time a fresh view on most matters of scientific interest, but in the end they chose to base much of it upon some strange and rather obscure interpretation of the thinking of much earlier philosophers; such as Plato, Aristotle and Ptolemy; not least by incorporating the concept of there being 'the Sphere of the Universe'. This is of particular importance since by electing this approach; they were choosing to employ Kepler's original 'perfect solids' concept, or a very close derivative of it. On the surface this was in total contradiction of the concepts within the Newtonianism system, which was for the most part the current preoccupation of those desirous of knowledge.

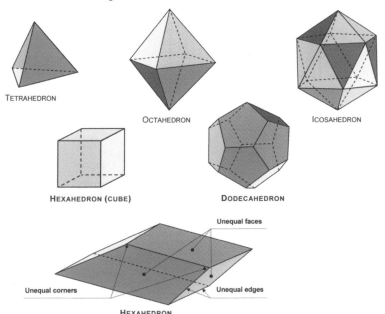

Figure 5.3. The five 'regular' solids and in contrast the features of one that is 'irregular'.

On reflection it is even stranger still, since as has been stressed already several of the Founders got a large portion of their income for lecturing on that very subject. It will be argued in Part V that this was likely due to their wish to preserve a close and hence more comfortable correlation between the science they were openly professing and the prevailing religious doctrines. Thus by discreetly distorting their own, outwardly professed, scientific beliefs they were able to retain the favour and support of the established church (from whom they were also deriving a goodly portion of their income) and perhaps their own innate beliefs and even if not their own, certainly those of the many they wished to attract.

This reluctance to depart from long established religious beliefs is quite strong in all people and especially understandable within the context of the period of interest here. Indeed, it appeared true of Kepler himself, who having rejected the Divine hand in relationship with the 'regular solids' in the very early 1600s, appeared to have second thoughts and returned to the notion in a publication he wrote shortly before his death (but actually published circa 1640). Even so, this publication was some eighty years before the time the Founders were constructing the Ritual of the Royal Arch – an extension of this anomalous behaviour is re-visited in Parts V and VI. Having now established the importance of this view of the Universe in the thinking of those who were around, if not directly instrumental, in the formation of Premier Grand Lodge, it is now possible to examine the actual words. Because of this strange phraseology it is helpful to consider separately the two aspects of the paragraph: 'It also serves to illustrate the jewel worn by the Companions which forms by its intersections a given number of angles: these may be taken in five several combinations, and when reduced to their amount in right angles, will be found equal to the five regular Platonic bodies which represents the four elements and the sphere of the Universe'.

The 'five regular (Platonic) bodies'. The word 'Platonic' is bracketed, for convenience, because the geometric concepts of a regular solid can be kept quite distinct from the more philosophical connotations implied by the word 'Platonic' – *see* Figure 5.3. It is therefore necessary to first consider the actual geometry of the solid and those factors that make them uniquely regular, whilst postponing for the moment any explanation of their connection with heavenly bodies and the elements. Again in order to develop this argument we must anticipate Part V a little to justify these particular explanations. Philosophers were ever concerned with the sublime order of (God's) Nature, however defined and the rigour and perfection of geometry was considered by some to be the most important piece of evidence to support the existence of the Deity. Conversely, by the 1720s a significant and persuasive minority of philosophers had adopted a counter argument and specifically reasoned against the need for there to be an inter-relationship between the perfection seen in nature and God's Creation (deism). They argued that there was no reason why the physical world could not develop in its own right and that the exactitude of geometry was a manifestation of the innate intrinsic order of things, although the majority were still of the view that geometric beauty was the very manifestation of God's presence. Indeed the utter perfection of 'mathematics' has been the foundation of certain eminent philosophers and branches of philosophy, right up to the present day – for instance that proffered by the late Bertrand Russel, being an example of perhaps the most extreme, mathematically argued, expression of total disbelief in the need for a supreme being. Whatever side of the argument used to establish an absolute interrelationship with a God (or Gods) or conversely to demonstrate a lack of it, the topic has never been ignored and all the evidence suggests that the Founders were totally committed to a belief in the Deity and this would have influenced their thinking greatly. An early realisation of such divine perfection was the fact (a 'fact' being the quintessential element of all scientific proofs and most philosophies) that only five regular solids were possible if the following law (requirements) were to be complied with:

(1) All its edges were the same length,

(2) All its face angles were the same,

(3) All its corners were the same,

(4) All its faces were the same shape, i.e., perfect symmetry

Planar shapes that are regular form the series: equilateral triangle, square, and the equi-sided pentagon, hexagon, heptagon etc. *see* Figure 5.4. However, it can be shown that only the first three when put together with replicas of their own basic form, have sufficient, three dimensional, freedom to move out of the plane (as it were; as if the attached forms are pressed down out of the plane of the paper on which they are drawn, whilst still retaining one corner in the original plane of the paper), rotating about their edges until their free edges touch and thereby close to form an elementary regular solid. The hexagon, with its six regular sides, would be next in the above series, but after the six equal forms have been attached to the central hexagon, it is clear that all their outgoing edges are in intimate contact with each other.

Thus the attached forms cannot, as was the case of the first three forms, be deflected (folded) down (or up) until their free adjacent edges touch, since the free edges are already in intimate contact with each other and there are no gaps. Indeed, it can be seen in Figure 5.4 that the heptagon, in theory the next in the series, would result in a theoretical overlap rather than there being gaps and so any attempt to extend the series further would be quite futile. From this realisation many of the Ancients (including it would seem the Founders, outwardly at least) concluded that these five solids were 'perfect' and quite fundamental to Nature. As a result these three forms were deemed of unique importance and hence inextricably linked with the perfection associated with a God or Gods and creation itself.

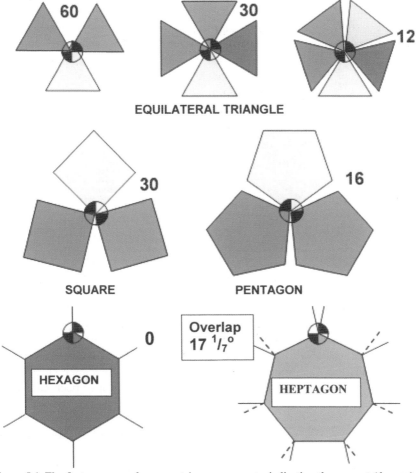

Figure 5.4. The first seven regular geometric arrangements, indicating the amount (degrees) of space between them. The sixth illustrates that there can be no space and the seventh would result in an overlap

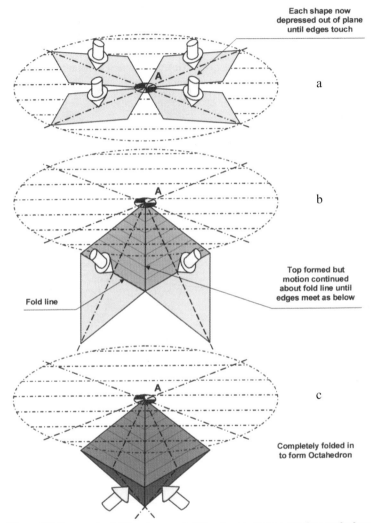

Each shape now
depressed out of plane
until edges touch

a

b

Top formed but
motion continued
about fold line until
edges meet as below

Fold line

c

Completely folded in
to form Octahedron

Figure 5.5. Progressive folding down out of the plane to form a regular octahedron

Thus it is reasonable to suppose that this was good and sufficient reason for those creating the Symbolical Lecture to associate these solids with the interlaced triangles and through the three rudimentary forms (equilateral triangles, squares and pentagons) to the Deity itself (and although not explicitly stated by the Founders, more particularly the Christian Faith).

'...the five regular Platonic bodies...'

The reasoning behind the concept; namely that there can only be five regular solids can perhaps be best explained by considering one of the simpler regular solids, the octahedron and then to apply the same principle to the others. The octahedron may be unwrapped symmetrically from one of its apexes, so that it lies in a plane as four equi-spaced diamonds, as can be seen in Figure 5.5a. If now, keeping point 'A' completely fixed in the plane, the diamonds are pushed down so that the corresponding sides touch, they form a regular four sided pyramid as shown in Figure 5.5b, with the remaining sides attached, but still pointing outwards. If, as shown in Figure 5.5c, those remaining sides are now hinged further about their free edge until again their corresponding sides touch they form the regular octahedron. The other four solids can be formed in an analogous way by adding appropriate extra regular units. Clearly the folding down process can only begin if there is space between the original forms lying in the principal (initial) plane. The equilateral triangle can be set symmetrically in the plane in three distinct patterns, consisting of three, four and five units, whilst still leaving space; the square and the pentagon only one; the hexagon is a perfect fit and all the sides touch and so the process cannot even begin.

If when forming the solids in this way, only simple deflections and rotations are used, it then becomes clear that it is only possible to form the five regular solids by this method. It may at first seem possible, from observing many everyday things, such as geodetic radar spheres and footballs etc., for there to be many solids formed in this way, but on closer inspection they remain contrivances and as such are outside the rules governing the 'regular' solids. There are other practical ways of demonstrating the uniqueness of the perfect solids,[1] but an even more rigorous, mathematically based proof, is possible, such as that found in the Appendices of Carl Sagan's book.[2]

Conclusion

Thus it is clear that by applying simple logic and without use of the more exacting geometrical proofs it is possible to show that there can be only five regular solids formed in this way and as such it was not unreasonable for the Founders to have considered them as being both 'regular' and 'perfect' and it is after all a Masonic imperative.

References

1. Rogers, E., *et al*, *Physics – Nuffield Physics Teachers' Guide,* V (Longman/Penquin Books, London, 1964), PTG 04216.

2. Sagan, C., *Cosmos* (MacDonald, London, 1981).

Chapter Six: The four elements

he whole phrase is: 'which represents the four elements and the sphere of the Universe', but the connection is vague and so they will be dealt with separately. Historically the four elements are defined as: earth, water, air and fire, although they are not actually named as such in the Symbolical Lecture, but it is reasonable to assume that this information would have more than likely been known by the Companions and the exaltee of those times. The literature of the times suggests they would have been aware, at least, of their designations. For instance some sixty years earlier Pepys wrote in his diary:

> 'So home; and my brother John and I up, and I to my musique and then to discourse with him; and find him not so thorough a philosopher, at least in Aristotle, as I took him for. he not being able to tell me the definition of fire nor which of the four Qualitys belong to each of the four elements.'[1]

However, to know a thing by a name does not of itself necessarily mean that there is an intrinsic understanding of that object. Once again in dealing with any aspect of the study it is important to resist the temptation to dismiss the thinking of these early philosophers and assume that they lived in a time of total ignorance, but rather attempt to first get it clear in our own minds what we understand by these terms and only then postulate or be critical of what they believed.

In practice this process is far from simple, since even today most people would think of these things in their own individual and abstract way; for example 'Earth' may be regarded by some as soil from the garden, or rocks, or a continent as opposed to the oceans, etc. depending greatly on that person's experience to date, but vague as these definitions may be, it is likely that they would have been even less clear when viewed from the standpoint of the contemporary thinking of the 1720s. The rationalisation of this factor is of great importance in this appraisal and an attempt must be made to reconcile the various strands of opinion extant at the time and that led to these particular concepts being inculcated in the Symbolical Lecture.

This dichotomy of view is illustrated well by considering the very essence of defining what constitutes 'matter', namely the physics of what we would now call chemistry. Robert Boyle (1627-1691), whose connection with Robert Hooke has been alluded to already, is considered by most historians to be the father of modern chemistry because of the strides that he and his disciples had made in overcoming the general prejudice toward chemistry, hitherto inextricably lumped by most people under somewhat dubious epithet of alchemy. More especially that he had challenged Platonism in a quite profound way. He (Boyle) believed that all matter is constructed

The four elements

of combinations of minute primitive unpolluted bodies, as could be argued, did many of the early philosophers and that he was in agreement with them was not of itself particularly special. However, where he differed was that he believed that fire was not an element as such. This revolutionary concept would also serve to explain Hooke's near fatal experiments to demonstrate that gunpowder required a supply of air for it to explode and despite the disastrous outcome due to the residual oxygen (still to remain unknown for well over one hundred years) in the saltpetre (KNO_3) he persisted in his belief. It is a measure of Hooke's intellectual powers, that whilst he was unable to explain the reason why the gunpowder inside the air-tight evacuated spheres exploded when it had been placed on a fire, he remained convinced of the concept 'that it was something in the air' that allowed the explosion (fire) to occur.

However justified Boyle (and later Hooke) may have been, he failed to dissuade the wider community and the near universal view (contemporary with the Founders) was that fire was an element or by the most influential, quasi scientific: a substance (phlogiston), which flowed into and out of things as combustion took place. Typically this served to explain why wood got lighter after it had been burnt because the phlogiston had flowed out of it, or exceptionally in say the oxidation of metals, phlogiston had flowed into it. Thus the contemporary view was that virtually every form of reaction could be somehow reconciled (and some explanations were, to put it mildly, 'imaginative') by using the phlogiston concept and only a glaring exception could have led to the rapid decline of the concept, so deeply was it entrenched.

(Al)chemists had long searched for some unifying agent that would explain the chemical behaviour of all reactions. In the late 1600s a German chemist Johann Becher suggested that all minerals had three basic constituents, but more importantly that they all contained *terra pinguis* (essentially the chemistry of sulphur compounds, one might conclude because historically it was those that had been the most easily disassociated from their metal derivatives) which they lost on combustion. George Stahl an influential professor of medicine at the University of Halle and an excellent self publicist, proposed the phlogiston theory, which enshrined Johann Becher's concepts. His phlogiston theory was to our modern way of thinking a complete nonsense, but simply stated it was: a weightless element, which was a constituent of all things that would combust. That during the burning process it flowed out from the substance being burnt and so anything containing carbon was extremely rich in the substance, such as oils and fats. Indeed there were some that considered charcoal to be pure phlogiston. This was typical of the differing concepts and serves to illustrate the bizarre arguments that were employed to support the various theories, since in this instance they failed to answer the obvious question of how can a substance without mass in its purest form be weighed? This is why these two otherwise obscure names appear on the historical diagram in Figure 5.1, rather than others who perhaps are much more worthy.

Thus phlogiston theory was the most widely (effectively only) accepted concept during the formative and working years of the Founders and as such fully supported the concept of Fire being one of the four basic elements propounded by the Ancients and indeed may have been the very reason why the concept of the 'four elements' was retained by them in the Symbolical Lecture. There were sporadic attacks made upon the phlogiston theory, but it survived up until Lavoisier's exceptional work and political endeavours in the late 1700's, when the discovery of Oxygen meant that it could be sustained no longer. Thus despite the fact that there were a few dissenters at that time there is little reason to doubt that the Founders would have been content to consider fire to be one of the Elements. However, given their innate intelligence, what is less certain is why the Founders would not have been more troubled by the concepts of 'Earth' and 'Air'. It is reasonable to assume that the fundamentals of 'matter' ('chemistry' would be too strong a word for it, although a chair in chemistry was established in Cambridge in 1698 it in no way represented today's discipline called 'chemistry' and they would have probably needed to glean each piece of knowledge) given to the Founders in their formative years would have been based upon vague concepts not far removed from alchemy.

The isolation of compounds such as salvolatile, quicklime and acetic acid (vinegar) had been isolated unwittingly for a very long time, but not recognised as such. Although Boyle's chemistry was quite basic (as were those in Cambridge initially), he had been very methodical and his work led to the isolation of substances formed by what would now be quite unsafe practices and producing extremely reactive and toxic concoctions. Although these experiments were crude, smelly and dirty processes and the manufacture of these compounds did lead to a number of complaints within the population at large; in hindsight his concepts were quite profound. He stated that these compounds were comprised of a number (clearly more than four) of elements:

> '... certain primitive and simple, or perfectly unmingled bodies, which not being made of any other bodies, or of one another, are the ingredients of which all perfectly mixt bodies are immediately compounded and into which they are ultimately resolved ...'

However, as already stated, this informed view did not gain favour until the late 1700s and his work was, to all external appearance, bracketed with the disreputable view of alchemy held by the public at large. Thus the first reaction disposes one towards the view that it was unlikely to gain acceptance within the group of Founders.

The four elements

Irrespective of how disreputable it may have been to the general public, Newton never gave up his interest in alchemy and that fact will be of importance in Parts V and VI. In many respects this generally unfavourable view was understandable since alchemists had been making brews like this for centuries in their attempts to change base metals into gold and clearly they had not been successful and so it is not surprising that they were viewed with some scorn. Because of his other scientific input Boyle was just a little more respectable and his chemistry had produced some interesting concoctions, but it was clearly unconvincing in any general way. It is of interest to note that once these compounds had been isolated there was a tendency to ascribe quite remarkable curative powers to them, as can be seen in some medicine chests of that and later periods (in the 1660s Samuel Pepys was disposed to take his tinctures), some such as mercury were so toxic, that by modern day reckoning, it is a wonder any patient survived at all. Chemistry in the strict sense that we would understand today did not really start to gather pace until the middle to late 1700's, but then accelerate at an astonishing rate and this is perhaps why it is difficult for us to now appreciate such naivety.

Thus, for whatever reason the Founders remained, outwardly at least, somewhere in the middle of 'mainstream' thinking on 'matter' and were not disposed to proffer any of these radical ideas, but rather to endorse a belief in the concept of the 'fundamental elements'. Holding on to this extreme conservatism, even though they were living through a time when there was an almost exponential increase in man's understanding of most other aspects of science that affected the Natural World. That they may have experienced difficulties in rationalising these new concepts to their own personal satisfaction will be returned to later. That amazingly sophisticated (and prophetic) concepts of matter had existed long before this time have been discussed earlier, such as where Greek philosophers considered matter to be composed of the coalescence of incredibly (to them) small particles, in essence what most people believe today. One can understand this since they could have reduced common salt down to an incredibly fine powder, but to then see it dissolve in water and become invisible, only to reappear as a powder when the water was driven off. But the greater majority would have sheltered behind an unchallenged, irrefutable belief that all creation emanated from some divine being/s and that somehow all things were constructed from a subtle fusion of the four elements. What precisely the Founders' views were in this formative period, is of course conjecture, but given the way in which it is presented (Symbolically) in the Ritual, their professed view was likely to be similar to that given in the 1931 explanation of the jewel referred to earlier.[2]

Thus whilst the definitions used in this particular version of the Ritual cannot be considered definitive, nonetheless it is reasonable to suppose that it will probably serve as well as any other guess, since it supports the broad concepts that the

Founders would have needed to adopt if they were to accomplish the important task of diffusing education within their members:

'... to the five regular Platonic bodies, representing the four elements and the Universal Sphere. These combinations will be found respectively to correspond in geometrical value with the five regular solids contained under equilateral triangles, equal squares, and equal and equilateral pentagons, viz., the Tetrahedron, Octahedron, cube, Icosahedron, and Dodecahedron which were used by the Platonists to express the four elements and the sphere of the Universe. It may be proper here to state that the Platonic theory was this, that the Universe itself as well as its subordinate parts, both animate and inanimate, were created by the Deity from the four elements – Fire, Water, Air and Earth. It was conceived according to this theory that all created matter must be both visible and tangible. Now, considering Fire as the source of light, it was plain that nothing can be visible without it; and since nothing can be tangible but what is solid, and that the earth is the most properly solid of all the four elements, therefore, all created matter was constituted of Fire and Earth.

Again it was supposed by the Platonists that no two bodies could cohere without some intervening medium to consolidate them; that planes required one such medium, and solids two. Therefore, the Deity constituted two intervening elements between fire and earth, viz., air and water, in such a manner that there might be an exact analogy between the four, i.e., as fire is to air, so is air to water, and as air is to water, so is water to earth; thus forming a regular and harmonious gradation from the lightest and most penetrating of the elements to the heavier and most obtuse. Now all the elements except the earth are without form themselves; yet, in order to assist the mind in arranging its ideas, it is necessary to attach some form to them. Therefore, since the elements are bodies and all bodies are solid, and bounded by superficies which consist of triangles either equilateral or otherwise, the Platonic theory assigned to each of the four elements the form of a solid, bounded by plane surfaces constituted of triangles; for although one of those solids is bounded by squares and another by pentagons, yet it will be evident that equilateral rectilinear figures may be resolved into as many triangles as the figures have sides united by their vertices in a common centre.'[3]

However well intentioned this portion of the 1921 'Explanation of the Jewel' is, it requires a comparatively sophisticated prior knowledge by the listener of the underlying subject area and is in this respect precisely analogous to the way 'Science' is portrayed in the Symbolical Lecture, requiring considerably more explanation before most people could be expected to understand it and the next Section is an attempt to explain at slightly greater length Plato's philosophical understanding of 'matter'.

The four elements

Again it is the thesis of this work that whilst the wording of the Ritual may have altered in ceremonial detail over the intervening years because of the uniqueness of the science with respect to contemporary belief, coupled with the short period it could be considered valid, its substance cannot have changed. This assertion is made on the premise that if it had been conceived at some other time it would, of necessity, been radically different (*see* Parts V and VI). Given that this proposition is true, it is necessary to present a basic scenario of what the Founders appeared to accept as representing Plato's interpretation of matter and to speculate later why they selected this particular explanation for inclusion in the Lecture. They would have received their basic education prior to or at the latest, very early 1700s and upon that foundation would be, as is the case today, the evolving 'state of the art'. We have already seen from Pepys' Diary that the concept of the 'four elements' was a 'textbook' concept of which they would have been made familiar with during their early schooling. The reality is that he/they elected to include in the Symbolical Lecture the concept of the Regular **Platonic** bodies and hence contended that the natural world consisted of the four elements: Fire, Air, Water and Earth. To understand the concepts better it is necessary to examine Plato's concepts more closely. However, as discussed already this will appear somewhat surprising since both philosophy and science were proceeding apace and the Founders were in the van of it. Although there was great potential for confusion, with its attendant doubts in certain areas, this would not appear to be true of their view on this particular subject area and so it will be necessary to search elsewhere for the most likely reasons (seemingly anomalous) for its adoption (*see* Newtonianism – Part V.)

Again the following is based on the pretext that it was one man or a small caucus of the Founders who decided to form a new ceremony which they were to call the Royal Arch. A major component of this innovation would be the formal extension of the concepts of Nature and Science that had now been enshrined, with considerable emphasis, into Craft ritual. This they chose to do in the form of a lecture. However in order to do this they were required to cover the topic in some detail and that would require them to take a stance. Since there were few workers (chemists) concerned with the substance of 'matter', other than the notable exception of Boyle, it is most likely that the Founders would have been disposed to think that chemistry was merely the respectable face of alchemy and would not have wished to 'rock the boat' since alchemy remained an active interest to Newton. Thus in the absence of clear evidence to the contrary it would have been unlikely for them to have incorporated anything into the Ritual other than the generally accepted doctrine of the time. It is of interest to note that this branch of understanding was grossly out of phase with the advances being made in all other areas of the arts and sciences, such as astronomy, mathematics, electricity, physics and associated technology, such as 'fire (steam) engines'; a particular interest of the third Grand Master (*see also* Figure 39.1). However, as stated already it was well before the discovery of oxygen and the massive impact its isolation had on the concept of combustion and chemistry in general. Devoid of any reasonable alternative explanation, the Founders were, if they were going to make sense of the world, required to regard fire as an element. To have not done so may well have numbered them among the scientific heretics or cranks.

The following therefore is based upon that which is in the Symbolical Lecture and whilst the above suggests possible reasons why the people involved may have adopted this explanation it continues to ask the question why such naivety and thus the whole matter remains uncomfortable, but to avoid distraction further consideration is left until Part V. An important factor to bear in mind whilst considering this résumé is that Plato's and perhaps more importantly Aristotle's (organic – living) concepts embraced the very essential, if not the imperative (to them at least), ingredient of Divine involvement. Plato had laid down a very sophisticated rationalisation of all matter and again it must be emphasised that they are specifically referred to in the Ritual as the '*Regular Platonic* Bodies'.

In order to gain some insight into what they believed and why, it is necessary to consider Plato's basic philosophy with respect to Matter. Namely that:

1) Fire, air, water and earth are all bodies,

2) All bodies are solids,

3) All solids are bounded by surfaces,

4) All rectilinear surfaces are composed of triangles.

In order for this to be consistent, certain precepts have to be established: the first of which is that Plato claimed that there were two basic types of triangle – each of which has one right angle and two acute angles:

(a) In one where the acute angles are half of a right angle 45°, (hence sides equal - eight juxtaposed forming a square).

(b) In the other the acute angles are unequal (notionally 30° 60° and 90°, although in the final analysis not exclusively so as we shall see, hence with all the sides unequal - in this special case when the two intermediate (adjacent) sides abut they form an equilateral triangle).

From this it was possible for him to conclude: that from these two triangular forms it was possible to construct the most perfect (four) bodies. Further that whilst they are unlike each other, they can in some instances be transformed or by some process transmuted into each other.

From this knowledge of the regular solids they (the Ancients) concluded that it was possible to reveal the truth about the (basic) fundamental components of earth and fire and the two that provide the means of their transmutation, air and water. Plato was disposed to making presumptions, which then took unto themselves the status of facts. In this instance he concedes that odd shaped triangular bodies could make a myriad of forms, but challenges anyone to show that there are more (than five) perfect bodies, in each type and on the assumption that there are no more than the two (basic triangles), he proceeds to argue that each can, by some process, be transformed into the other. Initially this concept appears to work well, but as it approaches the square it begins to require some 'ingenuity' of thought and falls into the classical textbook category of 'it can easily be shown that ...', but then chooses not to do so.

The **tetrahedron** (four faces), **octahedron** (eight faces) and the **icosahedron** (twenty faces) can clearly be **constructed out of equilateral triangles,** however with the fourth, the **cube**, he is obliged to use **isosceles triangles**. The fifth, the **dodecahedron**, presented him with an even greater problem, because this cannot be constructed out of either of the two basic triangular forms. However, this he explains with an amazing feat of ingenuity and without further verification; by stating that this convoluted concept is allowable because it approaches nearly (in volume) the form of a sphere – more in the manner of a politician than a philosopher it would seem.

This technique of failing to elaborate appears to have been a characteristic ploy of his when confronted with difficult matters, or to be more generous it is perhaps where his explanation may have been lost in its transmission over such a vast time period and frailties of the recorder, who in the absence of Plato's own precise explanation, has been obliged to write something. Whatever the explanation, unless they were privy to other sources of information, it is most likely, that the writings of Plato in the early 1700s and hence those available to the Founders, would have been the same as those found in the present day versions quoted here.

He asserts that God used this 'near spherical' configuration to 'arrange constellations' - literally to 'embroider with figures'. This he conceded raised the possibility of there being many worlds, which he at first considered worthy of serious debate, but after further reflection, decides to take the debate no further and rejects the notion in favour of there being just one divine world.

It will be argued later that it is this essentially 'divine' concept that may well explain why this philosophy lasted for 1200 years and it would appear was sufficiently plausible, to influence the Founders very much later than Kepler. Kepler, with his otherwise clinical, essentially mechanical explanation of the Universe, had somehow managed to retain the belief that: the Sun was the immobile centre and divine source of power and as such represented the *Father*, the surrounding celestial sphere containing the fixed star and the inter-space which allow the motion of the planets represented the *Son*. The motive force originating from the Sun and permeating the universe represented the *Holy Ghost*.

The reason the 1921 ritual quoted earlier may be regarded as somewhat deficient was that whilst it stated what they believe, it gave no indications of precisely what, why or indeed any explanation of the subtlety behind their reasoning. The following is an attempt to at least begin to develop their likely understanding of Platonism a little further. To do so it is necessary to return to Plato's basic precept:

1) Fire, air, water and earth are all bodies,

2) All bodies are solids,

3) All solids are bounded by surfaces,

4) All rectilinear surfaces are composed of triangles.

What did he/they who were proffering his philosophy in the 1720s, understand by the precepts above? It is reasonable to assume that their concepts of fire, air, water and earth were not those that one would expect to be in the minds of most people today, or for that matter the ritualists of 1921. To illustrate this point it would be of interest and indeed can be quite revealing, if before going on, the reader first writes down their own and if convenient some other person's immediate understanding of the terms: **Fire, air, water and earth**, for this is where the 1921 'Explanation of the Jewel' and the most recent Ritual leaves its readers, requiring them to form their own opinion, but without the wherewithal to do so. Given that the reader has responded to that suggestion, they will have written down their concept of the four Elements, with these in mind it will now be of interest to contrast them with Plato's which are briefly outlined below.

It is reasonable to suppose that those without prior knowledge of Plato's basic philosophy will have made their assessment, formed their own understanding of those terms, it will be quite individual and almost certainly markedly different from that of another person, since each definition will have depended upon that individual's prior (worldly) experience. However, the interesting point is that whatever those concepts may be, they are almost certain not to be those found in Plato's interpretation, or presumably those of the Founders three hundred years ago. This comment is based on the assumption that the Founders would have been influenced by the curricular of their early schooling/education, which was likely to have included the teaching of Aristotle and in consequence they would have been made familiar with and given a more specific understanding of Plato's concept of the four elements.

Again given the actual content of the Ritual they were seemingly constrained by their need to reconcile the cold clinical realities of the scientific discoveries unfolding before them, with their (imperative) need to convey a belief in the omnipotence of God. Unlike the average person of today, they would not have been exposed to the influence of the numerous strands of (media, Internet type) communication, or in more modern parlance 'information technology-transfer'. Modern scientific and technological discoveries are now presented in a popular way, at virtually every hour of the day. This information is usually dispensed by 'experts', presenting their individual interpretation of the 'facts', leaving everyone to reconcile these 'facts' with their previous understanding of the matter under discussion, which may or may not correspond with those embedded through their school, college curricular and/or experience to date. Thus we must presume that they (the Founders) were obliged to state in their Lecture that all natural phenomena could be explained in terms that were consistent with their audience's latest overall concepts of reality. Which judging from the content of the Symbolical Lecture, was that the most likely (informed) explanation of 'matter' in the material world was that there were just the four basic elements as set out below. Whilst these basic components may have provided the essential ingredients to define all matter they became less and less adequate with time. Those who followed, starting with Aristotle were progressively obliged to depend upon associated characteristics such as dryness and wetness, hotness and coldness and if that failed then the 'occult' came to their rescue.

Much of Plato's philosophy or at least the manner, in which it has been handed down, was in the form of dialogues between various people discussing philosophical propositions. Plato's explanation of the 'four elements' is achieved by eavesdropping on the conversation between two such philosophers: Timaeus and Critias. The format of the translation used here is typical of most authors, in that it has in addition an 'explanatory' Introduction. In this case it is those by Sir Desmond Lee,[4, 5] which of course reflects his interpretation of this ancient dialogue. The work is much broader than that implied by the peripheral explanation of the 'Elements' given below and does include the physical and psychological constituents of man. Even then that which is set out below is merely a further extraction and hence interpretation of their total question and answer dialogue. The following therefore is a summary of their conversation and attempts to convey the basic conclusions of their understanding of the four elements.

fire – is in the form of a tetrahedron:

Why the tetrahedron? This because this geometrical configuration was in the opinion of the Greeks, the lightest and sharpest (hence most penetrative) form of the regular solids.

They needed to explain 'fire' in this way because natural occurrences such as: flame, light, combustion, smoke, steam, ice, melting, radiation, convection, conduction, etc. were everyday experiences. Conversely there were clearly substances, such as rock, which to them appeared incombustible.

Underlying mechanism: their whole beliefs would take too long to explain, but it is hoped that the following explanation will serve to indicate their thought processes:

Fire is an incredibly small, sharp (tetrahedral) solid capable of penetrating the conglomeration of heavier particles of the solids and as such was capable of flowing into and out of a body.

Typical examples of the influence of fire:

The various phases of water: ice + fire goes to an intermediate state of snow, snow + fire goes to the next state of water, water + fire then goes to (steam) vapour, vapour + fire then goes to (air) æther (the water now no longer being an observable vapour) and vice versa, explaining physical events such as the formation of early morning mists.

Solubility metals etc.: metal + fire go to water (by water they meant all fluids), but no further – *see* water below.

Combustion: fire enters the solid and its piercing action breaks it up into minute particles and air, but when the heat flowed out (cools) this intermediate state resettles back to earth, but now without form (dust, ash, soot). etc., etc.

Light: this is the non-burning (and purest) part of the flame a derivative of which is the glow (in embers) once the actual flame has been extinguished.

The whole concept of fire is returned to in part V, since it is necessary for us to reconcile why the Founders embraced this seemingly outlandish concept. From the standpoint of our present day understanding, few would now question the chemical reaction of oxygen and combustible substances when conditions are favourable and so the concept of fire takes on a completely different meaning.

Air – takes the form of an Octahedron:

Why the form of an Octahedron? This was because they needed to explain its functionality, which required it to be able to infiltrate the structure of the more stable 'earths' and combine with water to allow the intermediate states between fire and earth.

There were several varieties of 'air', but the two that they considered of special significance are the very brightest termed æther and the muddiest which is called mist or darkness.

They had observed air bubbling out of solids and events such as the hissing of sap or smoke out of burning solids etc. and so it was air in combination with water that represented the intermediate (transitional) elements between fire and earth.

Water – takes the form of an Icosahedron:

Why the Icosahedron? Again because its shape would allow it to permeate (absorption) the more solid earth, but clearly in their minds it would not do so as readily as air or fire. Further that there were essentially two types of water:

1) Liquid: this was composed of a myriad unequal units, which in consequence cannot settle into a regular structure, remains constantly mobile and therefore totally lacked uniformity.

2) Fusible (they needed to explain things that would melt, but there was also the problem of softening under heat, but without actually melting completely and solidification): particles are larger and of uniform size and are thus able to solidify. Fire however can penetrate the structure and force it to become mobile and break down (melt) and because the air was pressing down upon it is forced to collapse (flow) all over the ground (they appear to have had no direct concept of gravity).

The reverse of this process – that fire escapes (cooling) – compressing the neighbouring air – which in turn compresses the liquid which fuses (solidifies) into the space left by the fire causing it to agglomerate – metals would have been seen to shrink on cooling.

He (Plato) then gives an explanation of the special varieties of water, namely the metals. He has an elaborate explanation for gold and why it retains its lustre and explains how the bright metal copper if reacted with earth is tarnished with verdigris.

He is now required to give some account of the mechanisms by which the two intermediate solids air and water cause changes of state and reactions. He is required to explain various states of actual water; mist, rain, hail, snow, hoar-frost, ice. This he does by an elaborate and somewhat obscure argument, contending that this behaviour is related to their position relative to the ground.

However, he concludes that most varieties of water are really juices. Juices, because most of them originate (are filtered) through plants.

He singles out those derivatives that contain fire:

1) wines – these warm the body etc.,

2) oils – smooth and shiny and some transparent: pitch, caster oil, olive oil etc.,

3) sweetness – those that contain sweetness to the mouth; of which he cites honey, but also fruit juices, root extracts etc.,

4) acids – fluids that burn the flesh or the mouth and froth. He refers to this group as being quite unique and completely separate from the other three.

Earth – takes the form of a cube:

Why a cube? Because of its obvious solidity.

All 'earths' are comprised of minute particles of varying sizes and so their structure is dependent upon their packing arrangement, or more importantly the spaces between them. This must be since to break them down requires there to be an interaction with some or all of the three other elements which have to first penetrate these spaces before they can be forced apart.

All the various states; such as the fusing of glass type structures, dissolving, brittleness of pottery, lava etc. are explained by the probability of the passage, penetration, retention, expulsion, combination etc. of the three elements, forcing themselves into the inter-spaces in the structure of a solid.

For instance he writes:

'There are two other substances formed in the same way when water has been extracted in large quantities from a mixture: and both are formed of finer particles, both taste salty, and both become only semi-solid and are soluble in water. The one, which cleanses from grease or dirt, is soda: the other, which blends well in various fluids, is salt, a substance traditionally accepted to heaven.'[6]

It is easy to speculate where the atomist concept (which was to have a considerable following in the philosophy just prior to the formation of Premier Grand Lodge) came from; for instance although salt was clearly a solid it could be reduced to an extremely fine powder in a pestle and mortar, would not burn easily, but would dissolve into such small particles that it was invisible, but it would return as a solid if the water was driven off; whereas Aristotle struggled with this behaviour and was obliged to use elementary qualities and divine providence.

Again these extensions to the basic concepts will be addressed when the complex social interaction of those with whom we are concerned and significance of Newtonianism within this process is discussed in Parts V and VI. Suffice it to say that Aristotle introduced four associated elementary qualities to refine his explanation. Further he was obliged to justify his account of certain physical effects that were anomalous in this otherwise simplistic view of there being just four elements. Thus he extended his definition by introducing the concept of hot, cold, wet and dry. Thus for instance he coupled these together with the elements – Fire is dry and hot, Earth of a certain type is cold and dry etc.

However whilst in his time this may have been just sufficient to ward off otherwise difficult phenomenological questions, by the 1720s there were a whole gamut of difficult items to address. For instance how did solids go into solution (dissolve), what was magnetic attraction, what was static electricity, what was toxicity etc? To overcome this problem the supporters of this doctrine introduced a further layer of qualities, so called 'non-manifest' or 'occult' characteristics (powers, virtues, forces, facilities, etc., used singly or in combination).

However, before we ask the question why those with whom we are concerned were even prepared to persist with this version, we have to remember that they were disciples of Newton and as we shall discover Newton was not averse to invoking the concept of divine intervention, for instance when he encountered difficulty in providing an explanation of certain aspects of colour. This subject is dealt with in much greater depth by John Henry.[7]

Conclusion

Because of their unambiguous reference in the Symbolical Lecture to the Platonic Solids, it must be presumed that the Founders had accepted this basic explanation as the basis of all material things. However, in Parts III, V and VI when discussing the rationale of some of Masonry's brightest and most important early characters, their interpretation was not necessarily precisely that of Plato's, but was rather an uncomfortable admix of philosophies (Platoism and Atomism) and the subtle interpretation within the thinking of one of the early Grand Masters is of particular interest.

Thus, the newly exalted Companions of the early Royal Arch Chapters were informed that the entire physical world could be rationalised by using a subtle contrivance of the Four Elements. Further that this could be extended to all living matter and was even used in great measure to explain the senses such as smell, taste, hearing, sight and even emotional states and dreams.[8]

N.B. Aristotle's later philosophical concepts were essentially 'organic' (namely: could be explained in biological terms) in nature rather than mechanical and became accepted generally as the true explanation of matter. Although challenged and often very well reasoned, by a number of notable philosophers, his views were not effectively or seriously threatened in any generally accepted way until the days of Copernicus and it would seem much later still given its inclusion in the ritual by the Founders.

References

1. Latham, R., *The Shorter Pepys* (Penquin Books, London, 1987), p. 301.

2. Anon, *The Perfect Peremonies of the Supreme Order of the Holy Royal Arch* (Private Publication, A. Lewis, London, 1921).

3. *Ibid.*

4. Sagan, C., *Cosmos* (Macdonald, London and Sydney, 1980).

5. Lee, D., *Plato: Timious and Critias* (Penquin Books, London, 1965).

6. *Op. cit..*

7. *Op. cit..*

8. *Op. cit..*

Chapter Seven:
Sphere of the Universe (Astronomy) – represented by the dodecahedron

aving already considered the geometry of the Jewel, the solids and the four elements, although as we shall see, this interpretation is not necessarily the abstract 'geometry' of the Seven Liberal Arts and Sciences which aspect will be considered again in Part VI, but for continuity 'astronomy' another of the Seven will be considered in the same way. However, in order to keep within the remit of Part I and to avoid distraction astronomy will be restricted to an assessment of what was most likely implied by the phrase 'the Sphere of the Universe' by those in receipt of the Symbolical Lecture in those initial days. Again the subtleties of the Astronomy of the Seven Arts and Sciences as then understood will be discussed further in Part VI.

Reference has been made already to the work of Tycho Brahe and Kepler, but in order to understand the presence of the word 'Platonic' it is necessary to consider the antecedence of their work in greater detail. Even today there still remains considerable amazement over the degree of accuracy with which Tycho Brahe was able to observe the orbits of the planets and other astronomical behaviour without the aid of telescopes as we would understand them. He had noted the orbit of Mars better than 8 minutes of arc (this is approximately 1/50th of the moon's diameter looking up from the Earth), which was most remarkable given that he was working with comparatively crude and fixed plane instruments and observing the orbits of planets that were orbiting the Sun on a planet that was itself orbiting the Sun. In much the same way as we now look with wonder at the early works of art undertaken by the Great Masters (however defined) in natural light and with relatively crude tools.

In a tempestuous and hence inefficient way, Kepler worked as Tycho Brahe's mathematician for nearly two years. However, despite their troubled relationship there was great mutual respect in terms of their technical abilities as shown by Tycho Brahe bequeathing his data to Kepler. After a protracted initial period and not inconsiderable prevarication from Brahe's relatives he finally gained possession of the bequeathed data. He continued his studies on these findings with great vigour over many years, the work having to be underpinned by various, but for the most part inadequate, sponsorship. That such profound work should come from this relationship was most interesting since they were so strikingly different in both personality and background, Tycho Brahe was a flamboyant aristocrat (he had a golden nose made to replace the one he had lost in dual); whereas Kepler came from a humble background, dependent upon patronage, was an extremely introverted character and reportedly a very poor communicator.

It is not appropriate here to go into further detail about the extremely interesting lives of these two extraordinary men, or how they interacted with each other, that is better done by others, although it would appear that the precise intensity of the relationship again depends upon the interpretation of the historian, with Carl Sagan's book being an interesting example.[1] However, what is universally agreed is the massive impact they each had upon astronomy and in Kepler's case science itself and later still the Founders. Despite the huge difference in social status, wealth and not forgetting their acrimonious relationship, they retained a very great regard for the accuracy of each other's work, which as it turned out was absolutely critical in Kepler's later analysis. He was certain that Brahe's readings from his astronomical observation were incredibly meticulous and so despite setbacks in his own calculations, he had the courage to acknowledge his own shortcomings and refused to find fault with Brahe's data. As a consequence he persevered by critically reviewing his own analysis of the data. This was not easy since after many years of effort he had been quite overjoyed when he was finally able to ascribe a 'precise' mathematical (geometrical) model of the orbits of the known planets with the perfection of Regular Solids and by implication demonstrate that this was indeed (could only be possible) by divine decree. However, once in possession of Tycho Brahe's observations he was able to calculate the magnitude of their relative orbits with greater accuracy and as with most propounded 'physical laws' his elegant model was not to last.

As discussed already many years later Newton was to demonstrate mathematically that all planets orbit the sun in elliptical orbits, but did acknowledge that it was only possible because of Kepler's ultimate discovery that the orbit of a planet sweeps out equal areas in equal times. Kepler's achievement was especially remarkable, because he had first to retreat from his own deeply ingrained concepts. It took considerable courage to throw away years of work, his wonderful Regular solids model and his innate belief in the perfection of the Creator in favour of a more secular scientifically/mechanistically justified elliptical based concept of the Solar system. His remarkable ingenuity was clearly demonstrated in his geometric model which will be discussed later.

However, it is first necessary to understand how he could have been deluded and why he had so much trouble rationalising planetary behaviour one has to realise that for the most part the orbits of the Planets of the Solar system are nearly circular; (for instance the eccentricity of the Earth's orbit is less than 2%) and it was this lack of pronounced eccentricity and Kepler's predisposition towards God's perfection that had caused him to be misled for so long. It was the one exception to this, namely the orbit of Mars (with *circa* ten times more eccentricity) that finally brought about the change. Even this proved to be a problem, because unfortunately for convenience of observation, Kepler had chosen to observe the orbit of Mars at times when the

Sphere of the Universe
Earth was at its nearest and furthest from the Sun. This strategy had inadvertently created an anomalous situation, since these readings chanced to coincide at a time when the resulting calculations of the orbit of Mars led him to believe that its orbit too was effectively circular (all the planets speed up and slow down as they orbit around the Sun – that is why the Seasons are not quite uniform).

As stated above the major constraint on Kepler was his basic disposition to believe that the universe was governed by some divine fundamental order, but this becomes less surprising when one remembers that this was equally true of the public stance taken by the Founders a hundred years later and hence dominates Masonic ritual. As discussed already the geometrical 'perfection' of the regular solids was considered a clear manifestation of this divine influence. Thus, having found, as a result of accidental timing, that the orbit of Mars was in keeping with all else he was observing, it was not unreasonable, indeed pleasurable, for him to find further, that this remained totally consistent with his fundamental religious belief and he would have been disinclined to challenge it further.

Indeed, Kepler was totally convinced by the facts that: in God's perfect heaven there were just six planets and that there were and only could be five regular solids. At that point he was certain that this celestial arrangement and perfection of the 'solids' could not have been created in vain. Indeed he was so convinced that he spent countless hours of meticulous study, in a quest to find the link. To his great joy he was eventually able to construct a model where the orbits of the known six planets could, using classical geometry, all be fitted into the perfect solids. That is where the tips of the solid were found to touch the inside of the containing orbital (concentric) spheres, or conversely the orbital spheres were such that they touched the inside of the containing solids in the middle of their respective regular faces.

Thus he was able to arrange, in the actual measured ratios, the orbital configuration of the planets, postulated on the basis of Copernicus' six planetary spheres, which he could fit around the skeletons of the five regular solids in the following way: that the sphere of Saturn could circumscribe a cube in which could be placed the sphere of Jupiter. The Jupiter sphere could be circumscribed a tetrahedron in which the sphere of Mars could be inscribed. Similarly the dodecahedron for the Earth's sphere, the icosahedron for Venus and the octahedron for the sphere of Mercury – *see* Figure 7.1. As stated earlier, the reality is that all the planets in the solar system travel round the Sun in a comparatively narrow eight degree wide band (not dissimilar to the way the rings go round Saturn), their orbital radii, as conceived by Kepler being a slice through Copernicus' six planetary spheres.

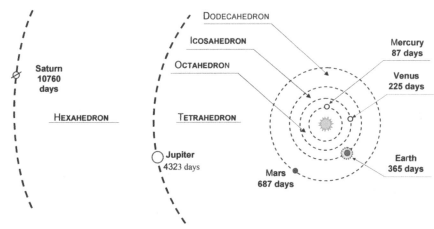

Figure 7.1   This shows Kepler's (and presumably condoned by the Founders) arrangement of the orbits of the known planets and the Platonic bodies. The orbits of the respective planets in the diagram are roughly to scale.

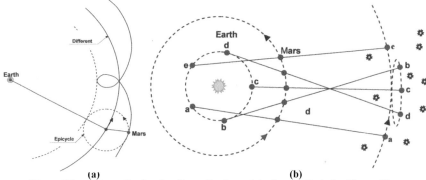

(a)   (b)

Figure 7.2a   Schematic showing the path of a point of a small circle either rolling on (quasi-spinning round) a point on a larger circle. Figure 7.2b how the erratic behaviour may be accounted for when observations of the orbit of one planet are taken from another.

He, like Ptolemy (120 AD) in his Tables all those centuries before, needed to actually reconcile and quantify the precessions or 'stop and go' motions, that had been known to occur in some regular, but unexplained way, since very early days, certainly they were known to the very early Greeks. Of course this is now known to be the result of taking observations of a planet whilst riding on another: namely the relative motion as the two planets pass each other in their respective orbits. The manner and extent of these eccentricities depending upon the length of each planet's year with respect to that of the earth and whether its orbit is inside or outside that of the earth's. These motions were catered for in Ptolemy's (calculations) Tables on the basis of quasi epicyclic or hypocyclic motion (epicyclic and hypocyclic motion being the motion of a point on a small circle rolling round the outside or inside of a larger circle). This concept was not new, but his version (if observed almost side on) provided an extraordinarily good approximation in terms of time and closely modelled the observed movement in the sky and hence lasted for *circa* 1200 years. Pythagoras (*circa* 550 BC) and many who followed adopted a Crystal Spheres concept and this whole subject makes interesting reading, but to go further at this point would be a distraction and so taking two giant leaps in time, via the Ptolemaic and Copernican System we arrive at Kepler. The basis of Ptolemy's epicyclical type model is shown schematically in Figure 7.2a. It shows how this retrogradation appears to take place when the Earth is taken to be at the centre of the Universe. Figure 7.2b provides an explanation of how in reality this eccentric behaviour was observed by them – *see also* Desagulier's acceptance of this revised concept in Appendix 1.

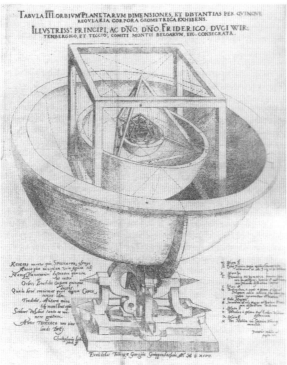

Figure 7.3. The 'paper' representation of Kepler's 'Cosmic Mystery' model of the six planets nestling within Plato's perfect solids. Sadly never made from precious metals.

Indeed in the beginning even to the brilliant mind of Kepler it was possible to reconcile this eccentricity by assuming that the skins of the spherical shells were in practice hollow and formed by two close concentric spheres (as though it were a thick hollow membrane between the respective layers of an onion) and that the hollow was sufficiently broad to accommodate these eccentric or epicyclical wobbles in their orbits. He was so committed to this interrelationship between the Regular Solids, the orbits of the planets and its obvious link with the 'perfection of God's Creation, that he asked his then patron to construct a model of his discovery of this interrelationship between the planets and the five regular solids in precious metals. However, his Patron's religious fervour did not extend to this level of expenditure and he suggested that Kepler should in the event 'construct (simply draw) it on paper', hence Figure 7.3.

The sheer genius of Kepler becomes apparent when one reads at some depth the extent of his mathematical ability and perhaps more remarkable his patience and industry. Such a study of the man is well done in a book on astronomy edited by Walker, which incidentally has an excellent explanation of retrogradation.[2] There were of course anomalies, but historians are of the view that he remained throughout his life, adhered to the concept that all things are intrinsically related to some divine order. He was a very brilliant man and contributed enormously to the advancement of science, and as we know from the earlier Section on geometry, he was later able to develop the mathematical concept that: 'that the radius of the terrestrial orbit sweeps out equal areas in equal times'; from which Newton's (geometry 'triangular' based calculus) gravitational law on planetary motion discussed above was evolved. However, for the purposes of this study, it is this interrelationship between the Regular Platonic Solids and the Sphere of the Universe claimed in the text of the Ritual that is of importance, since the more one probes the less there seems to be a rationale for its inclusion in the Symbolical Lecture in the first (1720s) place and exponentially less plausible at some later date.

This is another example of the different factors which affect the precise dating of the science of the Symbolical Lecture and one that will have to be addressed in Parts V and VI, because by 1605 (120 years earlier than the period of interest here) Kepler's work had forced him to now accept that the planetary orbits were in practice elliptical and in 1609 published a work to that effect. However, strangely in 1625 in the Second edition of his book *Proromus*, he returned, with only minor changes to the concept of the perfect solids and hence God's geometric perfection. Kepler died in 1630 which is relatively early in the 17th Century and it is therefore surprising that those beliefs appear to have persisted up until the time that they were included by the Founders in the Ritual of the Royal Arch. This may have been attributable to the paucity of books on the subject, particularly in schools and libraries or the

Sphere of the Universe

lack of a viable/acceptable alternative which allowed the concept to persist. Perhaps more likely was that the Founders may have decided that this interpretation was more consistent with prevailing religious precepts and that they merely intended their reference to the Platonic solids to comply with some vague common notion and not to be necessarily consistent with the new and more rigorous scientific analysis.

As will be discussed later, this may point to the likelihood that the astronomy of the Symbolical Lecture was in practice a judicious conglomeration of the old and the new and hence palatable to the church and deliberately retained some of the basic, still widely accepted, concepts of the 1600s. At least that would appear to be the most likely scenario, since after 1700 there was such a rapid upsurge in the understanding of science that these ageing concepts would have been open to ever increasing challenge. However, as has already been stated, in the edicts of the Constitution there is an implicit undertaking that its rules and indeed whole ethos were enshrined in the Ritual and that 'it was not lawful' to change them in any fundamental way; quite unlike today where this traditional inviolability is often replaced by the greater need of political expediency. If indeed this was their 'approved' understanding of our Planetary System, then we are now in a position to consider the contention made of the last 'regular solid' that the dodecahedron may be described as representing the Sphere of the Universe.

The Ritual of the Symbolical Lecture states that the fifth regular (Platonic) solid represents the Sphere of the Universe and hence we have to assume that in view of those responsible for the Lecture the term relates to the 'Copernican' model. However we must take the precaution of assuming that they, like all mankind before or indeed since, would have had confused thoughts on the very nature of their 'being', both in this life and the next and that this new concept of a now expanded heaven still had to remain consistent with their ultimate salvation. Now that these astronomical facts were before them, they were obliged to at least give some account of the newly revealed vastness of the heavens and the anomalies highlighted by such phenomena as the appearance and subsequent disappearance of comets. The concept of a single perfect (heavenly) crystal like sphere that contained the 'fixed' stars was now becoming rather strained. However we shall see in Chapters thirty-six and thirty-seven that there was some confusion on the subject and in order not to cause (social) disquiet it may have been prudent for them to adhere to the inaccurate, but generally accepted view within the Church.

Modern astronomy and space exploration continues to bewilder our present generation by exposing the seemingly unending extent of the universe and very few would now seek to challenge the basic validity of these revelations as they occur, thus making it increasingly difficult to reconcile the metaphysical realities of the immensity of the Universe, with that of some divinity of human ('Father' like, 'Supreme Governor', 'Architect of the Universe' etc. used in all the prayers throughout the Ritual) dimension. That the average person was nonetheless able to somehow rationalise this situation should not come as a surprise if we consider the current position which makes the situation far less understandable if not implausible. Few would now challenge the current view of the unimaginable vastness of the Universe and its evolutionary timescale, thus making reconciliation of the interrelationship between God and man an even greater philosophical challenge to the diverse philosophies of all the present major religions, as well as the many other splinter groups, with even more diverse beliefs. Yet it would seem that somehow or other each religion is perfectly able to rationalise the doctrines of their faith within these awesome discoveries; all somehow able to readjust and rationalise these realities with their faith. On the basis of this it is perhaps much easier to make a case for the Founders' naive acceptance of the more modest dimensions of their Universe as opposed to an effective infinity confronting this generation. At least their Universe was contained (visible) within human dimension and to them it would not have been inconceivable that there was a celestial (crystal like) sphere place called Heaven into which one could ascend, as opposed to infinite space and endless time that is postulated at present. Indeed, when rereading this particular paragraph in the constant process of reviewing this work, there appeared in the bottom of the centre pages of the Times newspaper on that day the comparatively insignificant (but absolutely typical) article shown in Figure 7.4. The numbers are in reality beyond comprehension in any physical sense, but if they are true then all concepts of space and time held hitherto need to be revised completely. However like computer technology it quickly became yesterday's news, but the significant factor is that it was obviously regarded by the editorial staff as 'throwaway' news and as such extremely unlikely to make the slightest ripple in the tranquil philosophical ponds of the theologians, even though if accurate it would clearly have profound implications with respect to the fundamental perceptions of their respective faiths.

Thus the recipient of these lectures in the 1720s may have been similarly untroubled, since they were blissfully unaware of the actuality of Space as we know it today and were able to accept the concept of there being some vast (crystal) sphere, albeit ill defined. However, unlike today their heaven was still finite and could, quite reasonably be considered perfect and thus irrespective of religious doctrine there was a conceptual (physically conceivable) Heaven. Copernicus was the first philosopher to propound in a way that had a general ('mind shift') impact on the public, namely the discovery that it was the Sun that was at the centre of the universe (heliocentric). That the Earth was merely a planet going around in one of the concentric celestial spheres that uniquely served to contain the other planets and that the outermost of

Hubble telescope rewrites theory of time and space

By Mark Henderson
Science Correspondent

THE standard theory of space and time may be undermined by observations from the Hubble Space Telescope, two American astronomers said yesterday.

The images of galaxies four billion light years from Earth show no evidence of an important effect that researchers expect to see under traditional notions about the nature of the Universe.

They suggest that time may work differently from the way in which astrophysicists have generally assumed. Instead of being composed of many incredibly small but finite individual moments, like grains of sand running through an egg timer, time may move in a seamless, continuous flow, the researchers, Richard Lieu and Lloyd Hillman of the University of Alabama in Huntsville, said.

If the results, published today in *Astrophysical Journal Letters*, hold up under further analysis, they would cause con-

sternation in the scientific community. They would imply, for example, that the Universe had infinite temperature and density at the moment of the Big Bang — a concept that cosmologists have always tried to avoid.

According to current theories, time should be divisible into 20 million trillion, trillion, trillion "Planck intervals". The shortest possible spatial measurement, the "Planck length", is the distance light can travel in one Planck interval 0.0000000000000000000000 00000000001 cm (10 to the power of minus 33).

Scientists say time and distances smaller than Planck scales are "fuzzy" because in a fundamental way they cannot be measured.

The theory allows for Planck-scale fluctuations in time and space which translate to minute variations in speed of light.

However, these variations would only be evident in light that has travelled a great distance. In a similar way, a sprinter running 1 per cent faster

than his opponents might win a 100m race in a photo finish, while a 1 per cent faster marathon runner would finish hundreds of metres ahead of the rest.

After billions of years, the faster components of a light wave would be far enough ahead of the slower components to make the beam's wave front noticeably distorted, or blurred.

The Alabama researchers sought to test the theory by looking for this blurring in the Hubble images, but instead each image showed a sharp, ring-like interference pattern around the galaxy.

This suggested that time was not a quantum function and flowed fluidly at intervals infinitely shorter than Planck units, they said.

Dr Lieu said: "This discovery will present problems to several astrophysical and cosmological models, including the Big Bang model of the Universe."

Shuttle commander, page 21

Figure 7.4 Extract from *The Times* newspaper with respect to a reported new discovery in Space. 1% of 100 metres is 1 metre and does not normally require a photo finish, but the point is made and the other numbers he uses are truly mind boggling. These findings were published c.2000, but are retained here to show how the Hubble telescope has now proved that these staggering findings to be comparatively modest.

them was a celestial 'crystal type' sphere, which contained the fixed stars. This outer sphere was still consistent with the ancient philosophers' belief in a place of utter perfection, a place in which God/s dwelt and in which was the ultimate residing place of a man's soul, Newton's latest concept simply meant that it was rather bigger than they had imagined.

Thus rather than being surprised at their apparent naivety, we should understand how easily they could, indeed needed, to have entertained this concept, because this is precisely how troublesome concepts are dealt with today. For instance, if one considers the stance taken by the advocates of the now widely accepted concept of the 'Big Bang' theory alluded to in the above article and which purports to explain the origins of the universe – they allow no room for further debate. However, without wishing to create a major diversion, their theory does not seem to deal with the questions such as: what existed before that momentous instant, or define in what was it contained, by whom was it created and who created the creator etc. These seemingly quite profound factors do not seem to deter the disciples of 'Big Bang' theorists in the least. Interestingly enough they are considered by many to be amongst the most profound scientists, mathematicians and philosophers of our time, clearly the Founders were highly intelligent men and so we need to exercise restraint before pouring scorn on their judgement, beliefs or mental faculties.

Conclusions

When first discussing the Platonic Bodies above it was stated that Plato argued, rather obscurely, that the fifth regular solid's volume approached that of a sphere (the ultimate perfection) and so it was not a great philosophical leap for it to be considered as representing 'the sphere of the (then known) universe'. To moot this matter further would be to invent reasons for their employing such outdated concepts and so the subject will not be pursued. However, what is perhaps more worthy of further consideration is whether there was a unique time at which all the concepts in the Symbolical Lecture could have been considered at their most reasonable and totally consistent with all other factors affecting the scientific world and Parts V and VI seeks to address this possibility.

References

1. Sagan, C., *Cosmos* (Macdonald, London & Sydney, 1980).
2. Walker, C., *Astronomy – Before the Telescope* (BCA. London, 1996).

Chapter Eight:
The science that is not included

he physical attributes of the science related to directly in the Symbolical Lecture has been discussed in terms of that which would have been expected in the well-informed person at the time of its conception. It is essentially one with pretensions towards the avant-garde, but which in the end remained consistent with the Aristotelian perception of the world about us and was in keeping with the generally accepted philosophy of the Church. As such it is reasonable to suppose that the Founders were quite happy to embrace it as a palliative, rather than confront a drastic analysis of the true implications that the emerging sciences might have on theology in particular. In this respect the original task of offering a reasonably comprehensive introduction into the 'science, of Freemasonry in terms of modern understanding has been accomplished. From this it is hoped that the reader and especially those who are Masons will henceforth have a better comprehension of the physical meaning of the words and phrases, such as 'the Liberal Arts and (especially) Sciences' they have heard repeatedly for many years, but not necessarily appreciated. As the research for the work reported here progressed the clearer it became that far more could be gleaned from the Science of Freemasonry than a simple explanation of its intrinsic meaning in the 1720s allied to current understanding and that there was considerable potential if it were pursued beyond a simple physical interpretation, hence the much broader analysis of the subsequent Parts.

However before proceeding to this second stage there is a need to deal with the loose ends of the science extant at the time, which are significant because of their absence. The fundamental reasons behind the extensive introduction of science into Masonic ritual have already been alluded to and in all the areas there was clear evidence of the progression towards the belief that there was a physical explanation to all things pertaining to the natural world and that severe cracks were beginning to show in the Aristotelian explanation of science (if it may be so described) which had dominated for the best part of the preceding 1200 years. It was now under attack from several schools of thought, none more so than those held by that group of scientists who were prominent in the very early years of Premier Grand Lodge. Not only was the basic physics under challenge, but also the underlying philosophical concepts. Science was not only affecting education, but also the whole of society.

From the start of the Aristotelian era the science had been encompassed within the 'logic' of his philosophy, but in the Fifth Century AD the Roman philosopher Boethius isolated and distinguished the Sciences (geometry, arithmetic, astronomy and music) from the Arts (grammar, rhetoric and logic), but it would seem with little impact until the relatively short period (the age of the 'Enlightenment' – a hundred years or so) prior to the founding of the Premier Grand Lodge. One could be forgiven for taking the meaning of these categories in their modern literal sense and because of the pressures of contemporary living and the plethora of information that accompanies it, it is easy to take things for granted, but in this instance one is likely to miss their original meaning completely and in the process miss some of the intrinsic philosophy of modern Freemasonry.

By taking this opportunity of looking more closely at this topic in terms of the 1720s we have in part avoided this trap, but before we leave the physical aspects of the physics/mechanics implicit in the science of Freemasonry, it is of importance to reflect on that which is omitted. Whilst it is now quite natural to think of science as being a collection of disciplines, it was not the case in the early 1700s.

The question of time, or rather date, is a constant issue in this work, because whenever the Ritual was adopted, it had to be at some particular date and at that moment its originators were disposed to specific views on all things, but particularly the current state of science given the emphasis laid upon it. In the 1720s chemistry (or rather the lack of it) and the measurement of longitude have been mentioned already but there were several others areas that would have been of considerable importance to them. Three in particular were conspicuous by their absence in the Symbolical Lecture, namely: the natural sciences that would now be one of a number of disciplines; such as, say, botany and biology, medicine and two other important areas: magnetism (often at that time associated with the attraction we now know as gravity) and electricity. Conspicuous because great advances either had been, or were in the process of being made in these areas. It is reasonable to suppose that they should have fallen within the remit of their umbrella term of 'Nature and Science'. Given the ingenuity with which they contrived to introduce the topics of the Symbolical Lecture, which have been discussed in some detail, into the ritual, it is comparatively easy to think of ways that those that were omitted could have been associated with say religious connotations, but more especially because of the particular disposition and interests taken in those topics by certain of the Founders. This 'disposition' is not only of central importance to this work, but it has occupied the minds of several Masonic historians since. Again, although not specifically in these terms, two other areas were of particular interest; Geology, for instance fossils were known about, but more especially because of the importance of the barber surgeons to this study, physiology – public dissections were quite common. This tendency to misconceive both the intellectual capacity and personal motivation of the individuals concerned is an important element when considering why events such as the formalisation of Freemasonry should have occurred. Thus before leaving this section which relates to the ritualist's likely scientific perceptions, it is important to make a simple appraisal of the science omitted by the originators of that early ritual and in particular the Symbolical Lecture.

Although only a 'straw-poll' it would seem that a freemason of today might consider: 'grammar' to imply to the structure of one's language; 'rhetoric' persuasive speaking; 'logic' the science of reason; 'geometry' Euclidean geometrical analysis; 'arithmetic' the science of number; 'astronomy' the study of Space and 'music' the study of the composition and rendition of music. Since there is effectively no specific indication within the ritual of the Founders' interpretation of these terms, it is reasonable to imagine that the majority of present day freemasons would most likely assume that the definitions above are essentially those which would have been generally accepted in 1720. However to do so would be quite wrong since the meanings of these terms have changed dramatically over the intervening period – *see* Appendix 2. For instance, and again it is speculation, it is reasonable to suppose that they wished to retain in their ritual the Grecian concept of 'logic' implicit in the Aristotelian School (*circa* 340 BC onwards). Namely a system propounded on truisms or the lack of them, as in the famous example: 'All men are mortal, Socrates is a man, therefore Socrates is mortal'. However this assumption may be incorrect, for as will be seen in Parts V and VI it was challenged by the very group of people with whom we are concerned and asks the question of whether the word, or indeed any other word, would have remained effectively unchanged in its basic concept? It was certainly not the 'binary' logic proposed by George Boole (1815-1864), which implies the absolute 'either/or' approach which underpins Boolean algebra – so enormously important today, because it is the basis of the modern computer, namely the certainty that a switch is either 'on' or it is 'off' and where there are no grey areas or room for debate. But there have also been deeper philosophical reappraisals of 'logic' since that time, by people like Bertrand Russell (1872-1970), that may well have influenced further a present day freemason's understanding of the word 'logic' – *see also* Appendix 2.

Again it is reasonable to assume that the same is true of their concept of 'rhetoric' and that our modern interpretation of the term is strongly influenced by more recent philosophers, notably Ludwig Wittgenstein (1889-1951) who made a significant contribution to the study of the way in which language is used in human understanding and communication, but this word has also undergone profound change over this period.

Their understanding of 'arithmetic' is even more difficult and requires an even greater degree of speculation. This is because by the time the Founders were forming the Premier Grand Lodge, there was, in certain schools, an astounding understanding of number (arithmetic) and its symbolic analytical extension (algebra). Those who have needed to use mathematics to the level of complex variables (imaginary numbers: $\sqrt{-1}$, or as in the more practical example of the Cosh function in Figure

2.1) may think of it as a modern concept, but it was developed and used long before the Premier Grand Lodge was founded, certainly as early as the 1500s. However, as suggested above and again considered in subsequent Chapters: it is reasonably certain that several of the Founders were dedicated to the notion of analysis through geometry. Again the modern concepts of 'number' or 'mathematics' are influenced greatly by more recent philosophy, such as that of Gottlob Frege (1848-1925) and Bertrand Russell.

Astronomy has changed in that it is the clinical study of the heavens, there is little or no thought of the occult, of astrology, of magic, of celestial bodies, of the so called 'music of the spheres' etc., just the bare facts of each mind-bending discovery as interpreted by the respective 'experts'.

'Music', the last of the 'Noble Arts and Sciences' is of extreme importance to this study, since their (the Founders') conception of music gives a very strong indication of their beliefs in general. The physical structure of music is of course a science in its own right and several of those with whom we are concerned were particularly active in this concept of music – *see* Part IV. However, even though the æsthetic nature of music is emphasised in the Ritual, the true impact of their fundamental understanding of music (harmony) is most germane and hence revealing. There are many historians who emphasise the importance of music in early speculative Freemasonry, but only in terms of rendition, but as stated above, the theory of harmony was specialised in by several likely Founders as well as by those within their sphere such as Newton.[1] But although there is a degree of uncertainty, it must be considered further in this study both as an interrelating interest of certain Founders and as a fundamental concept of the philosophy of the period. Certainly the only other Masonic references to music, relating to this period,[2,3] encountered in this study have been keen to report the fact that freemasons' meetings were often regaled with the raucous singing and by implication, enhanced by an adequate supply of beverage.

In Parts V and VI it will therefore be necessary to make reference to the sciences that have been omitted, since they too will have a part to play in determining; who, why, where etc.

Conclusions

Although the sciences in the early 1700s were not compartmentalised and it was reasonable to suppose that certain of the Founders would have had a keen interest in the raft of subjects that were conspicuous by their absence in the Symbolical Lecture or elsewhere in the various rituals of Freemasonry. Because several obvious areas would have had quite profound spiritual and scientific implications it indicates that

The science that is not included

their omission was more a question of discretion, for one reason or another, rather than neglect and as such is a serious component of any study into the instigation of formalised Freemasonry.

References

1. Gouk, P., *Music, Science and natural Magic in Seventeenth-Century England* (Yale University Press, New Haven, 1999).
2. Jacobs, M., *Women and the Enlightenment* (The Haworth Press Inc., New York, 1984), pp. 69-91.
3. Edwards, L., 'Three early Grand Masters', *AQC* 43 (1930), pp. 226-238.

Part II

Che case for claiming that the ethos of early Premier Grand Lodge was influenced by predominance of Nature and science expressed within a humanitarian context and a description of an analytical approach that demonstrates such an assertion?

Chapter Nine:
Che ramifications and implications of the science of freemasonry

he circumstances that led to this particular investigation were explained in the opening remarks of Part I but as with most research, in the process of establishing the background upon which the investigation would proceed, it soon become clear that this seemingly simple process, was in reality multi-faceted and hence quite complicated. The consequence of this complexity was that areas were being chanced upon that appeared to offer greater understanding or touched upon topics of considerable interest to anyone seeking an insight into the origins of formalised Freemasonry and that many were quite outside of the original Masonic remit. Connections were found to exist between areas which up until then had either never been considered or adequately explained. Much of the problem was that there has been such rapid changes, in philosophy, science, technology, but especially society over the last four hundred years, that if one was to attempt to gainsay what the Founders had envisaged shortly after that process had begun, on the basis of their repeated use of the term 'Nature and Science', it was necessary to repress one's own preconceptions and attempt to understand theirs and indeed those who came before. If, in practice, it were possible to build such a picture, a meaningful attempt could then be made to comprehend what they believed and to understand further why they did so. In order to do this it would be necessary to gather together the many strands that had led up to and now formed the basis of their society and from that gain insight into the narrow climate of their tightly knit circle. An appreciation of the general (principally technical) understanding of science and technology at that time was the objective of the work undertaken in Part I, however because there are no direct indications of the Founders' precise intentions, such as contemporary records, the research was thereby forced to broaden substantially. It was obliged to include that which at first sight appeared to be extraneous factors such as whom, when, where, what, why etc. this in turn revealed associated factors that promised to unravel the likely origins of the Premier Grand Lodge, but in particular the Royal Arch itself.

Historically, most of these topics had been the subjects of extensive research, but although much has been claimed, little of real substance has been found. This

The ramifications and implications of the science of Freemasonry

painstaking and at times scholarly, but largely unsuccessful research may have been due to excessive introspection. Unfortunately, there is such a paucity of Masonic archival material during that initial period that it makes looking for substantial information a thankless task. However once the shackles of confining the investigation to that which was specifically 'Masonic' had been removed it became clear that there was a great deal more data available and because of its nature a considerable portion of it was verifiable. This approach was directed along lines not attempted before or at least not in a meaningful way, neither was it solely reliant upon Masonic archive material, but rather using it in a supportive roll and gaining additional strength from using an analytical (quasi mathematical) approach to certain of the data. The research necessary to study Freemasonry's 'Nature and Science' in the 1720s was outlined in Part I, but was for the most part restricted to merely establishing the contemporary 'state of the art' and the scientific reasoning that surrounded it. Except in passing, it had not required the systematic consideration of the chronology, individuals, opportunities, places etc. and the social/political/religious machinations of that prevailed and the years leading up to it. Even so this procedure had nonetheless revealed a unique insight into the interrelationship of many of the principal players who, strikingly, were the very same characters that were centrally involved in the formation of Premier Grand Lodge. But more significantly it showed that a similar analytical approach could reveal a much more comprehensive and authoritative understanding of the prevailing circumstances than would otherwise be gleaned from single strands of unsubstantiated information taken in isolation.

As stated above, most people who attempt to research this area pursue Masonic literature as the obvious source of material, but it soon became clear that there was very little known about the actual substance or precise content of the first or indeed any of the very early ritual. Neither was there very much definitive data on many other matters, such as when precisely the Royal Arch was founded, by whom, for what reason, where held etc. Maybe, it is because of this dearth of knowledge that one finds it replaced by a plethora of essentially fictitious (perhaps too strong an adjective) works on Masonic history, most claiming to be based on that period, but with little authority. This apparent wealth of information was encouraging at first, but unfortunately on closer examination it quickly becomes clear that there is very little indeed that has sufficient objectivity to be considered definitive and that this deficiency had been replaced by retelling the same story in different ways and employing the expedient of using invention in place of reality. If this study was not to be numbered in amongst that larger group and some progress made, it was clear that a different strategy had to be employed.

A reasonable basis upon which to start seemed to be that all institutions bear some relation to the society in which they exist or from which they emerge and are usually centred around some distinct faction or interest group with its own particular and often very narrow objective in view. Virtually every piece of official literature that is now released to characterise the *raison d'être* of Freemasonry, rightly points out the extremely laudable objectives of the Society; the question that needed to be addressed was whether it was ever so? Did the newly emerging Premier Grand Lodge fit into this general pattern of the needs of an individual group and if so what was it? Could this factor then be used to make progress on other interesting factors such as: who, why, when, how etc? The following makes the case that Premier Grand Lodge was very much a product of its time and that the Founders were a unique blend of remarkable individuals who usurped a concept started by others for subtle and quite different reasons. Although each of the Founders derived benefit, it seems reasonable to conclude that such benefits were not universally or equally rewarding, but unique and sufficient to the requirements of each person. In particular to answer the question of whether the amazingly successful Institution of formalised Freemasonry resulted from the force of their peculiar involvement and foresight or was it more by accident than design?

Thus the premise adopted henceforth is that the *raison d'être* behind the Premier Grand Lodge and the establishment of the Royal Arch is far more likely to be deduced from the sociological realities of the period, its people and the events leading up to it in general, than to seek a complete answer from the writings of Masonic (and others in cross reference to it) historians of a much later period. This because by the time these historians undertook their work, there had been great cultural changes within society at large and especially within those concerned with defining (for the most part justifying it on moralistic/esoteric grounds) speculative Freemasonry itself. That altruism which was to become its banner was to manifest itself very soon after Premier Grand Lodge was founded when it was used to justify (or excuse) the battle between the two Grand Lodges (Antients and Moderns), where the two sides exchanging fire on moralistic (quasi philosophical/religious) grounds, but where in reality the underlying cause was essentially political power. Intrinsic humanitarianism was then and remains an essential component of the interrelationship between the various constitutions and at the time especially the version adopted in the East coast of America and the other burgeoning colonies. Later in that same century the intrinsic appeal of Freemasonry was clearly illustrated with the emergence, both in terms of their structure and content of the first of the many so called 'other degrees' or 'side degrees', by those who are not particularly disposed towards them and the 'higher degrees' by those who are.

It will be seen that when this 'outside looking in' approach is adopted the problem becomes that of dealing with a wide range of factors, all of importance, of which the science in Part I is not only a clear demonstration, but is an essential

The ramifications and implications of the science of Freemasonry

lynch-pin. This because the subject is comparatively well documented and the certain knowledge that those with whom we are concerned were both intimately involved in the formative years of Premier Grand Lodge and the science and technology of the time. Further, the closer one delves into the social history and in particular science, of the preceding century the more one is struck by the way in which certain names keep reoccurring. Thus it will be argued: that it is the interaction of people from within and outside of Freemasonry, both before and during that period that gives the greatest clue as to the origins, timing, justification etc. for Premier Grand Lodge in the form we know it today and the early foundation of the Royal Arch.

However before retreating from recorded Masonic history it is helpful to reflect on that which is available. The study related to a remote period in history has a number of drawbacks, but there are two in particular: those of hindsight and preconception. Neither of these limitations can be suppressed easily, since one arrives at any subject with the disadvantage of ones experience and continued education to date and hence one is bedevilled with a preconceived view on things. Second one is aware already of the outcome of those events, again the accuracy of which depending upon its derivation as well as how faithfully in the interim the nature of those events has been transmitted. As has already been stated a number of times in the case of Freemasonry this chronicling appears to be a collection of sparse factual data, heavily supplemented by jaundiced views and invention, but sadly it is now all that remains. Bearing these points in mind it is perhaps opportune to reiterate that it is from the general history of the period, namely the widely recorded events up to 1744, that are used to distill a more precise understanding of likely circumstances surrounding the formation and basic constitution of the Premier Grand Lodge and the formation of the Royal Arch. 1744 is taken as the upper (date) limit because there is wide agreement amongst Masonic historians that there was unambiguous use of the term the Royal Arch after that date, albeit that there is no understanding of what it meant precisely.

There have been numerous studies concerned with the internecine conflicts of various schisms within Freemasonry, but more especially the Antients and the Moderns, from *circa* 1730 through the remainder of the eighteenth Century, into the nineteenth Century, until the United Grand Lodge of Ancient Freemasons of England was formed in the early 1800s and ratified finally on 27 December 1813. It would be possible to give many references relating to this topic, but once again the appraisal given is extracted from Jones' book; *Freemasons' Guide and Compendium*[1] may be considered an above average and fair assessment of that which has been written to date. Here, because of the period, we are concerned primarily with the pejorative term 'Moderns', otherwise the Premier Grand Lodge. If these historians are substantially correct, then the present day understanding of early Freemasonry is

111

that it went from rapid expansion in the early 1720s into a period of marked slowing if not decline through the 1730s. For the most part this malaise was because it was ill served by its leadership, who appeared to have no great passion for the Institution, managing to offend the 'purists' (as well as those precluded or disaffected) and to have their main interests in other areas or as in one or two cases nothing of any importance at all and by the middle to late 1730s Freemasonry had effectively lost its way. Indeed it had departed to such an extent that it had fostered the nucleation of the major splinter group that would form the 'Antients' – who claimed the 'higher (moral) ground'. It will be argued later that this process of decline was an inevitable consequence of its origins and that the seeds of such a decline were sown no later than two years after the initial concept in 1717 when it was usurped and that in reality 'the cuckoo's egg' had in effect been laid, even as it started.

Thus it is necessary to search for the reasons why the comparatively simple notion of a Premier Grand Lodge quickly changed into what was to become an incredibly successful social venture, only shortly to decline to a state of mediocrity and almost founder. Of especial interest was to gain an understanding of the individual disposition and motivation of those who were influential in the early stages of its development, for it was becoming quite evident that each had their own agenda. Indeed, if the conclusions of this study are correct, namely that the driving force behind the formation of the Premier Grand Lodge was far more sociological and insular than esoteric, then the loss of direction was understandable and that the wrangling and posturing of the various groupings was essentially one of individual politics and not substance. Thus it could be argued that the Masonic ethic as it is known today was not an inevitable ingredient (although no doubt discussed and considered an admirable garnish); but that its great attraction relied upon its powerful social involvement which was already a dominant feature of the disparate freemasons' lodges from which it emanated. However the esoteric, history and essentially moralistic and altruistic aspects that are a predominant if not imperative feature of Freemasonry today, were embellished to their present level at a later date, blossoming in the Freemasonry of the Victorian era.

Despite a considerable amount of work within Masonic Archives and to an even greater degree outside of it, in an attempt to gain some understanding of these early days, the reality was that there was in reality precious little direct factual evidence to work on. In consequence it became clear that an alternative indirect and/or integrated approach was required. Fortunately the data (if it may be so described) presented here when used in this way proved to be of sufficient quantity, impartiality and integrity, to justify the conclusions arrived at. The problem with adopting this approach was that almost immediately it became apparent that within certain of these earlier writings and snippets of contemporary archival information, such as the Premier Grand Lodge Minutes (although there is evidence that even these have been tampered with at some later date and are in any case incomplete – *see* Bibliographies) have at some time been surreptitiously combined with other strands of less reliable information, such as the quasi factual evidence of Pritchard's *Masonry Dissected* and Anderson's *Book of Constitutions* (1723 & 1738). Thus with judicious backward extrapolation, integration from other, much later, writings and further 'rearrangement' these findings are then presented as being somehow factual. This observation is phrased in this ungracious way, not to be critical of the originator's outstanding efforts, far from it, but to emphasise the inordinately difficult task of repressing one's own preconceived view and preferred interpretation. This has already been demonstrated in several of the scientific dictates in Part I. A typical example of how it affects this aspect of the work, is found in the following extract taken from Chapter Seven of another exceptionally fine book by Jones, *Freemasons' Book of the Royal Arch*:

> The origins of the Royal Arch are as uncertain as those of the Craft. It is now generally accepted that the Royal Arch originated in the 1730s, but whether in England, Ireland or, possibly, France is still highly arguable. There have been various theories published as to the origins of the Royal Arch [here he includes a reference]. It has been suggested that it either evolved from material discarded when the third degree was settled in the 1720s or that this degree was deliberately mutilated to provide for a new degree. As we have little evidence concerning the development of the third degree, and none at all for its mutilation or splitting in two, those theories have been discounted. Vibert [here he gives another reference] suggested that the Royal Arch originally formed part of the ceremony of Installation of the Master of a Craft lodge, but there is no evidence of this ceremony, at the time at which the Royal Arch was developing, being anything other than a ceremonial placing of the Master in the chair without any esoteric content, and Vibert's theory has generally been dismissed. Others have suggested that the Royal Arch was a natural extension of the third degree: a loss having been made in that degree, it was necessary to invent a further degree in which the loss could be repaired. Others would argue that at the time in which the Royal Arch was evolving in the 1730s, the loss was repaired in the third degree by the introduction of the substituted secrets [again reference]. Some, less charitably, have suggested that the Royal Arch was an inevitable result of human vanity. They argue that initially the third degree had been very strictly controlled but was becoming more widely practised in the 1730s, resulting in the development of the Royal Arch as a 'special' and limited degree to replace the former exclusive Master Mason's degree, etc., etc.[2]

However, his use of the words 'generally accepted' suggests that he has in some way been able to make some form of measurement. However, in practice this would not appear to have been the case and perhaps the phrase 'a strong body of opinion' or 'one school' would have been a better description. Thus from here on, when dealing with such information there is special need to avoid the temptation of claiming speculation as fact. Even so, there are very strong reasons to conclude from literature dating *circa* 1742/4 that there was a ceremony referred to as the Royal Arch within English Masonry, which because of the normal delays due to publication, means that it had been in existence for some time (say before 1740), but none that indicate exactly when it was introduced, or precisely the nature of its content or ritual. Another excellent example of the many attempts by learned and extremely dedicated people, is the painstaking work of the comparatively modern historian W. Bro. Clarke.[3, 4] It is also of interest that in these papers he makes a limited attempt to go outside the confines of Freemasonry. By his extensive cross-referencing, he acknowledges the work of many others, who have researched into the tenuous strands of the history of Royal Arch. From this work, it is clear that many have attempted to gain some insight into the nature of this early ritual and other Masonic matters, but that despite their considerable effort, they have met with only limited success. Clearly this situation was principally due to the absolute dearth of actual definitive documentation, but the inescapable reality that it is unlikely to change and that the device of simply rearranging the existing data offers little value or promise. Thus if progress was to be made it was clearly necessary to look elsewhere for further evidence and only after that had been done and to a large degree verified, should an attempt be made to find some correlation with the existing findings of the Masonic historians.

So far as it had been possible to ascertain, there had been no in-depth research into the actual concepts of the 'Sciences' or indeed the 'Liberal Arts', even though they are referred to repeatedly in both Craft and Royal Arch ritual of today. Given that there so little hard direct data on the Freemasonry practiced in those formative years, there appears to be even less (although in Alice in Wonderland terms 'it is difficult to get less than nothing' [except perhaps misinformation]) early information on these specific subject areas and so it is easy to understand why little work has been undertaken. Although this assertion is almost certain to be challenged by some, if there is evidence, then it is awfully obscure. Even much later Masonic literature appears to be effectively barren on matters scientific and since Freemasonry in its present day guise is expressly apolitical, it would be of advantage to gain some insight of the contemporary thinking in both these areas at the time and to ascertain whether a technique based on a scientific/sociological format would constitute the basis of a fresh approach. Having decided upon this approach, just as in Part I and indeed with most research, matters that at first appeared to be routine, when they are pursued at depth proved to be bedevilled by a host of complexities, both within and

The ramifications and implications of the science of Freemasonry

especially, in this case, outside of the actual science and Masonry itself.

The greatest obstacle is the lack of irrefutable truths; for the politics of the situation were such that even if it had been possible to have read the contemporaneous words of the actual people themselves it would have been unreliable, for it seems that most of these characters were innately devious. In the normal course of events historians rely heavily on such pieces of information, but it was quickly realised that any 'facts' that might have been derived from their writings, statements or actions would have been tempered by the extent of their social involvement, their psychology (aspirations and motivation), the political constraints and especially the social standing of those for whom their words had been intended in the first instance. It appears almost inevitable that however many times one undertakes research in a new area, problems occur at the very first hurdle. Even more strange is that when it occurs, one is always surprised and saddened that it should have happened in this latest instance, since it is certain that nothing then remains, other than to start trawling through a whole raft of data, knowing that little of it will be particularly reliable and with little or no certainty of what or where that small gem of information resides.

Thus the following appraisal is based upon the rationalisation of very many different strands of historical information all conveying some scientific, technological, philosophical or sociological nuance of the period which may reveal a common (consistent) strand that is close to the truth. This approach accepts the fact that none of the data is of itself likely to be totally accurate or convincing and avoids the trap of having to rely on any one specific item as the lynch-pin. Unfortunately there are too many strands of information for them all to be incorporated, but if sufficient of these could be used in combination it is very likely that a much more cohesive understanding could be gained. In Part I it was necessary to make reference to the work of many authors and in every case those authors have spent literally hundreds of hours in researching their chosen topic before publishing their findings. If this research was to span the many scientific disciplines and embrace the sociological climate during this time of dramatic change, then it too was not only going to be a comparatively painstaking task, but of necessity, was going to rely on making a balanced interpretation of the 'facts' as seen by these and the authors in many other fields, for to research every aspect in detail 'from scratch' was clearly impossible.

The problem was where to begin and the decision made was to start with those factors that appear to contribute towards the identification of those persons most likely to have founded the Order. Clearly whilst much may have been borrowed from elsewhere, the actual ritual adopted, especially that of the Royal Arch ceremony itself had been compiled (or adopted and adapted) by those already within Freemasonry and because there were a very limited number of lodges involved during that early period, the choice of possible individuals was comparatively restricted. The 'bad news' is that there were, amongst that small group, a number of extremely articulate, educated and very influential people, any one of whom taken in isolation, could be considered capable of consolidating the disparate Craft rituals and conceiving a unifying extension to the remit of the new Premier Grand Lodge, by introducing a ceremony called the Royal Arch.

However, it will be argued and one hopes sufficiently demonstrated, that factors relating to the sociological climate of the time and those within it, appear to have had a very strong influence indeed. Fortunately this factor would restrict the choice of likely individuals who were in a position or would have had the wit to anticipate the need to found the Royal Arch and hence restricted possible candidates to a select few from within those who were primarily involved during the very early development of the Premier Grand Lodge itself. Further, it is intended to show, that there was much more than merely the choice of a supplementary ritual involved in the very early developmental stages. Although this task still remained a daunting undertaking, it was helped to a large degree by the fact (one may fairly use the term fact since these were actual lists, but again there is strong reason to believe that they were incomplete and subject to some later tampering) that there were comparatively few lodges involved in the formation and early years of the Premier Grand Lodge. Given the unique skills required of a person/s capable of undertaking such an initiative, it was reasonable to suppose that in practice the choice would be restricted to a very few individuals. Whilst this person or few persons were likely to have been aided and abetted by other able men, the task of identifying them was now at least feasible. As will be seen, the challenge was then to provide a convincing argument as to who he or they were likely to have been. The assumption that there had to be a uniqueness to the choice of a capable person was taken as the basis of this approach, but asked the question of whether it was valid, however during subsequent research the following passage in a quite remarkable book on social history by Barzun was chanced upon:

> 'The men who came to lead factions or who gained power for a time lacked mature political talent. To govern well requires two distinct kinds of ability: political skill and the administrative mind. Both extremely rare, either in combination or separately. The former depends on sensing what can be done, at what moment, and how to move others to want it. Anyone who has served open-eyed on a committee knows how many "good ideas" are proposed by well-meaning members that could not possibly be carried out, because what is proposed consists only of results, with no means in sight for getting from here to there. After serving on a local government body, Bernard Shaw guessed that perhaps less than 5 percent of mankind possess political ability, etc.[5]

He goes on to reiterate the rarity of such people and in this sense reinforces the notion that although there were a number of talented people within that small band of the Founders in reality the actual number of viable candidates was extremely restricted – reference to Desaguliers in Part VI.

References

1. Jones, B.E., *Freemasons' Book of the Royal Arch* (George Harrap, London,1969).

2. *Ibid.*

3. Clarke, J.R., 'The Medical Profession and Early Freemasonry', *AQC* 85 (1972), pp. 298-311.

4. Clarke, J.R., 'The Royal Society and Early Grand Lodge Freemasonry', *AQC* 80 (1967), pp. 110-119.

5. Barzun, J., *From Dawn to Decadence*, (Harper Collins, New York, 2000), p. 426.

Chapter Ten:
Factors affecting the Investigation and proposed analytical model

hroughout ritual of Freemasonry there are repeated incantations, for its Members to first embrace its spirituality and hence its attendant morality, but in addition and with almost equal insistence, the injunction that in order to do so they must strive to appreciate the essence of 'Nature and Science'. From this it is reasonable to suppose that whoever the originators were; Nature and Science were to them of the utmost importance. From the many historical, essentially reliable, records outside of Freemasonry it is possible to consider the personal attributes and likely aspirations of the principal players who were known to have been in place when the Premier Grand Lodge was founded and who were most likely instrumental in its formation and to have influenced greatly its destiny. Further that within this group there was a disproportionately large number, whose main preoccupation outside of Freemasonry was with 'Nature and Science'. Again these contemporary sources, such as the minutes of the Royal Society, leave no doubt of the great importance of Nature and science to them and why they would have been considered essential suitable core components of the basic philosophy and *raison d'être* of this foundling society. Clearly a central aim of this work is to show by the superposition of these many (historical) facets the validity of this assertion and further, to demonstrate that there was a fashionable requirement within that discreet element of society for the totally 'educated' man to possess a good understanding of Nature and science, or in modern terms of natural philosophy and the emerging technology, although they would have been unlikely to have viewed it in this rather abstract way. If therefore it is reasonable to conclude that the fundamental (educational imperative) precepts of Masonic ritual over the intervening years had not changed, then it would confirm this pre-eminence in their thinking.

However, it will be shown that there were even more compelling reasons for their enthusiasm, because, leaving esotericism aside, contemporary science affected them in many other ways, not the least of which being financial. Indeed, for several of those with whom we are concerned it became a major part of their income, not least in terms of the fees they received for delivering lectures and involvement in technological projects. Further at this time in their careers there was within this tight-knit group an influential employer/employee relationship, the proceeds of these joint endeavours forming a substantial part of their respective incomes and social standing. These facts emerged whilst researching the archives to test the validity of the underlying assumptions that would support or prove otherwise the importance and physical nature of the science of Freemasonry, but in addition it brought to light the possibilities and potential of conducting a much wider investigation.

Factors affecting the Investigation and proposed analytical model

Further, the realisation that these complex interrelationships extended into their social life and provided a window of opportunity to understand more clearly how these men came to be involved in the eventual form of the Premier Grand Lodge and the way in which they wished and seemingly engineered it to be. This was exciting because the science and to a lesser extent the sociology (outside of Freemasonry) of this period was documented with much greater certainty. However, if the Study was to be successful it required a strategy that addressed any possible uncertainties. The difficulty was how to capitalise on the opportunity because the basis of any such investigation was so very broad; which would mean that to be sufficiently convincing each aspect would require adequate (detailed) consideration. Another facet was that if the interrelationship of those involved was indeed as significant as it appeared, it would almost certainly entail the need to consider factors much earlier in the process and *ipso facto* the need to contemplate the basis on which the Premier Grand Lodge itself was founded, including the antecedence of the Founders.

In the time that has elapsed since the initial Premier Grand Lodge was formed there has been considerable emphasis placed upon the profundity of its content and the integrity of those who were responsible for the metamorphosed version of the Premier Grand Lodge. But throughout this investigation there has been little to suggest that those responsible were anything other than astute and pragmatic socialites. Most research is predicated on the verification or otherwise of some hypothesis or hypotheses one of which in this instance was:

a) That if their social ambitions were to be realised the Founders needed such a fraternity and especially one such as this for a number of reasons: its altruistic connotations; its adherence to religious principles; its latent feedstock of existing freemasons' lodges already populated with men of influence; its restricted and elitist nature.

b) That they were in no sense evil men within the context of the prevailing climate, neither were they angels, but just practical, uncompromising businessmen who had a good 'game plan', the right model, at the right time and fortunately the right men to ensure success.

c) That they were extremely busy men, who were quite content to work with all the best ingredients of the Freemasonry presently practised and whilst they were perfectly capable of the esotericism claimed by later historians, they had neither the time or inclination for the type of the deep epistemological concepts postulated by later generations.

There is of course considerable complication when attempting to address a scenario as intricate as this, especially in the almost complete absence of irrefutable evidence and as with any study of this type much will remain speculative, but the real test of such speculation is to show that all else is consistent with it. This is especially true of this study because as will be shown, leading up to and during those formative years, there were intense political connotations, ensuring that even if there was actual (contemporary) documentary evidence, the real motivations and rationale of the Founders, would in all probability, have been couched in terms that were intended for external consumption. The underlying motivations of these individuals would be very much more obscure and restricted to their innermost thoughts, although outwardly expressed as conforming to the politically correct view. It must be assumed that as normal in such amalgamations there would have been a need to overcome all the numerous difficulties of persuading a number of totally autonomous lodges to unite together into some centralised form. However, it would appear that fate, aided and abetted by group behaviour, played a part in overcoming this difficulty. A group of senior (in their own lodges that is, but otherwise of no great social standing) freemasons, conceived the notion of holding a semi-formal quarterly gathering, which proved successful. Flushed with success and no doubt influenced by self-aggrandisement, they decided to formalise it, by establishing a structure and appointing officers and naming it with the grandiose title of the 'Premier Grand Lodge'. It is only possible to surmise what the underlying motivation was of those who first hit upon the concept of quarterly meetings, which then led on to the creation of a more formalised and ostentatious structure. It will be argued here that whatever the original aims may have been when first started in 1717, it very quickly metamorphosed into something quite different and with a completely new agenda. As is often the case with many inventors (except perhaps Desaguliers in this instance, if he was in fact one of the originators of the concept) they gained little from their invention. Certainly when shortly afterwards leading aristocrats appeared as butterflies from the chrysalis, the metamorphosis was complete and the original format bore little relation to the new. Given its new format, it required some compromised (in relation to that currently practised) ritual that would be acceptable, or at least insufficiently unacceptable, to the majority and ideally a supplementary piece of ritual, such as the Royal Arch that would provide a unifying element and serve as an expedient way of overcoming an organisational necessity of establishing a group identity. Such a strategy in comparison to introducing a completely revised or otherwise controversial (Craft) ritual would have been a much simpler expedient. Central to this contention is that: those responsible for this usurpation of the original initiative would have been obliged to declare an outwardly agreed common aim, although the motivations and ambitions of individuals within this core group were certain to have been markedly different and it was expedient to abide by the old adage 'least said soonest mended'. This concept of individualistic motivation will be returned to throughout.

Factors affecting the Investigation and proposed analytical model

If the findings of Masonic historians are afforded anything like equal status then the conclusion must be that there is no general consensus view on the way in which events unfolded during the early 1720s or the nature of the ceremonies that were enacted. However, clearly some agreed form of ceremony or sequence of ceremonies was in place. If the assumption made herein is correct; namely that the lectures have remained substantially unchanged, then there is no reason why Royal Arch ritual, at least in terms of its lectures, should not have been essentially the same as it is today. This because to a large extent it would have satisfied their innate need to 'put their own stamp' on this new initiative, establish a ceremony unique to Premier Grand Lodge, which would provide a vehicle for the exaltation (a unique qualifying element) of a member and meet the essential injunction placed upon all freemasons: that of continued learning. The case that its ritualistic content is a logical consequence of the sociology of the times and the personalities of the individuals involved is also demonstrated. As in every period of history, the immediate situation will afford an opportunity for talented individuals to seize upon a concept and by force of their dominant personality, some good fortune and occasionally good sense make an impression upon their times – 'cometh the hour, cometh the man/men'. In this instance the principal sociological factors were:

a) The rapid expansion of science and technology,

b) The expansion and commercial exploitation of science and technology, especially in the form of steam, hydraulics, mining, navigation etc.,

c) The wider distribution of wealth and (sometimes bought) social influence, the influence of the entrepreneur,

d) Expansion of general commerce, both at home and abroad, at home in enterprises such as share trading, insurance and the exploitation of patents etc. and abroad (colonisation and world trading) in areas such as slavery, commodities, land acquisition, legalised piracy, raw materials etc., especially in the granting of sole rights,

e) Development of the infra-structure (water, to a lesser extent roads, but sadly not sewage) which led to the relocation and sustainability of whole communities,

f) The public appetite for knowledge, given its perceived potential for advancement of whatever kind,

g) Other aspects of the social climate, such as profound changes in the monarchy and political/religious expression.

h) Increased leisure time and hence socialising activities of the influential, but increased decadence of the lower echelons of society.

If the original basis of this study, the narrower goal of the influence of science, is taken as an example, it serves to illustrate the potential complication of the task of research in this much wider area. During the 1600s throughout Europe there was an ever-increasing emphasis placed upon the importance of science and in consequence many learned academies of science were founded and flourished. However, in general historians seem agreed that religious repression of this emerging science was considerably greater on the Continent than in Britain. There was sufficient freedom for the Royal Society to be formed in 1662 which soon became of influence; although not very long after its formation, for other, principally financial, reasons, it suffered a lean time. However, by the turn of the Century the Royal Society had re-established itself and had by then become perhaps the most (socially perceived) influential group in society; since to be accorded membership was an implicit recognition of ones intellectual and social prowess. It did however, in company with most all else in that period, have a congenital problem of always being short of money, which influenced its development and functionality. Its nature and structure is an interesting study in itself, but it is sufficient here to realise that by its very nature it excluded some people of considerable intellect and/or social standing and hence influence. There were persons within the Royal Society who not only saw the injustice of this, but because of the social/economic importance of these notable exclusions, were themselves socially, politically, financially, or in some other way disadvantaged by the ostracizing of these influential individuals.

Whatever the motivation, they (the people of concern here) could see that there were justifiable reasons, not to say benefits, in forming an analogous (equally influential) liaison, contrived to embrace this important, otherwise excluded, group by creating a new society. Such an innovation would need to have the same basic aura and prestige of the Royal Society, but with a different *raison d'être* and although its members would not be constrained by such formal academy, however defined, education because of its social importance would have to be explicit in its constitution. The problem was that even if such an institution could be formed, simply populating it with a significant number of members of high social status was no guarantee that it would of itself be sufficient to convince society at large and so it requires a further dimension. The instigation of such societies and clubs was becoming a popular pastime, indeed, as we shall see, those with whom we are concerned continued to do so elsewhere, but these withered on the vine and at no stage did any even begin to rival the Royal Society. It was clear that some subtle blend of additional ingredients was required, but up until then no recipe had been found. It is the thesis of this study that: the time was especially right for such an initiative, all that was needed was a springboard and that this comparatively innocuous quarterly meeting of the masters of a few lodges, that assumed the grandiose title of the 'Premier

Grand Lodge', was the perfect vehicle to fulfil this function. If this was indeed the underlying motivation, it would go a long way towards explaining why, from the point of view of subsequent 'purists' groups (such as the Antients) that Grand Lodge had lost its way (lost its esotericism and moral purpose) and why it was in difficulty by the middle of the 1730s. By this point it had been proclaimed 'impure' by those excluded for whatever reason from what had now become an extremely influential mainstream institution, but in the late 1720s and 1730s few of the influential people within Premier Grand Lodge were listening to these protesters. Certainly not the immediate hierarchy, or at least not enough to shake them from their complacency to the extent where it would cause them to refocus, although the threat was so marked that they should have done so. Indeed it was to remain in its *laissez-faire* format (*see below*) for many years, despite the formation in the 1730s of an active major schism (the 'Antients'). The 'Moderns' were finally forced to galvanise their thinking some twenty years later in the 1750s.

When these quarterly meetings began, Freemasonry in the form of independent lodges was flourishing and although highly individualistic, their purpose seemed to be similar to that of present day businessmen's clubs, such as the ROTARY and PROBUS meetings, but because of the more elitist social status of the members of these Masonic lodges it would have more likely adopted a much higher sociological/sectional/political agenda. Such organisations are, or at least start out as individual groups, say within a district, where a number of like-minded people are happy to meet and engage in social intercourse. However, within such groupings there will be people who seek a somewhat grander role. Such individuals then proceed to organise such groups into formalised associations, with rules, presidencies (to which most will aspire), secretaries, treasurers (to which few aspire) etc. and all else besides. Today there is scarcely one aspect of human activity that does not have its national/international association (even tiddlywinks one imagines) and whose presidents or spokesmen appear never to miss an opportunity to court the media on every conceivable occasion to give the 'authoritative' view.

Given the fact that the Premier Grand Lodge came into being it is reasonable to suppose that several such persons sought to organise matters in a similar way. They would have created the basic framework and precepts of the intended group, selling the concept to its ordinary members on the basis that there would be some rational advantage in doing so. In this instance the notion was that these disparate lodges of freemasons who were meeting in London at this time would be well served if their individual Masters were to gather on a regular basis to discuss matters of mutual advantage. On this same premise and because it is the usual way such initiatives work, it is reasonable to suppose that the first three Grand Masters; Anthony Sayer, George Payne and John Desaguliers, not forgetting the fourth who remains unsung, played a key role in this persuasive process. Whatever the original motives for setting up these regular meetings may have been, at least for the remainder of this study, it is argued that those in the shadows who had been seeking some means or 'springboard' of opportunity, quickly realised that here was an ideal vehicle. Further that it was the exceptional wit and talent of John Desaguliers who was the 'lynch-pin' and proposed that link and that in turn he had great influence over, if not was the author of, a unifying ceremony which is now referred as the Royal Arch.

The formal organisation of the initial gathering of the Masters of the four respective lodges, commonly referred to as the Premier Grand Lodge, and first recorded in an official way in 1717, will for the purposes of this Study not be taken as the precursor of the Grand Lodges as known today, but merely the basis on which it was formed. The term 'Premier Grand Lodge' used in this text is taken to be the quite different organisation that grew out of it, very shortly (two or three years) afterwards.

If this burgeoning society were to flourish, it required a number of attractive facets, such as the ingenious device retained by its operative predecessors as well as freemasons before and since, that secrecy should be a constituent part of their fraternity. This device would at once, enhance exclusivity within its constitution, would add greatly to its ambience, strengthening the appeal to be numbered amongst those within it, whilst at the same time enhancing loyalty and *esprit de corps*. An unavoidable consequence of such 'secrecy' (a factor already true of the prevailing freemasons' lodges) was that it would almost certainly alienate it from large sections of the general population, but ironically, by doing so it simply added to its appeal for those qualified to join. In the event such external animosity did appear very soon after. However as forecasted, far from weakening its appeal it went into a phase of rapid expansion and if these early years are taken as a guide, secret exclusivity proved to be an important element and certainly outweighing any possible disadvantage. Its significance can be gauged by the severity of the now 'Traditional Penalties' contained in the earliest known rituals. Indeed they were not averse to flaunting their status as freemasons, as reference to Lord Kingston's short biography set out in Chapter Eighteen will bear witness, *see also* later reference to Freemasonry in the USA and George Washington in particular and even today there is a refreshing openness with respect to the rôle of Freemasonry in the USA.

Perhaps less critical then, because of the way society was structured, but for the same basic reasons as today, they would have had to deal with the antithesis of the public at large, anticipate likely reactions and formulate a counter strategy; but they were however, spared the intense media/political problems that have bedevilled Freemasonry in the United Kingdom since the 1990s. Even so malevolence towards Freemasonry was there, as Prichard was to show, but more sophisticated attacks were

Factors affecting the Investigation and proposed analytical model

made as Picard[1] found in her research for her book on Samuel Johnson's London:

> Then as now, there was a popular perception that Freemasonry pervaded the judiciary. Hogath's print of 'Night' published 1738, portrays a drunken magistrate still in his Masonic regalia, being supported home by his clerk. The viewers would have immediately recognised him as a notorious Bow Street magistrate loathed by the poor not only for his savage sentencing, but for his attempt to enforce the Gin Act. The legal profession was popularly thought not to be above corruption. An 'ambidexter' was a lawyer who took fees from both the plaintiff and the defendant, (here quotes) presumably before the case came to trial.[2]

Thus they had, so far as it was possible within the code, to demonstrate clearly to others that its aims and objectives were laudable, that its members were recruited from only the most worthy of individuals, that it was governed by the principles of morality, religious conviction, loyalty to King and Country etc. Especially important, in the context of the contemporary needs within society (and central in terms of this study), was their declared intent of promulgating learning amongst its Members, so that they might possess a profound understanding of Nature and science, to the benefit of all.

Hence this newly conceived Premier Grand Lodge was clearly an ideal foundation for the establishment of this exclusive society of the good and the great. It was well placed to expand, for within it existed a ready made 'feed-stock' in the form of the existing freemasons' lodges, each already boasting most of the requisite qualities and that in no small measure. These lodges did conform to a certain pattern, but each had their own autonomy, being only loosely affiliated as a group by the protocols within their meetings and general laudability of their declared aims. As entities they could not, in any formal way gain, or for that matter lose, universal respect or claim a high social profile, but neither did they as disparate groups present a particular threat to members of the greater society who were not freemasons. Perhaps their most attractive feature was that they were for the most part comprised of people of very high social (both local and national) standing. However, it would have been realised by this caucus within the Founders of the Premier Grand Lodge, that if they were to succeed in bringing these lodges into some formalised grouping, they would have to address the problem of present dispersion and lack of cohesiveness. Whatever the perceived difficulties may have been, the way in which this initial *ad hoc* meeting of Masters had come into being, showed that some enhanced form of unification was feasible. Clearly to meet this hidden agenda some major changes would have to be made, but if it could be brought into operation, then it had enormous possibilities, which history has proven to be the case.

However, the fact that these regular meetings of Masters were taking place was one thing, creating the climate for a potential 'take over' was quite another, with a real battle to be won. There is today and almost certainly then, a very serious sociological problem surrounding any attempt to amalgamate established groupings of this kind, since by its very nature it creates a system of winners and losers. Put bluntly the various hierarchies of these several independent lodges would have needed to be persuaded of the 'benefits' of surrendering their autonomy and rather distinguished position. This would have been especially true of the influential few in each of the respective lodges, who were waiting in line for accession and hence destined to occupy the highest possible role in their Masonic world. For them amalgamation would mean that they would then become comparative subordinates in a much larger organisation, with only a limited prospect of individual advancement within it, especially since all the top jobs were already spoken for.

To counteract this limitation there was another important sociological factor; the desire by most of those not so privileged, to be associated with the rich and the famous and the obvious collective or implied strength and social prestige that comes from such association. Whatever the rationale, the unqualified success of the Premier Grand Lodge is testimony to the politically persuasive powers (and one might ponder social standing and influence) of the Founders. Neither is it surprising to see that the body (if not the hierarchy) of senior members of Premier Grand Lodge, now in the new format, were recruited from amongst the most influential people in society. Whilst they had very close social affinities, it is of some interest to note that they appeared to come from a surprisingly wide range of lodges and this balance has in some measure been preserved even today. This apparently random association will be returned to after the history leading up to the sociology of the period and the individuals concerned have been dealt with in greater detail. Suffice it to say that all the above elements that were present then are intact in the hierarchical structure of present day Freemasonry.

However, because effectively nothing concerning that period that may have been committed to paper has been preserved; thus little may be concluded with any absolute certainty about the political ramifications leading to the eventual formation of the Premier Grand Lodge. Indeed as stated above, even if there had been some form of documentation, it is unlikely to have contained the underlying truths and so the 'facts' would still have been within the licence of the writer and thence the interpretation of the reader. Nonetheless, even in this age of so called 'spin doctors' and 'sound bites' or the more defensive 'public relation officers', little is gained by taking such a cynical view and it is perhaps better to attempt to interpret as fairly as possible the most likely scenario from such information as there is. There is no option, but to work with the data that is available and so a strategy has to be employed that will allow a distillation or purification of the metal from the dross. The means of achieving this goal by interpolating between the diverse strands in their complex relationships became evident as the research necessary in Part I indicated that their intimate involvement in science was matched by their interaction within their social sphere.

Although going outside of direct Masonic sources was a great improvement there was still only a comparatively small amount of direct authoritative contemporary evidence such as documents, biographies, artefacts etc. If this new approach was to be convincing it needed to adopt an indirect procedure that would give (if it was indeed possible) due weight to the various facets that had affected the ethos of this new centralised Freemasonry; the form of the 'standardised' Craft ritual it was obliged to adopt; the reasons behind the foundation of the Royal Arch and content of its format. Such data would rarely be direct, but needed to be teased out and if it were to remain credible it was necessary to adopt a procedure that was based upon a proven and generally accepted technique. Although science is referred to constantly throughout the Ritual and without doubt there was a considerable amount of all types of contemporary scientific and technological evidence available, there was no scientific (specific) explanation within the Craft ritual itself; except for that contained in the Symbolical Lecture of the Royal Arch, which is why it was important to consider it in depth in Part I. However, science was plainly of enormous significance to those of interest here and for that reason it is true of this work also. Science and technology represented a new approach to solving this riddle and this search for evidence and method outside of the obvious Masonic sources needed to have a focus. Clearly the prevailing science of the time did not exist in a vacuum and consideration of the surrounding infrastructure and in particular the social climate that supported it would also prove to be exceptionally useful. Much of that which was written in Part I and that will be discussed still further in the remaining chapters is nonetheless an interpretation, of some (its clearly impossible to say all) of what is known, reasonably accessible and sufficiently well documented, of the contemporary scientific thinking of the time. From this body of material it is possible to begin to speculate on the perception and to some extent the intent of those likely to have been responsible for including 'Nature and Science' in the initial Ritual. Similarly other sociological parameters may be interpreted in a like manner and hopefully they too will continue to support and even add to the possible identification of the individuals involved and other factors such as time and place, although on such an emotive subject as naming names there is little doubt that there will be a number of dissenters to the choice of persons cited herein.

When Alice in Lewis Carol's profound book asked 'where to begin' the reply was 'to start at the beginning', on the presumption that: 'it was as good a place as any other'. However, in this instance each piece of the story is contingent upon another and whilst in the final analysis it has a clear outcome; namely the eventual format of the Ritual and formation of the Premier Grand Lodge and the Royal Arch, the beginning is most obscure. It was decided to approach the complex array of information by adopting a well established technique ('set theory') that is based on the probability or the 'logic' of association. This concept will be used (although not fully explained or rigorously applied) in the usual schematic form of a Venn diagram shown in Figure 10.1 below. With this approach each element is deemed to exist in its own right, but where appropriate respective areas may be overlaid (in this case by destiny) and thereby incorporate other areas of mutual association. The resultant diagram will indicate area/s where certain elements are uniquely unified. Thus if this procedure is repeated for the whole gamut of respective variables under consideration the outcome will indicate any areas of common association. Further by providing evidence of a mutually inclusive zone it enhances greatly the probability of it representing the actual reality, even though some of its constituent parts may not be totally verifiable or quantifiable. It is presumed that the worth of approaching the problem in this way will become self evident, but in attempting to explain the nuances of the interrelating parts, there is regrettably a need for some repetition as the various strands do in practice criss-cross and the forbearance of the reader is required.

By using this diagrammatic concept it is possible to show the structure of the original organisation and indicate why this seemingly oddball organisation should still be flourishing nearly 300 years after its inception whilst virtually all others had faded. However, to use this quasi Venn diagram approach requires that these essentially (at times intimately) linked factors be somehow broken into discrete and hence somewhat artificial, conceptual blocks. Thereby allowing them to be researched in isolation on the presumption that very little would be lost by so doing and that once refined it was reasonable to reunite them by dint of their common parts. If the birth of the Premier Grand Lodge was to be tested in this way and found in a conclusive manner to occupy the common core, then a number of sociological, religious, financial, political, philosophical, historical etc., factors must be seen to combine in appreciable measure. These may be written as a set of generic cells (primary questions) categorised as follows:

Why? Given that there must have been a need, was there such a need?

Who? Since the process requires the vision, ability and drive, were such people available and who were they?

Where? Since the general environment must be sufficiently conducive to foster such an organisation, what factors made London favourable at that time?

Which? Given the numerous choices of clubs, societies, associations, coffeehouses, meeting places etc. what other factors were there that made this

Factors affecting the Investigation and proposed analytical model

venture so different and uniquely superior?

What? To succeed it needed to be in a format that would set it apart and have some innate appeal and be of an enduring nature, if so why did it take the form it did?

When? What were the circumstances that made this precise time so opportune?

Having defined the basic questions of each enquiry cell, before proceeding further the intended process to achieve that goal will be discussed in a little more detail.

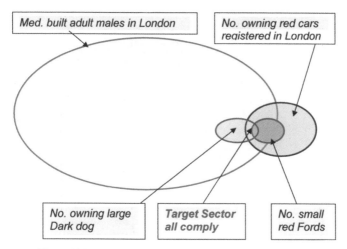

Figure 10.1 A Venn diagram concept depicting the relative value and disposition of the witness' statement.

The concept may be explained by employing a more familiar model. Suppose a witness in an investigation of a crime, committed say in a West London open space, claims to have seen a fairly tall person (reasonably confident that it was a man). Although conceding that it could have been a woman in boots and a heavy coat, but thought it unlikely from their manner. The person had presumably been walking a large dog. They had then got into a small, likely Ford, red car. He had needed to stoop rather awkwardly on getting in, but then drove off towards the City. This data must be deemed comparatively vague, however, it becomes substantially more helpful if the following approach is adopted.

Although difficult it is possible to obtain some quantitative as well as qualitative data with respect to some of these parameters, such as the number of adult men in London, the registration of small red cars. The Kennel Club or Royal Society for the protection of animals would no doubt have some measure of the level of dog ownership (unfortunately with respect to this technique dogs are no longer licensed for if they had been the data would have quantifiable instead of qualitative) etc. From such information it would be possible to construct a Venn diagram similar to the type shown in Figure 10.1 with the information elements, referred to here as cells, having discrete size.

From the fictitious model used in Figure 10.1 one can see that about one fortieth of the likely men in London own a small red car. Of these about one eighth are presumed to be Fords. Of this group those owning a large dog is say one in one hundred and fifty. This process has progressively reduced the likely suspects from every man in West London at the time to a substantially reduced and hence manageable number. Of course if any of these factors can be actually verified or measured then the more satisfactory the analysis becomes.

It is of course possible to keep adding constraints, such as their height, where they reside etc. If when a likely person is found, further constraints such as was he in the area at the time, did he know the victim, was there motive etc. add weight to the case. However, before condemning the person out of hand converse factors have to be explored. For instance if the offence occurred during the morning, he may well not have been able to be there. If it were a public holiday it may well have been a visitor etc. In the final analysis it is the jury, and in this instance the reader, who will decide the validity of the data and, in the case of this Study, it is the reader. For those who have difficulty with this evidence by 'probability', because it is so vital to this study and experience has shown that the Venn diagram approach is either not fully understood or accepted with respect to early Freemasonry the reader is recommended to read a paper by Lawrence[3] that further addresses this approach.

Without wishing to minimise the possible limitations it is believed that this approach is very powerful and if, as in the model used above, one can verify or better quantify the data it is possible to apply a rigorous mathematical analysis to such problems. However, in the work here there is precious little hard data and much has to be deduced or inferred from the restricted historical sources available. Thus it is not possible to put scale on the respective cells that have been selected to describe this set of circumstances and so for convenience they are shown in Figure 10.2 to be of equal size. Clearly that is not so and their relative size will change with time and this factor will be taken into consideration in the final summing up and for this reason an alternative way of considering the data is suggested below. In the work here the question of time is of great importance, especially with respect to contemporary understanding. The reason why the cells cannot be quantified is that each is an amalgam of non-specific factors and so the cell is an assembly of many parts which may vary in emphasis with time and circumstances. There is a more comprehensive explanation, whilst remaining comprehendible to the non-mathematician, of the scientific/mathematical basis of this technique in a book by Keith Devlin.[4]

Factors affecting the Investigation and proposed analytical model

Since size cannot be taken as a measure in this instance another approach is used to indicate the range and importance of the cell. It is suggested that they be perceived as having the capacity to light up according to their current level of favourability; in which case the brightness of each would contribute towards the overall intensity of any unified section. Historically we know that the relative intensity of each cell is very prone to change with time. For instance in the case of say 'why', it is reasonable to suppose that in a time of conflict society would be preoccupied with other matters and the cell would be dull and as a result the overall intensity will be moderate, but if the 'who' is also favourable it will add to the intensity. Whereas in time of peace and prosperity people would seek diversion and the cell would glow. It is self evident that however good the climate for development, if there is not the right calibre of person from the right social background, then there is not the right 'who' and the cell will remain switched off. Similar analogies can be drawn for any other combination of cells.

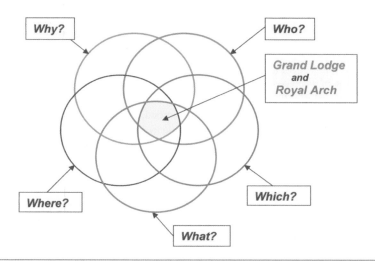

The symbolic concept of a Venn diagram used in this Study. Whilst it claims no pretence to scale, its area of conjunction offers an answer to the burning question when?

Figure 10.2. Venn diagram of the interacting facets surrounding Craft ritual and the foundation of the Royal Arch that have to be addressed before it is possible to speculate on the importance of any one of them.

'When' is of particular interest here and it too would glow according to the particular circumstances of the time. Thus if we were to integrate 'when' into the Venn diagram we could expect its impact to have a dulling effect at a time of plague or depression and brightening effect when society was untroubled. However for this study 'when' is considered to be the 'condition state' that is the focus of the investigation and therefore not a variable in that sense.

Thus it is assumed that at any point during the time under review a Venn diagram could be drawn and from it an assessment made of its present standing from the favourability or not of the other variables. Clearly if all the conditions were favourable and all the cells were switched on it appears to glow sufficiently brightly, as appears to be the case in the early 1720s, then the conditions would have been favourable for the concept of Freemasonry as we know it today, to come into being. The adjective 'sufficiently' is used here because it will become evident that the internal politics of the early years of the Premier Grand Lodge were not all sweetness and light, but rather there was a series of skirmishes with its fair share of winners and losers. But ironically, it is in large measure because of this turbulence that one can make an even stronger case for its actual dating and the formation of the Royal Arch.

It would be remiss to leave this summation of events without stating that the overall social climate during the initial twenty year period of the Grand Lodge was, in comparison to the preceding years, exceptionally stable (only one prime minister for example) which allowed all the cells to be lit sufficiently and hence make it possible for this form of Freemasonry to become well and truly established. It has, since that time, gone through periods where certain of the above cells have approached extinction. But by that time it was well founded, contained some very powerful ingredients and in consequence it has been able to sustain itself through those times. Indeed, because of its innate strength, not least its outstanding fellowship, that in subsequent times it has been of great solace to its members and others in periods of depression, wars and other difficult situations. It is well documented that in times of war members stationed far from home have gained great comfort from the warm embrace of local lodges. Indeed in a paper read by Morris to the *Quatuor Coronati* Lodge he was able to show that freemasons from both sides in the American War of Independence actually contrived to hold joint lodge meetings in between skirmishes.[5] Having once adopted a basic strategy for the research it was necessary to find a way forward and given that it continued to be valid, attempt to extract the *raison d'être* for the Royal Arch.

As with most historical appraisals where there are little or no concrete facts there is a problem of credibility. In order to overcome this difficulty a strategy has been adopted that is based upon the presumption that all the influential factors concerned with the formation of the Premier Grand Lodge can be compartmentalised into one of the discrete segments illustrated in Figure 10.1. That whilst these targeted cells clearly ranged over a wide spectrum of human activity they would, if the conditions were right, be found to converge in a way that was mutually consistent.

Factors affecting the Investigation and proposed analytical model

That the pronounced presence of a common core resulting from the integration of the cells would provide much stronger evidence than that coming from any one of its constituent parts. Clearly the more these factors were found to correlate, then the stronger the reasons to suppose that the correlation represented the actual conditions prevailing at its (Premier Grand Lodge) conception and inception. But since 'opportunity' was a dominant factor in the effective size of all these cells, then time (date) itself would in the end be the determining factor. However, there is when using this approach, a temptation after initially expressing a few minor doubts and in compensation to insert several discrete caveats, to quickly (conveniently) forget the earlier conditional statements and proceed to represent the original speculation as now forming a set of irrefutable facts.

In this instance there is a further factor, namely that there is little doubt that there have been changes, despite the almost menacing injunction not to make innovations in the 'Body of Masonry'; with the implication of dire consequences to anyone who actually does so. Research in Part I suggests that until recent times these changes, at least in its scientific content, were comparatively modest and peripheral and there has been a strict adherence to the actual basic 'scientific' content, even though as time progressed these 'facts' would have become progressively and so very clearly outdated. From the recent determined resistance to change there appears to have always been a fierce pride taken in preserving the Ritual in its original form and that despite or maybe because of, its archaic format form of words or concepts. Indeed any understanding of the early years of Freemasonry depends upon there having been a faithful transmission of ritual and what limited written evidence there is of other aspects/artefacts of Freemasonry suggest that this was indeed the case. In terms of the requirements within this Study it is most fortunate that this adherence to the original format is particularly true of science; mainly because there has been little political pressure to change it and the scholars who have rewritten the respective rituals over the years seem to have been satisfied with its content or ill qualified to amend it. Of course the degree of reliance that may be attached to faithful transfer will have to be examined carefully, especially because much of the analysis below depends upon it. The question of whether this is done more faithfully through the process of dogged repetition of the spoken word (particularly so in the absence of any written aids) or by the device of some scholar writing the words down, will be returned to later.

References

1. Picard, L., *Dr Johnson's London* (Weiderfield & Nicolson, London, 2000), p. 203.
2. *Ibid.*
3. Lawrence, C., 'Within and Without : the Hidden Mysteries of Nature and Science', *AQC* 118 (2005), pp. 92-132.
4. Devlin, K., *Mathematics: the Science of Patterns* (Scientific American Library, 1994).
5. Morris, S. Brent, 'The Polite Revolution – The Formation of American Grand Lodges, 1777-1806', *AQC* 116 (2003), pp. 65-82.

Chapter Eleven:

Raison d'être of Royal Arch Masonry, its content and its relationship to Craft Masonry

All human activity outside of those driven by the need for survival such as providing against hunger, thirst, excessive heat or cold, ensuring procreation etc., appear to be illogical, such as twenty-two people kicking a ball up and down a field, or 'trooping the colour', wedding ceremonies etc. If all such activities were to be viewed in this cynical way, those enacting Masonic ritual would certainly merit such reproach. Yet the passion of a football supporter for his team is unquestionable, that a man will die for the honour of his regiment has been shown many times. That a person will dive into icy waters to save another is equally true, but in clinical terms of self preservation of the person attempting the rescue it makes little sense, even foolhardiness. Because these extraordinary reactions appear to be so irrational it is convenient to avoid further analysis by referring to them as manifestations of abstract innate social behaviour, all part of the inexplicable 'human psyche'. But whatever these motivations may be, they are absolutely crucial to Freemasonry and there is a very strong case for claiming that ritual is a most potent expression of this characteristic of human behaviour and that it is indeed so innate, it can be seen in even the most primitive of cultures.

Thus whatever the deeper reasons for this complex behaviour are, there is little doubt that the profound camaraderie and a desire within them to preserve an ancient tradition is the underlying bond within Freemasonry. Neither can it be dismissed as simply the ulterior motive of enjoying influential association, since there are other ways within society of ensuring that. As with all such organisations there will be some who seek to exploit it for their own gain, but by far the greater majority devote many selfless hours to benefiting others, both inside and outside of Freemasonry. It may therefore be asserted with some confidence that it is the meeting together to enact the Ritual as faithfully as possible and to afterwards join in a convivial festive board and enjoy the mutual pleasure of having done so, which has been the cement that has bound the Order together throughout its history. The conviviality of the 'after proceedings' that usually accompany a lodge meeting, is somewhat analogous, clearly in a more formal and one might say exaggerated way, to the camaraderie that ones sees in the changing room after a game or by a group of mountaineers at base camp after some joint project. It is clear from the contemporary writings that report such 'after proceedings' that they were also of great significance in these early gatherings.

However, experience suggests that such camaraderie evolves over time and that devotion to a cause or institution is a consequence of, rather than it being the reason for, such bodies coming into existence. Thus the aims and objectives behind the formal coming together of the disparate Masonic lodges to form the association called the Premier Grand Lodge, were likely to have been quite prosaic and stimulated by other factors; economical, social, political etc. It is reasonable to conclude that some time had elapsed before it was enhanced and refined and that it has only evolved into its present day (ethos) form over the intervening years. That its present high moralistic aura has resulted from the efforts of those who have been dedicated to the task of emphasising and promoting its more altruistic aspects and who have trawled through literature to provide evidence of that aspect and have predicated their Masonic research upon it. However, even if there had been contemporary writing to that effect or other evidence, it is virtually certain that there has rarely, if ever, been a case where politicians or those in a privileged position would tell the voters their innermost reasons, for say offering themselves for election, but rather to proclaim their profound desire to serve the community. However, in the final analysis, whether an institution such as Freemasonry will survive or not, will depend upon its relative merits, the basic tenets of its constitution, but above all its ability to inculcate and sustain devout affiliation. The thousands who have devoted enormous energy in establishing new lodges and chapters and/or promoting other Masonic causes and charities provide overwhelming evidence that this is especially true of Freemasonry. How laudable in practice the intentions of the Founders of the Premier Grand Lodge and Royal Arch were, will have to be left to the judgement of the reader given their present knowledge and the data presented here.

Founding the Premier Grand Lodge had now for the first time formally regularised and in a sense expressly politicised Freemasonry and brought it into much sharper focus within society. Indeed a great deal of what Masonic historians assumed to have been the purpose and practices in the early ritual is inferred from that which in fact is essentially vindictive, exposures of Freemasonry, principally that of Prichard. Prichard's *Masonry Dissected*, published in 1730, complained of the powerful and by implication undesirable influence that Freemasonry was then having on (current) Society, which he evidenced by exposing the worrying nature of the practices within Freemasonry. Most Masonic historians take the view that he was unlikely to have actually been a freemason, or that if he were, he had deliberately distorted his exposure, but equally they agree (tainted no doubt by the absolute dearth of alternative information) that it was sufficiently accurate for it to merit serious attention and for that reason it has been and is still used by some historians as almost definitive. If one extrapolates upon their interpretation of his exposure, it is possible to hypothesise the reasons why this amalgamation of the various lodges within the London area came about and it is in a sense the process of testing that hypothesis, in quite another way, that is adopted here. Clearly Prichard was antipathetic towards Freemasonry and he encouraged the notion that his disparaging stance was due to

Raison d'être of Royal Arch Masonry

his selfless and righteous concern for society and had nothing to do with any other ulterior motive, such as profits from the sale of his writings. He would have been comparatively unique if that had indeed been the case, but whatever his intent, we cannot deny his impact on the history of Freemasonry. It depends therefore, upon the level of ones preconception (one might say degree of cynicism) with respect to his underlying motives, compared with the motives of those who founded the Premier Grand Lodge before arriving at some ultimate conclusion as to the merit of his work and hence his view of Freemasonry.

However, one thing is certain, that whatever the reasons behind the formation of the Premier Grand Lodge it cannot be denied that it was clearly an immediate and resounding success. Whether success came despite itself it is difficult to say, since even those Masonic historians who have a tendency to look through rose tinted spectacles, write about the period with varying degrees of scepticism. That everything was far from (the currently perceived) Masonic ideal, became clear whilst researching the bibliographies of the leading contenders set out in Part III. It revealed that there were a number of unpleasant feuds, with attacks made upon it, by so called (Masonic) purists, even in its very early stages. An immediate priority of the Founders would have been to establish its (the Premier Grand Lodge's) 'identity' and impose its authority. As part of this process it is argued here that they would have wanted, or perhaps considered it essential, to add to their Masonic protocols by imposing some order or unification to the wide range of existing rituals. To have attempted to tinker around the edges of existing ritual would have been most difficult and divisive, a simpler ploy would be to introduce an essentially new sanitised version and supplement that by adding an original extension to the ritual (now known as the Royal Arch). Since this would have been instigated under the auspices of the new Premier Grand Lodge, it would be uniquely identified with it, thereby providing the vehicle for achieving a further unifying factor. Clearly whatever they originally intended (or more likely borrowed and then modified from somewhere else, such as the French *Arche Royalle*), it would have to be sufficiently attractive and compelling for it to stimulate men of substance to join. Perhaps more important, it had to engender sufficient loyalty and regard for the ceremony to maintain commitment to the Royal Arch, the particular Chapter concerned and in time nucleate others. Since a ceremony under the name Royal Arch was in existence by *circa* 1740, the really interesting question is how soon after the inauguration of Premier Grand Lodge did it come into being?

The nature of Craft Ritual will be considered in later chapters, but the thesis adopted for this analysis with respect to the Royal Arch is as follows:

a) That the actual body of the (initial) Exaltation ceremony was substantially of the same basic form as that in use today and that its purpose was simply one of facilitating the formal introduction of the candidate into the Chapter and that it did not aspire to the more recent, now often stated prime objective, of restoring 'the loss' that had occurred in Craft Ritual. That as with most ceremonies of this type it was embellished by a moralistic tale that points up some of the most desirable features of human behaviour and yields the ultimate rewards for acting in this altruistic way; but in addition there was a need to have a further purpose to the degree other than the simple introduction of a new member; namely:

b) That such was the contemporary preoccupation of society in general, but in particular certain of the Founders with the need to embrace all forms of learning, that to have a ritual that relied greatly on lectures was totally consistent with their aim of providing a complete and purposeful ceremony.

The strength of the assertion made in (b) above is based upon the public demand for this form of learning; self improvement being a particularly strong fetish of the period and the fact that there was this need is reinforced many times throughout Craft Ritual. It is upon this basis that it is considered reasonable to propose that it could have been an important element and certainly worthy of especial inclusion in the first Royal Arch Chapter Ritual.

Before proceeding further with this list it is reasonable to assert that this was indeed the case, since there is a tendency for human beings to create things within their own image, for instance a carpenter would make his coat hanger out of wood, the welder from steel and the blacksmith from wrought iron. Similarly the Oxford Don might wish to foster a student whose peculiar talents were mirroring his own and knowing that he (the Don) was at the leading edge of scholarship would be completing his mission if he were now to transfer that knowledge to a man truly worthy of that gift.

c) That to make progress in this analysis it is first necessary to stand outside of Freemasonry and look in, before attempting to rationalise the findings of Masonic historians. That in the course of doing so there will be correlation with factors within Freemasonry and aspects with respect to Craft and Royal Arch ritual will become apparent.

This work is therefore written with some trepidation, since historically, any attempt to re-examine and likely challenge the established view is most dangerous. This is particularly true where those views are deeply entrenched and/or the subject matter has assumed an almost religious aura, the likely outcome being certain to attract fierce criticism and indignation. Unfortunately some of the views expressed and conclusions drawn here will fall well within this category.

Raison d'être of Royal Arch Masonry

For instance there is considerable (one might say overwhelming) evidence that the legend of the secret vault in various guises was well established a very long time before 1720, especially in ceremonies in France. It is therefore equally certain that the essential plot of this Legend was adapted and woven into the exaltation ceremony, thereby enabling the Sojourners to make their discoveries etc., but having no basis whatsoever with respect to historical reality. It is a very good yarn, adds interest and excitement to the ceremony, but it remains pure fiction and nothing whatsoever to do with the Legend of Hiram. This in itself is somewhat contentious and the subject of some imaginative and romantic speculation, each nuance depending upon the aspiration of its author. An outline of such evidence is given below, but it is doubtful that it will prove sufficient to prevent argument.

The background to the various 'Legends of the Vault' have been well researched and equally well summarised in Section Eleven of Jones' book.[1] In it he gives many examples of these Legends and demonstrates that they are all basically the same. He reinforces the claim further by quoting books that contained reference to a Legend of this basic concept and which had been either published at the turn of Century (1700) or were in common use at that time. He writes as follows:

'The Sojourners (a word made familiar chiefly by biblical usage and only occasionally found to-day outside of Freemasonry) may have been introduced by the early eighteenth-century arrangers for the excellent purpose of allowing the story to be unfolded by the Candidate (or some one speaking for him), he being an Eyewitness of and partaker in the discoveries upon which the ceremonial depends'.

Consequently, whether the original Ritual was connected with the legend of Hiram at all, must be regarded as very far from certain, especially as suggested above, there are some Masonic historians who claim that the legend of Hiram Abif did not appear in Craft Masonry until some time later. For instance: Victor Langton in the transcript of one of his lectures, 'The Origins of the Three Degrees in Freemasonry' suggests that it was not until the late 1730s that the 'Legend' was introduced into the third degree, he too relies on Prichard and Anderson for much of his source material – although extensive it adds but very little to any verifiable understanding or actual content of the degrees. Clearly if this independence from the 'Legend' is valid, it suggests that the present connotations made in the closing remarks of the Exaltation Ceremony and obliquely throughout '... on the front were engraven the names of the three Grand Masters ...' , 'those secrets were lost for a period of nearly five hundred years ...' etc., must have been added somewhat later and have arisen out of the need to create some continuity with the then newly revised Third Degree and to provide an answer to some of the questions posed within it. In practice there was no great necessity for the 'Legend' at all, since the discovery of the Sacred Name and associated symbols would have provided reason enough to expand upon them in the three Lectures that followed. Thus the following is based therefore on the premise that the Hiramic Legend was not a necessary component and was not part of, or needed to be part of the original Exaltation Ceremony. The object of the Ceremony being that of introducing a candidate into the newly created Royal Arch and in the process of doing so to introduce more forcibly the latest fetish of 'learning' inculcated in the earlier degrees.

The last paragraph provides a good example where someone about to rewrite the ritual might be tempted to make a 'factual' change, for if indeed the double cube was 'a perfect figure', placed in the very 'centre of a vault' which was, by implication, underground, there was presumably no door, the double cube may logically be said to have a top and bottom, but certainly not a 'front' and so in a clinical sense it would be more correct to write that: 'on one of its sides was engraven' rather than 'on the front...' etc. No doubt this would represent a more precise description, but it would no longer be that which, until the time of the rewriting, had been the original form of words.

Clearly a vitally important ingredient of the Legend of the Vault was the description of the discovery of these sacred artefacts and their symbolic allusions to the deity etc., which they (the Founders) considered to be of great interest and importance. Although in recent times, much of this part of the Ritual, because of political expediency, has been deleted from the Ceremony, particularly from the Mystical Lecture. Thus it is reasonable to suppose that the narrative running through the Exaltation Ceremony could have contained essentially the same story as it does today, but for the subtly different reason, that of preparing the Candidate for the Lectures. In view of the way in which the 'Sheffield Ritual' of the late 1790s is presented, some researchers are disposed to believe that the original or earlier ritual may likely to have been in the form of a catechism – a dialogue between master and pupil, observed by others. This may of course be true, but that would not have meant necessarily that the presentation of the Lectures themselves could not have been delivered in essentially the same form as they are today.

Thus the currently popular injunction, by many of the wiser and more established brethren, to use this Legend as good and sufficient reason to impress upon all new Craft Masons to 'complete' their introduction into Masonry, may be an artefact of more modern thinking and by no means the reason why the Royal Arch was conceived in the first place. However, it would not serve any great purpose to debate further whether this presumption is true or false, but was raised at this juncture to reinforce the notion that there was no imperative need for the Hiramic Legend to be introduced in order for there to be a link with the Third Degree and hence a need to complete it; since an equally reasonable link with the Third and earlier degrees could have been education. Again because there was at that time and still remains the eminently laudable requirement to fulfil the repeated injunction found in all three degrees: the constant quest of all men and especially freemasons to search for knowledge. In this respect the lectures fulfilled the repeated injunction throughout Craft Ritual. At the very start of their Masonic career a freemason is told that 'the chisel points out the benefits of education', claiming that only by that means could they 'be rendered fit members of regularly organised Society'. More important still in the 'Charge after Initiation' is the injunction to (seriously) study '… more especially such of the liberal arts and sciences as may lie within the compass of your attainment and without neglecting the ordinary duties of your station to make a daily advancement in Masonic knowledge'. This of itself would have been a totally justifiable reason why all Masons should meet his obligation by 'completing' their third degree, by joining the Royal Arch. It is important to reiterate that this was totally consistent with the notion that: formal (public) lecturing was an important component of the income of several of the Founders and an important component in the lives of the remainder.

Taking Part I at face value it is clear that during that period, man's knowledge of Nature and Science was experiencing exponential growth and whilst this was an exciting time it was also a confusing one. The Founders would have been bombarded with numerous, ever changing, concepts, many challenging their most basic understanding of religion, morality, philosophy, science etc. Above all they were rational human beings, it is therefore reasonable to assume that they would have chosen a form of the Ritual consistent with the 'facts' as they understood them and not some ancient concept. When they do refer to the historical past they employ such phrases as 'scripture informs us' and yet everywhere else they talk of 'Nature and Science', implying that it alludes to contemporary understanding! Not until much later in the research was it realised that they were operating at several levels and this very important complication is dealt with in Chapters Thirty-six and Thirty-seven.

At first it was difficult to understand why they (the Founders) had chosen to ignore the dramatic changes that were taking place, since several were at the very forefront of conventional scientific thinking and were actually instrumental in making the changes that were driving science and technology forward. Further to that, an exceptionally high number of them were Members of the Royal Society whose declared purpose was to inform society on such matters and there had been a constant flow of papers under its auspices; conveying one must presume the latest 'truths'. However, whatever their personal understanding, for some important tactical reason, they took the decision that henceforth the Ritual would remain consistent with the then generally accepted (informed) understanding of the sciences. They ensured that it would remain so by making the Ritual inviolable, thereby freezing the scientific 'facts' in time. If success were to be measured in the terms used in modern ('marketing') psychology, their strategy was absolutely right, because much of the appeal of modern Freemasonry rests upon its traditional (strict) preservation of the past. The rapid expansion in the United Kingdom of Freemasonry after the Second World War and the more recent re-entrenchment has led to subtle changes, some have already been referred to, but de-mystification and aggressive recruiting, has now changed the original marketing strategy of maintaining discreet silence that had been used so successfully over the bulk of the preceding three centuries. Given this fundamental change in strategy it raises the question of how Freemasonry will extend into the twenty-first century or in the extreme whether it will survive at all and this is now the subject of serious debate.

The corollary of this effective inviolability, was that since they were extremely intelligent and well informed men, it has to be supposed that, for a reasonable length of time (several years) at least, the 'facts', as they presented them, needed to remain ostensibly true and unchallenged if the tradition was to become sufficiently well established and for it to be considered reasonable that henceforth the Ritual should remain inviolate. This process of cementation was assisted further by the cultural shift in the nature of the hierarchy of the Premier Grand Lodge from the late 1720s onwards, who for the most were insufficiently versed in science to offer any challenge and they were almost indifferent figureheads. By the device of insisting on the precise retention of the original ritual they ensured that all future candidates would undergo exactly the same ceremony as their predecessors and thereby avoid academic challenge.

Indeed if there was to be stability then they needed to avoid repeated challenge, for as we shall see they were extremely intelligent men and they would have realised that there was never likely to be stability in scientific thought and without some constraint the Ritual would have required constant and in that sense quite arbitrary revision. It is argued here that the science of the Symbolical Lecture was only tenable within a very short period, almost certainly early in the 1700s and only then because it was engineered to be so. This was because by the middle of the 1720s Newton and his disciples were becoming less able to defend themselves from heavy criticism, both inside (e.g. the Cambridge Set) and outside of the UK (e.g. Huygens and Leibnitz). Such criticism was no longer restricted to internecine wrangles between academics, but because of general publication, lectures etc. it was now the subject of wide public debate. Whether or not it was indeed their intention to lock up or freeze the Ritual in this subtle way is perhaps debatable, but what is certain is that by imposing this strict regime it suppressed for all time the pressure for change, whenever confronted with the latest set of 'facts'. All such pressure could be resisted and totally justified on the basis of the powerful Masonic ethos of retaining the traditional adherence to the established ritual. Notionally at least, this inviolability is enshrined in today's Ritual, for that very injunction forms one of the Regulations read to the incoming Master, to which his 'unqualified assent' has to be acknowledged. Inviolability is implicit in the injunction read to him: that changes may only be made by 'Lawful Authority', but it is hoped that the plethora of 'lawful' changes that have taken place in recent times is indeed a modern affectation, otherwise much of the historical data based upon the faithful transfer of ceremony etc. that has been relied on hitherto, must be regarded as 'bunkum'. The extent, if at all, of this inviolability is challenged by some historians, an example of which can be found in the 'questions' in response to a paper by Lawrence.[4]

However, this is not the view held here and the thesis of this study is that:

1) This adherence to the original concepts (especially those of science) was then and has, until recent times, left the essential content of the Ritual unchanged and especially their injunction within it: namely the need to pursue and inculcate learning. Given that in the strata of society with which we are concerned there was an essential prerequisite that all 'educated men' of the period should continually enhance their knowledge and because of this fact it is reasonable to assert that:

a) A dominant educational content within the Ritual is absolutely consistent with the other evidence regarding Craft ritual and the formation of the Royal Arch, albeit undocumented in any absolute sense,

b) That the purpose of the newly introduced Royal Arch Ceremony was to exalt freemasons into a unifying (inter-lodge) extension of Freemasonry; of which an imperative component was to implant a knowledge of Nature and science; in particular its relationship with the Deity.

2) That this body of knowledge could have only remained sufficiently 'factual' in the minds of the lay brethren over a very short (several years only) period. Given the people in question and the nature of its scientific content this concurrence of view would have needed to be in the early 1700s; certainly before 1730.

The above in a sense pre-empts much of which is to follow since in effect it assumes the basis of 'why' the ritual of Freemasonry took the form it did. Given that there has been little factual evidence to support this, or indeed any other such claim, asks the question are there other possibilities? At this point it is perhaps advisable to reiterate the fact that in any study such as this, one is heavily reliant upon the work of others, several have or will be recognised by name, but it is hoped that the reader will forgive any failure to acknowledge specifically the many others that have been omitted, except by implication. One of the most important sources has been referred to already, namely the commendable work of Excellent Companion J.R. Clarke.[2,3] His papers on the Craft Masonry and Royal Arch in particular, range over many aspects of the Ceremonial and basic concepts, but of particular interest here, are his investigations into the association of early Masons with the Royal Society and other learned bodies. He points out that there was scarcely one Grand Master in the early years of the Premier Grand Lodge who was not also a Fellow of, or in some way closely associated with, the Royal Society. Whilst he acknowledged that the accuracy of recorded names was less than perfect, he demonstrated that there was in many instances very substantive supporting evidence of the connection. That eminent people such as Wren, Hooke and Newton showed keen interests in the physical (analytical) nature of architecture that is of direct relevance to freemasons, is generally accepted, even though there is no concrete evidence of their direct involvement in Freemasonry from giving lectures and writing. However this has not prevented many learned people within Freemasonry from giving lectures in the certainty that Wren was a freemason. Others outside, such as Fara,[5] refute such optimistic claims.

However, more important to this study he (Clarke) implies that there was a confluence of factors which indicate that the Royal Arch was conceived by a group of people, many of whom were in a learned fraternity often referred to as the 'Barber Surgeons'. This at first sight appears to conflict in a minor way with the main thrust of this work, until it is realised that it is essentially the same argument, but with different personnel and timing. It is clear that whoever these people were, they were closely associated with other eminent academics, most of whom had strong affiliations with the Royal Society, several of whom were themselves members. No attempt will be made to paraphrase his (and the many others – for he too relies upon others for his data) extremely detailed work, but rather to assume that the names he lists are substantially correct – he appears to have largely suppressed the temptation of many genealogists, of making 'convenient' connections and looking no further.

Indeed, it will be argued here that the roles were in practice reversed, that in reality it was the 'academics' who were responsible for the foundation of the Royal Arch, that they received strong, but only secondary, support from other (professional) worthies such as the Barber Surgeons and other influential groups, including the aristocracy. On this basis it will be assumed that a caucus of eminent thinkers conceived the Royal Arch early in the early 1720s. The thesis here is that the 'science' in the Symbolical Lecture substantiates this dating and indicates most strongly the nature of the Ceremony.

Raison d'être of Royal Arch Masonry

Having considered some of the factors which may have influenced the nature and content of both the Craft and Royal Arch ritual, it is now appropriate to consider other forms of influence, such as who, why, where etc.

References

1. Jones, B.E., *Freemasons' Book of the Royal Arch* (George Harrap, London, 1969).
2. Clarke, J.R., 'The Medical Profession and Early Freemasonry', *AQC* 85 (1972) pp 298-311.
3. Clarke J.R., 'The Royal Society and Early Grand Lodge Freemasonry', *AQC* 80 (1967), pp. 110-119.
4. Lawrence, C., 'Within and Without: the Hidden Mysteries of Nature and Science', *AQC* 118 (2006), pp, 115, 126.
5. Fara, P., *Sympathetic Attractions* (Princeton University Press, Princeton, NJ, 1996).

Chapter Twelve:
Sociological factors behind the formation of the Premier Grand Lodge and the Royal Arch

ustification for such a pretentious heading is based upon the presumption that a rationale can be found answering the questions of whom, why and when etc? Unfortunately there is no simple way of answering these questions directly as there is no contemporary Masonic documentation with respect to the formation of the Fraternity currently available or ever likely to be. However, as has been suggested already a possible way forward would be to establish a correlation between the scientific, historical and sociological data, such as it is, before and at the time of its inception. The likely motivation and reasoning behind each of the Founders is clearly central to this analysis but as has been suggested already, there appears to have been only limited common motivation and that the success of the venture had been due to each deriving considerable benefit from an integration of the needs of each individual. This would make more sense if there had been no especial higher goal, but simply a requirement to have a friendly society, whose objective was merely that of meeting the requirement expressed in the present day 'Address to the Brethren': 'I therefore trust that we shall have but one aim in view, to please each other and unite in the grand design of being happy and communicating happiness'. However, it is far from certain that there was any altruistic 'grand plan', but rather that each could see the means of achieving their own objectives, whilst at the same time all were deriving sufficient mutual benefit to maintain great enthusiasm. Even so, if this was to be more than an extra special 'club' then not only from the point of view of its members, but also in terms of public perception it was essential that its aims and objectives should be seen against a humanistic, educational (especially in terms of Nature and science) charitable and patriotic backdrop. In order to test the merit of this assertion and before moving on, it was of interest, if not a necessity, to divert away from the original (scientific) theme of the study and search for other evidence, related to the likely men responsible and search for other contributory factors.

Whilst much of this work is concerned with the basis of early Freemasonry, Craft ritual and the formation of the Royal Arch, it is necessary to actually review its place within the context of the social climate of the time. This leads automatically to the need to try and identify the people most likely to have been concerned in the formal consolidation of the then disparate strands of Freemasonry into what is referred to here as Premier Grand Lodge – the reason for doing so will become apparent as the various subject areas are discussed. The rather turbulent period of British history after the comparatively tranquil reign of Elizabeth up to and during the formation

Sociological factors

of the Premier Grand Lodge was extremely colourful and an enormous amount has been written on this period. Almost in equal measure the scholarly historians have exhibited considerable ambivalence in such matters, such as posing the question of whether Cromwell was a great reformer or a scoundrel. That this immediate pre-history has enormous bearing on this study is without question and consequently accuracy is of great importance. However, it would be an impossible task to reappraise the individual scholarship of these historians and commentators. In any case even if sufficient time had been available and a concerted effort made it would likely be just as partial. Whilst considerable care will be taken, the final assessment of this study may nonetheless be prone to being that of a highly personalised view of the circumstances, the possible motives, the personalities (and hence integrity of the individuals concerned), the nature of the newly formed Premier Grand Lodge and the reasons for the subsequent formation of the Royal Arch.

Clearly it required a collective of people to found the Premier Grand Lodge, but it will be argued below that there were only a few who were crucial (and most likely conceived it) in that process. But again it is argued, that it was from these same people and more likely one in particular, that the conception and subsequent founding of the Royal Arch was to come. However, it is first necessary to reflect on the circumstances of the period and discuss factors that affected the unification of Freemasonry and led to this final assessment.

In the process of trying to understand the (Masonic) science woven into Freemasonry by reference to that in the Symbolical Lecture it was essential to establish the likely consensus of the contemporary view of science. In order to do this in a meaningful way it became evident that there was a need to study the scientific climate outside of Freemasonry, both during and leading up to that time. Again, a great deal has been written on this much narrower topic in relation to this period and it is somewhat gratifying to find that, for the most part, there is good overall agreement, differing only in detail or emphasis. However, whilst there have been many books and papers written on or around the topic, there are three that are of particular merit with respect to this Study and they have been used as the basic text for this Section. That by Dijcksterhuis[1] covering much of the period leading up to that time of the foundation of the Premier Grand Lodge; that of Stewart[2] on the science and technology during this critical period and that on magnetism (a surprising omission from the Symbolical Lecture) by Fara.[3] Whilst it is wise to question the objectivity of all historians, if progress is to be made it is necessary to take a stance and the extremely thorough research practices of these authors strongly recommends their work for this purpose. There is a fourth written by Jacobs[4] in which, in one Chapter, she covers a number of aspects that relate science and Freemasonry, but much of her work is concerned with foreign lodges and the notable exclusion of specific

The Key to Modern Freemasonry

groups, not least women. Although her work adds to an overall understanding of the subject, the objectivity of her assertions with respect to the impact of science *per se* on Freemasonry is less convincing.

Dijcksterhuis explains in a most comprehensive way that which is agreed by virtually all historians, that in the hundred and more years leading up to the formation of the Premier Grand Lodge there was a massive explosion of interest in all that was scientific and technological. As has been discussed already the reasons can be ascribed to many causes, such as the vast opportunities created by the opening up of trade with the rest of the world, the change from a rural economy, the slow but improving communications, the profits from mining, the potential rewards from exploiting technology, the printed word etc., but the emergence of entrepreneurial activity, especially in the coffee houses, clubs, societies and similar venues, of London appears to be crucial to this overall process and this appears to be particularly true with respect to the establishment of the Premier Grand Lodge.

One manifestation of the importance of science and technology (there was little distinction between the two at that time) was the patronising of those talented individuals by the socially powerful. Whether or not their intentions were entirely laudable has been reflected upon earlier, but whilst to possess knowledge of the sciences was considered a social grace, it was also recognised that 'knowledge was power'. It is at this point that a position has to be taken with respect to the motivation behind the formation of the Premier Grand Lodge and marks the beginning of the inevitable subjectivity when trying to rationalise such data and the controversy it will most likely engender.

The emergence of the entrepreneurial class started long before 1700 and economic benefits of such enterprise was not lost on many of the established gentry, even to the extent of establishing mines on their own property, building canals etc. and investment in different ventures both at home and abroad. Although started by his grandfather, when Charles II was restored with kingly power there was to be a very large increase in the upper echelons of the aristocracy (to a high degree related to the issue of his mistresses). It is of significance that also included within this burgeoning aristocracy were entrepreneurs, who were there by dint of their wealth and not birth. Within the established families, there were those disposed to commercial and scientifically based ventures in a large way, such as the Dukes of Montagu. This was also a time when certain aristocratic families were not ill disposed to marriage into the then *nouveau riche*. It was essential, if they were to survive, to avoid injudicious political involvement, the trick was being able to make the right choice and often opportune changes of allegiance, for as we shall see, at least in the case of the families with which we are concerned, they proved to be master magicians.

Sociological factors

It is necessary to establish an important sociological (hierarchical) component of most, if not all, institutions: namely the kudos and power of being numbered amongst and/or associated with its leadership and the derived benefits. For the lesser mortals, it was that of being part of such an elite fraternity. However, whilst rarely acknowledged, it is the corollary of this: namely the importance of those who may have been excluded that is of particular interest, if not central, to this study. By the time that the Premier Grand Lodge was founded the Royal Society had become a most prestigious institution within British Society, but by the very nature of its constitution it excluded men of rank and fortune who would, if only by implication, have considered themselves to be greatly disadvantaged by such exclusion. To substantiate the sociological importance of this claim and to show that it is equally true today, as well as not appearing to be churlish, it is helpful to revert (*see also* Part I) to the comments of Richard Feynman a Nobel Prize winner and perhaps one of the most outstanding theoretical physicists of the Twentieth Century and clearly a most eminent man, well worthy of the very highest distinction:

'Honors! I had trouble when I became a member of the National Academy of Sciences (the USA's equivalent of the Royal Soc.), and I had ultimately to resign because here was another organisation which spent most of its time choosing who was "illustrious enough" to join. This included such questions as "we physicists must stick together because they've got a very good chemist that they are trying to get in, and we haven't enough room" or whatever ... What's wrong with chemists? The whole thing was rotten, because the purpose was mostly to decide who could have this honour, etc.'[5]

To be so included was/is perceived to have four possible ramifications, first, being that of status, second, the opportunity to exert influence, third to exploit openings, fourth to exclude others. Again the corollary: to be so excluded having the reverse effect, which may manifest itself in hostility or ridicule or as some mixture of them, or personal antagonism, usually dressed up as objective critique, i.e. ... (The) Royal Society as a gentlemanly club of *virtuosi* dreaming up unrealizable projects.[6] Whether the reader shares this view is problematic, but based upon the social historians' assessment of the time and contemporary (analogous) experience, it is taken to be true for the purposes of this work. Based on this presumption, the four factors cited above would have featured largely in the Founder's thinking and this tacit assumption is assigned to the remaining text.

It is first necessary to consider the original format of the Premier Grand Lodge formed in 1717. The facts, such as they are, can be found in a number of places, but because of its additional relevance to early Royal Arch Masonry those of J. R.

Clarke[7, 8] are relied upon here to a large extent.

At this point the research had reached a stage where it was necessary to gain some understanding of the Founders' likely view of Nature and Science. Their motivation as individuals will be considered in much greater detail in Chapters Thirty-six and Thirty-seven, but for the present the chronology of the research will be adhered to. This because it is believed that the basic scientific phenomenon in the current Ritual is presumed to relate to the time (1720s) of its inception in the form as we know it today and whilst an explanation of its essential physics has been attempted in Part I, except in passing, it did not explain why it was adopted in this outmoded form. Would this anomaly prove to be a strength or weakness in terms of the basic presumption of the dating of the Premier Grand Lodge and the instigation of the Royal Arch? It was clearly necessary to seek some rationalisation of a number of apparent paradoxes that existed and ask the questions why did the Founders adopted that particular interpretation and why in that form? Of course immediately prior to that period the improved level of general education, the printed word, ease of communication and freedom of expression had brought about a general consensus of what might be regarded as the 'basic realities' of Nature. Among the present population few would now challenge such things as the vastness of the Universe, the existence of the 'atom' however defined, that light is electromagnetic radiation, that fire results from the combustion of matter with oxygen etc., but to paraphrase Newton: there still remains an ocean of things to be discovered. It therefore comes as no surprise that even within current scientific thinking there are still fundamental disagreements between today's so called experts. However, today we are inured to these 'breakthroughs' and these internecine disputes are regarded as local skirmishes with the body of fundamental science remaining intact. But for the 'informed' few with whom we are concerned they were then being asked to contemplate and in that sense wrestle with quite radical conceptual changes that were fundamentally different from their present understanding. This was especially troublesome because these changes affected not only their concepts of the actual physics (mechanics) of Nature, but also their philosophy of life, spiritual being and even their place within that sector of society. In consequence any alignment with some new discovery or philosophy would require concessions that were appreciably more difficult than would be the case in the blasé world of today. Nowadays for instance quite astonishing discoveries; say an announcement of a new phenomenon in space, or that an animal or humans may be cloned, or where almost daily some clinicians, scientists, engineers or astronomers give (self protective) forecasts of even greater discoveries just around the corner. Indeed they come with such frequency, that there is no time to assimilate them in terms of their impact on one's own general view of things, before the next revelation reduces them to yesterday's news. Indeed as mentioned in Chapter Seven whilst undertaking this research there was an article inserted in the middle pages of *The Times* (London), by their Science Correspondent – *see* Figure 7.4.

Again there is no merit in attempting to update the article cited above since each revelation of this kind becomes more and more expansive, but rather to consider that if this, or any similar announcement is indeed correct then it would revolutionise most of our thinking on the Universe and further reinforce our infinitesimally small place in it. But such was the impact of this particular article that it glimmered for half a day at the bottom of the inside pages and was quickly extinguished by the need to provide tomorrow's revolutionary find. It is interesting therefore that Fara's book illustrates the very same thing, although at a much slower pace, that this delayed assimilation occurred then, since the various ramifications of magnetism were being debated well before and during the eighteenth century, not least during the period with which we are concerned and although there were strong connotations made between the forces of magnetism and some divine power, they were to play no part in the Nature and Science of the Ritual.

However, before becoming too dismissive of the confused and rather naive reasoning that the Founders seemed prepared to adopt, it is as well to remember that in the intervening years, it is only by some remarkable circumflexure of human (highly inventive) reasoning that has allowed matters spiritual to have become somehow separated from matters scientific/mechanistic. Superficially at least, it would appear that all major religions are extremely slow to embrace contemporary thinking on scientific matters and by what can only be described in some cases as very ingenious reasoning, are they able to provide arguments that somehow reconciled these scientific truths within the tenets of their respective faiths. In defence of the Founders they received mixed messages, for instance even one hundred years later (early 1800s), Linnington felt able to write on these matters in his Compendium of Astronomy, subtitled 'comprising a complete treatise, adjusted to the improved state of the science, and an Astronomical Dictionary'. He informs us that his primary task was to write a book for the use of youth of both sexes (no less!),[9] when discussing the subject of whether the Moon is inhabited or not, writes as follows:

> From her constant serenity, and apparently uniform lustre, it has to be supposed that she has no atmosphere [he goes on to refute this somewhat], and consequently no vapours, clouds, nor rain, which might have been strengthened by the supposition of her not possessing either oceans or seas, on which account, as far as we can judge, she would be incapable of supporting animal or vegetable existence, and we might thence conclude, that she is wholly and solely formed for the express purpose of subservience to our earth. But as this supposition would be at variance with the uniform conduct of the Deity, in regard to creation,

we may infer thence, as well as analogically from similar forms of motion of the moon with that of the earth, that she is inhabited and provided with every necessary for the support of her inhabitants, wherefore we may conclude, that she has an atmosphere similar to that of the earth; and although we are unable to discover oceans or seas, that must not be considered a proof that she does not possess them; but independent of these, it would not be a task too hard for omnipotence to accomplish, to supply her with water in various other ways, sufficient to support life and vegetation.[10]

Interestingly, 200 years later still, we are still debating whether or not there is unequivocal evidence of water on the Moon. However, it is reasonable to conclude that in the early 1700s there was much greater polarisation of religious belief and matters scientific had to be reconciled with an individual's intrinsic belief. It is not the purpose of this study to enter into the psychology of religious belief, but in order to understand the difficulty of their position it is necessary to repress our contemporary understanding and recognise that in practice, even after all these years of enlightenment we have no definitive answers either.

By definition there can only be one of the many faiths (or in the very worst case none in the religions presently practised) that can represent the absolute reality and so the believers within any of the other sects of the diverse faiths are clearly suffering under a delusion. Notwithstanding, this fact does not dissuade the millions practising within those other persuasions from the absolute conviction that they are right. They use patronising terms when referring to the others by proclaiming their right to religious freedom and that they respect the other person's right to do so etc., but in reality from their self-assured viewpoint it is a position of simply tolerating the intellectual failings and misconceptions of the others. If one follows this argument to its logical conclusion, it is quite clear that there is a multitude of highly intelligent people who have anchored their eternal salvation on profoundly conflicting (and to the devoted believer in any other faith than their own, patently wrong) views. In some instances these various faiths can have quite fundamental differences in basic beliefs and yet can even be within the same intrinsic faith and this, in a bizarre way, is even more difficult to rationalise. However, to the individual concerned what they believe is absolutely rational and will brook no challenge. Premier Grand Lodge Freemasonry came into being at a time when politics and religion were especially intertwined and although it protested its non-sectarianism it was or quickly became, essentially Protestant; only subsequently to actually adopt the philosophy that a freemason is merely required to profess a belief in a Supreme Being.

Thus despite the quantum leaps in scientific understanding since the early 1700s, it is quite clear that people's capacity to reconcile the irreconcilable has not

Sociological factors

really changed. We must accept, that despite our modern sophistication, it was much more logical for them to reconcile these conflicting messages than it is for people today, for we are in possession of the 'fact'; that Heaven is no longer a tangible crystal sphere clearly visible for all to see, but an ever changing universe of unimaginable size – we have to grapple with the concept of infinity, but although their universe was huge it was at least somehow finite. Thus if this research is correct, it indicates that at some stage (argued here to be early 1720's) some important concepts of science and technology were introduced into the initial portion of the Symbolical Lecture by a group of highly intelligent, educated and devout men. However with the proviso, that in their case there was a greater imperative; that any scientific discovery introduced into the Ritual would have to be consistent with the very strong (ingrained) religious convictions of society in general – *see* Chapters Thirty-six and Thirty-seven.

The overriding factor that was bringing about this change (and the cause of considerable consternation in some quarters) was that there was emerging a large body of opinion that these scientific facts did not appear to be reliant upon divine providence. It adopted the stance that all phenomena could be tested and hence explained experimentally (the very essence of the scientific method). The Founders were living in a time where the techniques developed in the sixteenth and seventeenth centuries; such as telescopes, microscope, more accurate clocks, chemical separation, vacuums, magnetism, electricity etc., were then advancing rapidly and because these discoveries were based upon better and better scientific method they were becoming irrefutable (as indeed they are today until someone comes up with a better concept). This posed the immediate question in this enquiry: since it repeatedly asks such things as: why were Kepler's concepts with respect to the orbits of the planets and their relationship to the regular solids (that even he had decided to abandon a century before) included in the Symbolical Lecture? It was in large measure an attempt to answer such questions that has led to the rationale presented here. Clearly an important factor in this study was to establish, as far as was possible, an accurate scientific dating and to understand why such a pronounced phase-lag was acceptable to them.

The concept of scientific and medical specialisation has become so much part of present day thinking that it is difficult to conceive a time when people attempted to obtain a complete understanding of all things. It is now quite normal to speak of say a 'paint' chemist, a 'rubber' chemist or a 'pharmaceutical' chemist, neurosurgeon, ergonomist or whatever. This hyper-specialisation is accepted as necessary because of the sheer complexity of the various disciplines and we acknowledge that these experts will likely possess only a comparatively peripheral knowledge of the other subjects. For the Founders to have understood the chemistry, albeit quite different, of that time they would have required about the same level of knowledge as a fourth year student at senior school. Although as with every age there would have been a huge amount of totally spurious knowledge; in that particular instance it would have been the distraction of alchemy. Their initiative in setting up the whole new concept of the Royal Arch suggests that they were not only receptive to new ideas, but also keen to pass them on to others. However, it will be argued that these contemporary (radical) concepts were perhaps coming too fast, had a much greater significance and were extending too far beyond the actual science itself for general acceptance and hence some discretion was necessary in its dissemination. This was especially true of their intended audience, who up until that point would have been shielded from radical concepts. If they were to then be asked to embrace some of these newer concepts it would have required them to throw away too many ingrained religious beliefs. If this assessment is correct, then it is easy to understand why certain outmoded concepts were retained in the Ritual after they had been rejected by those (erstwhile specialists) at the frontiers of that particular aspect of the science/ technology. In the 1600s two great philosophers had arrived at this conclusion, John Locke (1632-1700) 'No man's knowledge here can go beyond his experience' and George Berkeley (1685-1753) 'Truth is the cry of all, but the game of few'. Wherein lay the knowledge and the truth of the Founders; perhaps some insight into their early education may help to provide an explanation?

References

1. Dijksterhuis, E., *The Mechanisation of the World Picture* (Oxford University Press, 1992).
2. Stewart, L., *The Rise of Public Science* (Cambridge University Press, 1992).
3. Fara, P., *Sympathetic Attractions* (Princeton University Press, Princeton, NJ, 1996).
4. Jacob, M.C., *Women and the Enlightenment* (E. Reimen ?), pp. 69-91.
5. Stokes, C., *No Ordinary Genius – the Illustrated Richard Feynman* (Weidenfeld & Nicolson, London, 1974), pp. 81-82.
6. Fara, P., *op. cit.*
7. Clarke, J.R., 'The Medical Profession and Early Freemasonry', *AQC* 85 (1972), pp. 298-311.
8. Clarke J.R., 'The Royal Society and Early Grand Lodge Freemasonry', *AQC* 80 (1967), pp. 110-117.
9. Linnington, R., *Compendium of Astronomy* (Wittaker, Teacher & Co., London, 1830), pp. 115-116.
10. *Ibid.*

Chapter Thirteen: Education

ecause of the likely influence of schooling and early social environment on the eventual personality of each individual it was deemed to be of particular interest to consider the source of any ingrained concepts the Founders may have possessed. To then speculate upon the degree to which these primary concepts may have affected their preference for a particular understanding of contemporary science and why in some instances they appeared to be quite out of phase with the most advanced (current) thinking. The innate difficulties of communication could account for much of the shortfall, but other, more subtle, factors may also have played an important part. For instance: a Roman Catholic (Jesuit) priest is reputed to have said: 'give me a child between seven and eleven and I will show you the man'. There is little doubt that schooling and religious instruction during one's formative years are likely to have a profound influence on a person's subsequent thinking and disposition to resist change. That the education one receives is in turn a function of the mode of its presentation, the books available and the thinking of the teacher, parentage etc. It therefore seemed necessary to look at their likely exposure to formal education more closely since that might prove to be a fruitful line of research.

Several avenues were explored in an attempt to verify and quantify the importance of this concept, but the two discussed at depth here were considered the most significant. The first was to research the background of those most likely to be among the Founders and especially the possible nature of their schooling.

The Founders were clearly highly educated men with particular 'drive', most having wealth and/or influence. In an attempt to determine who these may have been, it became necessary to return to the work of other Masonic historians. It was fortunate that early in the course of research in the Library of the United Grand Lodge of England, Great Queen Street, London, it had been possible to enter into discussions with E. Comp. J. Hamill (not forgetting others of the Library staff before and since) and together with his own extensive work in this area, his almost encyclopaedic knowledge of the work of others[1, 2] and copies of the actual lodge registers of names of the period, a collection of likely freemasons began to emerge. Thus from this beginning it was possible, to isolate further likely groups of people by cross-referencing influential freemasons referred to Masonic writings such as those found in E. Comp. J Clarke's papers[3, 4] which alluded to the Royal Society and other influential groupings such as the Barber Surgeons. The crucial step in this research was to take this potential list and correlate those names with those cited in the publications of non-Masonic social and scientific historians such as Stewart.[5]

This proved to be an iterative process, since this second list revealed names that were then found to be within this early group of freemasons, but who had not previously been afforded too great a significance in the surviving Masonic literature.

A study of those particular papers and others related to the subject strengthened the possibility that the Founders of both the Premier Grand Lodge and the Royal Arch were in practice confined to a very small group of people and were almost certainly one and the same. The disappointment was that Clarke's careful study had suggested that earlier claims of this inter-relationship with the Royal Society had been exaggerated somewhat (although he may have been too premature in arriving at that conclusion – *see* individual bibliographies of those early freemasons). Whilst he was able to show that the numbers of *FRS*s who were also freemasons was staggeringly high, finding who they were and connecting them with specific lodges and their Masonic involvement was much less easy, with many anomalies. Although very useful insights had been gained from this approach, because of the limitations cited above, this line of enquiry was deemed limited and that it would only advance understanding by a small amount and so only a limited amount of specific work was done on it, although from time to time it was necessary to return to it with respect to certain people.

In a similarly way, because of their large representation in the Royal Society, the Barber Surgeons who were also freemasons was considered to be of particular interest by some Masonic historians. This was more likely true since at that time they would not have been constrained by the protocols of modern specialised (professional) affiliations. Indeed many entitled their particular bent as 'physiks' (which one might be dispose to think of as 'medicine' in the broadest sense). They nonetheless would have regarded themselves perfectly competent to range over a whole spectrum of topics and it would appear many did. Although there is much talk in the ritual of 'Nature' there are no actual examples in the Ritual to indicate those topics that would now perhaps be described as 'life sciences' such biology or physiology etc., as one might be led to expect, if there had indeed been a major input from the Barber Surgeons. This conclusion is reinforced further by earlier and contemporary accounts of the public's predilection (one might be tempted to describe it as macabre perversion) towards rather lurid dissections, typically those described by Pepys and other diarists etc. Thus whilst there is no doubt that there were many Barber Surgeons who were members of the lodges which combined to form the Premier Grand Lodge and subsequently the Royal Arch, as would be expected because of their social standing, there is little to support the notion that they were instrumental in the basic concepts inculcated in the adopted ritual or that of the Royal Arch. Further if one studies the list of these Barber Surgeons in Clarke's paper, it is apparent that their numbers increased markedly as time went on and that they became more influential in the late 1720s and 1730s. Since there is a tendency for people of like interest to affiliate, this phase-lag may have been due to the lodges to which they belonged not joining the Premier Grand Lodge until a later date. This again could be taken as another small indicator of why they seemingly failed to have influence on the adopted ritual or the Royal Arch to any great extent.

However, although there are few 'facts', there is very strong, if not irrefutable, evidence that the Royal Arch was founded between 1717 and 1740 and that by highly motivated, extremely intelligent, educated, politically active individuals of considerable substance and social standing. Whilst it is now virtually certain that no actual written evidence will ever be found as to who they were or precisely when it was established, it is possible that this indirect approach may be more successful. Again two things may be taken as fact; one that they were highly educated in comparison with the rest of the population, whatever their social origins. Second, because it is repeated many times in Craft ritual; that they regarded the possession of 'knowledge' not only as an essential social grace, but a vehicle of power and influence. It is on the basis of this that the case will be argued later that the choice of the men who were likely to have founded the Premier Grand Lodge and subsequently the Royal Arch is limited by this factor alone. However, it is necessary first to attempt to understand the means by which they would have gained their knowledge and thereby influence of any preconceptions they may have carried into adulthood.

This approach was based upon the supposition that the number of grammar and public schools capable of affording this level of education was small. In particular to challenge their capacity, or indeed desire, to teach the rudiments of Nature and especially science, given the structure of their (the Church mainly) constitution. This antipathy towards science and technology was because these subjects would have been considered to be heretical by most school authorities and as such their teachers would have been actively discouraged from venturing into these subjects. This anti-science trait was found to limit dramatically the choice of likely institutions.

This same antipathy would also be true of private tuition of the type afforded in privileged homes, since the availability of suitable tutors would have been equally limited and most of those would have studied in a church environment. One could be forgiven for making the broad statement that a person of comparatively low social standing, but of high intelligence could only reconcile these two states by entering the church, since a large number of the influential men in science and other disciplines were the sons and daughters (outstanding examples: Hooke, Austin and the Brontes) of vicars or to a lesser extent school teachers.

The following presumption may not be true necessarily, but is taken to be so: namely that the average schoolmaster was unlikely to have moved in that upper echelon of influence. That in consequence his or her education would have been somewhat out of phase with the rapid advancements in knowledge that were occurring elsewhere. Similarly scientific text was extremely rare, would have been expensive, confined to private libraries and that it would be somewhat dated, but more especially, very partial. Thus unless these school teachers or tutors had taken rigorous steps to modify their thinking they would have had a view of matters scientific dating much earlier than the time they were actually teaching, in particular those boys who were destined eventually to found the Royal Arch. Because it is often difficult to disabuse people of entrenched preconceptions, it is reasonable to assume that there may well have been a latent effect on the boys' adult thinking and hence influenced that which they selected to include in the Symbolical Lecture.

The question then arose as whether this thesis could be given credence by finding samples of these early documents and better still to be able to examine examples of a student's actual written work, during the period 1670 to 1700. It has been stated already and will be returned to later, that Robert Hooke was, during this period, of immense importance to science in general, but also in a convoluted way Freemasonry itself. His importance with respect to understanding the transfer of knowledge (if only because he was pivotal in the preservation of the Royal Society, the quasi model and spur of the Premier Grand Lodge during the time when it was experiencing considerable difficulties) is by example. Robert Hooke was born, again the son of a clergyman, in the Isle of White, one may assume because of this fact and his obvious talent, that after his father's death his mother was able to petition that he be allowed to receive his education at Westminster School (regarded by many historians as the finest school of that period); although there is some dispute over the precise nature of his acceptance into the School. This incidentally had also been the school for several of the early Grand Masters and so it was an obvious place to begin such an investigation.

At the very beginning of this book it was stated that the work has extended over very many years and that during that time it had become necessary to be beware of historians and now we must add archivists to that list. Because a study such as this is never ending and by the time it is necessary to make a final appraisal of the work prior to publication other matters have come to light. In view of the cautionary note above in this instance the next few paragraphs will be left as they were originally recorded some eight years ago:

'Herein we encounter the difficulty of conflicting intelligence and are once again obliged to accept one or other of two contradictory positions or some vague compromise between them. In this instance the logic was to consult the archivists of these famous schools for some clue of the curricula of those times and examples of student's work and written text. However on enquiry, the School Archivist said that the School Curriculum during that period was purely Latin and Greek and that there

Education

is absolutely no evidence that any scientific text, other than Euclid would have been available and even then such a book would not have been freely accessible, but loaned on an individual basis to a bright student, such as Hooke. That such individual tuition was likely was reinforced by the fact Richard Busby the headmaster throughout the whole of that period, was keen on mathematics (geometry in particular) and had in fact tried to establish a chair in the subject at Oxford, but his attempt in fact failed. Whilst this indicated a likely scenario, it was also quite tenuous and so that avenue (Westminster School) had to be abandoned. He (the Archivist) felt that apart from Busby's likely personal involvement, Hooke or indeed any other erstwhile scientist would have to wait for university or discover some other fount of knowledge, as appears to be the case of third Grand Master.

The next school of such calibre nearest to London during that period and likely to have an archivist was Harrow. The lady archivist was most helpful, although not in the sense of scientific association, but by emphasising the lack of it. This, for the most part, was due to the rather peculiar ecclesiastical connections, which influenced (in this school at least there was unequivocal evidence, but most likely Westminster also) the curriculum greatly. She explained that Harrow School had been instigated by the parish priest because the local school had ceased to teach Latin and Greek and he was greatly concerned that these classical subjects would no longer be taught. Right up until nearly 1700 the pupils were taught in a large church hall on the 'Hill', with the records kept in a large trunk in the corner of the room. Thus she regretted there were no books or student work kept of that period. However, she did have a syllabus of a much later (1750s) period, giving the times and nature of each lesson throughout the week. Sadly there was absolutely no mention of formal science, even though by that time science was coming on apace. However, she did afford details of the archivist at Eton and the enquiry was made there.

Unfortunately Eton's Archivist was of exactly the same view as that of Westminster, namely that there was no place for the sciences or mathematics within the system, only Latin and Greek. She said that the boys did not have as full a curriculum (timetable) as today's pupils and felt that the may well have been encouraged to develop other interests. Nonetheless, she felt that in the case of science, other than the chance that there may have been a shared interest with one of the masters, a boy's access to books was severely limited. There was no School library *per se*, only one kept strictly for the Head Master and Fellows; not, she was keen to point out, the ordinary Masters. However, that scientific stars could emerge from such a system was eminently illustrated by the fact that Robert Boyle (Hooke's employer/benefactor although again there is dispute over the precise relationship between them – *see* Part I) was educated at Eton.

The research up to this point was indicating that there was little left but to accept that those Founders who had developed a strong interest in science had done so despite their school's educational philosophy, rather than because of it. Given that it is not possible to be wise in all things and the obvious status of the sources, although the outcome had been very disappointing there seemed to be little value in pursuing this line of enquiry further. Clearly it was then necessary to look beyond any the individual's schooling, since it now seemed most likely that it was their parents or family associates that encouraged that interest and influenced their study at university. They would have also needed to be atypical students, since most historians are agreed that academic standards at places like Oxford were extremely lax – 'mould growing on the books in the library', complained one contemporary critic.

Despite the above reservation, the question still remained of how was it possible to instil that level of understanding into the minds of these young people other than by a formal educational process. For example Wren was a fellow pupil of Hooke and he became a don in mathematics at Cambridge when he was barely twenty and was appointed professor at twenty-five. There seems little doubt that he must have had an exceedingly good grounding, but from where? The latent belief that there was merit in pursuing this line of enquiry was reawakened when there was a need to consider the nature and intent behind the founding of the 'Mathematical School' endowed by Charles II at Christ's Hospital (Blue Coat School) in relation to the sociology of London. Once again the School Archivist was somewhat discouraging, but said that records prior to 1900 were held at the Guildhall Library in London. The keeper of the records at the Guildhall Library also shared the gloom of researching them directly because they were a huge and extremely tedious list or items such as bills of sale etc., but indicated that there had been a number of books, held in the main Library, that had been written on the subject.

Although they were many of great interest only that of Pearce[6] referred directly to that which was actually taught. From the morass of data he had managed to isolate the nature of the syllabuses and some aspects of teaching practice at various times between inception in 1662 and 1700 (Pearce's examples of 1697 being perhaps the most appropriate). As with all the royalty during this period Charles' generous endowment was more imagined than real and the School struggled in several ways. However, its greatest shortcoming was that it tried to engraft its very advanced and concentrated nautical mathematics onto its already tough teaching schedule. The boys were not necessarily the brightest and it would appear that the Regime adopted the view that any aspect that could not be taught by normal process could be 'beaten in' [*sic*]. As indicated above the mathematics was that directly associated with navigation at sea. There was a temptation here to reproduce the syllabus to give an indication of its severity, for example its complex spherical trigonometry, but it will be left to Isaac Newton who had been invited to comment on the syllabus. Newton

Education

stated that such a syllabus could not be taught in the time or in that way, indicating that it would require at least twice the time and more significantly a change of staff. However, he may not have properly allowed for the 'leather strap' parameter. It would seem that if the pupil was bright enough to have achieved the desired level, he should have been bright enough not to have started, given the following extract from a letter received by the School:

'I now have the honour," wrote Sir Francis Wheeler in 1691, "to command the Albermarle, and am very desirous to have one of your mathematical boyes … by assignment. I had about a yeare ago one that was bred up to accompts by you, and found him quick and so hopefull that upon his death I was very sorry, which leads me to beg favour that you'l please oblige me with one, and I'le engage in any security to breed him according to institution … and onely desire him to be well provided with two suits of Clothes and Linnen'.

One can find consolation from the fact that the Captain at least got a few months out of the original boy and that he had likely not worn out his two suits of clothing in that time. Thus we have a least some indication of the standard and the degree of understanding possible in pre-university education.'

However, a second a more direct insight into the possible education standards in science at that time was derived from chance meeting at a conference on Robert Hooke which was to commemorate the tercentenary of his death. A very erudite paper was presented by Smith,[7] the new archivist at Westminster School, on the level of science taught at the School in the time of Hooke and since Dr Busby remained the head master for over fifty years, right up to the period of interest here. He paints a completely different picture of the availability of science and mathematics and the level attained by the pupils. He showed that there were the necessary books and equipment and above all competent tutors. He further shows that boys, such as Hooke and Wren, went to university 'hitting the ground running' and not as previously imagined having to make the huge educational leap that would have been necessary otherwise. Both his paper and subsequent discussion left the impression of a profound piece of research; the danger is that his interpretation is consistent with the stance adopted in this book and could have indicated partiality and in order that the reader may make a judgement the views of the previous archivist's have been left. Despite this possible reservation the assumption made here is that the Founders of interest here would, by one means or another, have received a reasonably profound grounding of science, based upon the knowledge of their tutors and the written text of the mid to late 1600s. Two final but significant parts of Smith's paper are worthy of mention: he indicated that Hooke was appointed surveyor of Westminster Abbey and one of the pieces of work he oversaw was: 'Hooke had also worked on the Solomon's Porch' indicating the universal 'love affair' with Solomon. Second: 'The histories of the School often highlights those whose talents have shone in the arts or as statesmen, but some further indicators of the breadth of the talent that the School nurtured are that before Busby's death twenty-four Westminster scholars had joined the Royal Society, including (Hoskyns, Montagu, Wren and Wyche) ...'. He says they included physicians, botanists and chemist and of course we know about Hooke's science and architecture; Wren's mathematics and architecture, but note especially Montagu the first of the aristocratic Grand Masters.[8]

At this point it was necessary to reconsider this approach, as there appeared to be a distinct danger if the research was continued in this way of it becoming polarised. Since by sieving out for selected study only those members of the Premier Grand Lodge considered the most likely candidates on the basis of their scientific background was likely to inadvertently exclude men who were equally motivated and similarly competent, leading to a strategy where the research would because of its selectivity become self-fulfilling. Unfortunately, to avoid this dilemma completely would require a whole new area of inter-relating the personal profiles of all these prominent people in a sociological study (possibly the next area of interest if this line of research is pursued further). Because a balanced view is so important an attempt will be made later to address this deficiency, at least for the principal players, but the difficulties of doing so will become apparent.

However, science is the new ingredient in this study into early Freemasonry and in consequence takes centre stage in this enquiry. In order to mitigate excessive bias due to an over emphasis on science an effort has been made to explore many other strands, but it would have constituted too great a distraction to have to have pursued them to the extent that the science has been considered in Part I; it was decided therefore to make as honest an appraisal as was possible within the time and space available.

Continuing along this line of investigation the next obvious source of influence would be that stemming from the universities. Unfortunately this too proved to be comparatively difficult because they were found to be radically different from the institutions we are familiar with today. The problem was exacerbated by the fact that we have little enough real knowledge of the people concerned and although they may have been credited with certain academic attainments, what that meant in terms of actual academic ability is often open to question. We shall see that some were simply 'awarded' academic titles, some in effect bought them, some may even have earned them (Montagu 'applied' for his doctorate), but that did not mean necessarily their 'qualification' was in the discipline for which they became known. For instance Wren was not a trained architect, but a mathematical scholar. Whereas Hooke, who worked in close partnership with Wren in architecture, was an outstanding applied scientist and covered a whole range of technologies. Both men would have had an enormous impact on the thinking of those who were to become the Founders of the Premier Grand Lodge. Indeed it is shown in Part I and Chapter Thirty-four that Hooke's concept of 'light' is a critical factor with respect to the search for the origin and concepts of 'light' adopted in the Symbolical Lecture. Desaguliers, the person we are perhaps concerned with most, will be dealt with later in the Section that considers those persons who were most likely concern with the formation of the Royal Arch.

It became clear that whatever influence there may have been as a result of attending university it was quite unlike that which would be expect today. That in practice there were no (specialist) course curricular as such. That any subjects outside of the compulsory Arts needed to be studied on an individual basis and as such were arbitrary and in any case were likely (historically) to have their roots in the Arts. The study process would differ from student to student and place to place, with the 'modern' sciences for the most part considered *infra dig.*, if not heretical. Because there appears to have been no specifically definable influence, any interest there was required considerable self motivation, the extent of which may be inferred from the short bibliographies of the key players discussed below – Hooke for example: his activities with respect to university science will be dealt with as being somewhat representative.

Most of those, with whom we are concerned, such as Desaguliers, Brook Taylor, Stukeley etc., had links with the old universities (principally Oxford and Cambridge). However, these universities were preoccupied with the classics and theology, but worse were otherwise steeped in political intrigue dressed up as fundamental theological and anti-science philosophy. It would appear that Oxford was slightly more disposed to study the emerging sciences, but only marginally so.[9] Thus the fact that our people excelled in science was despite rather than because of the teaching of scientific subjects within the universities. Gascoigne's book[10] is such a complex piece of collected wisdom that it is effectively impossible to condense and so a trivial assessment will be made: namely that within the confines of the university one could think what they liked, within reason do what they liked, but in no sense were they allowed to proclaim any of it as university policy. This was particularly true of religion where there were many radical thinkers in the upper echelons of the Church, who discussed freely the various implications of science on religion and philosophy, but the overall conservatism persisted.

References

1. Hamill, J.M., 'English Royal Arch MS Rituals *c.*1780-*c.*1830', *AQC* 95 (1982), pp. 37-54.

2. Hamill, J.M., private communication.

3. Clarke, J.R., 'The Medical Profession and Early Freemasonry', *AQC* 85 (1975), pp. 298-311.

4. Clarke, J.R., 'The Royal Society and Early Grand Lodge Freemasonry' *AQC* 80 (1967), pp. 110-117.

5. Stewart, L., *The Rise of Public Science*, (Cambridge University Press, 1992).

6. Pearce, E.H., *Annuals of Christ's Hospital – The Mathematical School*, (Hugh Rees Ltd., 1908), pp. 109-127.

7. Smith, E., 'Hooke and Westminster [School]', pp. 215-226, paper delivered at Hooke 2003 International Conference, Royal Society & Gresham Collge, London, July, 2003.

8. *Ibid.*

9. Gascoigne, J., *Cambridge in the Age of Enlightenment*, (CUP, Cambs., 1989).

10. *Ibid.*

Chapter fourteen: Persona of the founders

At this juncture it is perhaps appropriate to consider the principal players before entering upon the background history leading up to the early days of the Premier Grand Lodge and the formation of the Royal Arch. The logic being that by already having their names and some understanding of their traits it will add relevance to some of the events in the years leading up to the 1717 initiative and in doing so reveal names not considered hitherto. Clearly there were a number of people who were likely to have been involved in the formation of the Premier Grand Lodge, since the process required the consensus of those lodges (four to begin with, but soon many more) who were willing to form such an alliance. However, it is usually the inspiration, efforts and persuasiveness of a determined few that make something such as this actually happen.

The following has already been discussed with respect to other aspects of this study, but because this Chapter is concerned with making some assessment of the likely individuals responsible for the actual inception of the definitive version of the Premier Grand Lodge the major points will be reiterated. It has been argued that the whole concept did not 'come out of the blue' but must have been started with some informal discussion between like minded people well before the accepted official inauguration in 1717. Further to assume that when the idea was first mooted: that there would be advantage gained in having an affiliation of several lodges into some formal amalgamation, it would have likely been a relatively modest proposal. But having once begun this ostensibly simple gathering of a few like minded people, it was recognised by one or more of them that it had far reaching potential and with his or their judicious involvement and one must assume 'discreet/discrete' lobbying it quickly assumed a quite different form. Given the modest social standing of those who were reported to have instigated these first few gatherings, it appears to have started as a 'rather nice thing to do'; namely to have a regular (quarterly) gathering of a group of the more significant lodge members to discuss matters of common interest or concern within the various factions of Freemasonry in London. Whether this initiative had the blessing of all the members of the constituent lodges is a moot point. However, once under way and appearing to work quite well, it quickly evolved to a stage where it took on the trappings of a formally regulated (constitutionally and initially styled as the 'Premier Grand Lodge') body. For this to happen at all, there would have had to have been some forfeiture of independence within the constituent lodges, although almost certainly not expressed in quite such forthright terms by those anxious to see it happen. Such a move would require them to conform (subjugated would have been a term they would have chosen to avoid) to this newly created supreme body, which once adopted, would dictate strategy, defined protocols from there onwards and almost certainly require support funding from the constituent member lodges. One must suppose that this must have required both extensive and extremely skilful negotiation, by this small band of influential members of these hitherto autonomous lodges. This because the senior people within those constituent lodges would have enjoyed already, or reasonably expect to be the most important person in their small fraternity, but if this more grandiose scheme should materialise, it would mean that they would now be faced with the prospect of being dictated to by some new supreme authority from outside. They would have realised that there was little chance of advancement (the top jobs were already filled) within it and it is easy to imagine the political skill required to reassure them that such an arrangement was in their best interest. Concomitant with gaining this agreement it would have been necessary to conceive an organisation that would inspire people to first join and then remain loyal to its precepts. However, the history of the Premier Grand Lodge suggests very strongly that this was a two or more episodic process – *see* later reflections on the founder members.

This new body would also be required to formulate or at least adopt/create a set of ceremonial rituals that would, if not replace, at least modify protocols sufficiently to in some way regularise any glaring variants within the constituent lodges. Again this needed to be managed in such a way that it would be sufficiently palatable to avoid antagonising the respective members. There were many logical reasons for there to be a selected and hence restricted membership in Freemasonry if an aura of privilege was to prevail. It would need to apply strict codes of conduct, retain the very strong elusion of ancient tradition and have secrecy as an important factor in their dealings. There is certainly little doubt that they got the formula correct and history confirms that this powerful cocktail was to add to Freemasonry's appeal and strengthened its members' loyalty towards it.

When time is taken to study the Ritual, as opposed to simply learning it by rote, most are struck by its profundity, ingenuity and scholarship and it is clear that its originators were highly educated and extremely talented in their prudent choice of adopted ritual. There has been a huge amount written by subsequent scholars about the profound nature of speculative Freemasonry, but for the most part this has to be regarded as pure romanticism rather than fact and reflects the ideology of subsequent generations wishing to read esotericism into every line, dot and comma. This because despite the fact that the Founders were closely related to the Church and otherwise capable, they were far too active in their social activities to have been involved to the depths implied in many of these later erudite and hugely academic contemplative studies of Masonic philosophy, which must have required their authors to spend many hundreds of hours of research.

This basic thesis of expedient simplicity will perforce have to be returned to several times over. Thus whilst much has been written on the early ritual, it is argued here that it was far from contemporary, but that most was borrowed from that already practised in existing freemasons' lodges and that its allegorical nature and symbolism was consistent with that found in all forms of the art, architecture, literature etc. of previous centuries, but which was still very much a component of what they would have construed as 'culture'. That for the most part the highly idealised interpretations of subsequent generations merely reflect this obsession and that the only contribution of the Founders was to base their appropriated version of it on the popularity of the emerging science and fetish for education. Thus in the absence of precise written evidence of its content, two basic components have to be taken as self evident that:

1) Some generally accepted ceremonial device had be established that could in future be used to formally initiate a person into a lodge/chapter and

2) That an essential element of any such ceremonial would need to maintain the strong tradition and establish an outward expression of obedience to those codes already part of existing ceremonies; namely shared objectives and in particular loyalty to their nation, this new Institution and to each other.

To a present day freemason this stark assertion that initially there was only a layer of superficial morality masking what was in essence a political game may not seem a fair assessment and so in the end it must be left for each person to decide the extent to which the concepts set out in this study are fair. However, before becoming too defensive of the perceived ethic it is important to take into account, the 'morality' of the time, the fullness of their (Founders) lives (*see* bibliographies in Part III), their social and political background, the need to support themselves and the living conditions of the times, such as lighting and heating restricting much of their activity to the daylight hours. Even so, experience dictates that if these ceremonies had been colourless and without embellishment, they would have not been in keeping with the contemporary expectation of such schemes and insufficient to inspire people to meet on a frequent basis. Thus they required additional inducements: the provision of knowledge, the prospect of attainment and possible progression within the framework of the fraternity would provide the incentive, but most of all social intercourse at the highest level. Further, there was a need to meet the inexplicable, almost primitive, requirement within all societies for rites and ceremony. This thesis is supported by the many derivatives that have been introduced since that time, such as Rose Croix,

Mark Masons, Knights Templar etc., but most especially by the early appearance of the Royal Arch. To reiterate, the important factor is to remain objective and ask the question: whether all the esoteric and deep philosophical meaning attributed to Freemasonry dates from time immemorial, or at least from the inception of the Premier Grand Lodge, or has it evolved since or been implied in the years after 1740? Again the view taken here is that there is a stronger and more likely scenario: namely that these esoteric and laudable interpretations have been introduced at a much later date and written by people with a quite different perspective and purpose. If we assume, or at least be prepared to test, that this assessment is valid, then it gives authority to the following assertions made in a most interesting note in Margaret Jacobs' book, where pragmatism and enjoyment replace morality, faith and rectitude:

> English Masonic records of the early decades of the century (18th) indicate that lodge meetings were festive events where, even without women, wine and song prevailed and where the largely non-scientific brethren received occasional instruction in mathematics and simple mechanics in the presence of Newtonian scientists no less distinguished than Brooke Talyor, Martin Folkes Jean Desaguliers. This enthusiasm for the new science, so characteristic of Enlightenment culture, is reflected in the fact that over one-fourth [but a greater proportion of those of importance here] of the early Masonic membership also belonged to The Royal Society, and that the Society's official experimenter, Desaguliers, played a particularly active role in the lodges.[1]

She continues; talking about science in Freemasonry, but since one must acknowledge the doubt expressed by some Masonic historians and analysts over absolute rigour of certain parts of her work, it will end here, but even so her book makes quite interesting reading. The simple mechanics that she makes reference to are difficult to find, other than the references to architecture, light and colour that were discussed above in Part I, and even more obliquely in that of the (lever) crow 'for taking purchases', in the Symbolical Lecture. All other lectures, such as the 'Sheffield Rituals' and Tunnah Manuscripts,[2] are perhaps better described as catechisms and were of a moralistic/ceremonial nature. There are of course Masonic 'Lectures', but it is in a sense an abuse of the word since they too are in the forms of catechisms and as such the person posing the question clearly knows the answers and the respondent clearly knows the responses (there would be some tut tutting if he did not) and so in practise there is no transfer of knowledge – the very essence of a Lecture. They (the lodges of that period) may, as in present times, have received informative (technical) lectures from time to time. Although presently this is usually only as a result of there being no candidate available, rather than a thirst for knowledge, which one suspects may not have been the case in those days, because then all knowledge was deemed important. So saying, other than the lectures found in the Royal Arch, there appears to be no contemporary evidence of this.

That there appears to be an innate need within people for 'group (socialising) behaviour' and this aspect of human behaviour must have been intuitively, if not expressly, realised by the Founders, for it appears to have been the essential component of the initial ceremonies. It is only necessary to consider the list of principal officers below (namely the senior officers of the Premier Grand Lodge itself, which does not include the bulk of the other members and those of the constituent lodges) to appreciate that their social status would have been in the upper echelons of today's society. Nor does it take much understanding of social behaviour to appreciate why there would have been a large number of similarly important people outside this immediate group, who would wish to join and be associated with such an august body. To maintain momentum, they needed to meet on a very frequent basis and the Founders would have appreciated that if the Institution was to flourish then they would need to introduce diversity, interest and purpose. The obvious device would be to extend the ceremony, invite supplementary talks or other activities or alternatively add another ceremony. History informs us that they chose the latter, which was in practice a contrived combination of the first two. This goes some way to answering the question why, but at the same time requires a greater need to reflect on the questions of who, what, where, when etc. The 'who' will now be taken another stage further by reviewing some of the likely people involved.

Unfortunately to answer the question of who these people were is a tedious process, because there has to be some justification given for either including or excluding likely candidates. As will become apparent simply considering the man is insufficient because he has to be placed within the context of the Institution and that requires some understanding of his antecedents and factors surrounding their evolution. It soon becomes clear that this group of people did not come together in a random way, but rather was the consequence of a complex historical process at the very highest level of society. That their positions in society were directly related to historical events of the preceding hundred years or so and in particular the fortunes of the royal dynasties during that period. Thus it was considered necessary to broaden the enquiry in this respect, albeit a somewhat tedious and protracted process.

Bearing in mind that the definition of the Premier Grand Lodge used throughout this study refers to the body formed by the usurpation of the original Premier Grand Lodge, it is reasonable to suppose that many of those (Founders) with whom we are concerned in this Study are in listed in Tables 14.1 and 14.2. But who among them was the person (possible persons) who had the initial inspiration that brought about the subsequent changes to the original concept cannot be known with certainty. Nor even if there had been some quasi-authoritative statement could it have been relied upon, because political expediency would have dictated that any official explanation would have ensured that their proclaimed objectives were quite remote from their actual intent. Ask any politician why they aspire to become President or Prime Minister and their reply will almost certainly be that their sole desire in life is to serve 'the people'. It is therefore left for the reader to speculate on the motivation of the various Founders, at the same time recognising how little factual information there is as well as taking account of the Social climate of the time. Unfortunately this means once again that the only source of data relies upon the perception of individual historians, who in turn have had to make their own assessment of the data available. Of course the same is equally true of this work. Indeed, because this data can be distorted in much the way as a 'trench whisper' can modify a command, the approach here has been to revert, as far as it is possible, to contemporary evidence. This is why science is important; papers and lectures were given, letters were exchanged and books were written all of which are dated and our people were totally immersed in it. It is true there was a level of politics and philosophical posturing within their science, but because of circumstances it was less covert and in view of this there is less likelihood of distortion. This is why it is reasonable to suppose that the Ritual's constant allusion to Nature and science reflects the fundamental interest of its authors and not that of a political expediency.

Whilst there were an appreciable number of people who could have united to found the Premier Grand Lodge any one of whom could have played an important role in the process, but as already argued in practice the choice was quite limited. During the preparation of this text many names were considered and then rejected for various reasons and this exercise will not be repeated here, but rather to present the final list, leaving the reader to judge its validity. Since there is a dearth of 'facts', it is helpful to at least start with the luxury of an almost certainty, namely the list of principal officers for the first twenty years or so of the Premier Grand Lodge.

Although one of the initial objectives of this study was to speculate on the wherewithal surrounding the founding of the Royal Arch, it was not possible to do so without relating it to the development of formalised Craft Freemasonry. More especially the injunction made throughout the Ritual that every freemason must strictly attend to their education, but then begs the question of its precise nature or who were to be their educators? This in turn supports the claim that the introduction of the Royal Arch, which is an exaltation ceremony with a series of lectures, came from within the same small group of men who were themselves educators and ranked among the most learned in the land. Because of their influence subtle (one might be tempted to say insidious) but profound changes took place within two or three years after the foundation in 1717 of the Premier Grand Lodge. The Tables 14.1 and 14.2 given below cover the period from 1717 until 1739. It gives the names of the Grand

Masters, Deputy Grand Masters and Secretaries in Table 14.1 and the Wardens in Table 14.2, but of course there were many other people of considerable status both within the membership of the constituent lodges and others associated with them, who may have been freemasons, but whose names were not recorded since the lists are known to be incomplete. Those that are printed in 'bold' type were also members of the Royal Society. Those marked with an asterisk are also mentioned in Stewart's,[3] Fara's,[4] Jacobs's,[5] Redwood's[6] and Taton's[7] books (namely authoritative authors who are concerned principally with those who are known to have a direct influence in the science) or others when mentioning the science of the period, each quite outside direct Masonic involvement. The list itself was compiled from various sources, but it also relies, as does much of this work, on many Masonic items such as the first Minutes of the Premier Grand Lodge, presented collectively by the *Quatuor Coronati* Lodge in 1913,[8] and Hogg and Currie's recently amended version of the list of Grand Officers found in the *Masonic Year Book Historical Supplement* (2008): Premier Grand Lodge 1717-1813.[9]

Nobody cited in the first few years of Tables 14.1 and 14.2 can be regarded as insignificant in the early history of the Premier Grand Lodge, but only those that are directly referred to later in this study will be considered more closely. As the study progressed other names appeared; typically that of Brook Taylor who was cited by Jacobs and then others as a major contributor to the science of that period. Superficially there was no direct reason to consider them any more than the many other lay members, but then it became obvious that whilst some of these did not hold high office they had dominant personalities, were socially active and highly motivated. However, it was impossible to consider them all at depth and some selection was necessary, although it is hoped not prejudicially so. They were chosen principally on the basis that they were referred to elsewhere in the literature with specific regard to the concepts proffered in this work and so it was essential that they should be considered in some depth. Because of their social status or influential position in the upper echelons of the early Premier Grand Lodge, it was deemed important to consider those individuals who have been highlighted in the above list. Many are from quite different backgrounds. Superficially at least they seem to have come from two social groupings, but destiny was to unite them in a common cause. Indeed it is because of this diverse background, that much more is known of some than others and as a result the following biographies in Part III are somewhat unbalanced in this respect, but somehow it seems to support, in roughly the same proportion: their likely influence. Unfortunately there may be some important omissions, as would have been the case of Brook Taylor until his name appeared whilst researching another topic. Fortunately in his case he was also referred to by Simon Schaffer[10] with respect to another matter (*see* section on magnetism etc.)

Table 14.1 LIST OF PRINCIPAL GRAND OFFICERS 1717-1742

Year	Grand Master	Deputy GM	Grand Secretary
1717/18	Anthony Sayer		
1718/19	George Payne		
1719/20	**John Desaguliers***		
1720/21	George Payne		
1721/22	**2nd Duke of Montagu***	**John Beal***	
1722/23	Duke of Wharton	**John Desaguliers***	
1723/24	**Earl of Dalkeith** φ	**John Beal***	William Cowper μ
1724/25	**2nd Duke of Richmond**	**Martin Folkes***	William Cowper μ
1725/27	**Lord Paisley***	**Martin Folkes***	William Cowper μ
1727	4th Earl of Inchiquin*	**John Desaguliers***	William Cowper μ
1727/28	**3rd Lord Coleraine**	William Cowper μ	William Read
1728/30	**4th Lord Kingston** φ	Alexander Chocke	William Read
1730/31	8th Duke of Norfolk	Nathaniel Blackerby	William Read
1731/32	**Lord Lovel** φ	Thomas Batson	William Read
1732/33	6th Viscount Montagu	Thomas Batson	William Read
1733/34	**7th Earl Strathmore** φ	Thomas Batson	William Read
1734/35	**20th Earl of Crawford** φ	Sir Cecil Wray	John Bevis
1735/36	2nd Viscount Weymouth	1st Vis. Dudley & Ward	John Bevis
1736/37	**4th Earl Loudoun** φ	1st Vis. Dudley & Ward	John Bevis
1737/38	**2nd Earl Darnley**** φ	1st Vis. Dudley & Ward	John Bevis
1738/39	**Marquess of Carnarvon***	1st Vis. Dudley & Ward	John Bevis
1739/40	**2nd Lord Raymond** φ	1st Vis. Dudley & Ward	John Bevis
1740/41	3rd Earl of Kintore	1st Vis. Dudley & Ward	John Bevis
1741/42	**14th Earl of Morton**	**Martin Clare** φ	John Bevis
1742/44	6th Lord Ward	Sir Robert Lawley	John Bevis

Persona of the Founders

Table 14.2 GRAND WARDENS 1717-1739

year	Senior Grand Warden	Junior Grand Warden
1717	Capt. Joseph Elliot	Jacob Lambell
1718	John Corwell	Thomas Morris
1719	Anthony Sayer P.G.M.	Thomas Morris (until 1720)
1720	Thomas Hobby	Richard Ware
1721	Josias Villeneau	Thomas Morris
1722	Joshua Tinson	Rev. James Anderson
1723	Francis Sorell	**John Senex***
1724	Francis Sorell	George Payne
1725-26	Francis Sorell	George Payne
1726	Col Daniel Houghton	Sir Thomas Prendergast
1727	Alexander Chocke	William Burdon
1728	Nathaniel Blackerby	Joseph Highmore
1729	**Sir John Thornhill**	Martin O'Connor
1730	**George 2nd Lord Carpenter** φ	Thomas Batson
1731	**George Douglas**	James Chambers
1732	George Rooke	James Moore-Smythe
1833	James Moore-Smythe	John Ward 1st Vis. Dudley etc.
1734	John Ward 1st Vis. Dudley etc.	Sir Edward Mansel
1735	Sir Edward Mansel	**Martin Clare***φ
1736	Sir Robert Lawley	**William Graeme***φ
1737-38	Sir Robert Lawley	**William Graeme***φ
1738	Lord George Graham	Andrew Robinson
1739	John Harvey Thursby	Robert Foy

    * Mentioned in the other sources (literature) used in this work, as having made a significant contribution to a particular branch of science, as opposed to say literature, the 'arts' or simple patronage.

    ** (HRH Frederick Lewis – Prince of Wales Initiated – the first direct Royal Blood).

    μ Although historically listed as *FRS*, in the *Masonic Yearbook Historical Supplement* the William Cowper who *was* a Fellow, was the uncle of the William Cowper in the above list – *see below*.

    φ (Authenticity depending on source – only the most recent version of the *Masonic Yearbook Historical Supplement* (2008), acknowledges the *FRS* and although it relies on only one reference source the balance of probability is that they were. – *see main text*.[11]

which made it necessary to investigate his involvement further. This showed that although he appeared not to have held any significant office in the Premier Grand Lodge he was intimately involved with those who had and this relationship was to prove of outstanding importance to this study – *see* the section on individual bibliographies.

References

1. Jacobs, M., *Women and the Enlightenment* (The Haworth Press Inc., New York, 1984), pp. 69-91.
2. Hamill, J.M., 'English Royal Arch Ritual *c.*1780-*c.*1830' *AQC* 95 (1982), pp. 37-54.
3. Stewart, L., *The Rise of Public Science* (CUP, 1992).
4. Fara, P., *Sympathetic Attractions*, (Princeton University Press, New Jersey, USA, 1996).
5. Jacobs, M., *op.cit.*
6. Redwood, J., *Reason, Ridicule and Religion* (Thames & Hudson, 1996).
7. Taton, R., *A General History of Science (1450-1800)*, (Thames and Hudson, London, 1958).
8. Anon. 'The Minutes of the Grand Lodge of Freemasons of England 1723-1725', *QCA* Vol. II. (1913).
9. *Masonic Yearbook Historical Supplement* (2008): Premier GL 1717-1813
10. Schaffer S. Private communication.
11. Clarke, J.R., 'The Royal Society and Early Grand Lodge Freemasonry', *AQC* 80 (1967), pp. 110-117.

Chapter Fifteen:
Bibliographies of the first three Grand Masters: 1717, 1718/21 and 1719

lthough the definition of the Premier Grand Lodge adopted for this Study would exclude the first two Grand Masters, for completeness and to justify their exclusion, as well as helping to develop the argument more fully later, it was considered necessary to reflect upon the personal details and social standing of the first and second Grand Masters as well as that of Desaguliers. This reveals immediately the inherent imbalance of basic information referred to earlier. In addition it exposes another limitation throughout this Section and indeed much else in this study, the difficulty of sieving out that which may be regarded essentially as fact, from a plethora of fiction. Obtaining information on certain aspects has proven to be extraordinarily difficult, especially as the various resources used have clearly relied upon each other, often perpetuating the same intrinsic inaccuracy. Thus discovering more about some of these individual characters was to prove tenuous in the extreme, since the list of references was often quite long, but the reward for having read them through was to find that little new was added or the 'facts' verified, in a way that might have been expected given their titles. However, having made this implied criticism there is little doubt that this biographical section could be undertaken rather better by an expert and dedicated genealogist, but such an undertaking was outside the scope of this study and so the work below is distilled from the efforts of many others and it is hoped fairly so.

The first two Grand Masters would, at least by contemporary standards, have clearly numbered amongst those accorded the title 'gentlemen' (usually Esquire in the Minutes,[1] but in terms of the group of people who were to become involved in the formative years of the Premier Grand Lodge as defined above, they were comparatively ordinary members of society in general and little record appears to have been kept of their lives. What little information there is relates to their Masonic activities and in that sense is somewhat outside the spirit of this study. An attempt was made in various libraries etc. to seek data outside of Masonic literature, but despite considerable enquiry there seems to have been effectively nothing written about them that has survived the passage of time. Indeed, the information given on the first two Grand Masters set out below is largely the result of some painstaking research conducted by two Masonic historians, specifically engaged upon that task. Their work, as no doubt this study will be, is open to criticism, especially with respect to the authenticity of the data and their objectivity/impartiality or rather notable lack of it, on some aspects of the work. The basic biographical details preceding most entries relating to the respective Grand Masters are those compiled by A.R. Hewitt,[2] with certain additions where there has been an obvious need.

Anthony Sayer
(*c*.1672-1742)

Gentleman. 'Invested with the badges of office and power' as first Grand Master, St. John Baptist's Day, 1717. SGW, 1719. Member of Lodge at 'Apple Tree' Tavern (*now* Lodge of Fortitude and Old Cumberland, No. 12)

'Suffered misfortune in later years and was relieved on numerous occasions' ['numerous' – is a term difficult to justify since there only appears to be actual evidence of three]. Became Tyler of the Lodge at the King's Arms (*now* the Old King's Arms Lodge, No. 28).

d.1742, 'aged about 70' and buried in St. Paul's Church, Covent Garden.

The following is essentially a précis of Theodore Beck's Prestonian lecture for 1975: 'Anthony Sayer, Gentleman the truth at last'.[3] By now however we should be somewhat suspicious of any document that purports to expound 'the truth' and that scepticism seems to be well founded here, for other than the actual (no doubt similarly partial) newspaper report of the burial ceremony and the entries of his claims upon charities, little hard evidence exists. Beck is therefore for the most part 'clutching at straws', for whilst his paper presumes to give a true account of Anthony Sayer it relies upon complete supposition, which he is later disposed to call 'fact'. A harsh appraisal of his study might be that it was undertaken to provide him with a vehicle by which he could expound his own philosophy on the development of Freemasonry up until that period. However, since it is probably the best we are likely to find, it should be considered. He contemptuously dismisses the views of an earlier historian, with the following dank praise: (that this earlier historian was) 'a Masonic scholar many years my senior' [*sic*], and whilst acknowledging he was 'older and wiser' he had nonetheless been quite wrong in concluding that: 'that he (Sayer) was a nobody'. Whilst reluctant to express it in such strident words, it will be argued here that, in the overall scheme of things he was indeed a comparative 'nobody'. It is possible that he was a bookseller by profession, since Beck established a tenuous link between him and a family of that same name, closely associated with the area and who were book sellers etc. Certainly at the time of Sayer being elected as Grand Master he must have been a man of some substance and to have been a bookseller was certainly consistent with that requirement. Beck quotes an extract from the *London News* of Saturday 16 January, to Tuesday 19 January, 1742:

Grand Masters: 1717, 1718/21 and 1719

'Buried St Paul's Church Covent Garden. A few days since died, aged about seventy years. Mr Anthony Sayer, who was Grand Master of the most Ancient and Honourable Society of Free and Accepted Masons in 1717. His corpse was followed by a great number of that Honourable Society of the best quality, from the Shakespeare Head Tavern in the Piazza in Covent Garden and decently interid in Covent Garden Church.'[4]

Beck implies from this that even though Sayer by that time was greatly impoverished, he nonetheless retained considerable social status, but there are many modern day examples that would lay challenge to that assumption, where the funerals and commemorations of fallen and/or destitute idols are attended by the good, the great and the powerful, all seemingly compelled to extol the erstwhile merits of the departed, leaving one to wonder, why if the deceased had been so meritorious and they being so rich and powerful, this dire situation should have been allowed to occur in the first place. For what ever reason, by the early 1730s he (Sayer) had become a Tyler and whilst there are of course examples where the Tylers/Janitors of ordinary lodges and chapters have received high acclaim, for the most part they are paid individuals and as such are effectively transparent to some Members of the lodge or chapter concerned.

Beck then spends much time on the mezzotint (a type of metal engraving - usually of copper) copy of Sayer wearing an apron and with the inscription Anthony Sayer, Gent., Grand Master of the Masons. The original has not been found and it is further suggested that the mezzotint had been modified, because there is some evidence to suggest that the original did not have the apron. There is comment that his hands were not 'those of a gentleman', but Beck counters this by saying that there is medical evidence to suggest that he was even at this age stricken with severe arthritis. This could also explain his financial decline if his income had depended upon his physical involvement in printing. But if this were the case it would also show how difficult it would have been for him to keep company with the (emerging) other half of the grouping, there would clearly have been a comparatively high financial burden on any person socialising in such company. Certainly by the early 1720s there is written confirmation of his seeking formal Masonic charity and again later in the 1730s, although it is not clear where the biographer got the words 'numerous occasions' from. Beck makes light of his being charged with 'misconduct' and having to appear before a board of censure; appearing to regard the state of his being deemed to be 'irregular', as somehow that of a mild reprimand. However, given the furore and political ramifications that would have accompanied the exclusion of the first Grand Master, it is more likely that this modest action was more one of expediency than appropriateness. The fact that these accusations were brought to light at all entailed the possible risk that his misdemeanours would be afforded significance.

Beck genealogy is suspect too, since as there appears to be no registration of his birth, or indeed where he was likely born and raised or irrefutable written documentation of his business affairs etc. Thus little of real authority is known of a man, originally of some substance, who had clearly peaked socially for a few years, only to suffer an impecunious and a seemingly ignominious end. Evidence that the onset of his decline had begun already by the late 1720s may be inferred from the description in Mackechnie-Jarvis' paper entitled 'The Grand Stewards'[5] (*see* James Kingston – Lord Kingston, below) of the protocols relating to the Procession formed preceding the Grand Feast in January 1729. It is included because it also helps in our gaining an overall picture, because it is a graphic example of the class structure of the period, but more especially Sayer's perceived position within it:

'... Procession of March, *viz.*

Brother Johnson to clear the way.
Six of the Stewards clothed proper with their Badges and White
Rods, Two in each Chariot.
Brothers without Distinction duly clothed, in Gentlemen's Coaches.
The noble and eminent Brethren duly clothed, in their own Chariots.
Former Grand Officers not noble, clothed proper,
in Gentlemen's Coaches.
Former noble Grand Masters clothed proper, in their own Chariots.
The Secretary alone with his Badge and Bag, clothed, in a Chariot.
The two Grand Wardens clothed proper with their Badges,
in one Chariot.
The D.G. Master alone clothed proper with his Badge, in a Chariot.
Kingston Grand Master clothed proper with his Badge.
Norfolk G.M. Elect clothed only as a Mason,
in one coach.
The Duke of Norfolk's Coach of State Empty

The Stewards halted at Charing-Cross till the messenger brought Orders to move on slowly, and till the Rest follow'd; and when the Grand Master moved from the Square, Brother John Pyne the Marshall made haste to the Hall to conduct the

Procession of entry at the Hall-Gate, *viz.*
The 12 Stewards standing, 6 on each side of the Passage,
with their White Rods, made a Lane.
Brother Johnson to clear the Way.
Former Grand Wardens walk'd one by one according to Juniority.
Former D. Grand Masters walk'd one by one according to Juniority.
Former Grand Masters by Juniority [essentially social?], *viz.*

Lord Colerane, Earl of Inchiquin, Lord Paisley, Duke of Richmond,
Earl of Dalkeith, Duke of Montague, [*sic*] Dr. Desaguliers,

George Payne Esq., and Mr Anthony Sayer. [note not even Esquire] ... etc. etc.[6]

From this one is disposed to the unfortunate conclusion that by 1729 Anthony Sayer had, because his exalted past rank made his exclusion from such ceremonies difficult if not impossible, but in every other sense he had become an embarrassment to the establishment and that his presence was tolerated rather than welcome.

There is suggestion that his misdemeanour may have been that of being involved in the plethora of publications of subversive pamphlets, books etc., that were a characteristic of the time; even to the extent of his being implicated in disclaimers similar to those of Prichard. However, other than timing there is no actual evidence of this and it must therefore, of necessity, be total speculation. It is easy to see where such speculation comes from, since book-sellers were quite often publishers as we shall see in the case of Senex. It is only referred to here to indicate that it would have been considered the kind of offence that would normally have been sufficiently serious to have prompted the hierarchy to bring such an offence by an outwardly 'important' figure into public gaze.

George Payne
(*c.*1677-1757)

Chief Secretary to the Commissioner for Taxes (1743).

Member of the Lodge that met at the 'Horn' Tavern (*now* Royal Somerset House and Inverness Lodge, No. 4): Member of the Old King's Arms Lodge, No. 28 (WM, 1749-50).

Elected Grand Master 24 June 1718. Re-elected for 1720. JGW, 1724.

Compiled the *General Regulations*, 1720 (basis: Anderson's, *Constitutions*, 1723). Member of Committee for revision of *Constitutions*, 1754.

*d.*1757 (buried St Paul's Church, Covent Garden)

The following is extracted from the Notes and Queries Section of the *Transactions* of the *Quatuor Coronati* Lodge.[6] Again it is essentially an account of his Masonic activities and little is known of the man or his actual social standing apart from the fact that he rose to be a senior civil servant and from that one may deduce that he possessed a good education. He was clearly a most active freemason and appears in several senior positions (including the critical time, from *circa* the middle of the 1730s through to the early 1750s, of the machinations of the 'Antients' and the 'Moderns'), right up to very near his death. From the positions he held throughout that time he was presumably held in some esteem, but not necessarily greatly so, since he like Sayer was there, because he was one of those who were involved at the very beginning and it would therefore have been difficult to exclude him.

However, the author of these 'Notes and Queries' dismisses the claim made by Dr Anderson, Sayer's fellow Warden in 1723, that he was 'a learned antiquarian', claiming that he could find no corroborative evidence of that fact. This laudable caution is to be applauded, but in this instance his conclusion is somewhat difficult to understand for two reasons:

1) He challenges Anderson's assertion, but it remains one of the few pieces of contemporaneous information available and written by somebody close to him and asks the question why he would have needed to lie about such an irrelevant matter? Although in fairness a number of Masonic historians challenge Anderson's accuracy in other respects and as we shall see later this is not without some justification.

2) There are instances where a person may have a profound knowledge of a subject, but have nonetheless not felt disposed to set it down or make public issue of it and despite being well respected by his contemporaries his accomplishments were never formally recorded as such. In any case there has been such a loss of documentation of that period, that he may well have lectured or written on the subject and those documents have been lost through the passage of time and so a true assessment of his academic ability remains in abeyance.

Again there was in any case an avid interest in that aspect of learning by many people during this period. Indeed the Masonic records show that in 1724 a notable young scholar (without stating who precisely) of Middle Eastern Languages was initiated and he was likely to have been proposed by someone of similar interest. There was certainly evidence of such interest in the second part of the (English version) 'Mystical Lecture' that preceded the current modified version and of course there is the inference in the 'Historical Lecture' itself.

Thus it would seem that George Payne followed the conventional career of a rather well performing civil servant, advancing by natural, time honoured, progression up through the ranks, although strangely not knighted. He had some social status and was related through his daughters to nobility. It is of interest to note that he succeeded his fellow civil servant colleague and immediate boss (and Grand Warden for 1723), Francis Sorrell in 1743 as Chief Secretary to the Commissioner for Taxes. His sole claim to fame appears to be his involvement in the foundation of the Premier Grand Lodge and subsequent commitment to its salvation and future development. Unfortunately there remains little record of his life, of which the 'Notes and Queries' from which much of the above is gleaned is perhaps the best attempt.

John Theophilus Desaguliers
(1683-1744)

b. 1 March 1683 at La Rochelle, France. Brought by his father to England from Guernsey, 1692.

BA (Oxon.), 1709. *MA*, 1712. *FRS*, 1714. *LLD*, 1718. Lecturer in Experimental Philosophy, Oxford, 1710-13. Holy Orders, 1710.

Moved to London, 1713. Several 'livings' in the Church, first 1710, all prudent, but most notable: Chaplain to Frederick, Prince of Wales, 1727. Author of numerous scientific works.

Member of the Lodges meeting at the 'Rummer and Grapes' (*now* Royal Somerset House and Inverness Lodge, No. 4), at the 'Horn Tavern and at the 'Bear and Harrow' (*now* the St. George's and Corner Stone Lodge, No. 5) and the University Lodge, No. 74. Master of the French Lodge at Solomon's Temple and of the Lodge of Antiquity (*now* No. 2). Acted as Master of Occasional Lodges when eminent persons were to be made freemasons.

Elected Grand Master 24 June 1719. DepGM, 1722-24; 1726.

Instrumental in the reviving (initiating?) the office of Grand Steward in 1728 and in the establishment of the Fund of Charity, 1724-30.

d. 29 February 1744, and buried in the Chapel of the Savoy.

However, it is the thesis of this study that it was the quite remarkable Dr John Desaguliers that had a tremendous influence in the formation of the Premier Grand Lodge and subsequently the Royal Arch. In consequence he is of great significance to this study and it is most important that we have a detailed look into the way in which latter-day historians perceive him. There have been many biographical studies of him, but perhaps the two most notable are those of Hurst in 1928[7] and the more recent by Stewart (regarded by many as the leading authority on the science of Desaguliers).[8] There is little that is contemporaneous and as in all cases, including this study, any assertions made are those of the investigator, no doubt reflecting their degree of sympathy for or disaffection with the man. Whatever those views may be, there can be no doubt that he was an outstanding intellectual and played a pivotal role in a huge range of activities. The problem is that of selecting one source of information, since some of these appraisals must be incorrect, because they tend to conflict with each another. It is therefore necessary to inject a note of caution, because the man was so complex and his career so diverse, as to encourage the notion that his life was one based more upon expediency than conviction. For instance Stewart writes of him 'currying favour in the Court of Queen Anne' [*sic*], by dedicating a poem covering all aspects of popular science, entitled – 'Newtonian Systems of the World'. This reference is a little worrying, since although this important poem in our story (*see* Appendix 1) was written many years before, it was not published until 1726. It is clear that at that time Desaguliers dedicated the poem to George II and Queen Caroline, but if Stewart is right and given that Queen Anne died in 1714, it would, for political impact, have needed to be written well before that; a very flexible poem indeed! His dedication and true conviction to Freemasonry is illustrated when Stewart refers to Desaguliers' closing years; noting that although by then he was plagued with ill health, speaks of his retained enthusiasm for his 'beloved Freemasonry'. Indeed, he and the circumstances of the society in which he worked is considered so important to the setting up and content of the Royal Arch and following some discussion with Larry Stewart he graciously allowed the following passage to be taken directly from his book:[9]

'The career of John Theophilus Desaguliers straddles the realms of landowners and industrialists. A son of the Huguenot Diaspora, educated by his clergyman father, who opened a school in Islington, near London, Desaguliers went up to Oxford, where he came under the influence of John Keill. Too much the product of the Protestant cause to be affected by the High-Tory cant of Christ Church, Desaguliers had no truck with the Oxford Jacobitism of the latter part of Queen Anne's reign. His sentiments were entirely with the supporters of the Hanoverian Succession. Desaguliers took deacon's orders from Henry Compton, the Bishop of London, in 1710, although he remained at Oxford until his marriage in 1712. His added responsibilities caused him to loosen the bounds that tied him to an academic life and he risked all in the rage for natural philosophy in London. His move into the metropolis was a dramatic change in the direction of his life and it was here that Desaguliers faced the dialectic that reshaped British Society.

As a lecturer, Desaguliers was enormously successful, a remarkable feat when one considers how many attempted to secure at least part of their livelihood from the practice. Of course, like John Harris, with whom he collaborated from time to time, Desaguliers was also a clergyman and even a small living promised to provide for body and soul. But the last thing Desaguliers wanted was to be expected to provide much in the way of religious service. He understood, as Harris had also recognized, that patronage was the predecessor of religious preferment. Indeed, it is conceivable that Desaguliers' presentation in 1717 to the living of Bridgeham in Norfolk in the gift of William Lord Cowper, then Lord Chancellor, was the result of his association with Harris, whom Cowper had long patronized. By far the most important of his clerical appointment, however, came from the largess of James Brydges, *FRS*, later the Duke of Chandos, who, as Earl of Carnarvon, appointed Desaguliers his personal chaplain in 1716. This made a great deal of sense for Brydges, who had an extensive interest in the affairs of the Royal Society and an increasing passion for things mechanical, especially if they might turn a profit. In 1718, Desaguliers obtained his *LLD* from Cambridge, seemingly indicating a hope for further ecclesiastical advancement. He was rewarded in 1719 when Brydges appointed Desaguliers rector of Whitchurch or Stanmore Parva in Middlesex. By this point, it must have become obvious that it was not the religious employment that interested Brydges, who was convinced Desaguliers was "certainly the best Mechanik in Europe". Like Hooke before him, Desaguliers' contemporary reputation was made not so much as a curator of experiments, but upon his mechanical skill.

We cannot now be certain why Desaguliers originally commended himself to James Brydges, although by 1716, the philosopher had made himself useful in the presentation of experiments before the Royal Society. In the summer of 1714, when he was elevated a Fellow as a protégé of Keill, Desaguliers had reproduced experiments to verify Newton's theory of colors and since then had obtained some income from the Society as had his predecessor Francis Hauksbee. In November 1716, shortly after Brydges had appointed him chaplain, Desaguliers was once again making important experiments at the request of Newton. Clearly, by 1716, Desaguliers was a man of increasing reputation. But he was employed by Brydges not in the making of crucial experiments and only marginally in his function as a clergyman.

Understanding where Desaguliers fit into the rush to the improving spirit is best obtained by seeing where his patron stood at the end of the seventeenth century. By 1694 Brydges was a Fellow of the Royal Society and in 1698, elected *MP* for Hereford, a promising and ambitious descendant of both the landed gentry and the merchant class. The brief diary of his early years in London from 1697 to 1702 reveals the range and convergence of his interests. Here he followed quite literally in the path of Hooke. He often dined with the Royal Society at Pontack's in Abchurch Lane between visits to Garraway's Coffee House in Exchange Alley to follow the progress of stocks before proceeding to the meetings of

The Key to Modern Freemasonry

the Society in Gresham College with Hans Sloane or Dr Hugh Chamberlen's land bank scheme, which was only one of the variety of financial fancies that he experienced during his lifetime. It was into this World that John Theophilus Desaguliers was soon drawn. There would emerge a history of much greed and just as much skulduggery as financial imaginations could devise.

From time to time, Desaguliers had need to set his course through Brydges' tangle of mechanics and finance. By 1717, Desaguliers was lecturing before the Royal Society on the breadth of the experimental program, from electricity and the barometer to improvements in the Savery engine. At this point ...'.[10]

Stewart's analysis continues to illustrate Desaguliers' increasing interest in what we would now consider technology and as the 1720s progressed its commercial implications, especially with the hydraulics associated with the transfer of potable water into the heart of London. But unlike modern technologists he was employed as an unquestionable expert in a wide range of disciplines. Such was the intensity of the commercial/political/legal (worsening: especially in his own case) implications of these projects that they could not fail to be a major distraction for him and divert his attention from what one may describe as pure science. Indeed he featured in the Press as being the source of a certain (conceivably true) impropriety and to add to his social discomfort, by the middle of the 1720s Desaguliers was plagued by severe gout.

Stewart does not mention (except as stated above and then only in passing when referring to his later years) Desaguliers' involvement with Freemasonry, but anyone who has experience of the setting up and running of even a much lesser society will acknowledge that the work is incredibly time consuming and one can only wonder at his peculiar social skills and abounding industry.

Much has been written on this extraordinary man, but during the course of trying to find information with respect to some of the more obscure Fellows of the Royal Society in our list, the following snippet was chanced upon whilst working through the Royal Society Minute ('Reports') Book *circa* November 1725 on quite another matter. The item in these (erstwhile) minutes was a short account of a talk given by 'Dr Desaguliers' at that meeting, in which he claimed that the discovery of the 'telescope' must have dated from a time very much earlier than that believed hitherto. The Secretary noted that Dr Desaguliers explained to the Royal society that he was able to make this claim as a result of discoveries made whilst researching another matter. In the course of his studies on fifteenth Century theology he had come upon works of a contemporary theologian, who had been writing a treatise on the 'Book of Revelations'. This cleric had proposed that the Devil was observing the world through a telescope and whilst Desaguliers expressed some scepticism about the involvement of the Devil in this way, the fact that the cleric had indicated his total awareness of such an invention and of its function, proved its prior existence

Grand Masters: 1717, 1718/21 and 1719

and he therefore deemed this to be a matter of some 'considerable interest' to the members. The Secretary readily agreed and was effusive in the way he acknowledged the gratitude of the Society for this snippet of information. So important is John Theophilus Desaguliers to our study that he will be returned to over and over again, but as we shall see his disposition to write and dedicate poetry proves to be one of his most revealing traits – *see* Appendix 1. Further insights into his engineering and scientific activities may be found in references below.[11, 12, 13]

Desaguliers represented the last of those who had come up from the ranks to occupy the office of Grand Master. The process can be expressed in physical terms as three quantum leaps: from immigrant, workaday speculative freemason to Grand Master and as a Grand Master of exceptional talent to have the acumen, foresight and political ability to put men of wealth and power into office. This third tier has remained intact (except for a minor hiccup of an erstwhile 'Walpolean' commoner Grand Master, Robert Raymond, GM, 1739-40) up until the present day. John Montagu(e) was the first in this almost three hundred year long list of men who have been part of the essential social engineering component within modern Freemasonry. Sadly, however, there appears to be no actual information on the fourth member of this interesting group.

References

1. Hewitt, A.R., 'Biographical Lists of the Grand Masters' in *Grand Lodge 1717-1967* (OUP, 1967), pp. 265-279.

2. *Ibid.*

3. Beck, T., *Anthony Sayer, Gentleman the Truth at Last* (UGLE, Prestonian Lecture, 1975).

4. *Ibid.*

5. Mackechnie-Jarvis, C., *Grand Stewards 1728-1978* (UGLE, Prestonian Lecture, 1978).

6. Anon. 'The Minutes of the Grand Lodge of Freemasons of England 1723-1729', *QCA* II (1913).

7. Hurst, W., 'An outline of the career of J.T. Desaguliers. Private Communication between himself and J. Clarke' (1928).

8. Stewart, L., *The Rise of Public Science* (CUP, 1992).

9. *Ibid.*

10. *Ibid.*

11. Stewart, L., *DESAGULIERS, John Theophilus, FRS, A Biographical Dictionary of Civil Engineers of Great Britain and Ireland 1500-1850*, Vol. 1. (Inst. Civil Engineers, London, 2001).

12. Anon. 'Desaguliers' in *Dictionary of Scientific Biography*, Vol. IV (Charles Scribner's Sons, New York, 1974), pp. 43-45.

5. Lawrence, C.C., 'Hell-Fire or Applied Science: The Origins and Personalities of Two Men and their Impact on the Hierarchal Structure and Ethos of the Premier Grand Lodge and Its Present Day Legacy', *Transactions of The Leicester Lodge of Research No. 2429 (EC)*, (2010-11), pp. 31-64.

Chapter Sixteen: Grand Masters 1720–1724
House (Dukes) of Montagu

his family name is very old and was first attested by Queen Maude in 1148 and was associated with the monastic lands at Montacute in Somerset. It suffered, as did most others, with certain breaks in its direct descendants. However the Montagues of the Premier Grand Lodge came from the largesse of King James. Indeed the Duke of Manchester and the Earl of Sandwich (who were intimately connected) came about at the same time. Thus this family which appears to come from ancient stock were in practice less than 100 years old by the time of Grand Lodge.[1, 2]

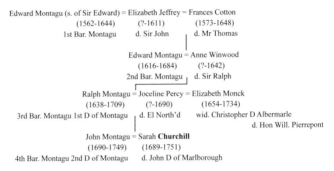

```
Edward Montagu (s. of Sir Edward) = Elizabeth Jeffrey = Frances Cotton
        (1562-1644)                   (?-1611)          (1573-1648)
        1st Bar. Montagu          d. Sir John        d. Mr Thomas

                        Edward Montagu = Anne Winwood
                           (1616-1684)     (?-1642)
                         2nd Bar. Montagu  d. Sir Ralph

        Ralph Montagu = Joceline Percy = Elizabeth Monck
          (1638-1709)     (?-1690)         (1654-1734)
 3rd Bar. Montagu 1st D of Montagu  d. El North'd   wid. Christopher D Albermarle
                                                    d. Hon Will. Pierrepont

             John Montagu = Sarah Churchill
              (1690-1749)    (1689-1751)
 4th Bar. Montagu 2nd D of Montagu   d. John D of Marlborough
```

John Montagu, 2nd Duke of Montagu
(1690-1749)

b. 29 March 1690. Lord High Constable, 1714. Lord Lieut., Northamptonshire and Warwickshire, 1715. *FRS*, 1718. *KG*, 1718. *FSA*, 1725. *KB*, and First Grand Master of that Order, 1725. *PC*, 1736. General, 1746.

Member of the Lodge at the 'Bear and Harrow', 1720 (*now* St. George's and Corner Stone Lodge, No. 5)

Grand Master, 1721. Ordered preparation of the first *Book of Constitutions*.

d. 6 July 1749 Dukedom became extinct.

It is the thesis of this study that the appointment of the second Duke of Montagu was the first watershed of Freemasonry in its present form and was cemented in place very shortly afterwards by the unusual selection of the Earl of Richmond (not that in Surrey or Yorkshire, but Ireland) in 1724. With the truly remarkable Philip, Duke of Wharton, sandwiched in between. Punctuated, as it were, by the comparatively (only by their standards) innocuous Francis, Duke of Buccleuch. Because of their undoubted influence the first four of the aristocratic (effectively now mandatory) appointees will be considered as a unit.

Grand Masters 1720-1724

Thus in the story of Premier Grand Lodge and the Royal Arch the Montagus are of especial interest, since within the Family there were those who were extremely involved in actual science, but more important they were also acutely aware of the potential wealth that might derive from its exploitation. They were in the forefront of entrepreneurial activity, both at home and abroad, well disposed to patronise men of scientific and/or technological learning and some even became members of the Royal Society. Although today there is now considerable deference to academic (scientific in our case) ability, the terms of entry into the Royal Society are only marginally less political today than they were then. Charles Montagu for instance was a benefactor of Isaac Newton (the President when John Desaguliers was appointed) no less. He (Charles) became president of the Royal Society in 1695, whilst at the same time being Chancellor of the Exchequer. John Montagu, the Second Duke of Montagu was the 5th Grand Master and Anthony Browne, the 6th Viscount Montagu, was its 16th.

However, perhaps a good place to start is with Edward Montagu who was born in 1602. After leaving Cambridge he went to Spain in 1623 with the then Prince Charles and in keeping with many of those who gained favour with Charles, he was made a Baron (of Kimbolton, in his case) in 1626. He later changed sides and joined, indeed fought with, the Parliamentarians, but was later removed from his military post after much wrangling with Cromwell. He was none-the-less given the post of Lord Chamberlain as a 'sop' to the Presbyterians and as such was representative of the pattern set by the Montagu dynasty over the next century and more. Other interesting examples were: one year after the formation of Premier Grand Lodge John Montagu was born, later to become the 4th Earl of Sandwich of tea-time fame. Edward born 1625 was to become an admiral, politician and ambassador. Charles (1st Earl of Halifax) born 1661, went to Cambridge, was a poet of note, MP, made Lord of the Treasury in 1692, created the first National Debt, responsible for imposition of the 'window tax', twice (unsuccessfully) impeached and following Queen Anne's death was made an Earl by King George I and became Prime Minister and much else besides, dying in 1715. Thus by any standards this must be regarded as a remarkable family. However, from this remarkable family we are primarily concerned with John Montagu, the second Duke of Montagu (1690-1749); his mother dying barely six months later. Whatever his title may have been at birth it is not given in the *CPE* the primary source of reference used throughout when referring to the aristocracy, but he became Viscount Monthermer on the death of his older brother in 1705. In that same year his father was elevated to the Dukedom and he became the second Duke on the death of his father in 1709.

He was related by marriage to the royal family through the daughter (who herself was a widow of the earl of Northumberland) of Charles II, the first of the three lines of his (illegitimate: over thirty is suggested by some historians, but only fourteen were

The Key to Modern Freemasonry

actually acknowledged by Charles II) children; namely the Earl of Southampton. In 1709 he succeeded his father and became the 2nd Duke of Montagu. He officiated as high constable at the Coronation of George I, who made him a Colonel of the Horse Guards. In 1717 he asked to become and as a result, was admitted a fellow of the Royal College of Physicians. To his credit he did actually attend many of their lectures and dinners and refrained from practising on patients. In 1722 George I granted him the West Indian islands of St Lucia and St Vincent and he sent out seven ships with settlers. However, it turned out to be a poisoned chalice, since the British Navy (funded rather differently in those days) would not offer assistance and the islands were eventually conceded to the French; not before it had cost him an estimated £40,000 pounds, a staggering amount in those days. Throughout his life he undertook many royal and military appointments and clearly loved ceremonial (he carried the sceptre and cross at George the Second's Coronation). He died of a 'violent fever' in 1749, but because of the lack of a surviving male issue, the dukedom became extinct.

He was obviously a man of considerable ability, with seemingly the sense of humour of the practical joker and was known to be involved in a number of high profile hoaxes. His mother-in-law wrote of him 'All my son-in-law's talents lie in things natural to boys of fifteen, and he is above two and fifty'. However, his importance to this study is his considerable (personal practical/economic) interest in science (Fellow of the Royal Society) and as a result his patronage of the scientific talent of others. His social/political drive coupled with his love of ceremony and involvement with Freemasonry.

House of Wharton

The notable history of this family appears to be as a result of Thomas Warton's military prowess against the Scotts, for which he was first knighted and then given the Baronetcy. Other than that he succeeded his father Thomas Wharton of Nateby, the history is quite vague before this time.[3, 4]

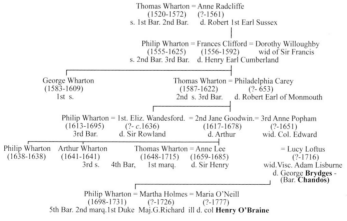

```
                    Thomas Wharton = Anne Radcliffe
                     (1520-1572)     (?-1561)
                    s. 1st Bar. 2nd Bar.   d. Robert 1st Earl Sussex
                                   |
                    Philip Wharton = Frances Clifford = Dorothy Willoughby
                     (1555-1625)      (1556-1592)      wid of Sir Francis
                    s. 2nd Bar. 3rd Bar.    d. Henry Earl Cumberland
              ┌─────────────────────────────────────────┐
      George Wharton                        Thomas Wharton = Philadelphia Carey
      (1583-1609)                            (1587-1622)      (?- 653)
        1st s.                              2nd s. 3rd Bar.    d. Robert Earl of Monmouth
                                          ┌─────────────────┐
         Philip Wharton = 1st. Eliz. Wandesford. = 2nd Jane Goodwin.= 3rd Anne Popham
          (1613-1695)      (?- c.1636)             (1617-1678)         (?-1651)
           3rd Bar.       d. Sir Rowland           d. Arthur         wid. Col. Edward
  ┌──────────────┬──────────────┬───────────────────┐
Philip Wharton  Arthur Wharton   Thomas Wharton = Anne Lee              = Lucy Loftus
(1638-1638)     (1641-1641)       (1648-1715)   (1659-1685)              (?-1716)
                  3rd s.    4th Bar,  1st marq.   d. Sir Henry         wid.Visc. Adam Lisburne
                                                                      d. George Brydges -
                                                                        (Bar. Chandos)
            ┌────────────────────────────────────────┐
      Philip Wharton = Martha Holmes = Maria O'Neill
       (1698-1731)      (?-1726)       (?-1777)
      5th Bar. 2nd marq.1st Duke Maj.G.Richard ill d. col Henry O'Braine
```

(Note: Thomas Wharton's Chandos/Brydges connection)

188

Philip Wharton, Duke of Wharton
(1698-1731)

*b. c.*21 December 1698. Viscount Winchendon, later Marquis of Wharton. Created Duke of Wharton in 1718. Died – by his (and perhaps by most, given his antecedents) standards penniless – (in the Spanish Cistercian Monastery of Poblet) 31 May 1731.

Initiated 1721. Grand Master 1722. RWM, Lodge meeting at the 'King's Arms', St. Paul's, 1725.

Anderson sets out in his *Constitutions* (1723), the method of constituting a lodge; as practis'd by his Grace the Duke of Wharton. '... according to the ancient Usage's of Masons'.

Credited with having established the first foreign lodge (Under the English system), at Madrid, in 1728.

Espoused the Jacobite cause and, in consequence, was outlawed. He fought for the Spanish against the British at Gibraltar, in which battle he was wounded.

d. 31 May 1731 in the Cistercian Monastery, Poblet, Catalonia, and was buried there.

In Masonic Ritual there is an expression 'one of the brightest characters recorded in the Annals of Freemasonry', if the adjective 'brightest' were replaced by 'colourful' then most certainly he would have been the favourite, for his career is truly remarkable. It is difficult to imagine how he could have begun better (or worse), since those sponsoring him at his christening were William III, Shrewsbury and Princess Anne. From 1709 (aged ten) to 1715 he adopted the title Viscount Winchendon. 'Worse' because of the example set by his father, for whilst he was a brilliant politician he was at the same time an unfortunate example to his son as is pointed out by Gila Curtis in her book on Queen Anne:

> 'Anne most detested, and who distorted her judgement of the other three [of the Junto – there were actually five with Lord Sunderland],[6] and of the whole Whig party. Lord Tom Wharton, "bluff, blasphemous and randy", was one of the most colourful personalities of the age, an extraordinary mixture "of the very best and very worst". As a politician his mastery of electioneering was equalled by none, and he was one of the very few members of either House who would never bend his political principles to gain favour or office. Yet in his private life Wharton was flagrantly immoral, a foul mouthed atheist who had once, it was rumoured, defecated in a church pulpit, and was one of the greatest rakes of the day ...'[7]

Philip received sound (personal) tutelage at home, under the strict observation of his father (euphemistically nicknamed 'honest Tom') who was keen to transmit his political, pure Whig, views to his son and inadvertently much else. Whilst in the event his father may have failed somewhat in his main objective, he transmitted his inherent deviousness to perfection. For example when just sixteen Philip married secretly (up until this unhappy event, his father had considered his son's marriage to be a major strategical weapon in the armoury of his own ambition) the daughter of Major-general Richard Holmes. It would seem that she was a most worthy person, of 'extraordinary education' and although he abandoned her shortly after their marriage, she appears to have behaved with great dignity, right up to her death in 1726.

In 1715 both his mother and father died and their joint legacy (comprised in part by that portion of his father's estate he could not prevent Phillip inheriting) which amounted to not inconsiderable sum of £14,000 per year, plus considerable property.

In 1716, in conformance with his father's wishes he set out for Geneva with a Huguenot governor to continue a strict Protestant education. Unfortunately their route took them via the Dutch and German Courts, in which he dallied and had very soon exceeded his allowance by a considerable amount. He neither liked the restraint imposed by his governor, nor those he found in Geneva and on the pretext of avoiding possible infection, abandoned both and left for Lyons. Here he wrote a letter together with a very fine present to the Pretender, who was then living in Avignon. James responded by inviting him to his court and it is alleged offered, in recognition of Wharton's promised support, the title of the Duke of Northumberland once he (the Pretender) had been restored to the Throne. Therein began a remarkable catalogue of intrigue; and if the biographers are right and they would appear to be substantially so, promised loyalty to both sides, depending on where he was and with whom he was dealing at the time; especially the colour of their money. Receiving money on the behalf of one cause, he returned, in 1717, to Ireland to espouse another and although just nineteen, was assimilated into the Irish House of Peers as the Marquis of Catherlough. He was most talented in this role and was soon the chairman of important committees. In which capacity he extended the Committee's congratulations to George I on 'a happy increase in the Royal Family'. Very soon after, the Whigs, in order to capitalise such unique skills, engineered that he now be created the Duke of Wharton and Westmorland. Historically Charles II had bestowed a number of Dukedoms on his illegitimate offspring whilst they were still children; this in its own way was equally remarkable, not least the absence of the extravagant plaudits normally given to justify the conferment of the honour.

For the next two years he appears to have behaved with unusual propriety, returning to his wife in 1718, who produced a son, who unfortunately died shortly afterwards from smallpox. He successfully reinvigorated his father's stud farm. He was introduced (in opposition) to the House of Lords. In 1720 he debated fiercely the extension to the South-Sea Company's Charter; prophetically it would seem, since it was later to become the principal component in the downfall of many, including to a large degree his own. He became a public moraliser, but at the same time became president of the 'Hell-Fire Club', which was ordered to be suppressed by the King in 1721.[8] In response he declared in the House of Lords that he was not blasphemous and in proof of his piety, quoted various texts from his family bible by way of demonstration. This overt parliamentary activity appeared to come to an end in 1723, but he remained in England for a further three years.

Later that year he founded the bi-weekly and strongly anti-establishment opposition paper *The True Britain*, but by then things were going awfully wrong for him personally and the paper stopped at issue number 74. Shortly afterwards his creditors moved in, causing his property to be placed under trustees and his allowance reduced to £1,200 per year. He had by that time already lost an enormous amount (£120,000 plus) in the South Sea Bubble. He continued to sell parts of his estates, but still the problems would not go away and by 1726 he was reputed to have had debts of £70,000. His strategy of selling paintings and property continued, most notably in the sale of his Westmorland estate in 1730.

He had by that time (*circa* winter 1725/26) left for Vienna, openly adopting the cause of James III, from whom he received the Garter and his patent: the Duke of Northumberland. From Vienna he went to Madrid. If the biographers are to be believed, his conduct as an ambassador proved to be far from perfect. He was reputed to be 'perpetually drunk and scarcely ever had a pipe out of his mouth', etc.

Within two months of learning of the death of his first wife in 1726, he married a Maria O'Neill, the daughter of an Irish colonel Henry O'Briane (a name we shall meet elsewhere in connection with the Earl of Inchiquin and various other marriages) in the Spanish service, by Henrietta O'Neill, a maid of honour to the Queen of Spain, who was less than disposed to the match, but relented after he became a Catholic.

He appeared to have treated communications from England with contempt, preferring to become active in an attempt to restore the Pretender, via a liaison between Russia and Spain. He went to Rome in 1726, but behaved with complete impropriety and to avoid scandal was forced back to Spain. In the spring of 1727 he asked the King of Spain to be part of the siege of Gibraltar and was appointed aide-de-camp to the *Conde de los Torres*. For this he was indicted for treason and outlawed by the House of Lords in 1729. He was wounded in the foot and was rewarded for his part in the affair with the rank of 'Colonel Aggregate' in an Irish Regiment that was in the Spanish Service. It would appear that his defection had begun earlier, after his visit to Rome where he had attempted to build bridges with the English, but this having proved unsuccessful, adopted the counter strategy. His last three years:

> '....were spent in rambling about Europe in a state of beggary, drunkenness and almost complete destitution. Such doles as he received from the Pretender were at once absorbed either in new acts of dissipation or by a clamour by a rabble of creditors'.[5]

During 1729 he did try to live on his colonel's pay of 18 *pistoles* per month, but it proved woefully insufficient for his needs. That coupled with the humiliation heaped upon him by the governor of Catalonia and the nature of his previous lifestyle, caused his health to deteriorate rapidly and in 1731 he died aged thirty-two. His widow returned to England and managed to survive on a small Spanish pension, living for a further forty-six years.

Those who have written of the man and there are many, whilst acknowledging his political adroitness, for the most part, appear to have very little good to say of him. They attach little regard to any of his (limited) written work, brand him an arrant coward and traitor, with 'a dominant characteristic of puerile malice', which they evidenced by recounting the occasion where he wantonly smashed windows at the Paris embassy or his placing of a 'libellous caricature of the Pope in the hands of Lady Wortley (or his term 'Worldly') Montagu', again a family name with which we are now becoming familiar, it is interesting to reflect whether those epithets would be applied so strictly in today's society.

Of course other than the historical detail of fact, these again are the views of individual historians and biographers and whilst we must temper our view with that in mind, the overall impression is not very encouraging and one is left with a decidedly uncomfortable view of the man. Our attention, or perhaps difficulty, will be in coming to grips with that part of his history which biographers outside of Freemasonry have not acknowledged: namely his meteoric rise (Initiated 1721, appointed Grand Master 1722) to the highest Masonic Office at the age of twenty-three.[9] Comparable acceleration is not unknown, even in more recent times, but he was the first to do so and in his case, he was so very young – except for the case of Edward, 2nd Earl of Darnley, who was made Grand Master in 1737; then just twenty-two. However, Edward Bligh was nowhere near so colourful or assertive and was likely 'engineered' into the post by others for political reasons, whereas Wharton was most certainly 'his own man' – *see* later discussion on the election of Grand Master in 1724. There is an interesting book by Blackett-Ord on the Duke of Wharton in which he reflects on the dubious dealings of the Duke with respect to Freemasonry, but his research seems a little thin and suspect in that particular area.[10]

Grand Masters 1720-1724

House of Buccleuch (Baronetcy/Earldom/Dukedom)

The history of this family is quite obscure prior to this period other than that they were of significance. The first Baron was the son of Sir Walter Scott (the famous writer is of this family, but much later). The title appears to have been granted for various military activities.[11, 12]

```
                        Walter Scott = Magaret Ker
                        (1565-1611)    (?)
                        1st Bar.       d. Sir William

                        Walter Scott = Mary Hay
                        (?-1633)       (?-1631)
          s. 1st Bar. 2nd Bar, 1st Earl    d. Francis Earl of Errol

  Walter Scott     Francis Scott = Margaret Leslie (née Erskine)        Walter Scott
  (1625-1629)      (1626-1651)     (?-1688)                             (1648-1650)
                   3rd Bar, 2nd Earl  wid. Alexander Ld. Balgonie
                                   (d. of Rothes/Earl of Mar)

                        Mary Scott = Walter Scott (House of Highchester – Mary then 11)
                        (1647-1661)  (1644-1693)
                                     4th Bar, 3rd Earl  s. Earl  Tarras

                 Anne Scott = James Scott (Anne then 12 - orig Crofts = Charles Cornwallis
                 (1651-1731)  (1649-ex1685)           (d.of Monmouth)   (1655-1693)
                              5th Bar, 4th Earl                         s. Bar, Cornwallis
                              1st Duke, ill s. Charles II , titles forfeited
```

Although titles were forfeited their son James continued to hold the title of Earl Doncaster/Dalkeith. The Francis with whom we are concerned was that James' son, to whose son the title Duke of Buccleuch was restored by act of Parliament in 1732 well after he had been G. Master.

```
  Charles Scott       James Scott = Henrietta Hyde
  (1672-1673)         (1674-1704)   (1677-1730)
  Earl Doncaster      Earl Doncaster/Dalkeith   d. Laurence Earl of Rochester

  (g. son Anne/James above) Francis Scott = Caroline Campbell      = Alice Powell (washerwoman ?)
                            (1695-1751)     (?-1729)                 (1697-1765)
                            6th Bar, 5th Earl, 2nd Duke  d. John D. of Argyle   d. Joseph Powell
```

Francis Scott: 2nd Duke of Buccleuch
(1695-1751)

b. 11 Jan 1695. Francis Scott *styled* Earl of Dalkeith, (his mother preferred the style Lord Whitchester), inherited the title 2nd Duke of Buccleuch on his father's death (1732). *FRS* [1724], *KT* [1725], d. 22 April 1751

Date of Initiation, unknown, but was a member of a lodge held at the Rummer and Grapes Tavern (Master 1722). Nominated (*in absentia*) GM on 24 June 1723.

Clearly Francis Scott the 2nd Duke of Buccleuch was of aristocratic stock, but for the purposes of this study it is of some value to consider his antecedents. Lady Anne Scott was the third and youngest daughter of Francis the Earl of Buccleuch. She attained that title by marrying James Scott, Duke of Monmouth, the natural son of Charles II. She had numerous titles of which one was Duchess of Buccleuch.

After her husband's execution she discretely conceded (traded) these various titles in order that she might retain her Scottish entitlements as Duchess of Buccleuch and Lady Whitchester. In 1688 she was married to Charles, 3rd Lord Cornwallis, a name not unfamiliar to present-day long-serving freemasons, since Lord Cornwallis has been a constant name on the toast list. Her second eldest son of the previous marriage: James Earl of Dalkeith married Lady Henrietta Hyde, the second daughter of Laurence, Earl of Rochester, one of Charles II's more notorious courtiers. To them, in 1695, was born Francis, styled, until his father's death, Earl of Dalkeith, at which time he assumed the title of Duke of Buccleuch.

Much of what follows has to be both conjecture as well as fact for, despite a prearranged marriage to Lady Jane Douglas which would have resulted in uniting two powerful dukedoms, this never took place and there is still speculation as to why. Later he *did* marry Lady Jane Douglas of Queensbury, second daughter of the Duke of Queensbury, by whom he had two sons and three daughters, a marriage seemingly approved by his grandmother.

Despite the fact that he was of Stuart Blood, outwardly at least he remained faithful to the Protestant cause and the Hanoverian Government; a factor that no doubt influenced the eventual restoration of the former family titles. He appeared to take a responsible role in the management of affairs:

> 'So far, save for the last suggestion (there was reference here to the alleged earlier jilting) and his marrying Alice Powell in 1742, (a Windsor washerwoman no less), there has been nothing to mar a portrait of a typical British *grand seigneur* as depicted, with perhaps a touch of pomposity, in the portrait shown herein, but there may have been another side of the picture. In 1757 was born to the third Earl of Bath, later the famous Prime Minister of George III, a daughter Lady Louisa Stuart.'

He informs us that she became a most respected author and in a privately funded publication on the Argyle Family, she recounted the Granddaughter's view of her father Francis. Lady Louisa writes the following:

> 'The Buccleuch family had rested in comparative obscurity for two or three generations past. However inclined King William had appeared to favour the unfortunate Duke of Monmouth, yet a direct attempt to claim the Crown was a fact to be jealously remembered by its successive wearers: and, so far from reversing his attainder and restoring his favours, as was done in other classes (for instance the Argyles themselves), William hastened to bestow the title elsewhere, creating Lord Mordaunt Earl of Monmouth. The Duchess presently married a second husband, Lord Cornwallis, who had his own interests in mind. Lord Dalkeith, the eldest son, died in her lifetime, at thirty years old; and her

grandson, now Duke of Buccleuch, a man of mean understanding and meaner habits, did no credit to his ancestry. In his youth a match was settled between him and your grandmother, Lady Jane Douglas (again reference to the jilting affair), but was broken off, and her brother the Duke of Douglas, fought a duel with him in consequence. Supposing the story true which was current at the time, that she owed the Duke of Buccleuch her repugnance, and, throwing herself on his honour, desired to be screened from the anger of her relations, this duel would seem to donate something chivalrous on his part, arguing better things than ensued. He married another Lady Jane Douglas, the Duke of Queensbury's sister; but, after her death, which happened in a few years, plunged into such low amours, and lived so entirely with the lowest company, that although he resided constantly in the neighbourhood of London, his person was scarcely known to his equals, and his character fell into utter contempt'.

If, as will be discussed later, the political ramifications within the hierarchy of Freemasonry during this period are as they are reputed to have been, or inferred, then these observations are truly remarkable. However, the author of the paper,[13] from which the above extract is taken, after pointing out other mitigating factors, does imply that he may have had a somewhat different personality and invites the reader to make their own judgement and that seems an eminently reasonable stance to take.

Ȟouse of Richmond

This family line descending from the only illegitimate son of Henry VIII as a result of his liaison with Eliz. Blount the maid of honour to queen Catherine, only to be repeated in the reign of Charles II. However, there is a further connection stemming from Esmé Stuart (6th Seigneur D' Aubigny in France) whose father was related to the Earl of Lennox. James I indulging his seeming passion to increase the aristocracy eventually created him Duke of Lennox, earl of Darnley etc. *see below*:[14]

Henry Fitzroy = Mary Howard
(1519-1536)   (?-1557)
s. Henry VIII. 1st Duke of Richmond   d. Thomas Howard D. of Norfolk

Title became extinct when the titles were re-conferred upon the Scottish nobility (Esmé) associated with James VI (Scot) and I (England)

Esmé Lennox = Katherine De Balsac
(1542-1583)   (*c.*1550-1632) very aged
XIV Earl. 1st Duke of Lennox   d. Guillaume

Ludovic Stuart   James Stuart
(1574-1623)   (1612-1623)
XV Earl, 2nd Duke of Lennox   XVI Earl, 3rd Duke of Lennox
Duke of Richmond etc.   later Duke of Darnley

Again the titles became extinct, but were reinstated when a title was required for one of the illegitimate sons of Charles II and Louise Renée De Penacoet.

Charles Lennox = Anne Belayse
(1672-1723)   (?-1722)
ill s. Charles II. Earl Darnley/March, 4th Duke of Richmond/Lennox   widow of Henry. d. Francis Brundenell
(unexplained: claimed to be G. Master Freemasons 1696/97)

Charles Lennox = Sarah Cadogan
(1701-1750)   (1706-1751)
5th Duke of Richmond/Lennox   d. William Earl Cadogan

Charles Lennox: 2nd Duke of Richmond
(1701-1750)

b. 2 May 1701. *FRS* [1724], *KB* [1725], *KG* [1726], *FRCP* [1728]. *LL.D* [Camb, 1728], *FSA* [1736], (President, 1749-50).

MP [1722-23], *ADC* to HM the King [1724-32], Lord High Constable for the Coronation of George III [1727], Elder Brother of Trinity House [1737], (Master, 1741-5). Master of the Horse [1735], *PC* [1735], Succeeded as Duke of Aubigny, France, and to the Seignory of Aubigny [1734], Ambassador to France [1748-49].

Captain Royal Horse Guards [1722], Brig.-Gen. [1739], Maj.-Gen. [1742], Gen. [1745], *later* [1750], CO.

RWM of the Lodge at the 'Horn' Tavern (*now* The Royal Somerset House and Inverness Lodge, No. 4), 1724. GM, 1724; at the end of his term of office was continued therein for a further six months. Established a Lodge at Chateau d'Aubigny, 1735.

He was the only son of Charles Lenox (Duke of Richmond), who in turn was the natural son of Charles II and (his mother) Louise de Kerouale the Duchess of Portsmouth. He (Francis' father) appears in his time to have been as duplicitous as Philip the 2nd Duke of Warton discussed above. Francis was the only son of Charles Lennox and Anne (widow of Henry Bellasis), by which time Francis' father had returned and ingratiated himself into the English Court. However, although Charles II recommended Richmond to his brother James II, James nonetheless removed effectively all his privileges. This was essentially due to the fact that James II positively disliked the Duchess of Portsmouth and this may well have been reflected in his treatment of Charles (Lennox). In the *Dictionary of National Biography* dealing with his father's life, in the final paragraph begins as follows:

> 'Richmond he had the easy, pleasant manners of his father, but was an unprincipled adventurer through life, and in his later years was addicted to drunkenness and other vices etc.'[15]

It would seem that Charles, who became the Second Duke, possessed much of the political agility of his father, but seemingly, without the former's (later in his life) excesses. Starting from a position of privilege, he was after all the natural grandson of Charles II and carried the title the Earl of March, he capitalised upon it and by the time he was twenty-one, he was a captain in the militia and elected a Member of Parliament. He occupied a series of important civic functions directly related to the

King succeeding to the title in 1723.

Of interest here, he was made a Fellow of the Royal Society in 1724 and made *LLD* at Cambridge in 1728 and much later in life a Doctor of Physics at the same University as well as the president of the Society of Antiquaries, but in the *Dictionary of National Biography* the following is written:

> 'Lennox had a defective education, and perhaps a somewhat sluggish intellect, but he had a wide fund of information, and certainly does not merit the sharp epithets of 'half witted' and 'mulish' which Queen Caroline applied to him. Harvey, in fact, calls him 'very entertaining,' and he was 'a friendly and generous man, noble in the way of acting, talking, thinking. This high estimate is confirmed by Henry Fielding (on 'Robbers', page 107). Martin Folkes [*q.v.*] the antiquary, in his letters written to De Costa in 1747, and dated from the Duke's seat at Goodwood, after eulogising his host's love for 'all natural knowledge,' describes him as the 'most human and best man living'. But from other writings, e.g. that quoted below, we know that Folkes was not given to making enemies in high places, but rather tended toward obsequiousness.'[16]

It is the view of Wonnacott in a paper on Charles Lennox[17] that he was indeed a very nice person, which may of course be true; the only need for caution is that he relies almost entirely on the interchange of letters between Lennox, Montagu and Folkes. But the favourable impression gained from this correspondence may be simply one of the style of communication, which is difficult to relate to in this present age and which would now be considered extremely sycophantic.

Thus again because of the differing views of the chroniclers we are obliged to 'take a view', but perhaps an insight of the man may be gained by reflecting upon his most unusual marriage. In order to overcome gambling debts his parents arranged a marriage between Charles and Sarah the eldest daughter of the Earl of Cadogan. Totally disenchanted with the whole notion, immediately after the ceremony he departed, with his tutor, to the Continent. On returning three years later, attending a social function at a theatre, he noticed this most beautiful woman and on enquiry discovered that it was 'the beautiful Lady March, his own wife, whom he had previously held in such low esteem. His subsequent love for her was truly remarkable and they had twelve children and the affection appeared to be mutual and she reputedly died of grief at his loss.

As to his political adroitness, charm and humour the two following extracts are from three letters: the first to Matin Folkes whom he intended to assist, by means of introduction to important persons, on his impending trip to Italy. The second and third were those to the two important people in question; Cardinal Albani and Princess Pamphili. Each letter giving some indication, thus avoiding the use of a more bigoted adjective, of his 'diplomacy':

Dear Martin,

Nothing but your goodness can excuse my laziness, for laziness is the only plea I have [...] that as I promised to send you letters for people in Italy [...] Dear Folkes, it is a very easy thing, yett to these damn'd people one must fill up one's letters with such a number of cursed stupid & insincere compliments to them, that its almost tiresome undertaking. However I have accomplish'd two, and hereafter will send you more, Cardinal Albani is an old Curr, Ignorant enough & proud as Hell, butt has the finest library, one of them in Europe [...] You must flatter him upon his learning, bon gusto.

The Princess Pamphili is the ugliest woman in the world Damn'd proud also, start staring mad, butt a Devilish deal of Witt [...] As to her, Dear Folkes, (I beg pardon if I am too free) I must tell you one thing tho, which is that I would not advise you to carry Mrs Folkes to her, for if the first Countess of England was to go and visit her, she would look upon her as a scrub, this I assure you is a fact, [...] I could send you letters to a thousand scrubs, but they would be of no use to you, & would ask you to lend them money or some such thing.

I hope that Mrs Folkes and all your little ones are well, I beg my humble compliments to them, & that you would believe me as I really am, with the utmost truth and Friendship, Dear Sir, your most faithful

& obedient servant,

RICHMOND.

However, to the lady in question a rather different letter altogether, which in view of the grammar and spelling would appear to have been proof-read by some third party:

As I know, Madam, that you are Protectress of Savants of all countries, and especially of ours, permit me to recommend to you Mr. ffolkes, who will have the honour of presenting this letter to you; he is one of my most intimate friends. He is a gentleman of very good family, and one of the leading savants of this Kingdom. Permit him therefore to pay his court to you and I dare swear that your Excellency will find his conversation agreeable, and instructive to others as well as yourself. But your Excellency knows too much already to require instruction from others, for devil take me if the Pope himself in his Consistory knows half as much as you, although he is infallible, we are told etc., etc.

With all these qualitys, I am sure, your Excellency, who is the chief Patroness of Learning & polite sciences, will soon forgive the liberty I have taken, of recommending him to the honour of your acquaintance. I am, Madam,

RICHMOND AND LENNOX.

At this juncture it is perhaps as well to reiterate that these short biographies are highly selective and this is for many reasons, but principally two: first, that although most of the Freemasons concerned with the early stages of the Premier Grand Lodge were men of substance, only a very few stood out. Second, because it is extremely difficult to get accurate, or indeed any, information about people during this period, unless they were in some way remarkable, there are virtually no sources of information on ordinary folk. It is fortunate therefore that the few with whom we are concerned were by any standards, rather remarkable and in a sense eminent people. The overt lives of the aristocracy were for the most part recorded because of their station in life, but these are either superficial cataloguing of their titles, marriages, social positions or occasionally their notoriety. Those who were not of the aristocracy, were people of achievement, distinctive personality and/or behaviour that demanded attention, but for whatever reason, it is virtually impossible to find documentary evidence of their inner thoughts or motivation.

References

1. Anon. 'Montagu' in *DNB* (OUP, Vol. VIII, 1968), pp. 700-701.
2. Cockayne, G., 'Montagu (Dukes of)' in *The Complete English Peerage* (St Catherine Press, Vol. IX, London, 1936), pp. 99-105.
3. Anon. 'Wharton' in *DNB* (OUP, Vol. XIX, 1968), pp. 1321-1322.
4. Cockayne, G., 'Wharton' in *The Complete English Peerage*, Vol. XII, Part II (St Catherine Press, London, 1953), pp. 598-602.
5. 'Wharton', *op.cit.*
6. Miller, J., *William and Mary* (Book Club Assoc., London, 1981), p. 184.
7. Curtis, G., *Queen Anne* (Book Club Assoc., London, 1981), p. 139.
8. Gould, R.F., 'Masonic celebrities, No. VI – The Duke of Wharton', *AQC* 8 (1895), pp. 114-155.
9. Blacket-Ord, M., *Hell-Fire Duke* (The Kensal Press, Berkshire, UK, 1982).
10. Anon. 'Buccleuch' in *DNB* (OUP, Vol. XI, 1968), pp. 963-964.
11. *Ibid.*
12. Cockayne, G., 'Buccleuch' in *The Complete English Peerage* (St Catherine Press, London, Vol. II, 1912), pp. 364-367.
13. Edwards, L., 'Three early Grand Masters', *AQC* 43 (1930), pp. 226-238.
14. Cockayne, G., 'Richmond' in *The Complete English Peerage* (St Catherine Press, London, Vol. X, 1945), pp. 829-835.
15. Anon. 'Lennox' in *DNB* (OUP, Vol. XVII, 1968), pp. 921-922.
16. 'Lennox', *op. cit.*
17. Wonnacott, W., 'Charles, Second Duke of Richmond (Grand Master 1724-25) ... etc., *AQC* 30 (1930), pp. 32-40.

Chapter Seventeen: Concurrent Men of Influence

We have already dealt with three men who were not members of the aristocracy, namely the first three of the initial seven Grand Masters. Having established the basic format of these biographies, in order to keep within the time frame it is perhaps appropriate at this juncture to deal with several other freemasons who were in an influential position during this period. These are: William Cowper, (first Secretary), Martin Folkes, William Stukeley, John Senex, Brooke Taylor, James Anderson, John Arbuthnot and John Beal(e). A ninth; the Duke of Chandos (family name: James Brydges), who unless, unlike the others, he was a member of an obscure lodge or omitted from the minutes[1] and hence not recorded was to that extent outside the remit of the known freemasons considered here; nevertheless because of his aristocratic background it is appropriate that he be considered after the last of the Grand Masters in this Study. Whilst it appears that the 1st Duke of Chandos was not a freemason he was nonetheless inextricably involved with those who were and because of this very strong interrelationship he is of necessity an intricate part of this analysis.

Although up to this point these short biographies have been in the chronological order in which the Grand Masters served, the following are interposed to indicate their likely influence during that critical period. There is no particular chronology or other factors that have determined the order in which these men are considered and although Chandos was extremely active and a close associate of those under this heading, during this formative period for convenience, style and continuity of presentation he will be dealt with somewhat later and after his less illustrious nephew who became the Grand Master in 1738.

However, it is perhaps appropriate to begin with the Cowper connection. Modern experience would lead us to the view that the secretary of a society or group and especially freemasons' lodges has a pivotal role in the running and general ethos of that organisation, especially since his term of office was through that period with which we are concerned most. But in this instance there was even greater reason to believe that there was likely to have been a very pronounced influence from the strategic office of secretary, because of his antecedence. The Founders had somehow managed without a formal secretary prior to this and so it was in 1723 some six years after the Premier Grand Lodge was formally opened that he became the first person to be appointed to that post, disregarding the necessary paperwork etc. prior to its launch. Given the politics of the time William Cowper was a name to be conjured with, but as with Henry Brydges, *styled* Marquess of Carnarvon (*later* [1744], 2nd Duke of Chandos), who was appointed Grand Master in 1738, they merely flattered to deceive.

Both the Cowpers and the Spencers were well-established and powerful families, not to say extremely colourful also, especially his uncle the first Earl Cowper (William) the Lord Chancellor; contemporary for much of the period with the William we are concerned with here. The first Earl Cowper was an extraordinarily astute politician and depending upon which account one reads was either a man '... with a reputation as a fair and incorruptible Lord High Chancellor of Great Britain',[2] or his other activities like being accused of murder (found not guilty, an outcome not the least bit unusual, since no peer of the Realm had ever been found guilty of that crime before that date and indeed for a long while afterwards). Unfortunately the first Grand Secretary did not appear to have followed in his uncle's footsteps. It is extraordinarily difficult to find any reference to him whatsoever, which, considering the characters with which he was surrounded – enormously influential, domineering and larger than life, albeit sometimes for the wrong reasons – one has to wonder whether he had any great influence at all. The following represents the best that could be found after considerable enquiry.

As stated above, in virtually every aspect of modern Freemasonry the function of Secretary (Scribe, Recorder etc.,) of a lodge is central to its efficient operation. It seemed essential therefore to determine whether this may have been true of the first Grand Secretary[3] and because this was considered likely in this instance considerable effort was expended in researching his characteristics, personality, and ambitions etc., to a greater extent than on any other character in these short biographies. At the beginning this appeared to be a comparatively simple task, because in Cowper's case there appeared to be two overriding factors: first his aristocratic origins and second that he was for a time Clerk to the Parliament, which then, like today, was the most senior non-elected role in Westminster. However, in the event, this was not the case, since very little could be found about him and what little there was, from places such as the archives of the House of Lords, was most uninspiring. However, to be able to hold on to a post without ruffling anyone's feathers is a manifestation of political adroitness and perhaps it is that very lack of overt charisma that says much.

Indeed, it is because of the political adroitness of our characters and their forbears, that they were able to survive and thereby create the environment that made the Premier Grand Lodge possible. Its constituent members and their motivation are therefore worthy of our attention. Their innate ability to survive is especially exemplified by the Cowpers, whose astute manoeuvrings throughout the 1600s allowed them not only to survive the violent political swings, but also to escape the consequences of several misdemeanours, not least of which, as stated above, was that of murder (indeed the first Earl was considered by some historians as extremely fortunate to have escaped almost certain conviction and that it was only by the implicit immunity of the peerage that he did so). Had the case been proven, it may well have changed the whole course of events discussed here. Alternatively one may read of Earl Cowper as: '... the most upright of men and one of the finest Lord Chancellors ever'. Certainly if one reads accounts of his behaviour in Parliament during the critical period with which we are concerned, not least the formation and subsequent bursting of the South Sea Bubble – this often referred to, but rarely explained event. The circumstances surrounding the South Sea Bubble, which seriously affected a number of our principal players, are nicely explained in a book by Mackay,[4] but more interestingly during the course of his explanation he makes detailed reference to some of our main characters and in his view William Cowper's actions seem most laudable. However, our William Cowper, in modern parlance '... kept his head so far below the parapet' as to be completely hidden from view, his family failing to even record the date of his birth, but the following may be of some interest.

William Cowper
(1689/93-1740)

b. during or shortly after 1689. Eldest son of Judge Spencer Cowper's second marriage (the younger brother of the Lord Chancellor and grandfather of the poet). If he carried a title he was never accorded it in the various Minutes of Grand Lodge, simply referred to as 'Esquire'. He was appointed Clerk to the Parliament. Called to the Bar 1712.

Although not known for certain it seems that he was a freemason prior to 1717. He was a member (JW) of the Horn and Tavern Lodge as was his brother the Revd Dr John (father of the renowned poet). He was made the first Grand Secretary June 1723 and in 1726 was appointed Deputy Grand Master by the Earl of Inchiquin.
d. 1740.

In the tradition of his family he began to study law in the Middle Temple in 1705, but according to certain accounts because of distractions, mainly family commitments, made slow progress and was not called to the Bar until 1712. Notwithstanding this inauspicious beginning he was appointed Clerk to the Parliament. Some dispute its importance; saying that he was only Clerk to the House of Lords and that at the same time there was a Clerk to the House of Commons. This was true, but then as now, the Clerk to the House of Lords (it being the senior Chamber) takes precedence over the House of Commons. However, this was very late in his career and it was most likely as a result of the Civil Service's tradition of 'Buggin's turn'; the post

Concurrent Men of Influence

being vacant due to the death of his good friend and erstwhile fellow Grand Warden Francis Sorrel, not forgetting that they were both members of the Lodge which met at the Horn Tavern in Westminster.

One can only glean scraps of information from here onwards, but extracting from two papers; Fisher's[5] and MacKechnie-Jarvis'[6] gives some indication of the man and the times, other sources are not worthy of quoting since they refer to him in passing with phrases such as: '... there were four children of which the eldest was William' adding nothing more.

In his paper 'A cavalcade of Freemasons in 1731 ...', Fisher writes, first quoting *AQC*, X, p. 49, as follows:

'From the Minute of the meeting of Grand Lodge held 24th June 1723, at Merchant Taylors Hall:

Ordered that "William Cowper, Esq., a Brother of the Horn and Tavern Lodge at Westminster, be Secretary to the Grand Lodge." '

The paper later continues:

'William Cowper belonged to a family, which held a distinguished place in the law offices of the Crown. His uncle, William Cowper, had a great reputation as a fair and incorruptible Lord High Chancellor of Great Britain. He (the uncle) had been created Baron Cowper on the 9th of November 1706, and after carrying out his duties as Lord High Steward at the trial of the Lords charged with High Treason in the Rebellion, he was advanced to the dignity of Earl, 14th March 1718.

William Cowper, who was the Secretary of Grand Lodge, was the eldest son of Spenser Cowper, younger brother of Earl Cowper, and a Judge of the Court of Common Pleas. William had two brothers – the Rev. John Cowper, Rector of Birkhampsted, who was father of William Cowper, the poet, and Ashley Cowper, who probably succeeded William (the Secretary of Grand Lodge) as clerk to the House of Lords. The Rev. John Cowper was also a member of the famous Lodge meeting at the Horn Tavern at Westminster.

Bro. William Cowper is sometimes described as "Clerk of Parliaments" which could lead to some misunderstanding. He was Clerk of the House of Lords, and the Clerk of the House of Commons at that time was Nicholas Hardinge, son-in-law of Lord Chief Justice Pratt.

Bro. William Cowper was JW of the Lodge at the Horn Tavern in 1725. In the 1723 list his name appears immediately in front of Nathaniel Blackerby, and it may be that he was also a freemason before the constitution of Grand Lodge. In 1726 the Earl of Inchiquin appointed him Deputy Grand Master. Apparently he continued to act as Secretary. He had been Chairman of the committee of thirteen members appointed by Grand Lodge to "consider the Best Methods to regulate the General Charity, and Report their Opinion". When the Report was presented to the Grand Lodge on 27th November 1725, however, Alexander Hardine was the Chairman. Bro. Cowper was succeeded as Deputy Grand Master by Alexander Chocke on the 27th December 1727, when Lord Coleraine was installed as Grand Master. In the Minutes of the meeting held on the 27th December there is a note in different handwriting: "Bro. William Reid chosen Sec^{ry}".

From this time Bro. William Cowper attended Grand Lodge from time to time, but there is no record of his holding office in Grand Lodge. He died on 14th February 1740, and his death was announced in the Gentleman's Magazine as follows:

"William Cowper, Esq. Clerk of the Parliament, Justice of the Peace for Middlesex and Westminster. The Revisionary Grant of the Patent as Clerk of the Parliament, comes to his eldest Son, William Cowper, Esq. Student at Oxford".'

The accuracy of the extract above taken from Fisher's paper may be questioned – *see* charts of Grand Masters in Chapter Fourteen.

However, MacKechnie-Jones' paints a rather different picture. His paper was about the function of the early Grand stewards. The piece with which we are concerned centres on a series of annual feasts, at first quasi-unofficial, but which became an established custom, where all 'the great and the good' were invited. By 1724 a series of regulations governing such feasts was declared to set the protocols for the next feast. Grand Master Richmond directed a Bro. Heidegger (an impresario at one time in partnership with the famous composer Handel), to undertake the task of organising it. He (Heidegger) appears to have assumed (implying that they were in fact new, assumed and illegal) the title of Grand Steward and engaged two brothers to assist him, one of whom was Bro. Edward Lambert. The following extract is taken from his paper, which shows that the capacity of people (brethren) to enter into heated debate over quite trivial matters is not a modern affectation, but was present from the beginning of formalised Freemasonry and how a certain William Cowper was keen to demonstrate that he had been in no way implicated with the present fiasco and employing the strategy of 'attack is the best form of defence' instigated the debate and then fired off the first salvo:

'In the following year Edward Lambert was apparently appointed sole Grand Steward, although Anderson says 'No Stewards, but Bro. Edward Lambert undertook to prepare the Feast'. Perhaps Lambert was acting in a professional capacity as a caterer? According to the minutes of the Quarterly Communications held on Monday 12 December 1726, Lord Paisley, Grand Master presiding:

Concurrent Men of Influence

His Lordship then acquainted the Lodge that he had designed to hold a Grand Feast on St Johns Day next ensuing [i.e., December 27] at Merchant Taylors Hall upon which Mr Lambert was called in being the Grand Steward appointed for the Sd. Feast.

The Grand Mar. read the Regulations agreed to by this Grand Lodge with the alteracon that the tickets not taken are to be returned by Monday next.

Appointed Deputy Grand Master in 1724 and 25 and because of the frequent absence of the Grand Master often presided in that capacity.

The quarterly Communication and Feast appear in fact to have been held two months later on 27 February 1727 at the Hall of the Mercers Company but no explanation for the postponement and change of venue were given.

It will be noted that the good intention of appointing twelve Stewards as planned in 1724 could not yet be given effect presumably owing to the reluctance of the brethren to undertake the office under the uncertain conditions obtaining.

The states of affairs prevailing at the time was ventilated at a special meeting of Grand Lodge held on Tuesday, 19 December 1727, when the arrangements for the forthcoming Feast to be held on St John the evangelist's Day, 27 December 1727, were considered. Grand Lodge had been summoned by the Deputy Grand Master, William Cowper, who presided in the absence of the Grand Master, Lord Inchiquin, in Ireland.

Anderson's account is as follows:

'D. G. Master Cowper in the Chair, eloquently excused the Grand Master's Absence in Ireland, and his sudden Calling them together; for that the Feast drew nigh, and the Grand Master had, by Letter, impower'd him to propose, his successor, the Lord Colerane Master of a Lodge, who was forthwith saluted as Grand Master Elect.

No Stewards being appointed, Brother Lambert again undertook to prepare the Feast.

The minutes of Grand Lodge treat the matter somewhat differently and at much greater length. After the preliminaries, the Deputy Grand Master 'proceeded to give the Grand Lodge an Account of his Reasons for Summoning them at this time in the matter following viz.': [Here follows an unusually long speech, reported in full, in which our brother discloses that, of the 500 tickets printed, only 81 have been paid for, Some lodges having not received any tickets and others not enough. With only ten days to go there was clearly an element of panic prevailing].

[The Deputy Grand Master blamed] 'your present Secretary' [but appears to concede that his own inaction had also contributed to the confusion that has arisen]. Brother Nathaniel Blackerby, Treasurer of Grand Lodge, 'taking notice of the Method used by some Brethren of taking Tickets at the Hall Door, as also

The Key to Modern Freemasonry

of the neglect complained of by the Deputy Grand Master, in the distribution of the Tickets, for the ensuing Grand Feast, proposed that the same may be taken into consideration by the Grand Lodge on St John's day next ensuing at Mercers Hall, and desired a Minute might be made thereof'. This Motion being made, and the Question put the same was agreed to Nemine Con. And the Brethren present were desired by the D. G. Master to be prepared with such schemes as they should Judge proper and necessary for the preventing such irregularities for the future. The Motion being made the Brother Lambert may have the Liberty to advertize in the publick News Papers, That Tickets will be deposited with him till Saturday. The Question was put, and it was unanimously agreed that he may advertize the same in such manner as he shall think proper'.

The 1727 Feast appears to have been successful as the minute includes the following:

'The other regular Healths were drank, as also Brother Lambert's with Thanks for his Care in the Entertainment of the day'. [The Secretary to the Grand Lodge for the previous year was not reappointed! This is of course inconsistent with the official records, which show Read survived for a further six years].

It would seem that very little has changed in the way in which the affairs of such bodies are run or indeed how quickly after vacating an office it is possible to forget the part one played in it or to acknowledge its innate problems. But as will be suggested later perhaps the first Secretary was rather more influential than it may appear on the surface.

Martin Folkes MA
(1690-1754)

b. 29 October 1790. Eldest son of solicitor Martin Folkes. Attended the University of Saumur (France). Cambridge 1706 (studied mathematics: graduated 1709, just nineteen). *FRS* 1714 (Vice President 1719).

d. 29 June 1754.

He was a highly educated man who studied at both the University of Saumur in France and Cambridge; reading mathematics. He was made a member of the Royal Society in 1714 and their President in 1724. He was also a Fellow of the Society of Antiquaries. His academic contributions were viewed by some to be of considerable merit, whilst others were less charitable. (*see* the biography of William Stukeley below). However, in his later years he was elected to the Academe of Antiquaries and further honoured by Cambridge University. Clearly there were a significant number of people who rated him highly and it is therefore reasonable to assume that even if one adopts the less charitable view that he was not brilliant, he was certainly not a dullard and clearly well above the average. Further it is virtually certain that he would have supported the concept of the enhancement of knowledge as a basic tenet within the cultural ethos of Freemasonry from that time onwards and that he was most likely to have been an influential part of that process. A further important factor, from the point of view of Masonic science, is that he was known to deliver (some biographers suggest rather indifferent) papers, talks etc., on Scientific matters.

Any contribution that he was likely to have made, is of particular interest with respect to the Royal Arch, since he was keenly interested in Egyptian and Middle Eastern antiquity and this association may well have influenced the inclusion of words on the triangle found in the earlier rituals. This particular association is also true of other (less conspicuous Masonic) scholars who were members during those formative years, some of whom professed an especial interest in ancient Middle Eastern languages. Above all he was very politically aware and 'tiptoed' his way through a highly (dynamic) political period; choosing 'sides' correctly and retaining influence in the most exalted of company. Stewart writes – in his book on public science, in the Section where he deals with *Patronage, Politics, and Subscription*, within general society at that time:

'... The Whigs, however, clearly dominated as they came to do politically, with Joseph Eyles, a Director of the East India Company, Richard Boyle, the Earl of Burlington and F.R.S., along with James Brydges (Duke of Chandos), Martin Folkes, Thomas Herbert, the Earl of Pembroke and a former President of the Royal Society, and Charles Townsend, F.R.S. and Secretary of State under Warpole.

Many of the Newtonian works of early eighteenth century were published by subscription. Political persuasion was an important factor in the connection that supported subscription between appearances of such prominent works as John Harris's 'Lexicon Technicum' in 1704 and the final volume of J. T. Desaguliers' 'A Course of Experimental Philosophy' in 1744. But politics was surely only one factor, and there were certainly many subscribers who cannot be identified with any certainty. It is impossible to draw any final conclusions as to the precise political motivation behind subscription to the Newtonian publications in general because some people subscribed infrequently or possibly only once through the entire period. It is not surprising, for example that James Brydges, later Duke of Chandos, should be among those who once purchased books by the area they were to fill on the shelves of his estate except the subscription may be a different degree of commitment than mere purchase.'[7]

Folkes' close association with the Royal Society involved him in other matters, which at first sight may be considered to be purely matters of scientific judgement, but which in reality were controversial to say the least. For instance he was a Member of 'the Commissioners of Longitude'. This topic is a subject in its own right and is better dealt with elsewhere,[8] but the feverish quest at that time to determine longitude at sea with greater accuracy had two quite distinctive characteristics. 1) There was a near fortune on offer for its solution and 2) the shear diversity of techniques proposed for doing so. Of these a strong contender was the use of magnetism, of which a leading proponent was a certain Dr. Cowin Knight. The degree of integrity with which Knight propounded his science or the level of his innate ability is again dealt with better by others, in particular Patricia Fara,[9] but he most certainly was a self publicist and politician; and in terms of this Section had procured the sponsorship of Martin Folkes. In modern parlance, one has to wonder why Folkes appeared not to declare 'an interest' when the ideas of this particular claimant were being debated.

Again there is the problem of historians failing to agree, illustrated by the short account in the brief passage on Folkes in the *Dictionary of Scientific Biography* where the following is written:

'Upon Sloan's retirement from the presidency of the Royal Society in 1741, Folkes succeeded to the office. His "literary style rather than scientific bent" was reflected in the society's meetings which, according to his friend [a 'one time' friend would perhaps be more accurate *see* Stukeley below] William Stukeley, became "most elegant and agreeable entertainment for a contemplative person." Other comments on Folkes were less charitable: the "philosophical Transactions" for the period of his presidency allegedly contained "a greater proportion of trifling and puerile papers than are anywhere else to be found" and the meetings merely allowed "personages acting the importants [...] to trifle away time in empty forms and grave grimaces" John Hill the society's severest critic, blamed Folkes for this state of affairs.'[10]

There are further examples where writers have been less generous, but for the moment the assessment of Martin Folkes will be left, until we have considered William Stukeley; the next of those people outside the aristocratic circle with whom we are concerned. However before doing so it is necessary to reiterate that the selection process of particular individuals used here, may well be overly prejudicial, for there were many men of considerable standing, who, potentially at least, may have played an important role in the early years of the Premier Grand Lodge. The rationale for limiting its number will be discussed where relevant, but the principal limitation is time and space. In deference of this approach, whenever a name has occurred, either inside or outside Masonic literature, an attempt has been made to cross-reference it with other data and where such links were found; they have been referred to.

William Stukeley
(1687-1765)

b. 7 November 1687. Eldest son of Farmer/Lawyer (Holbeach, Lincolnshire) John Stukeley. A solitary, very bright child, had many interests and was taken into father's law practice, but could not settle and went to Cambridge University in 1703, but family commitments interrupted these studies and he did not qualify as a *MB* until 1708. He studied many topics, especially antiquities. Began his Medical studies at St Thomas' Hospital under Dr Mead. Returned to Lincs. in 1710. Returned to London 1717 and by 1718 was made *FRS* – proposed by Dr Mead. 1719 a founder of the Society of Antiquaries. Was Initiated on 6 January 1721. Founded and became Master of a new lodge just over eleven months later on 27 December. *

He researched extensively into archaeological buildings and delivered many papers on that subject alone. He formed or was part of many important societies.

d. 3 March 1765.

* Given his otherwise punishing life style and wide range of interests and the restrictions due to daylight hours, it would be of interest to know the extent of the Ritual they were required to memorize, both in terms of action and words and how much of this expected 'retention' in and degree of 'perfection' was expected of its officers.

Stukeley was a quite remarkable man and it will not be possible to elaborate on him to the depth that perhaps he deserves. Most of the material used here comes from two extensive papers[11, 12] and a biographical reference,[13] but an even better understanding may come from reading his numerous writings, many of which exist in their original form in the National Register of Archives; although this also is quite difficult given the sheer extent of them. The following is an attempt to précis those elements that give an indication of 'the Man' and which determined his changing disposition towards Freemasonry and much else besides.

As with most of those who join Freemasonry, curiosity must have played an important role, but because of Stukeley's interest in archaeology, his 'curiosity' was reputed to have been especially heightened by the prospect of enlightenment in the 'ancient secrets and mysteries'. Given his scholarship and the state of knowledge at that time, if he had been merely exposed to the basic Ritual, he would almost certainly have been disappointed. Indeed it may well have been so, for even today most lodges and chapters of improvement, doggedly rehearse ritual, seemingly oblivious of the need to communicate its meaning or underlying philosophy. However, it is argued here that far from being deterred by the meagre amount he found, he appears to have at least supported (his personality was such that he would have vehemently opposed it otherwise), if not contributed towards the ceremonial. It would also be consistent with his personality to rectify any lack of depth, through the medium of the Royal Arch Lectures. As we shall find from Chapters Thirty-six and Thirty-seven another factor would have been the extent to which he was embraced within the 'inner circle' of the hierarchy, since if perchance he had been effectively excluded, it could have been a further factor in his comparatively early disaffection with the Premier Grand Lodge.

From his writings one has to conclude that he was constantly obsessed with the need to seek recognition and was especially flattered by the company of influential men and this too would have affected his basic motivation for joining Freemasonry. This is reflected in the way he boasts of his various meetings and association with people such as Newton and Wren and sundry members of the Aristocracy. He was keen to progress within this society so far as it was possible, given the social constraints and the fact that by the time he arrived on the scene the aristocratic exclusivity of any appointment to the office of Grand Master had been established irrevocably and so he would not have even entertained that possibility. Nonetheless, he must be regarded as having been most successful, for by any standards; his rise in Freemasonry was meteoric. He would have appeared to have a good relationship with Martin Folkes in the initial stages, but they were both vying with each other for position in a very close, highly political grouping. Since it was inevitable that there would only be one winner, it was almost certain that sooner or later there would be some resentment or animosity, if only coming from the loser of such a contest. Long after his retreat back to Grantham, seemingly by then having accepted that he was unlikely to ever progress further in the Premier Grand Lodge hierarchy, he recounted this opinion of Martin Folkes:

> Martin Folkes has an estate of £3000 got from his Father in the Law. He is a man of no economy. Before at age he married Mrs Bracegirdle [a parody since her actual name was Lucretia Bradshaw] off the stage. His mother grieved at it so much that she threw her self out of a window and broke her arm. His only son broke his neck off a horse back in Paris. His eldest daughter ran away with a book-keeper and who used her very ill. Quarrelling with Sr Hans Sloan about the presidentship of the Royal Society, and being baffled, went to Rome with his wife, & dau^r, dog, cat, parrot, & monkey. There his wife grew religiously mad.

Concurrent Men of Influence

He went to Venice and got a dangerous hurt upon his leg. Returning he was the Successor to Sr Hans, Presid^t of the R.S. Loosing his teeth, he speaks so as to not be understood. He constantly refuses all papers that treat of longitude. He chuses the Councel and Officers out of his junte of Sycophants that meet him every night at Rawthmills coffee house, or that dine with him on Thursdays at the Miter, fleet street. He has a good deal of learning, philosophy, astronomy: but knows nothing of natural history. In matters of religion an errant infidel & loud scoffer. Professes himself a godfa^r to all monkeys, believes nothing of a future state, of the Scripture, of revelation. He perverted the Duke of Montagu, Richmond, Ld Pembroke, & very many more of the nobility, who had an opinion of his understanding; and this has done an infinite prejudice to Religion in general, made the nobility throw off the mask, & openly deride & discountenance even the appearance of religion, which has brought us into that deplorable situation we are now in, with thieves, & murderers, perjury, forgery, &c. He thinks that there is no difference between us & animals; but what is owing to the different structure of our brain, as between man & man. When I lived in Osmand Street in 1720, he set up an infidel Club at his house on Sunday evenings, where Will Jones, the mathematician, and others of that heathen stamp, assembled. He invited me earnestly to come thither but I always refused. From that time he has been propagating the infidel system with great assiduity, made it even more fashionable in the Royal Society, so that when any mention is made of Moses, the deluge, the religion, Scriptures, &c., it is generally received with a loud laugh. He dyed in a deplorable manner. Two years after, his daughters both married to indigent persons.

This comment on Martin Folkes has been left until this point to convey an indication of both men; Stukeley's petulant 'clutching at straws' condemnation and ridicule of Folkes' prophetic views upon man's origins, which appear to pre-date those of Darwinism by over a hundred years. However, throughout the history of science, such 'pearls of wisdom' may in reality have not been his (Folkes') thoughts, but that his position allowed him to claim those of other workers, a ploy certainly not unknown today. It also emphasises the change from the close relationship that these two characters had in the early stages of the Premier Grand Lodge and although Stukeley's comments are somewhat pathetic, they put a counter view of Folkes. However, Folkes was diligent in his attendance at meetings of the Royal Society, presiding over many in a seemingly efficient manner. In researching through these minutes, it was clear that he 'led from the front' and delivered a number of papers of some merit and diversity and this should be borne in mind when considering Stukeley's account. Further, it is clear that Stukeley wrote this a considerably long time after he had returned to Grantham, doing so with the same degree of conviction as all else he did, not least his increasing involvement with Christian (Anglican) religion and even more bizarre, his conviction of its close affiliation with the Druids. A few snippets of his writings are as follows:

> 'That the clergy of England, under God's Providence, are the main support of religion now upon the face of the earth, is a truth that may not easily be denyd by good men, and those that consider things about 'em ∴ ∴ So great an influence has religion ∴ & how foolish are statesmen not to encourage it.

> Infidelity. I find one half of our half-witted philosophers in London, our R.S. people, are infidels: the other half are lunatics. So hard a matter is it to keep a golden medium, or to see the great beauty of the Ch. of England in particular, of religion in general.

> (5th June, 1726). I left London in the 38th year of my age, at that time Censor of Physicians, one of the Council of the Royal Society, & Secretary to the Antiquarian Society, In the full career of my studys, in the highest favour with all the great men of quality, learning or power, to live at Grantham; a resolution thought by many, executed by few. I chose Grantham, because it is a very pleasant place, in a very fine country, in my own county, & near my estate & place of nativity at Holbeach.'

Both Spurr [14] and the compilers of the *Dictionary of National Biography* [15] have trouble with what appears to be a rapid deterioration of his objectivity from the middle of the 1720s onwards, seemly becoming more and more extreme. In the second instance they write:

> 'Warburton, bishop of Gloucester, one of Stukeley's oldest acquaintances, describes him as a learned and honest man, but a strange compound of "simplicity, drollery, absurdity, ingenuity, superstition and antiquarianism." [ref. here]. Thomas Hearne says he was "very fanciful" and "a mighty conceited man" [...] Stukeley's plan of "Caesar's Camp" at the Brill (Somers Town), seems to be purely imaginary. Evans (Ancient British Coins p. 7) pronounced his drawings and attributes of British Coins untrustworthy, etc.'

From the above we have to form a view on this person. There is little doubt that he was a man of considerable talent and vigour, who clearly threw himself into a task. It is also clear that he joined Freemasonry and tackled it with similar verve; this assumption is made on the basis of his rapid progression. It was at a time when his work was most thorough and motivated with a profound concern with science. It is clear also that his Masonic career was blighted by the need (ambition) to choose sides. Although there is no direct evidence, it is reasonably certain that he was not in the camp that favoured the second Duke of Buccleuch and was disposed to let that be well known. Given the direction in which events were to unfold, this outward expression would have likely jeopardised any ambitions that he entertained. He had by that time, that is just before he left in high dudgeon, been severely affected with the gout and so was not enjoying the best of health. It was consistent with his apparent impetuosity that he finally decided to return to Grantham and far from having his 'tail between his legs' proceeded to claim the moral 'high ground'. But it is more likely this was a case of 'making a virtue out of necessity', that this move was not by dint of choice, but rather because he had 'painted himself into a corner'. Thus from the point of view of this work, his effective scientific input would have been restricted to the few years prior to his disaffection in 1725.

John Senex
(*c*.1673-1740)

His date of birth has not been established, but is *circa* 1673. Cartographer, Globe maker, printer and publisher, public lecturer, businessman, shopkeeper.

His date of entry into Freemasonry is not known either, but he was likely to have been a freemason well before 1717. He became a Junior Grand Warden, but it is reasonable to conclude that he was much more influential than that post normally implies.

d. 30 December 1740.

Little has been written on his origins and what is written here comes from two main sources.[16, 17] It is clear that by the turn of the century he was a businessman of some standing and from that it is reasonable to conclude that he would have been in his twenties and so his birth has been assessed as being around 1673. His principal occupation (expertise) varies according to source, but there is little doubt that he was a leading purveyor of print, instruments, globes and maps. In addition he was clearly a most learned person and since it was likely self taught – most exceptionally so, indicating a fine brain and initiative and was also a public lecturer of some repute. He commanded the friendship and one might fairly assume the respect of many very eminent, scientifically minded, people, in particular Desaguliers. He was clearly a talented engraver and for the most of ten years (1717-22, 1724 -27) executed cuts for the London almanacs and in 1723 for Sir William Brown's *Account of Microscopes and Telescopes*. He was perhaps best known for his cartography and in conjunction with other well-known persons such as Maxwell, published maps of both Britain and overseas. Indeed many of his maps are in the special collection of historic cartography in the Library of Trinity College Dublin. However, it must be understood that he was not simply a producer and seller of these things, but had a profound knowledge of their content.

Even so, despite his considerable scientific merit and powerful connections he was not admitted a member of the Royal Society until 1728, his principal delivery at which was on the Earth's rotational (precessional) behaviour, producing models, both actual and predictive.

There is very little known of him as a man and so it may be useful to attempt a reprise of his scientific, social and business association and activity and perhaps deduce a little insight from this. His close association with Desaguliers has been alluded to already, but he was clearly at ease with many others of high scientific standing. That he was socially astute, or just plain fortunate, is well illustrated by his continual support of Whiston following his expulsion from Cambridge because of his extreme (or at least anti-establishment) irreligious views. This outward support was best illustrated by his agreeing to publish Whiston's work on philosophy and astronomy, as well as making instruments for him. Although, insofar as those of influence in the Premier Grand Lodge were concerned, this may not have been such a disadvantage; for as we have seen already other members in the hierarchy of the Premier Grand Lodge Freemasonry were flirting with extreme philosophies at this stage in their career. It was not until later that prudence and political expediency (discretion, not necessarily persuasion) prevailed.

Hodgson and Ditton gave public lectures in the early 1700s and Senex published their work on the establishment of Longitude at sea. Senex published accounts (predictions etc.) and sold special glasses for the solar eclipse in May 1724. He stayed in London for the event, but Desaguliers travelled to Bath to observe it – it is clear that little has changed with the passage of time, including the perversities of the weather on such occasions.

Ephraim Chambers (of encyclopaedia fame) was his apprentice at the turn of the century and assisting in its publication in direct opposition to Harris' Lexicon. The full title was *Chambers Encyclopaedia of the Arts and Sciences – see* Appendix 2. He was involved also in joint publications on works dealing with the measurement of the speed of sound and with Desaguliers in refuting claims of 'perpetual motion' or as would be regarded today as their reaffirmation of the 'second law of thermodynamics' – showing that they had a most clear understanding of that very profound physical concept.

He appeared to remain successful throughout his life, his wife continuing to run his business long after his death and like most of those concerned with the development of the Premier Grand Lodge may be accorded the label of being extremely astute politically.

Brook Taylor
(1685-1731)

b. 1685 in London.

Educated privately and then at St Johns College Cambridge. *LLB* (1701) *LLD* (1709). Well connected: his grandfather was in Cromwell's Assembly, his father was of the squirearchy, his mother the daughter of Sir John Tempest. Admitted *FRS* 1712, becoming its first Secretary in 1714 and remained so for four years.

Married twice, both for short periods, both his wives died in childbirth or shortly afterwards. First was a certain Miss Brydges (Chandos connection?).

d. 1731 (buried at Somerset House).

Brook Taylor is recognised as a most outstanding scholar.[18, 19] Whilst he did not hold high office in the Premier Grand Lodge, there can be little doubt that he is an important character in our contemplations and this for a number of reasons.[20]

First, he was a truly out-standing mathematical scholar, but much else besides. Those who have studied mathematics to some depth, could not have failed to encountered his famous (calculus – finite difference) series – Taylor's Theorem, which is used today, but which was so profound that its true importance was not realised until one hundred years later.

Second, he was a talented musician (and artist), but in addition he had a profound interest in the physics of the vibration of strings (musical instruments) and produced his famous formula that connected the frequency with the physical parameters, namely the length of the string, its mass per unit length and the tension within it. This particular interest would have given him a close affinity with James Hamilton, the Earl of Abercorn the ninth Grand Master. It would also support the inclusion and emphasis on music within the ritual.

Third, and on the same vein, was his interest in geometry, on which he published a notable book 1719. He also published a treatise on 'perspective'.

Fourth, he wrote papers on the significance of the catenary (*see* Chapter Two), which would have been consistent with originators of the Symbolical Lecture.

Fifth, he was a noted disciple of Newton and a renowned public lecturer, which is consistent with the concept of enlightenment through the medium of lectures.

Sixth, he was known to be a close friend of Stukeley in those early years.

Seventh, he was elected on to the Charity (Grand) Committee which, because of Desaguliers' close association with that body suggests that he was likely to have been encouraged to do so by Desaguliers himself.

Eighth, he was a member and Secretary for four years of the Royal Society during this critical period and so would have known his fellow Royal Society members, who were also freemasons, very well.

Ninth, in 1725 he is recorded as having been Senior Warden of the lodge that met at the Bedford Head at Covent Garden and so he must have been a keen ritualist.

Tenth, he too was hit by the collapse of the South Sea Bubble and the (first) Duke of Chandos supported him. He must have been close to Chandos because Taylor was a well known friend of the Whig Bolingbrooke, whose overt support for the Pretender's cause was so strong that he (Bolingbrooke) had been forced to flee to France. By extending such support Chandos was exposing himself to criticism. In a passage of Stewart's book where he was discussing Chandos' interaction with science and politics, recorded them as a series of facts, but preceded it with the comment 'Self-interest and ideology are really separate currents – and of course, they could intersect'.[21]

Eleventh, amongst his papers was found a treatise on 'Logarithms' addressed to his friend James Hamilton, who was later to become the seventh Earl of Abercorn.

Twelfth, for the first time he determined the differential equations of the path of a ray of light when travelling in a heterogeneous medium.

Thirteenth, through this period he became interested in theology, which would have supported the retention of religion in any matter with which he was concerned.

Fourteenth, his health was never good, but deteriorated towards the end and although he still remained active much of his outstanding work was in the period 1710-25.

Brook Taylor exemplifies perhaps better than any of the others with whom we have dealt, the intricate manner in which this small band, who formed the caucus of the Premier Grand Lodge, were interrelated. It will be argued that they needed a focus and Desaguliers would have brought their attention to this new 'club' that had recently been set up by himself, Payne, Sayer and a few others and that it appeared to be the ideal vehicle for their purpose. It would provide a forum where great men of science, literature, religion, commerce and society could meet together under a common banner.

James Anderson
(1679-1739)

b. 1679. Educated Marischal College (U. of Aberdeen), where he received *MA* and *DD* degrees. Moved to London 1708 and formed a new congregation of expatriate Scotsmen. Published on a number of matters, but is known best Masonically for his two *Books of Constitutions* (1723 and 1738).

Served both as Junior GW (1723) and acted as Senior GW (1730).

d. 1739.

As with Stukeley there appears to be no obvious or natural link with those who were of importance during the first few critical years of the Premier Grand Lodge and that would have led to the influential position he eventually held. A possibility that has been suggested by several historians, but especially by one, was that his new congregation on moving to London, happened by coincidence to meet in a defunct church that had once belonged to French Protestants, of whom Desaguliers was a most influential member. [22] That he was Scottish and because his father was a Scottish freemason, it is most likely that James had become a Scottish freemason prior to leaving for London, again strengthening the possible basis of a link. There is very strong evidence to substantiate that his father was both an operative mason as well as a speculative freemason. This assertion is made on the basis that in 1670 his father published a most informative and quite delightful list of Apprentice and Master Masons and their adopted Marks. [23]

He was clearly a most devoted Protestant, which is interesting considering the pronounced ambiguity of many of his influential associates. He wrote on several matters, but one of the most remarkable is his defence ('No King Killers') of the execution of Charles I. This public declaration of his views may well be an indication of the confidence he had in his position, or simply irrepressible personal stridency. He was known also for his robust sermons, being popularly referred to as 'Bishop Anderson'. Another reason for his rigorous defence of the extreme action against Charles I, was his keen and seemingly main interest outside of Freemasonry, that of the genealogies of all royal and analogous dynasties; from Adam onwards. Herein lay the problems associated with his Masonic writing, because he does not seem averse to 'invention' when reality appears to intrude or his preferred view is impeded by some alternative viewpoint. He appears to be the main source of the assertion that Sir Christopher Wren was a freemason. However most pour scorn on his claim because he had very little indeed to say with respect to Wren when he compiled his first Book of Constitutions, but in his second effort he counteracted that by elevating Wren to having held the position of Grand Master for many years. Indeed, he makes the accusation that during the last few years of his reign, Wren was in fact guilty of culpable neglect – most scholars are deeply sceptical of its authenticity. This would not of itself be so terrible, except that it colours one's view of the authenticity of his other writing, for example, his imaginative provenance of Freemasonry. But in this respect it would be churlish, if not imprudent, to assume that because he actually lived through this period that he would, wherever possible, have preferred to have reported the facts as he saw them, rather than fictionalise.

He married well and by 1719 he would by the standards of the period have been considered comfortably placed, but it would appear that despite his reputed 'Hell raising' sermons, he too was subject to the lures of Mammon and no doubt influenced by his brother who was a clerk in the Company, invested heavily in the South Sea Company; suffering hugely, both spiritually and financially, from the experience. Indeed, his brother spent some time in a debtor's prison and it is clear that John was, because of his own situation, not then in a financial position to rescue him.

Apart from his *Books of Constitutions*, he was influential in Freemasonry in many ways; for instance it is claimed that he introduced the Scottish terms of 'Entered Apprentice' and 'Fellowcraft'. Much has been written about Anderson's Masonic activity and all that has been attempted here is to get some understanding of the man and his place and likely influence in our analysis. That he was likely to have been listened to during any discussion on the content of any matters of ritual, is perhaps best summed up in the following extract:

'He has been described as a good man, industrious but imprudent, with a brisk temper and pushful character. Much of his writing is unreliable ...'[24]

Concurrent Men of Influence
John Arbuthnot
(1667-1735)

b. 1667. Son of a Scottish Episcopal clergyman. Studied in Aberdeen, but was awarded a Doctors Degree in medicine at St Andrews in 1696. After father was forced into seclusion (for political reasons), his sons left Scotland. John came to London and gave lessons in mathematics, but published and became famous for his satirical writings, but also published on quasi-scientific matters. Elected *FRS* in 1704. Became a member of the 'Brothers Club'. He was a friend of Pope and Swift and was respected by them. He was a musician.

He was a member of the Bedford Head Lodge (Covent Garden) as were Folkes and Brooke Taylor.

d. 1735.

Much can be said of this remarkable man, of his political adroitness, his social charm, his wit, his obvious skills as a physician (especially his 'bedside manner'), his mathematical ability, his grasp of matters scientific etc., but we will only consider him in terms of his activity within the Freemasonry of the Premier Grand Lodge. Superficially he would have been simply an ordinary member of a constituent lodge, but many factors challenge that assumption.

a) he was not a man to be ignored, nor was he content to be so,

b) he was an *FRS* and a most active one at that,

c) he was a close associate, if not friend, of many with whom we are primarily concerned, such as Stukeley, Desaguliers, Folkes, Sir Tom Thornhill (also a freemason) etc.,

d) When deposed from his position of physician to the Royal Court on the death of Queen Anne (he was a close friend of Abigail Marsham – *see* Bibl. of Queen Anne), Montagu made concerted efforts to get him reinstated, but failed. However, the bitter animosity between George I and his son provided the opportunity of gaining favour with the Heir Apparent and more importantly his politically astute wife Caroline,

e) his scientific/mathematical works were predicated on a belief that they in some way described God's perfection – he was the first person to use 'statistics' as a tool,

f) he was the personal physician to the Duke of Chandos,

g) he was famous for his satirical and humorous writings and was admitted readily within the elite literary band that included Dean Swift and Pope,

h) His scientific contributions were of sufficient merit to gain acceptance at the highest (Newtonian) level.

i) He was an accomplished public speaker and lecturer, etc., etc.

Whilst it is almost certain that we will never know the extent if any of his influence over the consolidated Craft Ritual or the formation of the Royal Arch, it is not unreasonable to suggest that he was likely to have contributed, if only tacitly.

Before returning to the list of Grand Masters it is perhaps worth considering Dr John Beal(e) because of his possible (influential) association with the founding of Grand Lodge and the claim by some historians of the supposed link with the Barber Surgeons. That he was of some merit may be gained from his status, but beyond this it is very difficult to find further evidence of his Masonic involvement, one way or another, but for completeness the following is given.

John Beal(e)
(?-1724)

Doctor of Medicine. *FRS,* 1721. Licentiate of the College of Physicians 1715.

Master of Lodge 1723, at the Crown and Anchor (*later* the Star and Garter)

d. 1724.

Although a practising physician, he was much more than that and as such was representative of that school of thought that believed in the universality of knowledge. Although qualified as a physician, he like Stukeley, Graeme and Beckett, was also noted for his lectures and published papers outside of what could be described under the generic term medicine. He was therefore somewhat Baconian, in that he preferred the exchange of ideas, rather than actual practise them, publishing on a range of matters, such as economics.

However, this information was like much else gleaned from small snippets in texts written about other people. When one attempts a more direct account of the man, there appears to be a dearth of information and whilst within the archives of the Royal Society there may be more information, after considerable searching, especially that undertaken by their Librarian, the only reference that related to his work was that he was a 'male midwife'. Again as no personal record appears to have been made in the Royal Society's documentation of a person's necessary

Concurrent Men of Influence

qualifications for acceptance until 1732. His appointment as a Fellow could therefore have been perhaps more political than academic. His overall disposition towards knowledge in general and science in particular would have supported, or at least not conflicted with, the concepts within the Symbolical lecture. However, because of his intense involvement elsewhere and *laissez faire* disposition toward most things it is not unreasonable to assume that he would not have insisted upon the inclusion in the ritual of some elements of biology, human or otherwise – although 'life' in its human form being regarded as the ultimate expression of God's creative powers.

References.

1. Anon. 'The Minutes of the Grand Lodge of Freemasons of England 1723-1725', QCA II (1913).
2. Anon. Cowper in *DNB* Vol. IV (OUP, 1968), pp. 1314-1318.
3. *Ibid.*
4. Makay, C., *Extraordinary Popular Delusions and the Madness of Crowds* (Barnes & Noble, 1989), pp. 46-88.
5. Fisher, W., 'A Cavalcade of Freemasons in 1731 as recorded etc.', *AQC* 74. (1961), pp. 32-34.
6. Mackechnie-Jarvis, C., *Grand Stewards 1728-1778* (Prestonian Lecture, UGLE, 1978).
7. Stewart, L., *The Rise of Public Science* (CUP, 1992), p. 155.
8. Sobel, D., *Longitude* (Fourth Estate Ltd., London, 1998).
9. Fara, P., *Sympathetic Attractions* (Princeton University Press, Princeton, NJ, 1996).
10. Anon. Folkes, M., *DSB* Vol. IV (C. Scribner's and Son, NY), pp. 53-54.
11. Spurr, M., 'William Stukeley: Antiquarian and Freemason', *AQC* 100 (1987), pp. 113-130.
12. Gould, R.F., 'Masonic Celebrities: No. 5. The Rev. William Stukeley', AQC VI (1893), pp. 127-145.
13. Anon. Stukeley in *DNB* Vol. (OUP , 1968), pp. 127-128.
14. Spurr, *ibid.*
15. Stukely in *DNB*, *op.cit.*
16. Fisher *ibid.*
17. Anon. Senex. *DNB* Vol XVIII (OUP, 1968), p. 1182.
18. Taton, R., *A General History of Science (1450-1800), Mathematics and Physics* (Thames and Hudson, London, 1958), pp. 379, 400 etc.
19. Anon. Brook Taylor in *DSB* Vol. XIII (C. Scribner's and Son, NY, 1976), pp. 265-268.
20. Taton *ibid.*
21. Stewart *ibid.*
22. Newton, E., 'Anderson, the Revd James, DD', in 'Brethren who made Masonic History', *AQC* 78 (1965), pp. 113-130.
23. *Masonic Square* (1975), pp. 56-57.
24. Newton, E., *op. cit.*

Chapter Eighteen: The Grand Masters 1726-1730

To reiterate: one element of the thesis of this work is that the Premier Grand Lodge was the brainchild of a few highly motivated individuals, or more likely just one very talented person. Further that this group was sufficiently cohesive in the first few years to have laid a very solid and effectively inviolable regime, but shortly afterwards (c.1726) for a number of reasons this cohesion began to break down and that progressively the enthusiasm of those who were responsible for its subsequent management and wellbeing began to decline. Thus the period between 1726 and 1730 was a time when there were sufficient of the old guard to have influence over the new, albeit progressively less so. The new Grand Masters were doubtless men of power, influence and reasonably educated, but was the required degree of commitment also on a downward trend, for the 'old guard' were beginning to run out of scientifically credible aristocracy? It is not unexpected therefore that some of the new appointees may still have wished to be rather more than just figureheads, but that only works well if there is compatibility between their concepts and the wellbeing of that which they portend to represent. The extent to which they conformed to that requirement is subjective and any assessment of it must in the end be left to the reader and so the brief outlines given below of this third strand of grand masters is meant to aid in that process.

Given the importance of the aristocratic involvement in the formative years of the Premier Grand Lodge and in particular their connection, or latterly their lack of it, with science, any involvement with the Royal Society is of major importance. It was indicated in Chapter Fourteen that until the recent work by Hogg and Currie the *Masonic Yearbook Historical Supplement* (2008): Premier Grand Lodge 1717-1813 (*MYBHS*).[1] Again their work relies heavily on just two sources (the Bullock's list of the Royal Society and the *OUP*'s *Dictionary of National Biography*), but they are extremely reliable and so where there is a difference between those found in all the earlier versions of the *MYBHS* and those included below they will be designated with an asterisk.

Ïouse of Hbercorn

This family descends through the line of Hamiltons the Earls of Arran (related through the marriage of James II of Scotland's sister). Claud Hamilton being the brother of James the third Earl (the more 'famous' line). This branch of the family were styled under the title Lord Paisley from which was created the Earl of Abercorn in 1606. [2, 3]

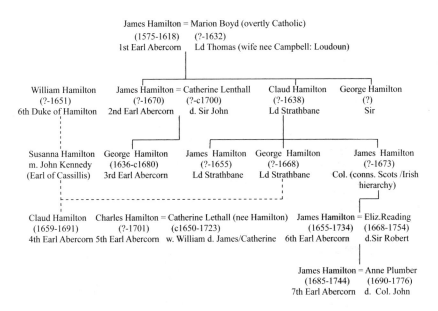

James Hamilton = Marion Boyd (overtly Catholic)
(1575-1618)   (?-1632)
1st Earl Abercorn   Ld Thomas (wife nee Campbell: Loudoun)

William Hamilton | James Hamilton = Catherine Lenthall | Claud Hamilton | George Hamilton
(?-1651) | (?-1670) (?-c1700) | (?-1638) | (?)
6th Duke of Hamilton | 2nd Earl Abercorn d. Sir John | Ld Strathbane | Sir

Susanna Hamilton | George Hamilton | James Hamilton | George Hamilton | James Hamilton
m. John Kennedy | (1636-c1680) | (?-1655) | (?-1668) | (?-1673)
(Earl of Cassillis) | 3rd Earl Abercorn | Ld Strathbane | Ld Strathbane | Col. (conns. Scots /Irish
 | | | | hierarchy)

Claud Hamilton   Charles Hamilton = Catherine Lethall (nee Hamilton)   James Hamilton = Eliz.Reading
(1659-1691)   (?-1701)   (c1650-1723)   (1655-1734) (1668-1754)
4th Earl Abercorn 5th Earl Abercorn w. William d. James/Catherine   6th Earl Abercorn   d.Sir Robert

James Hamilton = Anne Plumber
(1685-1744)   (1690-1776)
7th Earl Abercorn d. Col. John

Hamilton, James, Seventh Earl of Abercorn (1686-1744)

b. 11 January 1686; Styled Lord Paisley until he succeeded as the Earl of Abercorn in 1734; FRS*;[4] in 1715 he was the author of scientific works on magnetism and music.

RWM of the Lodge that met at the Horn Tavern (*now* Royal Somerset House and Inverness Lodge No. 4), 1725; Grand Master, 1726.

d. 13 July 1744 – re-interred in the Duke of Ormonde's vault in Westminster Abbey, 13 July 1745.

Once again it is difficult to find anything of great substance about the man *per se* and inference rather than fact prevails. However, from the scientific aspect there are at least some (reasonably reliable) facts although the two sources[5,6] seem to have been compiled one from the other. Whilst his life may be described as relatively conventional, as with most of the aristocracy with whom we are concerned, the same was not true of his ancestors, who had 'ducked and dived' their way through the preceding turbulent years, some even imprisoned for periods having momentarily (imprudently) chosen the wrong sides. As with many others quoted in Masonic literature James Hamilton had not attained the title to which he is accredited (i.e. the earlier versions of the *Masonic Year Book*) until long after being Grand Master and would at that time have been titled Lord Paisley; in his case the title of Earl followed the death of his father in 1734. Similarly belated was his appointment to 'the Lord of the King's Bedchamber' and English Privy Council in 1738 and that of Ireland 1739. He was made a Fellow of the Royal Society in 1715 and this one has to assume was by dint of merit and not status, for he later published notable scientific works.

It would have been of interest to have ascertained more precisely what his early interests were, but this is not easy to do because the minutes (Accounts) books of the Royal Society for this period are extremely difficult to research, because they are so random in nature and during that period only occasionally do they report the precise reason why a person was nominated. This may well have been because there would have been some embarrassment in doing so, since a number of those elected were there because of their social status and precious little else.

An insight into his early interests would have been a considerable help in this study, because his published interests, music and magnetism, are quite profound and in the case of magnetism, as with Desaguliers, Senex, Folkes, Stukeley, (Brook) Taylor and Montagu, are quasi commercial. It is generally the case that music in the physical sense of playing an instrument or singing is a natural attribute. Its presence is normally recognised when a person is quite young and it is reasonable to suppose that his interest in the science of musical composition would have resulted from such a natural disposition and that his (joint) publication on that subject in 1730 was a consequence of that process, although as we shall see that in Newton's case that was not necessarily so.

His interest in magnetism is however of considerable interest to this study, not simply because of its profundity and commercial implications, but because magnetism and electricity were becoming of increasing interest to members of the Group of interest here and society in general, not least their spiritual connotations. In Edwards' paper he writes the following:

'... he wrote a treatise entitled "Calculations and Tables relating to the Attractive Virtues of Loadstones. This was serving to find out the comparative degrees of goodness between Some of Them also to Know how much any Loadstone being of any proposed weight would sustain and also for to know the Value in Money of any Loadstone, published in the year 1729". It was apparently written anonymously. The principles of the pamphlet, which was founded on experiments, as expressed by the author, was to prove "that if any Two Loadstones were perfectly homogeneous, that is, if their Matter be of the same Specifick gravity, and if the same Virtue in all parts of one Stone as in the other, and that Like Parts of these surfaces are Cap'd or Arm'd with Iron, then the weights they sustain will be as the Squares of the cube part of the weights of the Loadstones: that is, as their surfaces".

He also translated a book on harmony which is published in London by James Watts in 1730, which contained the statement of truly Masonic feeling expressed in the rhythm of eighteenth century ritual that "Composition is the Part of Musick which teaches how to make use of concords, and of the Discords in a proper Manner; so or that the Union of the Parts, shall make Good Harmony", being no doubt accidental but to me, at any rate, sufficiently curious to deserve mention [one might go further by suggesting, as with much Masonic esoteric commentary, it to be pure invention, which of course is perfectly reasonable, so long as it does not then become 'fact']. Paisley was also concerned under the Duke of Richmond as President, with the formation in 1736 of the Society of the Encouragement of Learning. [However] The Society seems to have been formed for the protection of authors as much as for the encouragement of learning, to protect them against making bad bargains with booksellers. The project however was not a success. As Nichols says, [here is inserted a reference] it was as a direct attack on the booksellers, who are "no bad rewarders of literary merit", in other words, their necessity as middlemen soon demonstrates itself. After the Society had been driven to making contracts with some of the booksellers, in 1742 it became its own bookseller – but to no great purpose. Finally, after once more having recourse to the trade, the Society seems to have died of its own incapacity.'[7]

We have to return to Fara's book[8] to gain some further nuances of the scientific climate in general, our little Masonic community and Abercorn's likely contribution in particular. She points out the society's general interest in the subject, its spiritual connotations, commercial ramifications, etc., but more importantly she refers on many occasions to the interaction of others of this tight Masonic group and Paisley in particular and their interaction with the leading lights in the subject outside of Freemasonry. The question of why there is no inclusion of this subject in the 'Nature and Science' of Masonic Ritual and the Symbolical Lecture in particular will have to be returned to later.

Edwards reaffirms the Masonic details above, but more significantly mentions the seemingly notorious St John's Day feast that wasn't (it never actually took place) and points out that whilst he was active in earlier years when he was a member of the Lodge that met at the Horn Tavern, Paisley's attendance after his appointment as Grand Master quickly and progressively faded.

House of Inchiquin

This family descends through the complex aristocracy of Ireland. This particular line started with renunciation of his entitlement in the Irish (O'Breene) lineage, thereby submitting to the English Crown, the reward for which was the baronetcy of Inchiquin.[9, 10]

Murrough O'Brien = Elenor FitzGerald
(?-1551)   (?)
Prince of Thomond 1st Bart of Inchiquin   d. Sir Thomas

Dermod O'Brien = Margaret O'Brien (1st Cousin)
(?-1557)   (?)
2nd Bart of Inchiquin   d. Donogh O'Brien

Murrough Macdermot (O'Brien) = Margaret Cusack
(1550-1573)   (?-c.1589)
3rd Bart of Inchiquin   Sir Thomas

Murrough O'Brien = Mabel Nugent
(1566-1597)   (?-c.1611)
4th Bart of Inchiquin   d. Bar Delvin

Dermod O'Brien = Ellen FiotzGerald
(1594-1624)   (?)
5th Bart of Inchiquin   d. Sir Edmund

Murrough O'Brien = Elizabeth St Leger
(1614-1674)   (?-1685)
6th Bart/1st Earl of Inchiquin   d. Sir William

William O'Brien = Margaret Boyle   = Elizabeth Herbert (nee **Brydges**)(4 times married)
(1640-1692)   (?-1683)   (1651-1718)
7th Bart/2nd Earl of Inch'n   d. Roger El Orrery   wid Bart Herbert d. Geo. **Brydges** 6th Bart **Chandos**

William O'Brien = Mary Van den Bempe   = (?) Margaret O'Brien = Mary **Villiers** (cousin)
(1666-1719)   (?)   (?-1688)   (?-1753)
8th Bart/3rd Earl of Inch'n   d. Abraham   d. James   d. Sir Edward/**Howard**

William O'Brien = Anne Hamilton (1st cousin) = Mary Moore
(?-1777)   (?-1756)   (?-1791)
9th Bart/4th Earl of Inch'n   d. George Earl of Orkney   d. Vis Mount Cashell

O'Brien, William, 4th Earl of Inchiquin
(1696-1777)

b. 1696; *MP*, 1722-34; 1741-54; *KB*, 1725.

Governor of Co. Clare, 1741; and *Custos Rot.*, 1762-77; Gentleman of the Bedchamber to Prince of Wales, 1744-51; *PC*, 1753.

Grand Master, 1726.

d. 18 July 1777.

As with several of the later Grand Masters with which we are concerned, he appears to be a man of little dynamism. 'Reading between the lines' he appears to have entered Parliament by dint of convention rather than having good reason. 'A Whig, but voting generally against the Court. ' "Anti-Walpolean Whig". He and Lord Limerick (*afterwards* Earl Clanbrassill) and Mountrath are classed together under date 2 April 1731 as "gentlemen who vote always contrary to the Ministry [i.e. Walpole's]", in the Diary of the first Earl of Egmont'

He married his cousin Anne (*suo jure* Duchess of Orkney) the daughter of Elizabeth (Villiers) the mistress of William III. He (William III) rewarded Elizabeth's husband George Hamilton's condescension, they having married only the year previous, with the Earldom of Orkney. His first wife died in 1737. Although his precise date of birth is not known it is clear he had comparatively long life; indeed in 1761 he secondly married Mary Stephen (Moore) a wealthy heiress. He had three sons, but all predeceased him. Unfortunately, little more appears to be known of him and from that fact one may be correct in concluding that this is because there was nothing of note worth the writing. However, he had the correct antecedents and that alone appears to be qualification enough for the purpose of acting as Grand Master.

ɦouse of Coleraine

This family descends from the John Hare family of which he (Hugh) was the seventh son and as was typical of the times was created a baron by King Charles I. To what extent this was associated with his marriage into the Montagu family is a matter of conjecture.[11, 12]

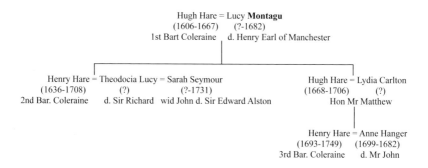

```
                    Hugh Hare = Lucy Montagu
                    (1606-1667)   (?-1682)
                    1st Bart Coleraine   d. Henry Earl of Manchester


  Henry Hare = Theodocia Lucy = Sarah Seymour              Hugh Hare = Lydia Carlton
  (1636-1708)     (?)            (?-1731)                  (1668-1706)    (?)
  2nd Bar. Coleraine   d. Sir Richard   wid John d. Sir Edward Alston      Hon Mr Matthew


                                              Henry Hare = Anne Hanger
                                              (1693-1749)   (1699-1682)
                                              3rd Bar. Coleraine   d. Mr John
```

Hare, Henry, 3rd Lord Coleraine
(1693-1749)

b. 10 May 1693; *FSA*, 1725; *FRS**, 1730;[13] Elected *MP*, 1730-34.

RWM, 1727 and 1731, Lodge at the 'Swan', Tottenham High Cross (*now* Castle Lodge of Harmony, No. 26); Grand Master, 1727; Grand Master of Ireland, 1743 (note: his grandmother Lucy, was a Montagu).

d. 10 August 1749.

He received a sound education under a personal tutor Dr. Uvedale (or Woodale depending on source). Following the death of his grandfather in 1708 he became Lord Coleraine. He was admitted a gentleman-commoner of Corpus Christi College, Oxford; his personal tutor being a Revd Dr. John Rogers, who later married his sister. He became a good classicist, specialising in civil and ecclesiastical history, publishing a number of notable (quite esoteric) texts and he was very highly rated by his peers.

He also possessed some artistic talents and recorded various antiquities, but most especially buildings, in his several trips abroad (principally Italy – whose Academy

– *Republica Litteraria di Arcadia* recognised him by admitting him a Member) in the form of prints and drawings (many now housed in the Bodleian Library).

He was elected Fellow of the Royal Society of Antiquities in 1725, frequently acting as vice-president. He too became a Member of the Spalding and Brasenose Society along with the others discussed above. He was elected as a Fellow of the Royal Society 1729. In that same year he became a Member of Parliament for Boston in Lincolnshire and remained so for four years.

In 1717 he married the daughter of the Governor of the Bank of England, who brought with her a huge dowry of £100,000. One has to assume that the marriage was an unfortunate one since she left forever in 1720. It would appear from his Will that it was a one-sided separation, for in it he goes on at great length to talk of her intransigence and his most noble attempts at reconciliation, but it is of course only one side of the equation. She appears to have remained genuinely unattached and he to have persisted in his endeavours of reconciliation for up to eighteen years, by which time he was forty-six years old, when he took up a relationship with a spinster Rose Duplessis, with whom he had a daughter and to all outward appearances and (given the circumstances) acted towards her most honourably, attempting to bequeath his estate to her, exclusive of the sum of the original dowry. The Government interceded and because his daughter was an alien, they escheated all entitlement to the Crown. This, after some substantial legal wrangling was afterward restored. It is of interest that he appointed George Paine (spelling was optional in those days) as executor of his Will.

His career as a freemason is also difficult to assess because, by this time and it could be argued appears to have remained true right up until today, it was predominantly the social standing and political correctness of the person that determined the appointment. This is exemplified in his letter of apology to the meeting of the Premier Grand Lodge that was due to elect his successor: 'that care should be taken that a person of honour and ability should be provided as G.M.', implying that they should consider Lord Kingston, which they duly did. It is of interest to note the outcome of a bid for relief at one of the meetings he did actually attend. He recommended that a sum of £10 should be donated to a Bro. North Stainer, but on finding that there was only £43 in the Treasurer's accounts, accepted the need to reduce that sum to £5, rather than attempting to provide the money by some further device, such as (given that he had proposed the donation) from his own extensive pocket.

He was politically astute, which became very apparent on a number of occasions, but not so overtly that he might be seen to be too embroiled. It is therefore difficult to arrive at the true nature of the man.

House of Kingston

This family descends from the Sir Robert King, who because of his military service to the king in Ireland was made Baron Kingston (Kingston of co. Dublin not Yorkshire or Surrey). [14]

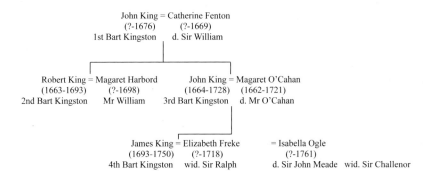

John King = Catherine Fenton
(?-1676)   (?-1669)
1st Bart Kingston   d. Sir William

Robert King = Magaret Harbord   John King = Magaret O'Cahan
(1663-1693)   (?-1698)   (1664-1728) (1662-1721)
2nd Bart Kingston Mr William   3rd Bart Kingston d. Mr O'Cahan

James King = Elizabeth Freke   = Isabella Ogle
(1693-1750)   (?-1718)   (?-1761)
4th Bart Kingston wid. Sir Ralph   d. Sir John Meade wid. Sir Challenor

King, James, 4th Lord Kingston
(1693-1761).

b. 6 May 1693; *PC* (Ireland), 1729.

Initiated 8 June 1726 (Lodge Swan and Rummer); Grand Master, 1728; GM of Ireland 1731, 35, 45/6; GM Munster, 1731; on one occasion (November 1729), his attendance being particularly requested at Grand Lodge, he left Ireland immediately, embarked for England and rode post from Holyhead in two and a half days, an example of 'his Worship's great love and regard to the Craft' (source of this plaudit unknown).

d. 26 December 1761.

As with virtually all of those with whom we are concerned, whilst James appeared to live a comparatively straightforward existence, the same was not true of his forebears. Thus to gain some idea of the man it is perhaps useful to start with James's uncle, who having served in the King's Army in the Rebellion (1641) became Governor of Boyle Castle (1642). However, by 1649 he was in the service of Parliament. He performed well as a military commander in the Revolution. Notwithstanding this handicap, in 1660 he was made a Baron (of Kingston Co. Dublin) soon after the Restoration. He went on to occupy many important posts and was granted substantial amounts of land in several Irish counties. He married Catherine Fenton, who in 1670 bore him a son Robert who in 1676 became the second Baron.

Robert on the other hand took an active part against James II and in 1689 was subject to attainder. In the July of that year he fled from Ireland, but later was in fact chosen to attend the King in Parliament with proposals for the settlement of Ireland. On the reduction of Ireland, he took his seat in Parliament in 1692. Although married he died without heir in 1693. The title reverted to John the brother of James above. He had earlier in his life renounced the Protestant faith for Catholicism and as a *PC* to James II had followed him to France and was outlawed accordingly. However, he obtained a pardon in 1695 and returned to England in 1697. He eventually integrated back, after a few hiccups, having been fined by the House of Lords in the meantime. When eighteen he married one of his father's servants and whilst in France she bore him a (second) son James.

It is interesting that in January 1707 he and his sister Sophia, being infants, petitioned for naturalisation, as 'born out of her Majesty's allegiance, but good protestant' (perhaps more prudent than Protestant). He was married twice, but neither provided an heir and his title became extinct on his death on 26 December 1761. He is accredited with no special virtues or talents and was sufficiently mundane to avoid mention in the various national biographies. So once again we have little of 'the man', but can infer quite a lot from his antecedence, which cannot have failed to influence him and colour his personality.

House (Duke) of Norfolk

This family descends from Sir Robert Howard, who married the daughter of Thomas Mowbray the Duke of Norfolk, the title falling to the male heir Thomas. Unfortunately he lost royal favour and was executed, but his son continued as The Earl of Arundel and was given the further title of the Earl of Norfolk. The Dukedom was eventually conferred (restored) on Thomas the 9th Duke's grandson. [15]

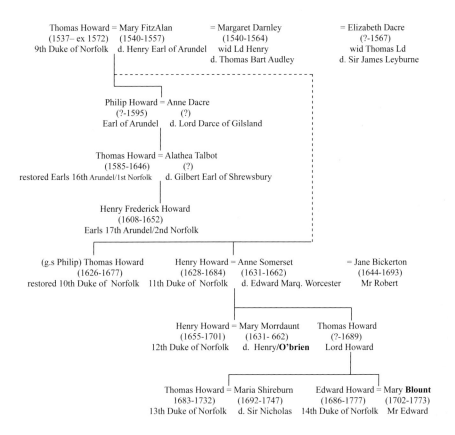

Thomas Howard = Mary FitzAlan   = Margaret Darnley   = Elizabeth Dacre
(1537– ex 1572) (1540-1557)   (1540-1564)   (?-1567)
9th Duke of Norfolk d. Henry Earl of Arundel   wid Ld Henry   wid Thomas Ld
                                           d. Thomas Bart Audley   d. Sir James Leyburne

Philip Howard = Anne Dacre
(?-1595)   (?)
Earl of Arundel d. Lord Darce of Gilsland

Thomas Howard = Alathea Talbot
(1585-1646)   (?)
restored Earls 16th Arundel/1st Norfolk d. Gilbert Earl of Shrewsbury

Henry Frederick Howard
(1608-1652)
Earls 17th Arundel/2nd Norfolk

(g.s Philip) Thomas Howard   Henry Howard = Anne Somerset   = Jane Bickerton
(1626-1677)   (1628-1684) (1631-1662)   (1644-1693)
restored 10th Duke of Norfolk 11th Duke of Norfolk   d. Edward Marq. Worcester   Mr Robert

Henry Howard = Mary Morrdaunt   Thomas Howard
(1655-1701)   (1631- 662)   (?-1689)
12th Duke of Norfolk d. Henry/**O'brien**   Lord Howard

Thomas Howard = Maria Shireburn   Edward Howard = Mary **Blount**
1683-1732)   (1692-1747)   (1686-1777)   (1702-1773)
13th Duke of Norfolk d. Sir Nicholas   14th Duke of Norfolk Mr Edward

The Grand Masters 1726-1730

Howard, Thomas, 13th (8th*) Duke of Norfolk
(1683-1732)

b. 11 December 1683; Earl of Arundel, Surrey, Norfolk and Norwich; Earl
Marshal.

Grand Master, 1730 and 1731. Nine PGMs. attended his Installation.
He donated £20 to general charity, Sword of State for use in Grand
Lodge, and a new minute book. That Sword is still used at the Quarterly
Communications etc.* In Masonic literature he is styled the eighth Duke,
but in Cockayne's Complete Peerage[16] he is sometimes classified as the
thirteenth Duke, the title having been restored in the mid 1600s as then
being the tenth in line.

d. 23rd December 1732.

As a comparatively young teenager he travelled extensively. At the age of twenty-six
he married a Maria Shireburn (then sixteen and half), who brought with her a fortune
of £30,000. It is reported in Lutteral Vol. VI pp. 439, 446, that: 'It was rumoured a
few months earlier that he was going to marry the eldest daughter of the Marquis
of Powys (*idem*, p. 350), but as long ago as 1706 it was known that he had "... a
design upon Sir Nich. Sherborne's, of the North, daughter and heir who has upwards
of £3,000. per annum and red lettered" (hist MSS. Com., Portland MSS., Vol. IV,
p. 329). The marriage proved unhappy: his wife, a staunch Roman Catholic and
Jacobite, is said to have separated from him in indignation at his having "truckled
to the Usurper", though she appears to have stood by him loyally at the time of his
arrest'. It is interesting to note that after his death she married, ten months later, in
November 1733, Peregrine Widdrington who had taken place in the Jacobite Rising
of 1715 (he was attained, but later pardoned).

As Earl Marshall (at the time of the Rising in 1715) he (Thomas Howard)
was able to exert influence in the acquittal of his brother and his heir presumptive,
Edward Howard, from the charge of high treason. He was arrested in October 1722
and imprisoned in the Tower for a time, on suspicion of being involved in the Jacobite
Plot. He was released on bail in 1723, on the surety of the Earl of Carlisle.

As a freemason it would appear that he was most conspicuous by his
absence. For instance he only attended the Premier Grand lodge to be installed,
left the selection and other matters necessary to appoint his successor to his deputy
Nathaniel Blackerby and even his donation of £20 and the Sword of State he did

by proxy. This observation is not intended to be an admonition, but to make the point that by the 1730s the post had changed to that of a mere figurehead, its only requirement being that of high social status. That the personal involvement with the new concept of Freemasonry shown by the early Grand Masters was missing and hence the likelihood of these 'cardboard' personages seeking innovation, such as the Royal Arch, within it was likely to be very low indeed.[17, 18]

He died after a long and uncomfortable illness on 23 December 1732. Again without issue and the title changed direction once more.

References

1. *Masonic Yearbook Historical Supplement* (2008): 'Premier Grand Lodge. 1717-1813'.
2. Anon. 'Hamilton' in *DNB,* Vol. VIII (OUP, 1968), p. 1609.
3. 'Abercorn' in *Complete English Peerage,* Vol. I (Ed. Cockayne, G., St Catherine Press, London, 1910), pp. 4-6.
4. Clarke, J.R., 'The Royal Society and Early Grand Lodge Freemasonry' *AQC* 80 (1967), pp. 110-117.
5. Hamilton in *DNB, op. cit.,* p. 1609.
6. Edwards, L., 'Three Early Grand Masters', *AQC* 43 (1932), pp. 226-238.
7. Edwards, L., *ibid.*
8. Fara, P., *Sympathetic Attractions* (Princeton University Press, Princeton, NJ, 1996).
9. Anon. 'O'Brien' in *DNB,* Vol. XIV (OUP, 1968), pp. 774-777.
10. 'Abercorn' in *CEP* Vol. VII (Ed. Cockayne, G., St Catherine Press, London, 1959), pp. 50-54.
11. Anon. Hare. *Dictionary of National Biography,* Vol VIII (OUP 1968), p. 1251.
12. 'Abercorn' in *CEP* Vol. III (Ed. Cockayne, G., St Catherine Press, London, 1913), pp. 365-367.
13. Clarke, J.R., *ibid.*
14. 'Abercorn' in *CEP* Vol. III (Ed. Cockayne, G., St Catherine Press, London, 1913), pp.
15. 'Kingston' in *CEP* Vol. VII (Ed. Cockayne, G., St Catherine Press, London, 1929), pp. 297-299.
16. 'Norfolk' in *CEP, ibid.*
17. Read, W., Let a Man's Religion ... Be What it May... *AQC* 98 (1985), pp. 69-89.
18. Anon. 'Notes and Queries' *AQC* 39 (1928), pp. 109-110.

Chapter Nineteen:

Grand Masters: 1731-1739 and the Dukes of Chandos

House of Leicester

his family descends from the Norman invasion in 1066. It went through a number of changes, but it was merged with all the other titles when Henry Bolingbroke became Henry IV in 1399. It reappeared as shown below.[1]

Robert Dudley = Amy Robsart   = alleg'y Douglas Sheffield   = Lettice Devereux
(1532-1588)   (1532-1560)   (?)   (1539-1634)
14th Earl of Leicester   d. Sir John   Wid. John d. Wil. Howard   Wid. Walter d. Wil. Cary

At his (suspicious) death the title became extinct. Robert Sydney was the heir of Sir Henry Sydney and Mary Dudley (Duke of Northumberland) and knighted by The Earl of Leicester. He therefore petitioned the queen (Elizabeth) for the title Lord Lisle. Through a series of such creations, he was eventually appointed Earl of Leicester.

Robert Sydney = Barbara Gamage = Sarah Smythe
(1563-1626)   (?-1621)   (?-1655)
15th Earl of Leicester   d. Henry/O'Brien   Wid. Sir Thomas d. Wil. Blount

Robert Sydney = (secretly) Dorothy Percy
(1595-1677)   (1598-1659)
16th Earl of Leicester   d. Henry Earl of North'd

Philip Sydney = Catherine Cecil
(1618-1697)   (1628-1652)
17th Earl of Leicester   d. Wil. Earl of Salisbury/Howard

Robert Sydney = Elizabeth Egerton
(1649-1702)   (1653-1709)
18th Earl of Leicester   d. Henry Earl of Bridgwater

Philip Sydney = Anne Reeve   John Sydney   Jocelyn Sydney = Elizabeth Thomas
(1676-1705)   (?-1726)   (1680-1705)   (1698-1759)   (1700-1775)
19th Earl of Leicester d. Wil. Earl of Salisbury/Howard   20th Earl of Leicester 21st Earl of Leicester   d. Lewis Thomas

Title once again became extinct and re-emerges via the Coke family, of which there exists some dispute over its origin, but which was generally believed to be that given to a master chef, who had the distinction of being called 'le Cok'. Whilst there is some mystery as to their origins, there is little doubt of the politics involved, not least his close alliance with Thomas Warpole. Whatever the underlying reasons, the reality is that he received a number of titles and eventually in 1744 was created Earl of Leicester. The irony is that the titles that he contrived to obtain for so long once again became extinct on his death.

Thomas Coke = Margaret Tufton
(1697-1759)   1700-1775)
22nd Earl of Leicester   d. Thomas Earl of Thanet

Thomas Coke, Earl of Leicester
(1697-1759)

b. 17 June 1697; Created Lord Lovel of Minster Lovel, 1728 and Earl of Leicester, 1744; Educated at the University of Turin.

MP, 1722-8; KB, 1725; *FRS*,* 1735[2] (*see* 2nd paragraph Chapter Eighteen),

Postmaster General, 1745 and 1758-9. Built the famous Hall at Holkham, Norfolk.

Grand Master, 1731. Whilst Grand Master formed an occasional Lodge at Houghton Hall (seat of Sir Robert Walpole) and made Duke of Lorraine (later Emperor Francis) and the Duke of Newcastle Master Masons.

d. 20 April 1759.

Again, it was not possible to find any extensive information with respect to his personality. From what little knowledge was found it appears that he was politically astute, but otherwise his character was not particularly wholesome. This is based primarily upon the following extract taken from the sub-notes in the Burkes Complete English Peerage.[3]

He was a neighbour and 'staunch supporter of Sir Robert Walpole', which was in stark contrast to his predecessor.

'According to a story told in the Earl of Egmont's Diary, under date 26 Jan. 1729/30, he was even then expecting or hoping for promotion in the peerage in return for voting with the Court, though he had to wait 14 years before his servility was rewarded'.

Ibid. 26th April 1737: "I was not pleased with the account of my Lord Lovell [...] as that my Lady Clifford his wife (who is a very agreeable and good lady) brought him £80,000, and when near undone in the South Sea year by that vile scheme, recovered his affairs, has so much as received of him her pin money; moreover, half a year after her marriage he resumed his debaucheries, and continues them with several ladies of quality and fashion".

Ibid. 12th February 1740, writes: "My Lord [Lovel] told me that his estate is £15,000 a year, his son about 22, and sober as to wine, and a meek temper [...]. That some might apprehend his son would live a wild sort of life, because himself does so, but that he had been careful of his education in that respect".

He built the present (1729) palace of Holkham, and stored it with choice works of art.

> ' Lovel, the oddest character in town;
> A lover, statesman, connoisseur, buffoon;
> Extract him well, this is his quintessence
> Much folly, but more cunning, and some sense;
> To neither party is his heart inclined,
> Voted with Warpole, and with Pultency dined".

> (Sir Charles Williams)

'A letter from E. Pile to S. Kerrich. (both of whom were Norfolk parsons), dated 10 May 1759, states that his death was the result of a duel with George (afterwards Marquis) Townsend, who had undoubtedly challenged him on 24 Jan. preceding. "A member of the Dilettante Society, a distinguished patron of the fine arts, also the great supporter of cockfighting in England of the day". The same writer describes him in his later years as "a waspish soured recluse, quarrelling with his neighbours, and still working on his unfinished house" '.

ɦouse of (Viscount) Montagu

The history of this family is another branch of the Duke of Montagu's family listed and described above and is hence repeated here, namely: that it is very old. It was first attested by Queen Maude in 1148 and was associated with the monastic lands at Montecute in Somerset. It suffered, as did most others, with certain breaks which prevented direct descendency[4], *see also* notes on the Duke of Montagu.

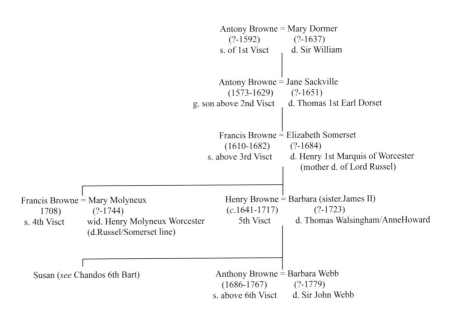

Antony Browne = Mary Dormer
(?-1592)   (?-1637)
s. of 1st Visct   d. Sir William

Antony Browne = Jane Sackville
(1573-1629)   (?-1651)
g. son above 2nd Visct   d. Thomas 1st Earl Dorset

Francis Browne = Elizabeth Somerset
(1610-1682)   (?-1684)
s. above 3rd Visct   d. Henry 1st Marquis of Worcester
(mother d. of Lord Russel)

Francis Browne = Mary Molyneux   Henry Browne = Barbara (sister.James II)
1708)   (?-1744)   (c.1641-1717)   (?-1723)
s. 4th Visct   wid. Henry Molyneux Worcester   5th Visct   d. Thomas Walsingham/AnneHoward
(d.Russel/Somerset line)

Susan (*see* Chandos 6th Bart)   Anthony Browne = Barbara Webb
(1686-1767)   (?-1779)
s. above 6th Visct   d. Sir John Webb

Anthony Browne, 6th Viscount Montagu
(1686-1767).

b. 1686. RWM. of the Lodge at the 'Golden Spike', Hampstead, 1731. GM1732.

d. 23rd April 1767.

Once again, it would appear that Anthony Browne the 6th Viscount Montagu was completely unremarkable. His only claim to fame being that he sold Battle Abbey shortly after he had succeeded to the Title on the death of his father, his older brother having died whilst quite young. He of course held the lesser title of Viscount, during a time where his more illustrious relation (the 4th Grand Master) held the title of the 2nd Duke of Montagu.

He was sandwiched (small 's' the Sandwiches were coming down the other line of the family) between two rather less creditable characters, if we are to believe the chronicler Mrs Roundell, who of his father wrote:

'He was profligate and superstitious, and having shot a priest who had refused him absolution, lived in hiding ever after', and of his son: 'His extravagance left the family estates much impoverished. His executors sold the borough of Mid-hurst for £50,000 to Lord Egremont. V.G. On his deathbed he rejoined the Rom. Cath. Church'.

Ҕousɇ of Strathmorɇ and Ꝃinghorn

This family descends from the John the second Earl of Kinghorne of whom Patrick was son and heir and was styled Lord Glamis until his father's death. However, in consequence of the Civil War this Scottish title was taken from them, only re-established in 1677 as an English title – 'the Earl of Strathmore and Kinghorne'. He wrote a book with respect to his (Glamis) family entitled: 'Glamis Book of Record'.[5]

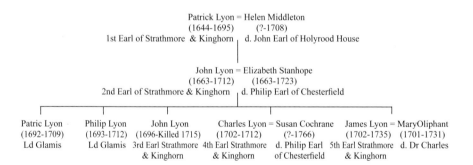

James Lyon, 5th Earl of Strathmore and Kinghorn (*see* note below) (1702-1735)

b. 24 December 1702, 6th Son of the 2nd Earl.

FRS 1732*;[6] RWM Lodge at the 'Bear and Harrow', Butcher Row (*later* University Lodge), 1731 and 1733; Grand Master 1733.

Said to have granted a deputation to eleven German Masons to open a Lodge at Hamburg, believed to have developed into Lodge Absolom.

d. 4 Janurary 1735.

N.B. In Hewitt's biography list it is claimed that he was the seventh, but he was not, for whilst his father had seven sons in all, the first predeceased him and it was his son John who became the third Earl, but was shortly after killed in action and was followed in turn by his brother Charles (the fourth Earl). Charles died in 1728 and it was then that James became the fifth Earl. The seventh son Thomas, two years his junior is not shown on the family tree above, but did go on to become the Grand master in 1744.

Once more, little appears to have been written about him, but he signals the second rash of military figures in the hierarchy of Freemasonry. He commanded a company of Barrell's Foot (22nd Regiment) in 1732. He represents yet another who contributed to the strong Scottish connection with the hierarchy of the early Premier Grand Lodge. Another similarity was the good fortune or adroitness of his forebears; since for some unexplained reason Cromwell saw fit to reduce the substantial fine that had been imposed on his grandfather after the Civil War, to a mere token. His father escaped the even more dire prospect of imprisonment for the crime of conspiracy in 1707, but avoided the almost certain likelihood of going to prison on the plea that his health was too poor for him to stand up to the journey to attend the trial. The reader will perhaps have thought this ploy to be a comparatively modern stratagem, but it seems that there is little that is new – to take the analogy further, in his case his clinical condition was so dire and life threatening that he lived for a further five years.

Although he became a member of the Royal Society there are no immediately obvious indications of its justification or of his expertise, but there was a need after 1732 for there to be a formal proposition, but since it is outside our remit it will be left there.

He (James) appears to have been 'a catch' so far as Mary (*née* Oliphant) was concerned. For her relatives had gone to considerable trouble to please his family: '... "her seize quartiers, apparently arranged with some difficulty to please the Strathmore family without too serious a deviation from the actual position" (if the report given in *R. R. Scottish Arms*, Vol. II, p. 416, is to be believed)'. [The 'pleasing' in this case was no doubt greatly assisted by a large dowry.][7]

Ꞙouse of (Viscount) Crawford

This family descends from the much older house and begins from the line of Sir David Lindsay 1314-55, the first Earl being his grandson David. The line jumped from one line to the next and this tree will start at the 13th (Henry). Sir David had a fourth son William: Lord of the Byres and this line continued independently until the Earl of Crawford's title was forfeited. It was restored to John in 1652.[8, 9]

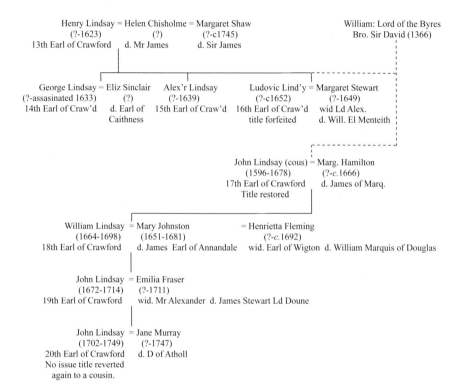

Henry Lindsay = Helen Chisholme = Margaret Shaw   William: Lord of the Byres
(?-1623)   (?)   (?-c1745)   Bro. Sir David (1366)
13th Earl of Crawford   d. Mr James   d. Sir James

George Lindsay = Eliz Sinclair   Alex'r Lindsay   Ludovic Lind'y = Margaret Stewart
(?-assasinated 1633)   (?)   (?-1639)   (?-c1652)   (?-1649)
14th Earl of Craw'd   d. Earl of   15th Earl of Craw'd   16th Earl of Craw'd   wid Ld Alex.
    Caithness   title forfeited   d. Will. El Menteith

John Lindsay (cous) = Marg. Hamilton
(1596-1678)   (?-c.1666)
17th Earl of Crawford   d. James of Marq.
Title restored

William Lindsay = Mary Johnston   = Henrietta Fleming
(1664-1698)   (1651-1681)   (?-c.1692)
18th Earl of Crawford   d. James Earl of Annandale   wid. Earl of Wigton   d. William Marquis of Douglas

John Lindsay = Emilia Fraser
(1672-1714)   (?-1711)
19th Earl of Crawford   wid. Mr Alexander d. James Stewart Ld Doune

John Lindsay = Jane Murray
(1702-1749)   (?-1747)
20th Earl of Crawford   d. D of Atholl
No issue title reverted
again to a cousin.

The Key to Modern Freemasonry

John Lindsey, 20th Earl of Crawford
(1702-1749)

b. 4 October 1702.

FRS, 1732.[10] Representative Peer of Scotland, 1732-49; Gentleman of the Bedchamber to the Prince of Wales in 1733.

Trained as a soldier. Capt. Scots Guards, 1734; Col., Black Watch; Col., Scottish Horse Guards; Col., Scots Greys; Adjutant-General, 1739-43; Brig.-Gen., 1744; Maj.-Gen., 1745; Lieut.-Gen.,1749. Served with distinction in numerous campaigns and was known as the 'Gallant Earl of Crawford'.

Initiated Lodge of Edinburgh (Mary's Chapel), 1733 (under the temporary presidency of Lord Strathmore, Grand Master of England); Grand Master 1734; attended the Premier Grand Lodge regularly during his term of office. Made far-reaching proposals regarding the irregular making of freemasons and administration of the Charity. He also drew attention to irregularities in regalia worn in the Premier Grand Lodge.

d. 24 December 1749, as a result of wounds received at the battle of Krotzha, near Belgrade, ten years previously, from which he had clearly never recovered fully.

His life started rather conventionally, but whilst a small child his mother died and when at the age of eleven his father died, he was placed under the guardianship of his grandaunt the Dowager-duchess of Argyll and from this event his Scottish affiliation was cemented. He was tutored privately and then went on to Glasgow and Edinburgh Universities and in 1721 was sent to the military academy of Vaudieuil in Paris. On completion he joined the Scots Greys. He became noted for his prowess in many forms of sport, including dancing and whilst (reportedly) continuing with, or rather 'did not neglect' his studies, although the source did not indicate their nature, but later suggested that they were 'military' studies. He then set out on a series of campaigns and because, in common parlance, 'he led from the front', they might almost be described as escapades. This gallantry and service, and one must assume his natural ability, led to a succession of promotions. His campaigns were legion, which included a significant role in the Scottish Rebellion and as we shall see, he was in this respect and in a number of other ways, very like the 20th Grand Master discussed below. Indeed their careers are remarkably similar, including receiving a serious wound, but in his case the wound never really healed and in the account of his later years it was implied that this eventually worsened to such an extent that it cost him his life.

His time of appointment as Grand Master was during one of the most active parts of his career and whilst he appears to have given it adequate attention, it was likely to have been little more than that. Similarly, his membership of the Royal Society was likely to have been even more peripheral. Indeed, Clarke[11] points out that, as today, one is elected by other Fellows, which in practice is not the same thing as the 'most worthy', although there is somewhat more academic rigor in the present system, it is nonetheless highly politicised. However, in those days it was metaphorically and often literally the case that they were elected by their peers. This seems most likely true of Lindsay, given the nature and extent of his other commitments and interests; this contention was further supported by the total lack of any academic reference whatsoever and so Clarke's scepticism was likely justified in this instance. Even if one presumes that he was accepted as a Fellow of the Royal Society, for social rather than academic reasons, if his citation for acceptance could be found it might at least throw some light on the nature of the man. However, it too appeared to follow the pattern in which the Royal Society members were recorded during that period, that are only rather scant details in a small book, giving little more than their name. Neither was it certain that any further detail would appear on the sponsorship forms of his application. In any case, these entries are most difficult to trace, since they are not in phase with the date of their acceptance. It is no doubt recorded somewhere, but in this instance it was not found, but even if it had been located, judging from similar entries, it would have carried little or no detail of specific justification or a list of achievements of the said applicant, especially if in reality there was nothing to write. Although these 'Accounts' or minutes are written in the most beautiful 'copper plate' handwriting, they are not particularly easy to read and because of the way they are compiled, it would seem that the entry for new members can appear anywhere within it. An extensive search was made in and around that period, but no entry could be found that indicated his academic interests/ qualification or ought else that would warrant his election.

Ḩousᴇ of (Viscount) Ⱳᴇymoutb

This family descends from the (Shropshire and Gloucester estates in both counties) family of Sir Henry Thynne. He had a brother Thomas, whose grandson became the 2nd Viscount – *see below*. For greater detail *see* works of Boyle – Marchioness of Bath.[12,13]

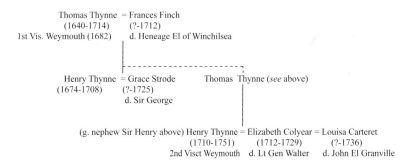

```
              Thomas Thynne  = Frances Finch
                (1640-1714)       (?-1712)
   1st Vis. Weymouth (1682)   d. Heneage El of Winchilsea


           Henry Thynne = Grace Strode        Thomas Thynne (see above)
            (1674-1708)     (?-1725)
                         d. Sir George


   (g. nephew Sir Henry above) Henry Thynne = Elizabeth Colyear = Louisa Carteret
                                (1710-1751)      (1712-1729)        (?-1736)
                             2nd Visct Weymouth  d. Lt Gen Walter  d. John El Granville
```

Thomas Thynne, 2nd Viscount Weymouth
(1710-1751)

b. 21 May 1710.

High Steward of Tamworth, 1733; Keeper of Hyde Park and Ranger of St James' Park, 1739-50.

Initiated 11 March 1734, King's Arms Lodge (*now* Old King's Arms Lodge, No. 28). RWM, 3 March 1735, but relinquished the office after two months (13 months in total) on election as Grand Master, 17 April 1735.

d. 12 January 1751.

Those who have read works by authors such as Jane Austen will know of the massive consequences (and good fortune or injustice – depending on the recipient) of the laws of inheritance during these times and this is a particular case in point, where there was a marked change in the line. When researching this section of the early Grand Master one is struck by how many are considered to be so inconspicuous by chroniclers and although they carried grand titles and moved within influential society their contribution was deemed to be of so little significance as not to warrant half a mention. Further, other than marking their chronological position in the family structure they even failed to merit inclusion in otherwise quite comprehensive reference sources such as the *Dictionary of National Biography*, which has over twenty volumes and which is biased towards the inclusion of any snippets of information related to those possessing such titles. This appears to be for two main reasons: first, dukes, barons, lords, etc. can co-exist within the same family at one and the same time. Second: these people, as in this instance, seem to lead a relatively empty life, simply 'bumping along the bottom' until perchance, inheritance lifts them from comparative obscurity into the limelight. Thus, as before, to gain some impression of the man we must first consider Sir Thomas Thynne, the first Viscount Weymouth. By contrast he was a man of some substance and was directly related through his brother (our Thomas's father) to the queen of Charles I. He was well educated and politically astute, judicially changing sides from time to time. It is amazing how such audacious juxtapositioning was possible. Perhaps in reality it was not so easy and the reason that it appears so simply is because we only are concerned with the few who were successful at it. Although, in truth, he does not appear to have been that secretive or devious, indeed considering the apparent risks, he seems to have taken quite the opposite approach. He would be best identified today by his development of the Longleat Estate (famed for its wild life park) in Wiltshire, where he spent much of his later life.

Unfortunately, his son pre-deceased him and when he died in 1714 at the age of seventy-four, he left no direct heir and in consequence he was succeeded by the comparatively obscure Thomas Thynne (*see* 2nd Viscount above), grandson of his (Sir Thomas's) younger brother, Henry Frederick, inheriting amongst other things the Longleat Estate. It is of interest that the second viscount was father to Thomas Thynne, who became the 3rd Viscount Weymouth and first Marquis of Bath.

He married into the Sackville family, marrying the second daughter when she was aged fourteen, but did not (according to the chroniclers) cohabit with her, since he left immediately on a military campaign and she died three years later before his return. He married again in 1733, but unfortunately his second wife died three years later shortly after giving birth.

A lengthy quote from the main reference used here in this appraisal is of some interest in understanding the man. It is for the most part a quotation from the 'History of Modern Wiltshire':

'After his 2nd wife's death he appears entirely to have neglected Longleat, where he never lived again. There is a story, related by Lady Bath [here a quote] that he may have "had a murder [*sic*] on his conscience". He is said to have fought a duel in a passage at the top of the house with an unknown man, who was his wife's lover [...] that he killed this man, and that he buried the body at Longleat [...]. When central heating was put in at Longleat, during the 5th Marquess's lifetime, the body was found buried in the cellars. He was wearing jackboots [it does not say what else], which crumbled away as soon as the body was exposed to the air. (Here some reference to a ghost is made) [...]. He appears from the autobiography. and corres. of Mrs Delany, [again a quote] to have been a selfish man, who nearly ruined himself and his sisters by his extravagance after his wife's death. Mrs Delany, however, in 1731, speaks of him as "good natured and affectionate, but liberal without distinction, warm in his temper, could not bear contradiction [itself a contradiction in terms], and had not discernment enough to be reasoned with" [ditto the above comment] and of his 2nd wife, she says that "she was very sensible, discreet, of a complying temper, gentle, mild, and withall very lively" (Idem). Mrs Pendarves writing, 21 July 1733, to Dean Swift, says of him, "he has honour and good nature, and does not want for sense: he keeps a very hospitable good house, and is always ready to relieve those in distress" (quote). [...]'.[14]

Once again, one is left to interpret from this account the nature of the man and how he would have performed in the role of 'the Grand Master' in Freemasonry. It was, after all, only two years after the death of his second wife and if we are to afford the above quote any credence, this was during the period where he began to behave rather strangely.

house of (Earldom) Loudoun

This family descends from an earlier strand, but is begun here with the marriage of Margaret the granddaughter of George Campbell, Master of Loudon who renounced his titles in her favour (essentially that of her husband).[15,16]

Margaret Campell = Sir John Campell
(1605-1661)   (1598-1661)
1st Earl, 2nd Baron Loudoun   s. James Ld Colvill
|
James Campell = Margaret Montgomerie
(?-1684)   (?-*c.*1685)
2nd Earl, 3rd Baron Loudoun   d. Hugh Earl of Eglintoun
|
Hugh Campell = Cous. Margaret Dalrymple
(?-1731)   (1685-1779)
3rd Earl, 4th Baron Loudoun   d. John Earl of Stair
|
John Campell
(1705-1782)
4th Earl, 5th Baron Loudoun

John Campbell. 4th Earl of Loudoun
(1705-1782)

b. 15 May 1705.

FRS;[17] *FSA*; Representative Peer of Scotland, 1734-82; Governor of Stirling Castle, 1741-63; *ADC* to the King, 1743-5; Governor of Edinburgh Castle, 1762-82.

Entered Army in 1727; Col. of several regiments; Major-Gen., 1755; Lieut-Gen., 1758; General, 1770. Governor General Virginia and C-in-C. of the Forces in America, 1756; C-in-C. of Forces in Portugal, 1762.

Grand Master 1736 (Styled then as Lord Mauchlane).

d. 27 April 1782.

As the name implies, there was a strong connection with Scotland. He succeeded his father the 3rd Earl in 1727 and became a representative peer of Scotland. He was appointed governor of Stirling castle in 1741. He joined the military in 1727 and from then onwards his career was dominated by military activity both home (especially in Scotland, for example the rebellion in 1745 etc.) and abroad. He later moved to America and was embroiled in many skirmishes there, not least with the French. (Note: the earlier Grand Masters' problems in defending their Caribbean Islands against the French). In 1762 when the war with Spain was declared he entered the fray there, principally in Portugal.

He remained unmarried and his title reverted to the son of the 2nd Earl. He was particularly noted for his interest in trees and imported many species. However, outside of his quite distinguished military career there appears remarkably little else and during the time that he was Grand Master, he was most active militarily and one has to wonder, given both this and his geographical location at that time, the degree to which he would have been able to carry out his duties. It is quite clear that he was one of the many, who one might say were obsessed with the military, who nonetheless were prepared to hold the highest office in Freemasonry, which would (should?) have not only involved their period as Grand Master, but presumably the important years before and after holding that high position.[18]

The Key to Modern Freemasonry

House of (Viscountcy/Earldom) Darnley (of Athboy Co. Meath)

This family descends from Sir Alan Stuart of Darnley who by marriage was related to Duncan Earl of Lennox, whose son John Stuart was created Lord Darnley in 1439. The title continued until the death of Matthew the 4th Earl, when they devolved to his grandson King James VI, who was the son and heir of the well-known Lord Darnley. Thus the titles became extinct until events in the 1720s, where the title was reinstated for essentially political and marital (she was Baroness Clifton and was a descendent of Esmé Stuart duke of Lennox, Earl of Darnley, thereby except for royal precedence was heir to those titles) connections – *see below.*[19]

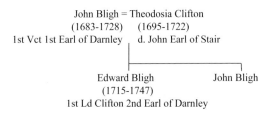

John Bligh = Theodosia Clifton
(1683-1728)   (1695-1722)
1st Vct 1st Earl of Darnley   d. John Earl of Stair

Edward Bligh   John Bligh
(1715-1747)
1st Ld Clifton 2nd Earl of Darnley

Edward Bligh, Earl of Darnley
(1715-1747)

b. 9 November 1715; Also known as Lord Clifton.
FRS;[20] Lord of the Bedchamber of the Prince of Wales;1742-47; Grand Master 1737; again very young – just twenty-two years old. d. 1 August 1747 and buried in Westminster Abbey.

He came of long established and notable Darnley stock, but even more strongly through the female line, through which he was related to the Lennox and Stuart Families and through which he could be traced into the Royal Line – the Earl of Richmond's (8th Grand Master) father was also the Earl of Darnley and was said to have been the Master of a Lodge in 1695.

He received a good education, first at Westminster School and then Geneva and his eventual fellowship of the Royal Society in 1737 may have been due to some merit, although there is no obvious scholarly output to support that assumption.

He became Grand Master when he was twenty-two and like several of his predecessors and indeed many successors, simply rocketed to (Masonic) fame. He died when just thirty-one and such was his status he was buried in Westminster Abbey. However, once again we are left with a cardboard figure, where nothing of particular merit seems to have been worth a mention.

House of (Baron/Dukes of) Chandos

This family descended from Sir Giles Brydges who married the daughter of Sir Charles Chandos the final heir to a very old family. His son the first baron served with Henry VIII in campaigns and politically afterwards, from whence the Barony and the line began. It is of interest to note that they became connected with the family of **Montagu** by marriage in 1637.[21, 22]

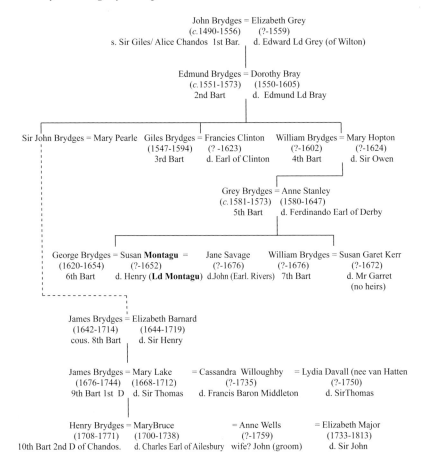

John Brydges = Elizabeth Grey
(*c.*1490-1556)   (?-1559)
s. Sir Giles/ Alice Chandos 1st Bar.   d. Edward Ld Grey (of Wilton)

Edmund Brydges = Dorothy Bray
(*c.*1551-1573)   (1550-1605)
2nd Bart   d. Edmund Ld Bray

Sir John Brydges = Mary Pearle   Giles Brydges = Francies Clinton   William Brydges = Mary Hopton
(1547-1594)   (? -1623)   (?-1602)   (?-1624)
3rd Bart   d. Earl of Clinton   4th Bart   d. Sir Owen

Grey Brydges = Anne Stanley
(*c.*1581-1573)   (1580-1647)
5th Bart   d. Ferdinando Earl of Derby

George Brydges = Susan **Montagu** =   Jane Savage   William Brydges = Susan Garet Kerr
(1620-1654)   (?-1652)   (?-1676)   (?-1676)   (?-1672)
6th Bart   d. Henry (**Ld Montagu**) d.John (Earl. Rivers) 7th Bart   d. Mr Garret
(no heirs)

James Brydges = Elizabeth Barnard
(1642-1714)   (1644-1719)
cous. 8th Bart   d. Sir Henry

James Brydges = Mary Lake   = Cassandra Willoughby   = Lydia Davall (nee van Hatten
(1676-1744)   (1668-1712)   (?-1735)   (?-1750)
9th Bart 1st D   d. Sir Thomas   d. Francis Baron Middleton   d. SirThomas

Henry Brydges = MaryBruce   = Anne Wells   = Elizabeth Major
(1708-1771)   (1700-1738)   (?-1759)   (1733-1813)
10th Bart 2nd D of Chandos.   d. Charles Earl of Ailesbury   wife? John (groom)   d. Sir John

Henry Brydges, 2nd Duke of Chandos
(1708-1771)

b. 1708 (christened 1 February)

Marquis of Carnarvon, succeeded to Dukedom of Chandos, 1744; *MP*, 1724-44; Lord of the Bedchamber and Master of Horse to the Prince of Wales, 1735; Clerk of the Hanaper Office; Ranger of Enfield Chase; High Steward of Winchester, 1754.

Grand Master, (*then* styled as Marquis of Carnarvon) 1738. Presented a golden jewel for use of the (Grand) Secretary.

d. 28 November 1771.

He again was someone who was acutely politically aware, but otherwise appears to have contributed little else of note. In his case he was one of the Whigs who were anti Walpole. He married three times, which may of itself illustrate his powers of persuasion, since it would appear, at least from one account that his physical appearance was not overly attractive: Mrs Delaney writes of her (Chandos' wife) and her husband as 'The ugliest couple this day in England'[23] and whilst it may be asked by what means she could have gained such an expansive knowledge of the population at large, it is nonetheless damning, since she must have at least known quite a few. Through his first marriage he became related to the Savile and Carnarvon dynasties, indeed his wife was styled the Marchioness of Carnarvon when she died. Notwithstanding this reported physical disadvantage, his next marriage was quite remarkable also, in that he married Anne Jefferies. Here the biographer suggests' *See* the story of her being sold 'with a halter around her neck' by her husband (Jefferies), an ostler at the Pelican Inn, Newbury, and purchased by the Duke of Chandos, in N and Q., 4th Ser. vol. vi, p. 179, G.E.C. She had been his mistress for some years. Lord Orrery writes of her, 15th Jan. 1744/5, '... of her person and character, people speak variously, but all agree that both are very bad...' He married for a third time when he was nearly sixty.

He died at the age of sixty-three and George III reportedly said of him, 'There my Lord Carnarvon, a hot headed, passionate, half-witted coxcomb' (Herveys *Memoirs*). It is perhaps sad that what little has been written of him is less than favourable, perhaps, like several of our characters, the good men do 'is oft interred with their bones ...'.

This connection between the Chandos dynasty and Freemasonry continued long after our period of interest when his son was made Grand Master from 1754-57, they (Grand Masters) had begun to hold the office for extended periods by then.

House of (Baron) Raymond (of Abbots Langley)

This family has a very short line and descends from Sir Thomas Raymond a justice of the King's Bench and Barony given to his son below, was essentially a political appointment.[24]

Robert Raymond = Anne Northey
(1673-1731)   (?-1720)
1st Baron Raymond   d. Sir Edward

Robert Raymond = Mary Blundell
(1717-1756)   (?-c1784)
2nd Baron Raymond d. Montagu Vis Blundell
title became extinct

Robert Raymond, 2nd Lord Raymond
(1717?-1756)
b. *c.*1717. Was also styled as Baron of Abbots Langley
FRS*;[25] PC 1756; RWM of the Lodge in Florence, 1738 (?); Grand Master, 1739.
Again only twenty-two years old which suggests very rapid promotion.
d. 19 September 1756.

Yet again, there appears to be very little written about him, with even his date of birth in some doubt. He travelled to Italy in his late teens and if the above is correct, was active in Italian Freemasonry.

His wife was Mary Blundell, the youngest daughter and co-heir of Viscount Blundell, bringing with her a £10 000 dowry.

He too was active politically and was the Chairman of the Committee, which moved the commitment of Astley and Cave for printing an account of Lord Lovat's trial in 1749. He died when only thirty-nine, when the peerage then became extinct.

This concludes the list of short bibliographies of Grand Masters during the period when it is virtually certain that the Royal Arch had been in existence for some time. It therefore remains to decide which of these twenty or so Grand Masters presided over its conception and introduction and by so doing begin to answer the question 'when'? Among those parameters must be their personality and commitment and hence drive. It only remains to reflect on other influential characters who may or may not have been freemasons, but who were nonetheless likely to be of extreme importance to this study. Whilst there are a number of others who fall within this category and may well be worthy of further investigation, for the moment specific

The Key to Modern Freemasonry

reference will be restricted to just one, others where applicable being left to comments within the subsequent text.

So last but by no means least is the remarkable Duke of Montagu who is left to complete this series of 'potted' bibliographies of significant persons in early Freemasonry. As suggested above there were one or two characters, such as Secretary Cowper's uncle, who whilst apparently outside of Freemasonry were nonetheless of extreme importance to it and in this respect James Brydges was especially significant. Just as the charisma of William Cowper was a mere shadow of his uncle's, the same may be said of the difference between the 2nd Duke of Chandos and his father James Brydges. There is no evidence that the first Duke was a freemason, or at least not in London (the greater likelihood being that he was not, because although he was seventy-three by the time his son was made Grand Master, since he lived a further six years it is reasonable to suppose that he was sufficiently strong for them to have provided, in the manner of Lord Kingston above, a 'chariot' for him to attend). But he had such a profound influence of many of our leading players that this short account has to be included.

James Brydges. 1st Duke of Chandos – *see* 2nd Duke for family tree
(1673-1744)

b. 6 January 1673. s. James Brydges: 8th Lord Chandos. *FRS*, 1694; *MP* for Hereford 1698-1714; created Viscount Wilton and Earl of Carnarvon by George I in 1714; Marquis of Carnarvon and Duke of Chandos 1719; 1707 Paymaster General (lucrative post).

d. 9 August 1744.

There is not the slightest doubt that he was a larger than life character. He spent prodigious amounts of money on property; the most famous of which was the splendid house 'Canons' (or 'Cannons' depending on source). He patronised 'The Arts', but managed to alienate their affection will similar aplomb. For instance he was reputed to have given £500 to the poet Pope only to come under serious attack by him later. He employed famous artists and commissioned Handel to write a whole portfolio of original pieces. He was reputed to have 120 staff and had a choir entertain his guests at dinner.

However, as we have seen from the biographies of Desaguliers, Stukeley and others, he was disposed to dabble in all kinds of things, not least those that were likely to bring profit. Another typical relationship concerning the important freemasons with whom we are concerned was his personal physician Dr. John Arbuthnot, who again was a *FRS* and a dabbler in many other things. However, Chandos got into trouble with his speculative investments. Swift (1734) in his verses on 'The duke and the dean', says that 'all he got from fraud is lost by stocks' Swift also accused him of neglecting his friends once he had become 'beduked' – this appears to have been over a request for some documents to be placed in the University of Dublin. It is perhaps not totally fair to dwell on the comments of Swift, but from his other work he seems to have been an objective commentator of the times. In Swift's 'Caricatures of the Court of Queen Anne', he called Chandos 'a very worthy gentleman, but a great compiler with every court'.

He was given various appointments by George II and was clearly astute enough to have negotiated himself through the various dynasties without great loss. He was married three times. The extent of his family was not listed in references used here, but he was succeeded by his second son Henry, five of his other sons having predeceased him.

However, from the point of view of this study it was his association with the 'scientists' of the early Premier Grand Lodge that are of particular importance, but it was his dealings with Desaguliers that are of especial significance. Although Chandos employed Desaguliers as the incumbent in one of the parishes under his patronage, his true reason for befriending him was the potential wealth of his scientific inventiveness. He commissioned Desaguliers to build him an 'improved' fire (steam) engine on his estate at Canons. Similarly when his African Company, essentially a slave trading venture was experiencing difficulties, for a whole gamut of reasons, both social and commercial, he asked Desaguliers to investigate the possibilities of exploiting the mineral (potash) wealth that appeared to exist on his African property – but not before he requested that they generate potash for soap manufacture, by exploiting the forests on his Scottish property. He was also keenly interested in mining on both his own and on anybody else's property that he was presently leasing.

It is impossible to go into a comprehensive discussion of all his activities, but primarily they stemmed from his entrepreneurial zeal and the subsequent attempts to recover from their unfortunate consequences (almost all it would seem) of them. Although it must be said that much of this mayhem was outside of his control. It was principally the hysterical financial climate that led to the South Sea Bubble affair and about which he tried to warn others. Unfortunately he did not heed his own advice and became heavily embroiled (a modern example would be the impact that advertising proclaiming the known dangers of smoking or alcohol seems to have on those seriously addicted to smoking and drinking). He subsequently went on to believe that their (attempting to involve other extremely influential people such as Walpole) salvation, and particularly his, lay in his African ventures. He soon realised that slavery and ivory were effectively no longer viable, but Africa's mineral wealth (not to mention the potential of gold) was immense. Unfortunately disease always intervened and wrecked every initiative, even leading him to embark upon a programme of inoculation for his adventurers. He realised that the key to solving his problems lay in medicines. Africa's flora and fauna held great potential in that field and the possibilities for domestic exploitation were potentially unlimited. This became yet another of his initiatives and whilst it was conceptually sound, it too went wrong. All sorts of schemes were entered into in and around this basic theme and which extended to the West Indies for a period. Many ended in disaster for a range of reasons, including mutiny, but for most he placed his faith in technology and science and for this he turned to that circle, which included some of our most important characters, principally John Desaguliers. He had a deteriorating relationship with him, but it would seem he never lost his respect for Desaguliers' ability (describing him as: 'The best Mechanick in Europe' a euphemism for 'World' one would imagine in the context of those times) until his death. Desaguliers was in many respects like the nineteenth century engineer Brunel, in that he took on too much (financial pressures forced him to do so) and then ran out of time and money, much to the annoyance of Chandos.

We leave Chandos with two things clear that he was a man who for the most part actually understood and recognised the importance of science, Nature (medicines) and technology and championed their exploitation. Second that he had enormous influence (he provided them with money and patronage) over the important people involved in the early years of the Premier Grand Lodge and society in general, not least by trumpeting the value of science and provided the financial support that enabled them to practice Freemasonry.

Chandos is better dealt with elsewhere,[26] especially in Stewart's book, which brings out quite graphically, through cross-referencing, his important connection with the scientist and technologists of this period.[27]

A case could be made for continuing this extended round-up of individuals such as Hauksbee and Derham who were likely to have been of influence in our appraisal and, as we have seen, Masonic historians have claimed that others even more famous such as Wren were actually freemasons. As for Cowper and Chandos there is no actual proof of any Masonic affiliation one way or the other, but their association with those who were so strongly involved with it, suggests that they could have been in Freemasonry outside of the London area or that the Records were incomplete. For instance there is no record of Walpole in the List of Members,[28] but in Curl's book[29] he states that Francis the Duke of Lorraine, later to become Emperor of the Austrian Empire was initiated into Freemasonry in Walpole's home Houghton

Hall in Norfolk. Incipiently changing the whole concept of Mainland Europe's Freemasonry adding a strongly English dimension. Jones[30] also mentions Walpole (Lord Orford) as being a freemason. This theme will be returned to in Chapter Thirty-eight when discussing Desaguliers, in the process of which the explosion in the number of clubs and societies is discussed. Within this discussion the claim will be made that there was a strong influence due to provincial societies. During this part of the research an interesting snippet[31] of information came to light which illustrated the possible significance of Provincial Freemasonry. Dr William Derham, *FRS*, also an Oxford trained cleric/astronomer was quoted as being a member of the Essex Mathematical Society, included in whose membership were many of those with whom we are concerned. But a matter of particular interest was that Derham's living was in Upminster (1689-1735) which coincided with the period in which the vicar of the neighbouring parish (Little Warley) was Dr John Desaguliers. Dr James Pound, *FRS*, another Oxford trained and effectively working freelance for Newton came from Wanstead another Essex Parish, again only just nine miles away. The giant maypole in London's Strand was offered to Derham, but he could not afford it and so Newton bought it for Dr Pound. Derham, Pound and Desaguliers exchanged instruments, but more importantly friendship with each other. To pursue this type of dialogue further runs into serious danger of becoming a distraction and so it will be left here and any further individuals will be alluded to in passing.

References:

1. Anon. 'Leicester' in *The Complete English Peerage,* Vol. VII (St Catherine Press, London, 1929), pp. 548-560.
2. Clarke, J.R., 'The Royal Society and Early Grand Lodge Freemasonry' *AQC* 80 (1967), pp. 110-117.
3. Anon. 'Leicester' in *CEP, op cit.*
4. Anon. 'Montagu' in *CEP* Vol. IX (St Catherine Press, London, 1936), pp. 100-102.
5. Anon. 'Lyon' in *CEP, Ibid.*
6. Clarke, J.R., *op cit.*
7. Anon. 'Montagu' in *CEP, op cit.*
8. Anon. 'Lyon' in *CEP, op cit.*
9. Anon. 'Hare' in *DNB,* Vol. XI (OUP, 1968), pp. 1184-1185.
10. Clarke, J.R., *op cit.*
11. *Ibid.*
12. Anon. 'Thyme' in *DNB,* Vol. XIX (OUP), pp. 848-849.
13. Anon. 'Weymouth' in *CEP,* Vol. XII, Pt II (St Catherine Press, London,1953), pp. 585-589.
14. *Ibid.*
15. Anon. 'Loudoun' in *CEP,* Vol. XIII (St Catherine Press, London, 1932), pp. 158-162.
16. Anon. 'Campbell' *DNB,* Vol. IV (OUP, 1968), pp. 828-829.
17. Clarke, J.R., *op cit.*

18. Anon. 'Campbell' in *DNB, ibid.*
19. Anon. 'Darnley' in *CEP,* Vol. IV (St Catherine Press, London, 1959), pp. 83-84.
20. *Ibid.*
21. Anon. 'Chandos' in *CEP,* Vol. III (1913), pp. 126-132.
22. Anon. 'Brydges' (Chandos), in *DNB*, Vol. III (1916), pp. 162-163.
23. Anon. 'Chandos' *ibid.*
24. Anon. 'Reymond' in *CEP,* Vol. X. (1945), pp. 151-152.
25. Clarke, J.R., *op cit.*
26. Anon. 'Chandos', *ibid.*
27. Stewart, L., *The Rise of Public Science.* (CUP, 1992).
28. The Minutes of the Grand Lodge of Freemasons of England 1723-1739. (*QCA* X. 1913).
29. Curl, J.S., *The Art and Architecture of Freemasonry* (Batsford, London, 1991), p. 52.
30. Jones, B.E., *Freemasons' Guide and Compendium.* (George Harrap and Co. London 1950).
31. Crouch, W., 'Astronomy in Wanstead' in *Essex Naturalist,* Vol. VII (1893), pp. 151-164.

Table 20.1 Status of family during the reign of ELIZABETH I (1558 – 1603)

HOUSE / CODE	1	2	3	4	5	6	7	8	9	10	11	12
Abercorn n/a												
Buccleuch n/a												
Chandos												
John Brydges	E	(c)K	(c)B$_1$		c		b	x	d	x	x	54
Edmond Brydges	E	(b)B$_2$					b	x	d	x	x	57
Giles Brydges	E	(b)B$_3$						x	d	x		73
William Brydges	E	(b)B$_4$						x	d	x		94
Grey Brydges	E	(b)B$_5$							d	x		02
Coleraine n/a												
Crawford												
David Lindsay	S	(b)E$_{11}$			cep		b	x	d	x	x	74
Darnley n/a												
Inchiquin												
Murrough O'Brien	I	(w)P	(c)B$_1$		i		b		n/a			43
Dermod O'Brien	I	(b)B$_2$			i				d			97
Murrough O'Brien	I	(b)B$_3$			i				d			57
Murrough O'Brien	I	(b)B$_4$			i				d			73
Dermod O'Brien	I	(b)B$_5$			i				d	x		97
Kingston n/a												
Leicester												
Robert Dudley	E	(w/o)D	(c)E$_{14}$	(f/r/e/)	c	(e & s!)	b	x	o	x	x	64
Loudoun n/a												
Montagu (Vct/Bart)												
Anthony Browne	E	(b) V$_2$			c							54
Norfolk												
Thomas Howard	E	(b)D$_9$		r	c/ex		b	x	g	x	x	54
Raymond n/a												
Richmond												
Henry Fitzroy	S	(w)E$_{14}$	(c)D$_1$	e	c	e(i)	b	x	d	x	x	25
Strathmore n/a												
Weymouth n/a												
Wharton												
Thomas Wharton	E	(w)K	(c)B$_1$		c		b	x	d	x	x	44
Thomas Wharton	E	(b)B$_2$					b	x	d	x	x	68
Philip Wharton	E	(b)B$_3$					b	x	d	x	x	68

Symbolic Key for each column

1. Family (basic roots) (E)nglish, (S)cottish, (I)rish, 2. Was (w) Became (b) Created (c), other titles (o), 3. Further elevation (c), 4. Title forfeited (f), Became extinct (e).Restored (r), Surrendered (s), Attained (a), Pardoned (p), 5. Executed (ex), Controversy (c), Exiled (e), Killed/detained (k): battle$_1$, murdered$_2$, imprisoned$_3$, insane$_4$, 6. Related to royal blood English (e), Scottish (s), Irish (i), 7. Politically active royal appointee: Intimate/sexual (a) other (b), 8. Politically active: Parliamentary (x), other science sc, trade/technology (t), 9. Line of decent: Direct (d), Brother (b), Grandson (gs), Illegitimate (i), Cousin (c), Uncle (u), Nephew (n), Stepbrother (s), Others say where recreated, revived etc. n/a, 10. related to others on list (x), 11. Militarily active (x), 12. Date of appointment *if after period of acting as Grand Master.

Key to title

(K)night, (B)aron, (V)iscount, (L)ord, (E)arl, (C)ount, (D)uke, (M)arquis, (P)rince, (Dr) doctor, (Mr) Mister, Honourable, Esquire, other.

Chapter Twenty: A potted history from the death of Elizabeth I to the establishment of the Premier Grand Lodge

he history of the British Isles during the 130 years or so prior to the forming of the Premier Grand Lodge is perhaps the most complex and difficult to understand of any period before or since. This is for a number of reasons, but principally for two: first because of the innate political instability, including civil war, it is difficult to extract true intent of the characters involved. Second the chronicling of the events was, because of easier printing etc., (contemporary) writing was much more prolific than in earlier periods. Unfortunately in this instance, more does not necessarily mean better, or more objective, or better explained, it just means more!

This because of the strong correlation between literacy and social status during that period, for it would seem that those so gifted, were at the same time obliged to adopt their own particular political and/or religious stance. However, for anyone taking sides it was of course fraught with danger and the content of contemporary reporting reflects this. Because of this factor and a plethora of others, latter-day historians have relished the scope afforded by the period, especially the heroics of some of its principal players. As most school children will testify, history is dominated by the principal events affecting the rich and famous, battles, plagues, famines etc. These milestones (dates) are snap-shots of events in the lives of otherwise privileged people; usually dwelling upon say their unfair trial, fall from grace, false imprisonment, or worse, execution; but only mention in passing the losses (horrendous death and suffering of lesser individuals, due to war, disease, retribution and poverty etc.) of tens of thousands of ordinary folk, who formed the extras in this erstwhile staged event.

There is of course considerable justification for this approach, since it was the action or inaction of the principal players and the degree of their various attributes of wit, stupidity, animal cunning, morality or immorality, religion, inhumanity, lust

From the death of Elizabeth I to the Premier Grand Lodge

etc., which affected the lives of the hapless majority. Any hope that this present contribution is going to redress this imbalance in any real way is sadly misplaced. The excuse here is that we are interested only in that narrow group of people who, because of their social standing, would have been likely to occupy the attention of historical researchers; hence the space devoted to the biographies in Part III. Indeed the principal reason for including this next section and its style is to show how the relationships between those particular individuals (in the period *circa* 1690 to 1740) were predetermined by the events and the manner in which their forebears survived during the preceding 150 years.

However, in order to understand how events such as the formation of institutions like the Royal Society, the Greenwich Observatory, the Premier Grand Lodge, or explain the expansion of the arts and sciences etc. and how they were brought about or became possible, it is necessary to at least reflect on the basic sociology during that period. Although all these factors are intimately linked, this short appraisal will for convenience, consider the history as three parallel streams: hierarchical, sociological (commerce, education etc.) and scientific, with some cross-reference made where it is either unavoidable or otherwise helpful. However, in modern parlance this package carries a 'health warning' and this for two reasons: first the writer has a view and despite all attempts to repress it, the fear is that it will nonetheless be present. The second and even more significant is that the only access to the information used here is through the work of other historians and archivists, who have most likely been influenced in much the same way. Neither can one hope to précis the many thousands of scholarly hours that have been devoted to the researching and writing of these quite remarkable studies, exemplified by well known authors such as Antonia Fraser (the life of Charles I)[1] and Sir Keith Fielding (the Period in general),[2] but also the many others that have been consulted and/or referred to (not necessarily all by name) here. No attempt will be made to emulate their work, but to distil the salient points of this period in history as it relates to our principal characters and Freemasonry and trust that by so doing there has been no massive distortion of the generally agreed reality.

There is a case for citing many points in this period as being the root cause of the change from operative masonry to the basic form of speculative (English) Freemasonry that was to become epitomised in the Premier Grand Lodge studied here. But as we shall see a very strong case can be made for having its basic foundation in the accession to the monarchy of James I. This because Elizabeth had an innate mistrust of the 'aristocracy' and had emaciated it to the point of extinction, whereas James I adopted a completely contrary strategy and he was to create the social (hierarchal) structure from which the Premier Grand Lodge was to evolve. Thus there will be an introduction of the position of the aristocracy up to the death of

Elizabeth, after which each regime will be dealt with in turn. Working on the basic premise of this study: that the Premier Grand Lodge (*c.*1723 as defined here) was the result of a contrivance of a narrow body of individuals, headed up and given credence by a similarly narrow band of the aristocracy. An attempt will be made to indicate how this incongruous and essentially unhealthy fraternal relationship seemed to evolve during this period. Thus for each epoch a chart has been constructed to show the status of the respective families during the period in question. We are concerned with three Royal Houses, the Tudors, Stuarts, Hanoverians and the intervening Commonwealth, but especially the quasi (illegitimate) house of Charles II. The family trees of these respective houses will be shown and the respective tables will precede each section.

House of Tudor

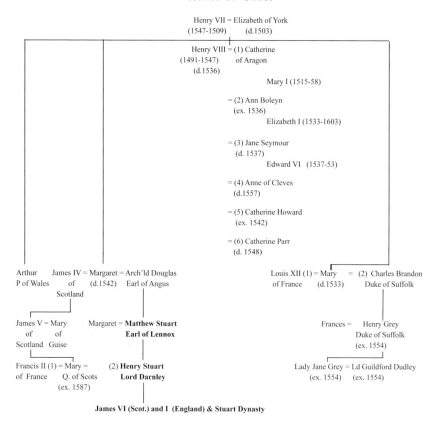

Henry VII = Elizabeth of York
(1547-1509)   (d.1503)

Henry VIII = (1) Catherine
(1491-1547)   of Aragon
(d.1536)

Mary I (1515-58)

= (2) Ann Boleyn
(ex. 1536)

Elizabeth I (1533-1603)

= (3) Jane Seymour
(d. 1537)

Edward VI (1537-53)

= (4) Anne of Cleves
(d.1557)

= (5) Catherine Howard
(ex. 1542)

= (6) Catherine Parr
(d. 1548)

Arthur   James IV = Margaret = Arch'ld Douglas
P of Wales   of   (d.1542)   Earl of Angus
Scotland

Louis XII (1) = Mary   =   (2) Charles Brandon
of France   (d.1533)   Duke of Suffolk

James V = Mary   Margaret = **Matthew Stuart**
of   of   **Earl of Lennox**
Scotland Guise

Frances =   Henry Grey
Duke of Suffolk
(ex. 1554)

Francis II (1) = Mary =   (2) **Henry Stuart**
of France   Q. of Scots   **Lord Darnley**
(ex. 1587)

Lady Jane Grey = Ld Guildford Dudley
(ex. 1554)   (ex. 1554)

James VI (Scot.) and I (England) & Stuart Dynasty

From the death of Elizabeth I to the Premier Grand Lodge

Indeed in many respects these tables may be regarded as the most significant aspect of this section of the work for the following reason. Freemasonry is conveyed by many as the present day version of that which has existed from time immemorial, but it is the thesis of this work that the formalised Freemasonry of the Premier Grand Lodge was a highly stylised and effectively new version of what was already a comparatively new innovation. That it was constructed by an individual or at most several individuals and fronted by men of an integrated group of aristocrats that had few historic roots. That even in the few families within this group who may be considered ancient, there had been dramatic breakages within the line and so there was little or no continuity there either. That effectively all of the principal players had a troubled history and financial difficulties. That a general ambivalence towards the Church meant that there were no great classical (cathedral type) buildings being commissioned that relied totally upon the unique skills of the stonemason. Thus in a sense the following short biographies merely set the scene and provide the backcloth for the enactment of the Premier Grand Lodge. As a prologue the demise of the House of Tudor is considered. However, because a title appears throughout in some cases that does not mean that there had been continuity. It is extremely difficult to illustrate this subtle characteristic and so the device of using a table is introduced. These tables show the state of the respective families during the reigns of the various monarchs/Lord Protector during the period from Elizabeth I and George II. But much care has to be taken when interpreting these tables and to illustrate this, notes are provided below Table 22.1, but the key and a similar analysis should be used on all the other tables in Part III.

The death of Elizabeth I marked the end of the Tudors, but more importantly it also showed the extent to which the upper levels of the aristocracy had been decimated. Those English families that were apparently extant at the time were, except for the Browne, only Barons. Those of the Whartons and the Cowpers who were Knights were in practice to expire. Thus the table would appear to show that families such as the Brydges, Dudleys and Montagus were thriving, but their lines of decent were in practice to be broken and if care is not taken the tables tend to give a wrong impression. It is especially important to note that the majority of names that were to survive throughout were in fact Scottish or Irish and so the stage was set for James I to develop his own aristocracy. Whilst the field was open for James I, to start afresh and establish a powerful team, he elected to be influenced by the gaggle of opportunist who clustered about him, especially certain of his family, erstwhile friends, sycophantic associates and a sizable Irish contingent who worked tirelessly, not to say shamelessly, to gain the King's approval and grateful largess. Chapter Twenty-one deals with matters concerning the Throne during this period and will show how the descendants of this group were to eventually become pre-eminent in the aristocratic element of the Premier Grand Lodge. Even then most were of quite recent origin, interrelated and many were of highly dubious character if not descent.

However, this section will start with a brief resumé of Elizabeth I. There have been numerous books and chapters written on the life of Elizabeth, such as that by Neville Williams[3] and like those written about the other heads of state in this list, each author has their preferred stance. Each of the short pieces in this work has been structured on the work of several authors and there has been an effort to remain objective, but it is difficult. As the reign of Elizabeth was nearing its end, its relative tranquillity had given it a distinct advantage (domestic, commercial, maritime, colonial etc.) over the warring factions of the otherwise competing (European) neighbouring nations. Of course Elizabeth engaged in disputes and wars – as the Armada is testimony, but in essence she abhorred war and recognised its futility and hence entered upon them with great restraint. Not that she would have needed to struggle to justify military action and it is certain that many another monarchs, especially given the urging from her contemporaries, would have done so with gusto. When all else had failed and she was forced to act, she would for the most part (greatly assisted by Lord Cecil) fund them in such a way that it would not bankrupt the country. Throughout her reign, because of rival claims, she was under both personal and political threat, not least from Mary Queen of Scots. Many attempts at arranged marriages were contemplated or proposed, but for whatever reason she remained single and most historians write that she was greatly influenced by her partiality for a succession of 'favourite' men. Although she was so successful in the way in which she steered her way through these turbulent times, if emotion did enter the equation, she kept it under great restraint.

Another interesting factor which is of direct interest here, was that for a number of reasons there had been a notable decline in the 'landed gentry', which may have been due to the caution resulting from experience gained during the earlier years of her reign. This strategy was based on the premise, one might say Tudor principle, that the fewer occupying a position of influence; the easier it was to maintain political control. Not that there was any lack of excuse or encouragement for internal conflict, from many, if not most, of those around her. For instance, there would have been sufficient reason to justify an all-out engagement with the Scottish and the Irish. Although the following is an understatement of the situation, in the event she made no significant move against or to overly interfere in the Scottish or Irish situation, leaving them to resolve their own destiny internally through private battles. This was not true in the case of Mary Queen of Scots, who, if the historians are right, spent most of her life involved in one intrigue or another, not least plotting against the English throne, to which she claimed title. However, her disposition towards political intrigue was not confined to this, but to the more general goal of the reinstatement of Catholicism, which led to escapades in Scotland, involving disputes over its crown, imprisonment and escapes. This ended eventually in her 'confinement' in England (Elizabeth would not have her imprisoned as such, and although she appeared solicitous of Mary's wellbeing she would not actually meet her) and after the discovery of plots against the life of Elizabeth and other misdemeanours, she was eventually executed. Another remarkable example of Elizabeth's political insight was that she would not name her successor, claiming that to have done so would in fact endanger her life further. Although plots were planned against her, they were discovered in time, which would imply that she was not totally correct in this respect, but even so died of natural causes in 1603. It is reported, not without invoking the scepticism of some historians, who argue that she was unable to physically speak at this late stage, that she did not nominate her successor and then only obliquely, until shortly (hours) before her death; namely James VI of Scotland, ironically the son of Mary Queen of Scots. In terms of this study her decision was of profound importance to the eventual structure of the Premier Grand Lodge, because it created the situation where English aristocracy had been so emaciated that it was in no position to resist that which would be imposed by James I.

Another outstanding feature of her personality – or perhaps shrewd management – especially the financial aspects, was her abhorrence of war, however, this may have been influenced as much by its cost as other matters. She roamed the country continuously, imposing herself and her huge entourage on a succession of unfortunate hosts and her lack of immediate family (as we shall see in the case of her successor, with its huge attendant costs) assisted in this prudence. However, towards the end of her reign she relaxed this tight grip and died with a national debt of £400,000, which was to prove the worst possible start for James I, whose almost total incompetence in financial matters was to greatly affect the way in which he reigned – not least the huge sums necessary to support the plethora of aristocracy he went on to create. A trait later emulated with great panache by his son and grandson, the adroit survivors of this largess are extremely well represented in those who founded the Premier Grand Lodge.

Whilst the history of the 130 years or more with which we are concerned is, because of its depth of infamy, intrigue etc. and collection of 'odd-ball' characters, one of particular interest in its own right, the real purpose here is to study and perhaps wonder how the families of those involved in founding the Premier Grand Lodge survived through it. Then, just as today, most attention is focused on those who have succeeded, little is said of the far greater number who tried but failed. Because of the complex nature of events during that period it is not possible to guess at numbers, but there must have been far more losers than winners, many rising and falling in quite spectacular fashion. Since Elizabeth had ensured that there were few powerful aristocratic (especially those of interest to us) families left, it is reasonable to start with the growth of the aristocracy following the accession of James I. It will become clear that most of the forebears of our characters emerged during this period, particularly the illegitimate children of Charles II. We can see from Table 20.1 that they were the only winners of what at times was quite literally, a deadly game. When reading these tables it is useful to refer to the personal bibliographies, for although the family name is maintained there are marked breaks in the continuity, with several dying out completely, only to be reinstated in the quasi royal aristocracy of the progeny of Charles II. Whilst it is possible that luck played a part in this process, it is much more likely they were the few who possessed the requisite guile and deviousness, requiring only a little good fortune to 'ease' their way through this long and dangerous period. Other than the Whartons who were alluded to earlier, of the surviving English families we are interested in three: the Darnleys, who despite the murder of Lord Darnley, were to reappear later, the Montagus and the Cowpers, who kept a comparatively low profile during the 1500s. A fourth was in Scotland where there were many people involved in various intrigues that surrounded the young prince and subsequent king. But at this time there was one in particular: the pro English conspirator, Esmé Stuart, created the Duke of Lennox, a family name that would appear later in the guise of Charles the 2nd Duke of Richmond, the 7th Grand Master, whose installation was to prove another watershed in the story of the early the Premier Grand Lodge.

To provide some understanding of the survival through these troubled times of the few established families amongst the first Grand Masters, it is useful to reconsider the family tree of the Tudor dynasty above and that of the Stuarts in the next Chapter. Of the eight families in the Chart, five were English (only one would go the whole way through) and three were Scottish or Irish, by the end of James I's reign there were eleven names, the original five English, but now six Scottish and Irish. Notice the name and line of descent of those highlighted, which may serve to explain the otherwise disproportionately large Scottish connection in the caucus of those who eventually formed the Premier Grand Lodge, intensified by having a monarch of Scottish descent. From this it can be seen that it was principally the Scottish and Irish seeds sown by James I, that were destined to grow and flourish during the greater part of the seventeenth century, with only the 'crop failure' of the Civil War stunting its growth.

Working on the notable human characteristic that; 'the grass is always greener on the other side of the fence', it is suggested by most historians that following Elizabeth's death in 1603, the general mood was not one of gloom, but rather that there was an air of relief, if not optimism, abroad and the advent of James I was hailed by most as a refreshing prospect; a view shared wholeheartedly by James himself, entering the fray with Messianic zeal.

References

1. Fraser, A., *King Charles II* (Futura Publications, Macdonald & Co., London. 1988).
2. Fielding, K., *A History of England*, (Macmillan, London 1966).
3. Williams, N., *Elizabeth* (George Weidenfeld and Nicolson and Book Club Associates, 1972).

Table 21.1 Status of family during the reign of JAMES I (Eng) VI (Scot) (1603 – 1624)

HOUSE / CODE	1	2	3	4	5	6	7	8	9	10	11	12
Abercorn												
James Hamilton	S		$(c)B_1E_1$			s	b	x	d	x	?	03/06
James Hamilton	S	$(b)B_2E_2$				s	b	x	d	x	?	18
Buccleuch												
Walter Scott	S		$(c)B_1$			s	b	x	n/a	x	x	06
Walter Scott	S	$(b)B_2$	$(c)E_1$			s	b	x	d	x	x	11/19
Chandos												
Grey Brydges	E	B_5					b	sc	d	x		02
Grey Brydges	E	$(b)B_2$					b	x	d	x	x	21
Coleraine												
Henry Hare												
Crawford												
David Lindsay	S	E_{11}					b		d	x	x	74
David Lindsay	S	$(b)E_{12}$			c k_3				d	x		07
Henry Lindsay	S	$(b)E_{13}$							u	x		20
George Lindsay	S	$(b)E_{14}$			c				d	x	x	23
Darnley												
n/a												
Inchiquin												
Dermod O'Brien	I	B_5				i	?		d	x		97
Murrough O'Brien	I	$(b)B_6$				i			d			24
Kingston												
n/a												
Leicester												
Robert Sydney	E	V_1	$(c)E_{15}$				b		n/a(m)	x	x	18
Loudoun												
John Campbell	S		$(c)B_2$		c			x	w	x		22
Montagu (Vis)												
Anthony Browne	E	V_2			c		b	x	d	x		92
Montagu (Bar)												
Edward Montagu	E		$(c)B_1$		c		b	x	n/a	x		21
Norfolk												
n/a												
Raymond												
n/a												
Richmond												
Ludovic Stuart	S	$(w)D$	$(c)E_{15}D_2$	e		s	b		n/a	x		13/24
Strathmore												
n/a												
Weymouth												
n/a												
Wharton												
Philip Wharton	E	B_3					b	x	d	x		72
Philip Wharton	E	$(b)B_4$							gs	x		25

For key to table *see* foot of Table 20.1

Chapter Twenty-one: James VI
(Scotland – 1566/1625) and I (England – 1603/25)

Before considering the reign of James I it is helpful to put it in context with the moral climate prevailing at that time. Any conclusion drawn will of course depend upon one's own level of moral perception since it has to be recognised that in more recent times there has been a considerable shift in public opinion and society's acceptance of what may be deemed morally correct. The public's perception on such factors as: illegitimacy, homosexuality, lack of honour in both word and action within the business world (considered now as 'part of the game'), matrimonial inconstancy as 'matter of fact', the

betrayal of state secrets for money, now seemingly legitimised by the courts etc., has replaced the superficial rigor of the 'Victorian' type ethical code. However, accepting all of this, one is still struck with an overwhelming perception of the seediness of the times and especially the moral fibre of the kings and queens with whom we are concerned and those associated with them.

Many historians ask the question 'why pick upon the behaviour of the Stuarts, since much the same could have been levelled at say Elizabeth who preceded him. However she was 'her father's daughter' and schooled in his image, but despite such brutal tutelage, she nonetheless made great strides towards humanising the relationship between the monarchy and the people: exemplified in, if only just as a token, the greater implication of Parliament. During this brief look at the sociology of the hundred years or so prior to the formation of the Premier Grand Lodge it will become clear that there was a massive change in the relationship between the monarch and the state. Although it may have been against her disposition, Elizabeth seems to have accepted the reality of the situation and adapted to the inevitable changes that were taking place. By doing so she deflected their impact rather better than confronting them head-on as appears to be the case with James I.

Most newspapers seem to flourish on 'bad news' and this human trait may explain the apparent tendency of historians to prefer comment on the warts, rather

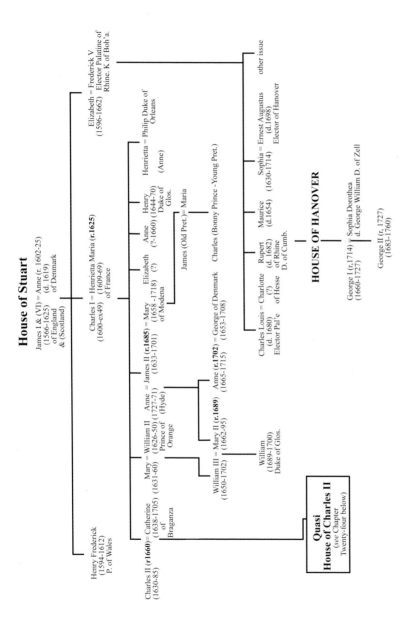

than seek any natural beauty of a person's outward appearance or personality. Or maybe it is a natural characteristic and that in order to survive in such a hostile environment, the 'winners' needed to be innately devious and unpleasant.

It is certain that if James I had ever needed to defend himself in a modern court-of-law, he could call on a host of expert psychiatrists who would willingly plead his case: his lonely impoverished childhood, desertion by his mother, her complicity in the murder of his father, physical ill treatment by those who were responsible for his care, a harsh court regime, severe tutelage, deliberate exclusion from female company, latent homosexuality, the machinations of the deep intrigues of those around him, his mother's eventual execution etc. would provide ample argument. Surely any one of these mitigating factors could be used to explain his actions and offer sufficient excuse for his subsequent behaviour; thereby making a case that his actions should be forgiven, if not condoned. If all these psychological factors were then coupled with what seems to be a universally agreed lack of conventional physical beauty and social graces, it would more than explain his strangely distorted personality and the inevitable defects in character. Whereas in the case of Charles II, for example, historians described him as having great beauty and charm, which for some peculiar reason, somehow excuses equally nauseating behaviour.

However, if we are to believe the historians (depending to some degree upon whom), James I in this respect had metaphorically, a huge personal and sociological 'millstone' about his neck. These historians differ to some degree, even on what might be considered factual data, such as his physical stature, beauty, charm, manners, etc., or rather lack of them. However, they are unanimous in the fact that he had 'spindly legs', which is somehow considered to be a particularly damming feature. Not that it really mattered, because there seem to be an absolute plethora of other things with which to beat him. Snellgrove for instance writes of him as follows:

'The first Stuart was neither heroic nor attractive. Small and plump, with thin legs, rolling eyes and over-large tongue, he seemed older than his thirty-seven years. Probably this was due to illness for he suffered from piles, catarrh and diarrhoea. His personal habits were revolting. He dribbled, picked his nose and was often sick through over-eating. He was a coward who wore extra padding in his clothes in case anyone tried to attack him. It was hard to believe his mother had been so beautiful and his father, Lord Darnley, so strong and handsome [...], James had been king of Scotland for most of his life. His childhood had been lonely and unhappy – left without parents, beaten by his teachers, bullied by lords who struggled for power. Slowly, more by cunning than force, he overcame both murderous nobles and intolerant priests'.[1]

Snellgrove goes on in this rather 'boo' and 'hooray' fashion of seemingly all historians to say that he was well educated, an authority on biblical matters, monarchy, witchcraft, sport and smoking. Stating that the much (of French origin) quoted 'Wisest fool in Christendom', should be interpreted as: 'meaning that he was cunning only in trivial not important matters', but in practice this was really 'not fair' comment. Followed immediately, by the fact that he considered him to be conceited, a bore and a drunk, but on the other hand he was generally kind, often witty, at times tolerant and peace loving. His major attribute was keeping England out of wars and his worst his treatment of Raleigh.

On the other hand, Kenyon using in places the words of another author D.H. Willson, writes that:

'James was thirty-nine, but looked rather younger, with his straggling adolescent beard, watery-blue eyes and thin brown hair. He was tall, [not older looking or 'small and plump' – as suggested by Snellgrove above] and the breadth of shoulders and chest was accentuated by contrast with his thin spindly legs [you were warned]. (Like his son Charles, he walked badly, rode a horse well). His tongue was "too large for his mouth, which ever made him drink uncomly, as if eating his drink, which came out into the cup of each side of his mouth". He dressed with an affection of simplicity that later degenerated into slovenliness, and "his skin was as soft as tafeta sarsnet [a fine cloth], which felt so, because he never washed his hands, only rubbed his fingers' ends slightly [note: not roughly in some uncouth way, its difficult to imagine how he could have washed the rest of the body if he 'never' washed his hand, and so it may be inferred body odour was another black mark] with the wet end of a napkin". His sense of humour matched his personal habits; always course and anatomical, it rose sometimes to "a fluorescence of obscenity" '.[2]

In virtually all the books consulted with respect to this period the historians set out to, or if they are to remain reasonably objective perhaps cannot avoid, illustrating the intrinsic unpleasantness of the personalities involved, but then as if by some compulsion or an innate tendency to see 'fair play', they seek by the device of subtle phraseology to excuse it. Much as in the fashion of the 'Walrus' in 'Through the Looking Glass' where these characters claimed to be most solicitous of the health and feelings of their erstwhile (oysters) victims as they effectively (ate) signed their death warrants. Perhaps it would be more accurate to say that these were extremely hard times and if they were to survive at all, it was necessary to 'meet like with like'. If that person was then possessed of peculiar unpleasant personality traits, that had to be indulged, that merely increased the need to be more ruthless and extreme in their actions. This scenario appears to be especially true of James I and it makes the précis of his life quite difficult if the account is not to appear churlish. Our interest is in those within his orbit who (have an eventually implication with the Premier Grand lodge) managed to survive intact and retained influence or even prospered, through these troubled times. Well before the death of Elizabeth, he had every reason to believe (a secret visit by Cecil, the receipt of a £4,000 pension from Elizabeth etc.) that he would inherit the English crown. By dint of necessity, he had been forced by both fair means and foul, to finally gain control over Scottish affairs, in so far as that was ever possible. However, Scotland was an impoverished kingdom and it would be reasonable to suppose that the view taken by historians is correct: that he considered the English Crown a potential El Dorado, even if not necessarily 'a land flowing with milk and honey'. His increasing belief in his omnipotence was made complete on acceding to the English Crown. One may be disposed to challenge this, on the basis that most historians claim also that he was quite 'intelligent' and as such would not have been so deluded. But then one realises that such delusions of infallibility are not confined to that period, since it would seem that it is a view enjoyed by many, if not all, modern politicians (who are similarly credited with intelligence and education). If indeed this were the case, this arrogant self-belief would, to some extent, explain why he would not face up to the political and financial realities, but rather to indulge in an unusual and for the most part unwholesome lifestyle. This would explain also his choice of associates, which feeding upon itself, became introverted, satisfying the self-interest of those about him, many of whom were not only more politically aware than he, but were even more devious and ruthless in the prosecution of their ambition; leading him to take irrational and impolitic decisions. He was king. His physical attributes were an accident of birth and his extreme unwholesomeness could have been explained if not excused, but those who associated with him (except for the queen who probably had little choice in the matter) did so by design. The fact that these associates were prepared to be closely intimate, some physically so, with someone so bodily and morally unattractive, indicates their depth of ambition. Given that he was as 'uncomely' as is suggested, then it is not surprising that he was so readily seduced by such attention and flattery. This susceptibility appears to have become accentuated with time, probably due to his progressive degeneration in every other respect, especially mental, so that by his late forties he has been described by some as prematurely senile.

Because his life is so unusual and was so influential in moulding the history up until the time with which we are concerned, it makes fascinating reading. From the works of most historians, it is usually possible to find strands of 'beauty' within it, but it would seem that however hard one searches into the life of James I it is mostly 'warts'. The following is a précis of his reign so far as it affects this Study; its function intended to show the ingenuity required of the forebears of the Founders of the Premier Grand Lodge to contrive or exploit their way through it. We will see that those families are comparatively few, that there is a very strong and steadily increasing Scottish stream, together with some Irish influence and that the one or two established English families that managed to survive 'hung on by their finger tips', the remainder were for the most part losing their heads (literally in some cases) in the process.

As has been stated already whole books have been written about the man and his time and the following is only a poor substitute for that level of scholarship. Historians generally agree that his English reign was in two somewhat unequal parts. The first part being that where he was more in possession of his faculties and objectivity and was prepared to be guided strongly by those who had formed the intrinsic elements of the administration inherited from the Elizabethan era. This initial stability was principally due to his retaining the counsel of Cecil (Lord Shaftesbury), the son of Elizabeth's Cecil. However, even during this period the elements that were to later shape events were already in place. As stated above the Tudors had decimated the aristocracy, with only one duke left by the time of Elizabeth and he was later executed. James for his part went berserk, creating knights galore; one historian suggests that he created around 200 simply on his way down from Scotland. Indeed he was perhaps the first to overtly adopt the ploy of 'cash for honours' and created his own price list and at one point obliged those in possession of a certain level of income to become knights, which of course required them to pay the appropriate fee!

Whatever the underlying psychology he failed to recognise that times had changed and that by then emancipation (Parliamentary) from monarchical domination was essentially unstoppable; a malevolent genie was out of the bottle. Elizabeth had managed, by political skill and womanly charm, to nullify the emerging importance of Parliament, but James was not so well blessed and because Parliament was such an anathema to him, he was to find the task extremely difficult, if not impossible. In a sense he was destined to fail from the start, for he was not only saddled with all the disadvantages mentioned above, but was given to wild monetary excesses, unwise patronage and other proclivities, the sum total of which was in effect to prove the task beyond redemption. For instance one of Elizabeth's ploys had been to have men of influence in Parliament to argue her case, James either through arrogance or imprudence took the opposite view, seeking to almost disregard Parliament's ever-increasing importance. Much as today the incoming administration has to work, at least for a time, with the existing establishment. James, wisely or of necessity, did retain the services of a few of the most influential people. Indeed he promoted Sir Robert Cecil (the then Secretary for State) to Lord Treasurer and created him the Earl of Salisbury. In the early years of his Reign he worked to promote peace both in terms of wars with foreign states and dissension between religious groupings at home. He steadfastly, one might conclude fatally, treated Parliament with disdain. However, in the final analysis Parliament controlled the purse strings and he would have been well advised to restrain his outward hostility towards it. Having started his reign in debt coupled with his excessively (by comparison to Elizabeth that is) lavish life-style and wanton generosity in rewarding his many 'friends'; who, because of their parasitic or ruthless personal ambitions, almost without exception proved to be most unfortunate, if not disastrous.

During this period two personal factors then became evident; first his desire to surround (and reward handsomely) himself with Scottish friends and second, despite the fact that he was married and had fathered children, that he was nonetheless, if his reported besotted actions are indeed accurate, essentially homosexual.

His desire to reward those who had assisted him during the difficult years of his Scottish reign (his mother Mary abdicated when he was one year old) was understandable. One in particular, Esmé Stuart, who was created Duke of Lennox on his return from France, is of immediate interest. It is a name which will reappear later in the century and in the list of Grand Masters and it is of interest to note that the father of Lord Darnley (James' father) was also a Lennox.

Saddled with the inherited debt of four hundred thousand pounds left by Elizabeth, his own lavish lifestyle and a compulsive need to buy his friends, James was quickly in serious financial difficulty. His perceived omnipotence (the God given right to rule) induced him to make unreasonable demands of Parliament, but worse, he had seriously underestimated their mood. As we shall see from the social history of the time, a different upper strand of society was emerging, that of the moneyed class, as opposed to landed gentry. They, and in that sense Parliament, had been waiting for the opportunity to gain greater control and although outwardly subservient and extolling allegiance, they were determined to take this opportunity to assert their influence and redress some old grievances. They were also most unhappy with the way in which the King was surrounding himself with 'favourites'. With neither side willing to concede very much ground, conflict was inevitable. Parliament acted as though they had already got, or presumed in a strident way, certain privileges, but historically these were more inferred than actual. However, the fact that their claim was not constitutional/legal was irrelevant, for they now felt able to demand that these privileges be recognised unambiguously and refused the King any substantial grants of money until he acknowledged them. Unlike Elizabeth, the few cronies of real power that the King had retained he had elevated to the House of Lords, leaving no spokesman in the Commons at all. He tried various approaches, such as cajoling, demanding, allowing minor concessions, but persisted in 'talking down to them', pointing out their inferiority in terms of actual power or wisdom when compared to his own, conceding them very little rights in any matter; clearly not a basis for fruitful negotiation.

He became active in the wider political scheme, negotiating peace deals, greater integration of English and Scottish affairs and religious tolerance etc. He had success in only a few of these ventures and never involved Parliament. Some indication of early success was the discovery in 1605 of the infamous Gunpowder Plot. However, as his financial problems increased, he tried numerous devices, such as trading concessions, imposing taxes (virtually always opposed by Parliament, if it were sitting, in which case he would dissolve it), but none were successful.

However, it would seem that his greatest problem was his choice of associates; they could hardly be called friends. Of the many to whom he had shown such favour, the first notable (seriously damaging) person was a reportedly handsome Scotsman, Robert Carr (more properly Ker) – his family portrait in the National Portrait Gallery Collection would support this, but James' portrait also hangs there and it is difficult to reconcile the unfavourable descriptions of his person given above, but then artists too have to make their way in the world. He (Carr) was (or elected to be for purposes of gain) a bisexual, whom the King made Viscount Somerset and later Earl.

Carr pursuing further political goals allied himself to the Howard family consorted with Frances, the wife of the Earl of Essex. He was aided and abetted in his (successful) pursuit by the highly dubious and politically imprudent intervention of the King. James compounded this indiscretion by promoting many of Frances' relatives, some to very high offices, almost inversely proportional to their ability (one Lord High Admiral, another Lord Privy Seal; Frances' father was appointed Lord Treasurer). The depth of the King's folly was to imprison in the 'Tower' one Thomas Overbury on a trumped up charge, principally because Frances did not like him. This punishment proving to be insufficient to satisfy her malevolent disposition, she then proceeded to contrive his murder. Somerset, who rose to be Lord Chamberlain, became the richest man in England, but as his riches grew so did his unpopularity. In order to allay some of this unpopularity and redress the Scottish imbalance, he introduced (disastrously as it turns out) a handsome young Englishman George Villiers (another name that will reappear a number of times in the family trees of our concern) to the King. The king was besotted by Villiers and when the poisoning of Overbury was exposed, Somerset and his wife were reduced to obscurity only narrowly avoiding an even worse end that one might be tempted to feel they merited under the rules of the day, but as a result any influence of the Howards was wiped out. The king made Villiers the Earl of Buckingham and Lord High Admiral, but in effect he became the real political (overall) power behind the King.

A common expression states: 'if this situation was not so serious it would be funny' and taking the analogy further it was as though the king was another Nero, except that the fiddle was replaced by hunting and extreme, if not licentious, behaviour. However, in his case the fire smouldered throughout his reign, relieved only by moments of conflagration, his ill chosen associates acting as bellows. A brief summary of the three most significant aspects of his downfall is attempted below, but in practice they were most complex and interrelated.

The first was his constant financial problems, which forced him to negotiate with Parliament, which was a complete anathema to him and because of this innate dislike all dealings between them were confrontational. Ironically this hostile defiance in the end caused him to make even greater concessions than ever and never with the desired outcome. Indeed, this in combination with blatant favouritism laid the foundations of the events that were to overtake his son and lead to the Civil War.

The second followed from the marriage of his sister to the Prince Frederick (Elector Palatine) who accepted the Protestant Throne of Bohemia which resulted in war. Because of his sister James felt some responsibility and hence a need to intervene, but due to Parliament's unwillingness to fund and lack of sympathy towards the notion, was unable to do so in any effective way.

This led to the third of the unfortunate episodes, that of trying to secure the hand of the Spanish Infanta for his son Charles. He had to some extent been deluded into believing that there would be a favourable outcome to such a ploy by the infamous Spanish ambassador Gondomar. Consequently Prince Charles and Buckingham (one might be tempted to ask whom else?) set out for Spain. The enterprise turned out to be an unmitigated disaster, but Buckingham was able to lay blame at the door of the Spanish and eventually nurtured a war against them.

Ironically, considering his clear preference for the company of men, James died surrounded by women, some suggesting in a less than coherent mental state, but not sufficiently deranged to prevent him from advising his son to be 'faithful to Buckingham', which unfortunately Charles appeared to have 'followed to the letter'.

The summary above is necessarily brief, but goes some way to demonstrating both the strong Scottish element in the upper echelons of society and the political adroitness of those that managed to survive intact and ensure that their families were well represented in the Founders of the Premier Grand Lodge – this is nicely illustrated by studying the respective changes in the family Tables that precede every Chapter.

References

1. Snellgrove, L.E., *The Early Modern Age* (Longman Group Ltd., London, 1972), pp. 115-123.
2. Kenyon, F.P., *The Stuarts* (Batsford Ltd., London, 1958), pp. 39-40.

Table 22.1 Status of family during the reign of CHARLES I (1625 – 1649)

HOUSE / CODE	1	2	3	4	5	6	7	8	9	10	11	12
Abercorn												
James Hamilton	S	E_2				s	b	?	d	x	?	18
Bucclauch												
Walter Scott	S	B_2	$(c)E_1$			s	b		d	x	x	11/19
Francis Scott	S	B_3E_2				s	b		d	x	x	33
Chandos												
George Brydges	E	B_6			c				d	x	x	21
Coleraine												
Hugh Hare	E	(w)M	$(c)B_1$		c		b	x	n/a	x		25
Crawford												
Geprge Lindsay	S	E_{14}			ck_2				d	x	x	23
Alexandra Lindsay	S	$(b)E_{15}$			ck_4			x	b	x		33
Ludovic Lindsay	S	$(b)E_{16}$		s	ce		b		b		x	39
Darnley												
n/a												
Inchiquin												
Murrough O'Brien	I	$(b)B_6$		f	c	i	b	x	d	x	x	24
Kingston												
n/a												
Leicester												
Robert Sydney	E		$(c)E_{15}$				b		n/a(m)	x	x	18
Robert Sydney	E	$(b)E_{16}$						x	d	x	x	26
Loudoun												
John Campbell	S	B_2	$(c)E_1$	r/s	c		banti	x	w	x	x	22/33
Montagu (Vis)												
Anthony Browne	E	V_2			c		b	x	d	x		92
Francis Browne	F	$(b)V_3$			c			x	d	x	x	29
Montagu (Bar)												
Edward Montagu	E	B_1		ck_3	c		b	x	n/a	x		21
Edward Montagu	E	$(b)B_2$						x	d	x		44
Norfolk												
Thomas Howard	E		$(c)E_{16}$	r		e	?		gs	x		44
Henry Howard	E	$(b)E_{17}$		r		e	?	x	d	x		46
Raymond												
n/a												
Richmond												
Ludovic Stuart	S	(w)D	$(c)E_{15}D_2$	e		s	b		n/a	x		13/24
Jame Stuart	S	$(b)E_{16}D_3$		r		s	b		n/a	x	x	41
Strathmore												
n/a												
Weymouth												
n/a												
Wharton												
Philip Wharton	E	B_4			c		bpro	x	gs	x	x	25

For key to table *see* foot of Table 20.1

275

Chapter Twenty-two: Charles I (1600-1649, r. 1625/49)

aurice Ashley starts his Chapter on Charles I by quoting the words of another historian Gwatkin on James I: 'a genius for getting into difficulties, but was not without a certain shrewdness in stopping short of catastrophe'. If he steered his ship straight for the rocks, he left his son to wreck it.[1] It would seem that the difference between the situation inherited by his father compared with his own was that James I did at least have some men of wisdom in place already. Unfortunately Charles had only the disastrous Buckingham, who had been especially responsible for the already parlous state between the King and Parliament and conflict within and outside of Britain. Charles was reported to have disliked Buckingham at first, but with the encouragement of his father and a 'charm offensive' by Buckingham, he was persuaded towards him. Indeed, by the time that he and Buckingham set forth in the pursuance of the hand of the Spanish Infanta, they were apparently close friends. Despite the fact that this friendship and seemingly blind faith in Buckingham was leading him deeper into disaster, he seemed blissfully unaware of the fact and it was only the eventual assassination of Buckingham and not any realisation that things were going badly wrong, that finally brought the liaison to an end. Historians claimed that up until this point Charles had entertained little regard for his wife, but now turned to her for consolation and even worse advice. This may have been because in the first instance the match was essentially political, she being the sister of the French King (Louis XIII), only fifteen at the time and with the secret proviso that he would promote the cause of English Catholics. Not that she could have been worse than Buckingham, but that it allowed him to continue to rule without thinking (politically) too deeply. Further, she was devoutly and overtly Roman Catholic and hence profoundly mistrusted by the public at large. Apart from a stutter, he did not inherit the physical disadvantages of his father, but on the contrary, if Van Dyck and Rubens are to be trusted, he was quite handsome, although their brushes may have been influenced by the fact that he gave them knighthoods. Whilst he stopped the device of directly selling titles, it did not stop him giving them away quite freely in recognition of one thing or another. Historians give him the usual catalogue of pros and cons, but it seems fair to conclude that 'the cons have it', tempered with adjectives: lack of insight and humour, sullenness, intellectual shortcomings, guided by sentiment and prejudices, shifty and unstable etc. However, he was a patron of the arts, a good father and husband, which because he relied so heavily upon his wife's advice, was a distinct disadvantage in the political climate of the times.

Charles also showed his Catholic tendencies and his choice of churchmen tended to reflect this. Indeed, when his father's Puritan Archbishop of Canterbury died in 1633, he appointed William Laud an avowed opponent of Puritans and an Arminian (a sect refusing to deny Roman Catholicism). Parliament clamoured for the enforcement of Puritanism, but the King's response was to appoint as his personal chaplain the intellectually gifted 'Arminian' Richard Montagu; who later still was appointed Bishop of Chichester.

However, this was not to happen until later in Charles' reign and in the meantime he had grown to rely principally upon the advice of Buckingham. Their period together was a catalogue of disasters, starting with the existing Spanish War that he and Buckingham had encouraged his father to declare. Further ill-advised strategies in foreign affairs and domestic politics occurred during this period, but they were mainly related to financial, religious, military fiascos and a determined antagonism against Parliament. Not least amongst this list was Buckingham's and indeed his own antagonism against his wife. Charles by then had squandered her marriage portion on an ill-fated military campaign, exiling her personal entourage etc. and quarrelling with her. She had responded in kind, for instance refusing to take part in his Coronation. Indeed, his manner towards her and the refusal of the English ships she had hired to attack the rebellious Huguenots in France angered Louis XIII, soured relations still further. Yet another of Buckingham's military disasters was the campaign to save an enclave of French Huguenots held up in La Rochelle. True to form, this venture was bungled and resulted in plunging the inhabitants into further trouble. However, it did create the climate that encouraged the Huguenot father of John Desaguliers to immigrate to England later in the Century. These various altercations continued up to the autumn of 1628, when, during the process of Buckingham setting up another military expedition to relieve (or more likely make worse) the plight of the Huguenots, he was assassinated. However, Buckingham's death was not sufficient to assuage the misgivings of Parliament and far from solving Charles' many (principally financial) problems it intensified attacks on his religious tendencies, not least from the newly elected Member for Huntingdon Oliver Cromwell. In early 1629, after declaring their rights in a strident fashion, Parliament elected to adjourn, not to be reconvened for the next eleven years.

The events of these next eleven years are too complex to detail here, but put simply was one of progressive deterioration, not in any marked way with the common people, but with those of influence. Not that this action was wanton on the part of Charles I, but more because he was under extreme financial pressures and the only method open to him was to take from those who had wealth. Thus by 'selling the family silver' (Crown Lands, Crown Jewels etc.) and aggressive taxation he built enormous resentment amongst those of influence. His astounding reconciliation, to the extent of utter devotion, with his wife (after Buckingham's death), merely increased his religious tendencies and encouraged the mistrust in his fervently Protestant people. He was sitting on a powder keg, waiting for somebody or something to spark it off. Ironically, it was in Scotland, where opposition to a new prayer book imposed by Laud proved to be the catalyst that allowed the reaction to begin. The Scottish Calvinists rebelled and Charles I set out to suppress this rebellion, scraped together an (totally inadequate as usual) army. It headed north, only to suffer another ignominious defeat. Laud and Wentworth (Earl of Strafford, overlord of Ireland) recommended that the only way to recover the situation was to reconvene Parliament and plead for the funds to form an army of repression and the King complied. Strafford returned to Ireland and raised £180,000, the House of Lords granted a similar amount of £120,000, but the remaining £840,000, required from the House of Commons was to prove a different matter.

However, the King and his advisors had mistaken the mood and their belief in the presence of an innate and deep-seated antagonism of the English towards the Scots was to prove to be more imagined than real. Instead a whole catalogue of new grievances arose from what is termed the 'Eleven Years Tyranny' and were then added to the long list of those that had existed before the last Parliament had recessed. Parliament was in no mood to comply with the King's demands and responded by providing a whole list of its own. Some negotiation was tried, but failed and the King dissolved 'the Short Parliament', with much resentment on both sides. The King continued his confrontation with the Scots, but was humiliated and was finally given little option other than to reconvene Parliament.

The constituent membership of this 'Long Parliament' was noticeably different; it was not disposed to compromise, but rather that of revolution and met in very black mood. Strafford returned from Ireland to aid the King, but he was charged with treason and despite a strident and eloquent defence was condemned to death, as was Laud. The King vowed he would defend him to the end and sent his son to plead for him, but in the end signed his death warrant. As matters deteriorated he feared that the queen and even he may be impeached and so he attempted to go on the offensive and arrest five prominent Members of Parliament, but this failed, which weakened his position further. He dispatched his wife to the Continent, for her safety and to raise arms. In June the two Houses sent an effective ultimatum the

'Nineteen Propositions', which they knew the King was almost certain to reject and once he had done so, they appointed a Committee of Safety and formed an army of 10,000 men, citing the king as an aggressor. On 22 August he departed with his sons, nephews and those loyal to him, for Nottingham and the civil war had begun.

The war was a strange, drawn out affair, with whole periods of inactivity and for a time the queen returned to the King's rather surreal court in Oxford. There were a few successes, but for the most part things were going downhill and with the subsequent arrival of Oliver Cromwell, the King was beaten. Cromwell had him retained (loosely) at Hampton Court. There followed a period of political indecision over what precisely should be the next sequence of events. A solution to this political dilemma was triggered into the next stage by the King making an escape, (the more cynical suggesting that Cromwell may have engineered the opportunity) to what he believed to be a better situation on the Isle of Wight. Yet again his strategy proved to be wrong, since he could now be represented as a 'loose cannon' and as such posed a serious threat to the Country's stability. This allowed his opponents to disguise their ineptitude and at the same time improve their own situation by moving against the King. The lack of a general consensus, the weakness of their case, the drama of his trial and the noble way in which he is reported to have met his death are well documented elsewhere. Indeed, most historians give the impression that this one noble act excused a lifetime of folly, (just as they seem to suggest that Charles II's beauty somehow ameliorates his boorish behaviour.)[2]

References

1. Ashley, M., *Life in Stuart England* (Batsford Ltd., London, 1964).
2. Watson, D., *Charles I* (George Weidenfeld & Nicolson & Book Club Associates, 1972).

HOUSE / CODE	1	2	3	4	5	6	7	8	9	10	11	12
Abercorn												
James Hamilton	S	(b)E$_2$				s	n/a		d	x	n/a	18
Buccleuch												
Francis Scott	S	B$_3$E$_2$			c	s	n/a		d	x	n/a	33
Walter Scott	S	(b)B$_4$E$_3$		f	c	s	n/a		d	x	n/a	51
Chandos												
George Brydges	E	B$_6$			c		n/a		d	x	n/a	21
William Brydges	E	(b)B$_7$					n/a		b	x	n/a	55
Coleraine												
Henry Hare	E	B$_1$			c		n/a	x	n/a	x		25
Crawford												
Ludovic Lindsay	S	E$_{16}$		s	ce		n/a		b		n/a	39
John Lindsay	S	(b)E$_{17}$		s	ce		n/a		c	x	n/a	52
Darnley												
n/a												
Inchiquin												
Murrough O'Brien	I	B$_6$	(c)E$_{1(ab)}$	f	ce	i	n/a	x	d	x	x$_{(ab)}$	24/54
Kingston												
n/a												
Leicester												
John Sydney	E	E$_{16}$			c		b anti	x	d	x		26
Loudoun												
John Campbell	S	B$_2$E$_1$					b $_{(ab)}$		wgd	x	x	22/23
Montagu (Vis)												
Francis Browne	E	V$_3$					n/a		d	x	n/a	29
Montagu (Bar)												
Edward Montagu	E	B$_2$					b anti		d	x		44
Norfolk												
Henry Howard	E	E$_{17}$		r		e	n/a	x	d	x		46
Thomas Howard	E	(b)E$_{18}$			i	e	n/a		d	x		52
Raymond												
n/a												
Richmond												
James Stuart	S	D$_3$		e		s	n/a		n/a	x		41
Esmé Stuart	S	(b)D$_4$				s	n/a		n/a	x		55
Strathmore												
n/a												
Weymouth												
n/a												
Wharton												
Philip Wharton	E	B$_4$			c		b pro	x	gs	x		25

For key to table *see* foot of Table 20.1

Chapter Twenty-three: The Commonwealth

gain, much has been written about this period and it is perhaps best characterised by the way in which various historians assess Oliver Cromwell (1599-1658) the man and his part in the process, typically.[1,2] They either consider him to be a laudable person and to have possessed a quite outstanding personality or a bounder and their analysis of the events during that period varies according to those views. However, to someone approaching the period without preconceived ideas it would seem that the people who were influential in occasioning the Civil War were united only in what they did not like, but otherwise were fragmented in what they saw to be the cause of the discontent or what they required to replace it, each seeming to have their own agenda. Numerous acts were passed that were to change for all time the relationship of Parliament and the Crown, but they were not prepared for and could not fully accept the notion of an absolute severance from a monarchical system. Indeed, Cromwell, who became Lord Protector, was under much pressure to become king and one of the most fervent advocates for this change was Lord Montagu. Even if one chooses to adopt the most pessimistic view of the period, it cannot be denied that much was done for the ultimate good of society, but any good there may have been was not immediately apparent in a climate of such uncertainty. Cromwell had become physically (prematurely) weakened by the huge pressures upon him, dying in the autumn of 1658. He had nominated his son Richard to succeed him, but he was not up to the task and given the widespread animosity towards his father at the end of his reign as Protector it is not surprising that he did not survive for long. Richard was ousted by a group of (forty-two) ex-members which included his own brother-in-law, who recalled the Rump Parliament dissolved by Oliver five years earlier. However, they were no less strident in their approach, failing to heed the protestation of other grandees, including Lambert. Finally Lambert took an armed force to the House of Commons and dissolved it. The fact that Richard Cromwell was allowed to depart without any further molestation and retire peaceably suggests that perhaps 'discretion was the better part of valour'. The climate was now one that would support restoration, but again for negative rather than positive reasons, since they knew what they were against, but could not agree on what they were for.

Whether one considers Oliver Cromwell to be a saint or a sinner there is no denying that he was a great man. Whether his policies were for the good or bad of society in general is therefore open to debate, but one thing is certain, their effect was to allow the families of those with whom we are concerned to survive and indeed some to prosper. The section is kept relatively short because Oliver Cromwell's surprising inactivity with respect to their affairs meant that in reality the consequence of the Civil War and its after effects had only a nominal impact on those of concern to this Study. However, in every other respect the opposite is true and his contribution and impact on the history of Britain was immense. Because the Commonwealth in its various guises had, essentially through human weakness, failed to provide a workable system that was acceptable to the Nation as a whole, the only viable option appeared to be the restoration of the monarchy. Before leaving this short period of history it is of interest to look at the family trees and Table 23.1 to see how our families survived through it and to realise that Cromwell was not as unkind to them as may at first be imagined or indeed warranted, given their previous affiliations and religious persuasions. One certain outcome however was that Britain would never be the same again. Although the monarchy was then 'restored', that too was in reality changed irrevocably.

References

1. Fielding, K., *A History of England* (Macmillian, 1966).
2. Reed, Brett S., *The Stuart Century 1603–1714* (George Harrap and Co., London, 1961).

Table 24.1 Status of family during the reign of CHARLES II (1659 – 1685)

HOUSE / CODE	1	2	3	4	5	6	7	8	9	10	11	12
Abercorn												
James Hamilton	S	E_2				s	x		d	x	?	18
George Hamilton	S	(b)E_3				s			d	x		70
Claud Hamilton	S	(b)E_4		f(l)	ck_1	s	b		c	x	x	80
Buccleuch												
Walter Scott	S	B_4E_3		f	c	s			w	x		51
James Scott	S	(b)B_5E_4		f	cex	s	b	x	d	(s)i	x	61
Chandos												
William Brydges	E	B_7							b	x		55
James Brydges	E	(b)B_8						x	c	x		76
Coleraine												
Hugh Hare	E	B_1			c				x	n/a	x	25
Henry Hare	E	(b)B_2					a	x	d	x		67
Crawford												
John Lindsay	S	E_{17}					b	xsc	c	x		52
William Lindsay	S	(b)E_{18}						x	d	x		78
Darnley												
n/a												
Inchiquin												
Murrough O'Brien	I	B_6	(c)$E_{1(ab)}$	f	ce	i	b	x	d	x	x	24/54
William O'Brien	I	(b)B_7E_2				i	b	x	d	x	x	74
Kingston												
John King	I		(c)B_1				b	x	n/a		x	60
Robert King	I	(b)B_2					b		d		x	76
Leicester												
Robert Sydney	E	E_{16}					b	x	d	x		26
Philip Sydney	E	(b)E_{17}		p	c			x	d	x	x	77
Loudoun												
John Campbell	S	B_3E_1		c					wgd	x	x	22/23
James Campbell	S	(b)B_3E_2		e					d			62
Hugh Campbell	S	(b)B_4E_3							d	x	x	84
Montagu (Vis)												
Francis Browne	E	V_3					b	x	d	x	x	29
Francis Browne	E	(b)V_4						x	d	x	x	82
Montagu (Bar)												
Edward Montagu	E	B_2						x	d	x	x	44
Ralph Montagu	E	(b)B_3			ck_1			x	d	x		84
Norfolk												
Thomas Howard	E	E_{18}	(c)D_{10}	af	i	e	b		d	x		52/60
Henry Howard	E	(b)D_{11}				e	b	xsc	b	x		77
Henry Howard	E	(b)D_{12}				e	b	x	d	x	x	84
Raymond												
n/a												
Richmond												
Esmé Stuart	S	(b)D_4				s			d	x		55
Chas (Lennox) Stuart	S		(c)D_6			e/s	b	x	i	x	x	75
Strathmore												
Patrick Lyon	S		(c)E_1				b	x	n/a	x		77
Weymouth												
Thomas Thyme	E		(c)V_1				b	xsc	n/a	x	x	82
Wharton												
Philip Wharton	E	B_4			c		b pro	x	gs	x		25

For key to table *see* foot of Table 20.1

Chapter Twenty-four: Charles II (1659-1685)

s may be deduced from the bibliographies of the early Grand Masters, only one or two were of any great social importance and most of that from notoriety rather than impact. However, in terms of Freemasonry in the form we know it today they were the very essence of its being.

With Charles II there are again huge discrepancies between the various historians, who seem obliged to either markedly love or hate him. This seems to be explained by whether one chooses to to judge him on basic humanitarian grounds (however defined),[1, 2] thereby justifying his behaviour on the basis of the moral and social attitudes of the times or to take a more critical stance.[3] Without attempting to explain why, the tendency here is to take the latter view as being the more realistic appraisal and to adopt the view that his behaviour showed all the tackiness of his father and grandfather, albeit expressed in different ways.

The difference being that he was less strident over his position and outwardly accommodating. He could be charming when appropriate, but his outstanding advantages over his grandfather, were his stature and looks, on which historians seem to be agreed universally, even those who choose to denounce him. However, it was his philandering nature that is of such importance to our study, since it was this core influence (and illegitimate progeny) that determined the nature of the society that surrounded him and created the establishment from whence came many of the influential Founders of the Premier Grand Lodge.

Although Montagu had argued so strongly for Oliver Cromwell to be made King, he contrived, in an almost heroic swap of allegiance, to be the very person who escorted Charles II back to England, behaviour not unknown in history, but rarely excelled. Like his grandfather Charles II was greeted ecstatically by the people, but in effect, it too was to prove a false dawn. This because the basis of his restoration was beset with many intrinsic problems, the two most important being his severe financial position, the second his uniformly agreed innate feckless personality. For essentially political and financial reasons he eventually married the Portuguese queen-regent's daughter Catherine of Braganza. She brought a dowry of £800,000 and the cities of Bombay and Tangier, both of which, like the West Indian possessions

Charles II (1659-1685)

Quasi House of Charles II

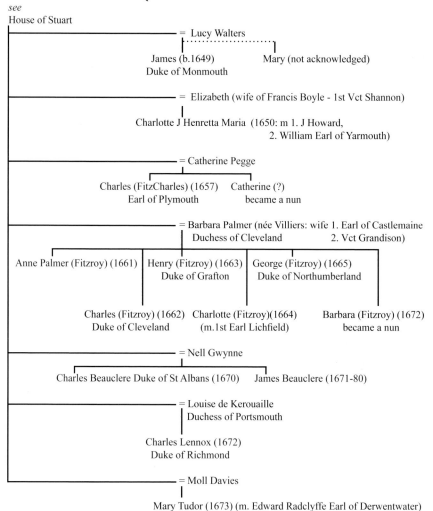

see
House of Stuart

= Lucy Walters

James (b.1649)   Mary (not acknowledged)
Duke of Monmouth

= Elizabeth (wife of Francis Boyle - 1st Vct Shannon)

Charlotte J Henretta Maria (1650: m 1. J Howard,
                                        2. William Earl of Yarmouth)

= Catherine Pegge

Charles (FitzCharles) (1657)   Catherine (?)
Earl of Plymouth   became a nun

= Barbara Palmer (née Villiers: wife 1. Earl of Castlemaine
  Duchess of Cleveland   2. Vct Grandison)

Anne Palmer (Fitzroy) (1661)   Henry (Fitzroy) (1663)   George (Fitzroy) (1665)
                               Duke of Grafton   Duke of Northumberland

Charles (Fitzroy) (1662)   Charlotte (Fitzroy)(1664)   Barbara (Fitzroy) (1672)
Duke of Cleveland   (m.1st Earl Lichfield)   became a nun

= Nell Gwynne

Charles Beauclere Duke of St Albans (1670)   James Beauclere (1671-80)

= Louise de Kerouaille
  Duchess of Portsmouth

Charles Lennox (1672)
Duke of Richmond

= Moll Davies

Mary Tudor (1673) (m. Edward Radclyffe Earl of Derwentwater)

given or franchised to several of the Grand Masters were to prove a distinct liability. The money was frittered away on just one of the fruitless wars (mostly with the Dutch) with which Charles II was associated. The last remaining potential advantage of this match, namely that it would produce an heir presumptive also failed.

This lack of progeny brought into prominence his blatant extramarital excursions, since in the eyes of some, these heirs became realistic contenders for the throne. Again the actual number of illegitimate children depends upon historians, but the Stuarts have attracted the attention of numerous historians for understandable reasons, since they were principal players of a frenetically changing world, amplified by a dishonourable and/or licentious lifestyle, Charles II representing the most outstanding example. Since many volumes have been written on his life it would seem unprofitable to introduce yet another attempt, but a few salient points that were to impinge on the eventual formation of the Premier Grand Lodge are discussed below.

Most historians are of the view that Charles II is rightly applauded for setting up or vigorously supporting a number of learned institutions; notably the Royal Society, the Greenwich Observatory and the Navigation School attached to the Blue Coat School. There is much evidence to suggest that he was, by the standards of the day, well educated and informed, but there must be some doubt as to whether his appreciation of matters scientific was more bravado than profound.

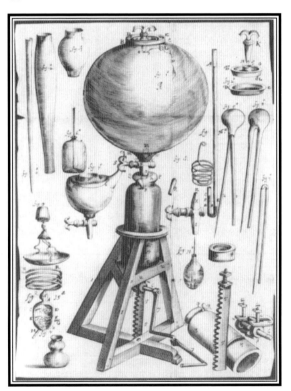

Figure 24.1

Boyle's air Pump as shown and explained in detail in his book published in 1662 – a mere two years after Charles II had ascended the Throne

For example he considered it highly amusing that someone (notably Boyle) should attempt to 'weigh ayre', but by the end of his reign atmospheric devices were at an advanced stage and were the very basis of the latent industrialisation and proved to be a major source of income for our principal player John Desaguliers. But if Charles had been truly interested in science and technology he was certainly in a privileged position to gain enlightenment. For example in the case cited above, Boyle was a highly respected member of the established aristocracy and could have been summoned to give an insight of his research to the king. He had after all just published a book on the matter and the apparatus in question is shown in Figure 24.1 There is no doubt that Charles' professed interest in and patronage of astronomy and navigation greatly encouraged support for the Greenwich Observatory and the Royal Society as is the case of any enterprise, not least Freemasonry. It will also prove to be of some importance in our story, because one of the principal judges (hence of social prominence in the early 1720s) in the quest for a prize of £20,000 for determining longitude, finally instigated by the Government in 1714, was a certain Martin Folkes, who as we have seen was greatly influential in the hierarchy of the Premier Grand Lodge. In 1714 this initiative, encouraged by an enormous prize, had been finally forced upon the authorities because of serious losses at sea, competition from other nations and other navigational difficulties, for the means of accurately measuring longitude at a point on the Globe, but it clearly had its roots in Charles' Royal Observatory,

However, Charles' greatest impact on the formation of the Premier Grand Lodge was through his illegitimate offspring; either through direct participation or very strong family or social links with the actual Founders, which at the same time ensured a strong Scottish presence. This whole caucus of new aristocracy imposed at the highest level was bound to have a large impact on the more established lines and would be difficult to assimilate. Whilst such an imposition on the establishment would likely be resented by many, some would grasp the opportunity to exploit, rather than oppose the new state of affairs. However the creation of an aristocratic line may be comparatively more easy than finding the wealth necessary to support it and Mainwaring's compendium on British Social History has a whole Chapter entitled the 'Rule of Money' which encapsulates the bringing together of these two elements during this period.[4] The King was committed to a policy that would enable his brother James to succeed him, but because of James' Roman Catholic tendencies this was widely opposed and there was a strong faction that demanded that his (handsome – the seeming prior requisite for success and acceptance) illegitimate son James Scott, the now Duke of Monmouth, should succeed to the Throne. Numerous devices were invoked, but the King's preference for his brother was in the end to prevail. Having thus far succeeded, Nemesis overtook him and on 1 February 1685 he suffered a stroke, but before dying, as if to exemplify his duplicity throughout and

The Key to Modern Freemasonry

willingly it would seem, received extreme unction.

Because he had flirted with the restoration of the Catholic Church, certain members of those (especially the Montagus) with whom we are concerned had a roller-coaster ride during this period. Their outward concern was principally that of anti-popery, but the real underlying concern was that many were resting on estates that had been confiscated from the Church and 'gifted' to them and therefore fearful that its re-emergence would restore these lands and entitlements. James was overtly Catholic and although he was to become King in a Protestant country and likely outwardly to comply with its constitution, the threat was there for all to see and troubled waters lay ahead and an outcrop of rocks similar to those upon which his father perished were close to the surface and unfortunately for him history was to repeat itself. Although our families were for the most part sailing with him they had donned their political lifejackets and positioned themselves close to the lifeboats; indeed some had gone ashore earlier and joined the wreckers.

References

1. Fraser, A., *King Charles II.* (Futura – Macdonald and Co. London, 1988).
2. Fulkas, C., *Charles II.* (George Weidenfeld & Nicolson & Book Club Associates,1972).
3. Reed, Brett S., *The Stuart Century 1603-1714* (George Harrap & Co. London, 1961).
4. Mainwaring, J., *British Social History* (Odhams Press Ltd., London, undated *c.*1944), pp. 51-73.

Table 25.1 Status of family during the reign of James II (1685-1688)

HOUSE / CODE	1	2	3	4	5	6	7	8	9	10	11	12
Abercorn												
Claud Hamilton	S	E$_4$		f(I)	ck$_1$	s	b	x	c	x	x	80
Buccleuch												
Dormant (Ex Dalkeith)												
Chandos												
James Brydges	E	B$_8$						x	c	x		76
Coleraine												
Henry Hare	E	B$_2$						x	d	x		67
Crawford												
William Lindsay	S	E$_{18}$						x	d	x		78
Darnley												
n/a												
Inchiquin												
William O'Brien	I	B$_3$E$_2$		a	c	i	b	x	d	x	x	74
Kingston												
Robert King	I	B$_2$		ar	ce				d		x	76
Leicester												
Philip Sydney	E	E$_{17}$						x	d	x	x	77
Loudoun												
Hugh Campbell	S	B$_4$F$_3$						x	d	x	x	84
Montagu (Visc)												
Francis Browne	E	V$_4$						x	d	x		82
Montagu (Bart)												
Ralph Montagu	E	B$_3$						x	d	x		84
Norfolk												
Henry Howard	E	D$_{12}$				e	b	x	d	x	x	84
Raymond												
n/a												
Richmond												
Chas (Lennox) Stuart	S	D$_6$				e/s	b	x	i	x	x	75
Strathmore												
Patrick Lyon	S	E$_1$					b	x	n/a	x	x	77
Weymouth												
Thomas Thynne	E	V$_1$					banti	xsc	n/a	x	x	82
Wharton												
Philip Wharton	E	B$_4$			c		banti	x	gs	x		25

For key to table *see* foot of Table 20.1

289

Chapter Twenty-five: King James II (1685-1688)

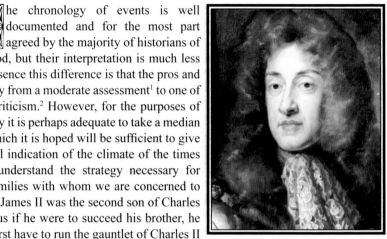

The chronology of events is well documented and for the most part agreed by the majority of historians of the period, but their interpretation is much less so. In essence this difference is that the pros and cons vary from a moderate assessment[1] to one of strong criticism.[2] However, for the purposes of this study it is perhaps adequate to take a median view, which it is hoped will be sufficient to give a general indication of the climate of the times and to understand the strategy necessary for those families with whom we are concerned to survive. James II was the second son of Charles I and thus if he were to succeed his brother, he would first have to run the gauntlet of Charles II having a son by his queen; although in the event his illegitimate sons were to prove to be a sufficient handicap in their own right. Failing which event he would have to survive his brother's death. This he also managed to do, but not until he was fifty-two, by which time (in his case at least) he had passed his prime, his health had deteriorated and he was by then not only intolerant and impatient, but a man in too much of a hurry to be prudent. He was tolerably good looking, but lacked the charisma of his brother. Try as he might, he could not quite match his brother's prodigious promiscuity, although he made a very noble effort and his first marriage was in modern parlance a 'shot-gun' affair. His comparative lack of success in his sexual exploits, both inside and out of marriage, were commented on by his brother, who asserted that James' mistresses were the ugliest women imaginable and were God's punishment upon him; which was a measure of Charles' concept of Divine intervention/retribution and sense of values.

However, in many other respects, James was like his grandfather. For example he had had considerable exposure in public affairs prior to ascending the Throne and in that respect was well prepared to take office; for instance, his brother Charles had appointed him Lord High Admiral. He was aided in this respect by two factors in particular; first that Charles just before his death had managed to subjugate the influence of the boroughs. Secondly, on the pretext of a failed assassination attempt and sundry other factors, James was able to remove the principal political group. They had assumed the generic name of 'Whigs' (after the Whiggamores a Scottish Presbyterian faction), a group who had been and were in direct opposition to James' plans. As with his grandfather, James II therefore ascended the Throne to general acclaim and because of the by then emaciated opposition, the first Parliament was the most pro-monarchist (Stuart) assembly ever. But, unfortunately history was to repeat itself and again like his grandfather, he miscalculated, failing to set realistic political targets that were both prudent and possible within the time available and as a result his actions were soon to bring disaffection and ultimate disaster. He started well, giving his maiden speech within hours of ascending to the Throne, which was conciliatory and since it appeared to be impromptu, gave an impression of sincerity. Many of the families with whom we are concerned were vulnerable to such skittish behaviour, but apart from Wharton, managed to keep a comparatively low profile. Many were of the faction that had been troubled by the prospect of James becoming king, because of his known Catholic persuasion, not so much because of Catholicism *per se*, but its attendant political implications.

Monmouth's ambition was to present James II with a golden (political) opportunity that might have set him in very good stead, but instead it merely proved to show that he had an abnormally malevolent disposition.

Monmouth was the illegitimate son of Charles II's mistress Lucy Walters and in consequence was afforded the title of Duke. He showed himself a competent officer, but had much higher ambitions, even to the extent of laying claim to the Crown. Because he was staunchly Protestant he was encouraged by many in this belief. Charles for his part did not support this view and although appearing to dote upon him, progressively stripped him of his various political positions he had at first held and at one stage sent him abroad. On his return Monmouth went around sounding out support, largely in the disaffected West Country. There was also a disaffected group in Scotland, led by the Duke of Argyll. By the time James ascended the Throne both had sought refuge in Holland and each attempted to form a sufficiently formidable group to dislodge James. Although they had the same basic objective there was to be no co-ordination between the two groups or indeed within the groups themselves and because they were both so ill conceived the whole initiative was destined for disaster from the start. Argyll landed in the Highlands, but the whole affair turned into a fiasco, failing to gain any real support and was routed, imprisoned and executed on the pretext of a former charge.

Even before Argyll had been executed Monmouth had landed in the West Country, he tried to drum up support, but few responded and those who did formed a disparate outfit of the disaffected, with little or no armoury, except any implements they could lay their hands on. In essence he, like Argyll, roamed around trying to gather support, but was finally confronted at Sedgemoor by a superior army which included a contingent of Dutch professional soldiers supplied by William of Orange (James' son-in-law) and competent generals such as Churchill. Monmouth's feckless band fought bravely and were surprisingly near victory and had they been better led it is suggested that they may well have achieved it, but history was to prove otherwise. Monmouth was eventually captured and was executed. Instead of being magnanimous in victory James displayed a level of vindictiveness exceptional even by the standards of those times. Much of this malevolence he enacted through the infamous Judge Jeffreys. The punishment meted out in the West Country was brutal in the extreme, but whilst it may have had the immediate effect of brow-beating any opposition, it laid the foundation for a climate of deep hostility that was soon to overtake him.

The effect of these routings sent a number of signals, but which in essence amounted to two; an ill placed sense of omnipotence to the King, that served to reinforce an already strident attitude and the other that of extreme intimidation and a sense of oppression and social injustice within the general population. Thus he began the process of exchanging rule by general consent with a regime of oppression, rapidly replacing the surprisingly high degree of sympathetic support given by the people at the commencement of his reign with rising disaffection and anger. Undeterred in any way he then set about imposing a hierarchical structure and political system. He replaced ministers of state and religion, gave increasing licence to religious expression (principally to Catholics, but also to other, some extreme, schisms; who being afforded that right of religious expression were likely to champion him). He attacked other sectors, by devices such as replacing the military command by those with declared Catholic persuasion. But in this frenetic process he appears to lose completely his sense of political discretion. He even imposed, one might say fatally since he greatly underestimated their influence, a Catholic management structure upon the universities and in particular Oxford who hitherto had been staunchly Stuart. As part of this system of oppression, outside the imposition of the so-called law, he had garrisoned a large force on the West Side of London, under the command of now Catholic officers. However, a storm of discontent was brewing and secret negotiations with William and James' daughter Mary were at an advanced stage. Despite a number of pregnancies James' second wife Mary had failed to provide a male heir, but now after a break of five years, the latest pregnancy produced a son. The circumstances surrounding the birth have been the subject of much debate, but most modern historians take the view that there is little doubt that it was actually his son and not a 'pretender' as was claimed by many at that time and since. The political storm that had been brewing was now whipped up into hurricane proportions by this event and his ship was now set to founder on the rocks. The 'wreckers', in the guise of Bishop Crompton, Lords Devonshire, Shrewsbury, Danby and Lumley, Edward Russell and Henry Sidney, were preparing for the event and collectively drafted a letter inviting the intervention of William, which he was to accept – mainly because the situation in Europe had changed; especially with respect to Holland – William's primary concern. Before James realised the seriousness of his situation he committed his final political blunder, by trying to enforce a religious edict, which was to bring him in direct conflict with the Established Church. When the bishops refused to do his bidding, he placed them in the Tower to stand trial. This also proved disastrous as the Court acquitted them, to the obvious joy of the population at large, but even worse for him was that it was also welcomed by his own standing army, who reportedly cheered when the news of the acquittal arrived. Realising the danger far too late, he tried various panic measures, rescinding many of the unpopular moves he had made earlier, but it was all too little, too late. Lord High Admiral he may have once been, but now the ship was out of his control. He tried a number of devices to save the situation, but remembering the fate of his father, first sent his wife and child abroad and then (was discretely allowed) to escape himself. As we shall see he did return to fight in Ireland, but true to form, was defeated by his own ineptitude at the Battle of the Boyne. He returned to France and frittered the remainder of his life away, dying as the result of a stroke in 1701.

His importance so far as this study is concerned is to reflect upon the degree of activity shown by the respective families with which we are concerned. Reference to Table 25.1 will show that most adopted a policy of distancing themselves from the Court, whilst not overtly exhibiting hostility towards it, with the exception of Philip Wharton and Thomas Thynne (Weymouth). But as his reign progressed the King's behaviour became more polarised and extreme, and seizing the opportunity, a good number of them or their close relatives became involved in his removal.

References

1. Earle, P., *James II* (George Weidenfeld & Nicolson & Book Club Associates, 1972).
2. Fielding, K., *A History of England*, (Macmillan, London, 1966), pp. 569-577.

Table 26.1 Status of family during the reign of William III and Mary (1688-1702)

HOUSE / CODE	1	2	3	4	5	6	7	8	9	10	11	12
Abercorn												
Claud Hamilton	S	E_4		f(I)	ck_1	s	b	x	c	x	x	80
Charles Hamilton	S	$(b)E_5$	(I)L(S)B	r(I)	c	s	b	x	d	x		91
James Hamilton	S	$(b)E_6$	(I)B		c	s	b	x	c	x	x	01
Buccleuch												
Dormant (Ex Dalkeith)												
Chandos												
James Brydges	E	B_8						x	c	x		76
Coleraine												
Henry Hare	E	B_2					?	x	d	x		67
Crawford												
William Lindsay	S	E_{18}						x	d	x		78
John Lindsay	S	$(b)E_{19}$						x	d	x	x	98
Darnley												
n/a												
Inchiquin												
William O'Brien	I	B_3E_2		r		i	b	x	d	x	x	74
William O'Brien	I	$(b) B_8E_3$		ar	c	i	b	x	d	x	x	92
Kingston												
Robert King	I	B_2		ar	ce				d		x	76
John King	I	$(b)B_3$		r	ce			x	b			93
Leicester												
Philip Sydney	E	E_{17}						x	d	x	x	77
Robert Sydney	E	$(b)E_{18}$						x	d	x		98
Philip Sydney	E	$(b)E_{19}$						x	d	x		02
Loudoun												
Hugh Campbell	S	B_4E_3						x	d	x	x	84
Montagu (Visc)												
Francis Browne	E	V_4						x	d	x		82
Montagu (Bart)												
Ralph Montagu	E	B_3						x	d	x		84
Norfolk												
Henry Howard	E	D_{12}				e	b	x	d	x	x	84
Thomas Howard	E	$(b)D_{13}$				e			n	x		01
Raymond												
n/a												
Richmond												
Chas (Lennox) Stuart	S	D_6				e/s	b	x	i	x	x	75
Strathmore												
Patrick Lyon	S	E_1					b	x	n/a	x	x	77
John Lyon	S	$(b)E_2$					b	x	d	x	x	95
Weymouth												
Thomas Thynne	E	V_1					banti	xsc	n/a	x	x	82
Wharton												
Philip Wharton	E	B_4			c		banti	x	gs	x		25
Thomas Wharton	E	$(b)B_5$					b	x	d	x		96

For key to table *see* **foot of Table 20.1**

Chapter Twenty-six: William and Mary (1688-1702)

ny political system based upon compromise rather than preference is likely to encounter difficulties. The contrivance which led to Mary's and hence William's accession to the English throne was predicated on the basis that the unpopular James II had to be removed.[1,2] Whilst William was far from ideal, he was Protestant and could claim legitimacy through his marriage to Mary. William and those who sympathised with him could point to James' implicit desertion and with sufficient licence, make their claim appear legitimate, but in any case 'might is right' and there were few of direct importance who would have wished to be seen to contest the situation. For consistency we should pause for a moment on his physical appearance and personal attributes (or rather lack of them). He may be described as a man of little charm and poor health (asthmatic, crippled, a tubercular lung – the sort of thing we have come to expect and if this was not enough: we are assured by most historians that he was most un-kingly). Although a declared Protestant, it is alleged that he had 'sown his wild oats', had a mistress Elizabeth Villiers (a name associated with our families and earlier monarchs – George Villiers with James I and subsequently Charles I; Barbara Villiers and Charles II and other members of the Villiers family who were placed in high office). He married James II's daughter Mary when she was fifteen. Historians suggest he had little passion for her, or indeed anything else except an all-pervading obsessive hatred towards Louis XIV of France. Indeed most historians claim that William's innate disdain for the English was only ameliorated by the opportunity of using their coffers to fund his war-machine, in the long-standing feud he had with the French.

He was nearly forty and therefore a seasoned politician when the situation arose that forced the dissidents to contact him. Unfortunately for them their need was marginally greater than his and in the bargaining process he was able to impose the condition that he should be made King in the absolute sense as opposed to a consort. Having so agreed, but significantly without parliamentary authorisation, a 'Council' was assembled, which contrived a general election. This device afforded a level of legitimacy, thereby allowing William to be declared King. However, with this strategy the time honoured kingly power of 'rule by divine rite' came to an end. As with most situations where there has been a pronounced degree of contrivance, there now existed 'an unholy alliance' between the various parties. Some historians argue that despite his irascible nature he was forgiving to the degree where it may be considered foolhardy. However, it may be argued with equal conviction that he considered the best strategy was to divide and rule. He therefore created an administration that was effectively a coalition of people at odds with each other, a number actively consorting with the deposed king. Most of those with whom we are concerned directly shifted their ground according to the direction of the political wind. The nature of his senior appointments is well illustrated in Fieldings' book:

> 'The curve of his power rose to a height and then declined within the Whig Junto's time, 1694-8. Generally his choice of ministers coincided with the advice of the very able men whose ambition coincided with national advantage. Godolphin was usually at the head of the finances, under whatever ministry; Sunderland advised a return to the Whigs; Marlborough would bridge a reconciliation with Anne. Tory administration, particularly Nottingham's at the Admiralty, was not successful, Danby (now Duke of Leeds) was always unpopular; while the Whigs were more united as a party, had more contact with the City and foreign merchants, and were more ready to support his Continental war. So during 1693-4 he dropped Nottingham and Seymour, while Leeds was attacked for taking bribes and lost influence.
>
> So came into power the Junto [*sic*]. Somers was Lord Keeper, a man of luminous mind and great charm, though a political partisan. Charles Montagu at the Treasury was exceedingly able, ingenious, and conceited [he introduced the Land Tax, Window Tax, Re-coinage and through the concept of Government Bonds what was to become the concept of the National Debt]. Russell, now Lord Orford, at the Admiralty was imperious, selfish and determined. Their party organizer was the violent irreligious "Tom Wharton", who nursed his native Buckinghamshire as a Whig stronghold, and whose horses were the best, as his head at table was the strongest, of his time. For nearly twenty years these men led the party that was bequeathed to Walpole, etc, etc [including many names from or related to the families of those with whom we are concerned].' [3]

King James II (1685-1688)

The level to which this jockeying for position was rife is illustrated by a short passage given in Ashley's book:

'Halifax, who was at first much with the King, said to his friend, Sir John Raresby: "Come Sir John, we have wives and children, and we must consider them and not venture too far" '. [4]

He spent nearly half of his time abroad (mostly in Holland) and when in England much of it in Hampton Court because he claimed the smoke and fumes affected his breathing. Although his frantic hunting exploits seem to put a lie to this claim and in the end were to lead to his premature death in February 1702, following an accident whilst hunting. This mode of indifference to his official duties, added fuel to the level of unpopularity he had inherited from the start. This mood of discontent towards him was held at bay by the presence and popularity of Queen Mary, but this came to an end with her death in 1694, which despite his dispassionate nature appears to have affected him deeply. After the Queen's death his personal standing deteriorated further. It is claimed that he was exhorted to re-marry, for obvious reasons of succession, but declined to do so.

As we have seen, William was a successful strategist and judicious administrator, was a moderately competent general, but an outstanding leader of men, all clouded by his obsessive antagonism towards France and its overriding implications with Holland. Assuming the veracity of the claim that he came to England in pursuance of this obsession his political skills may be judged by the way in which he managed to organise the British people to finance wars they had no real desire to fight. However, this success may be accounted for in another way, for there was a factor which in effect was much more powerful and that was to prepare the foundation for the eventual construction of the Premier Grand Lodge; namely the new environment of expanding (seemingly endless) wealth creation. Individuals and institutions tend not to 'rock the boat' when things are going very well financially and our families were at the very heart of this bonanza and amongst its major beneficiaries.

References

1. Miller, J., *William and Mary* (George Weidenfeld & Nicolson & Book Club Associates, 1972).
2. Fielding, K., *A History of England*, (Macmillan, London, 1966), pp. 578-597.
3. *Ibid.*
4. Ashley, M., *England in the Seventeenth Century (1603-1714)* (Penguin Books, Cox & Wyman Ltd., London, 1960), p. 182.

Table 27.1 Status of family during the reign of
Queen Anne (1702-1714)

HOUSE / CODE	1	2	3	4	5	6	7	8	9	10	11	12
Abercorn												
James Hamilton	S	(b)E$_6$	(I)B,		c	s	b	x	c	x	x	01
Buccleuch												
Dormant (Ex Dalkeith)												
Chandos												
James Brydges	E	B$_8$						x	c	x		76
Coleraine												
Henry Hare	E	B$_2$					?	x	d	x		67
Henry Hare	E	B$_3$					?	x	g	x		08
Crawford												
John Lindsay	S	E$_{19}$						x	d	x	x	98
John Lindsay	S	(b) E$_{20}$							d	x		14
Darnley												
n/a												
Inchiquin												
William O'Brien	I	(b) B$_8$E$_3$		ar	c	i	b	x	d	x	x	92
Kingston												
John King	I	B$_3$		r	ce			x	b			93
Leicester												
Philip Sydney	E	E$_{19}$						x	d	x		02
John Sydney	E	(b)E$_{20}$						x	d	x		05
Loudoun												
Hugh Campbell	S	B$_4$E$_3$						x	d	x	x	84
Montagu (Visc)												
Francis Browne	E	V$_4$						x	d	x		82
Henry Browne	E	(b)V$_5$						x	d	x		08
Montagu (Bart)												
Ralph Montagu	E	E$_1$	(c)D$_3$					x	d	x		05
John Montagu	E	(b)E$_1$D$_2$					b	xsc	d	x	x	09
Norfolk												
Thomas Howard	E	D$_{12}$			e				n	x		01
Raymond												
n/a												
Richmond												
Chas (Lennox) Stuart	S	D$_6$				e/s	b	x	i	x	x	75
Strathmore												
John Lyon	S	(b)E$_2$					b	x	d	x	x	95
James Lyon	S	(b)E$_3$					b	x	d	x	x	12
Weymouth												
Thomas Thynne	E	V$_1$					banti	xsc	n/a	x	x	82
Wharton												
Thomas Wharton	E	B$_5$					b	x	d	x		96

For key to table *see* foot of Table 20.1

Chapter Twenty-seven: Queen Anne (1702-1714)

gain historians are divided over Anne's qualities and so a more or less general description will be attempted on the views of a spread of historians, typically.[1,2] She was thirty-seven on her accession to the throne. She had buried fifteen children; most at birth. One, the Duke of York, who died aged ten in 1700, effectively removed all chance of continuing that particular line of the Stuarts and was the reason why Parliament, fearful of the Pretender's claim ensured that the Hanoverians would succeed by passing laws that would prevent any likelihood of James returning. The corollary of that was to set the political climate, which in combination with the fact that her Consort George, unlike the overwhelming dominance of William in the William and Mary reign, was, if the historians are right, a wimp, albeit one much loved by Anne.

Probably due to the stresses of bearing so many children, followed by their almost immediate loss, her health was, by the time she ascended to the throne, very poor indeed – gout, dropsy and she was barely able to walk. She was, perhaps quite understandably, said to be most irascible at times. She was a fierce guardian of the Church of England and it was this factor at the time of her accession and not any great political persuasion that disposed her towards the Tories. As with James I, the other critical factor in the way in which she behaved was her disproportionate disposition to choose 'favourites' and once chosen to then rely far too heavily upon their political proclivities. However, unlike James I, these were fewer in number, comprising of the ubiquitous Godolphin, the fence straddling top civil servant of succeeding administrations, the Duke (then Earl, but elevated late in 1702 to a Dukedom) of Marlborough and his wife Sarah. Both the Duke and his wife were handsome and vivacious (the essential ingredients of all 'good' monarchs that we have now come to expect, albeit rarely found), but he was also brave and an outstanding soldier. But more importantly both he and his wife were both extremely astute politicians. He was the eldest son of Winston Churchill, a Dorsetshire squire. A staunch loyalist, who on the Restoration had become a Member of Parliament, quickly knighted and steadily progressed through the ranks in all reigns, principally

The Key to Modern Freemasonry

due to his prowess as a soldier. In 1678 he married Sarah Jennings who was also in the service of the Duke of York. Reportedly it was a marriage of deep affection that no doubt added to its formidable presence.

Thus the scene was set and so it was not surprising therefore that the members of the Junto cited above, who whilst central in our consideration, were, as Whigs, a complete anathema to the Queen. With the encouragement of Sarah they were quickly ousted from power – ironically one of the Junto was Charles Spencer, Marlborough's son-in-law. It would appear that so close was the relationship between Godolphin, the Marlboroughs and Anne that the Queen is reported to have declared that only death could dissolve their friendship. However, even in this précised account of the previous one hundred years it is sufficient to show that such faithfulness was unlikely to last, especially in this particular period, where intrigue is everywhere, supplemented by wars, the tenuous nature of friendships, the arrogance of power and in her case personal bereavement.

The Marlboroughs with the assistance of their friend Godolphin exercised extreme influence in these early years of the reign, with Sarah in particular becoming more strident. As part of this largess she (innocently) introduced a poor distant relation Miss Abigail Hill (later to marry in 1707 Marsham, a 'gentlemen' of Prince George's household) into the Queen's service, who eventually became a woman of the bedchamber. Although occupying a lowly position, Abigail was nonetheless in direct communication with the Queen and became her very close confidant and advisor, the result of which was to prove fatal to the Malboroughs and their friend Godolphin. It is not possible to go into the complex external and internal ramifications, but by the time Prince (Consort) George died in 1708, which affected the Queen greatly, the tide had turned. With the unification of England and Scotland now agreed, and commerce expanding, the Continental wars were having some success. This in any case did not intruding very much on domestic affairs and the Whigs regained power. Just as Mrs Marsham had quietly infiltrated the Queen's affections, so had a hitherto unknown politician called George Harley inveigled his way into a position of exceptional political influence. He had been chosen more by default than design, because the feuding between the main contenders had distracted them from keeping an eye on him. He quickly exploited a 'friendship' between himself and the Marshams and through them was able to have direct, although covert dealings with the Queen.

Although their path was still not an easy one, our friends of the Junto could now begin to emerge from the gloom, some regaining significant office; Wharton for instance as Lord Lieutenant of Ireland. It is generally agreed that it was Sarah's sheer arrogance that had alienated the Queen's affection and whilst she would have preferred to have retained the services of the Duke himself, he remained stubbornly loyal to Godolphin and eventually the two were relegated, although the Duke retained considerable general popularity. However, the members of the Junto and their close associates such as William Cowper, were not favoured by Harley and because they were Whigs, neither were they overly so by the Queen. So once again they went on the retreat, but this time it was tactical, since it was clear that the Queen had little time to live and by dint of their outward disaffection with the Queen, they could now manifest their disposition towards a Hanoverian accession. Further their loss of power also excused them from making unpopular decisions, whilst at the same time allowing them to make open contact with the incoming regime, clearly no ill store. The Tories for their part were divided, a few sensing the 'way that the wind was blowing' actively courting the Hanoverian cause; whilst others blatantly opposed it, with Bolingbroke chief amongst those, but most were content to sit on the fence. Sensing the imminent demise of the Queen the Hanoverians attempted to exert influence, which was not welcomed by Anne and led to heated disputes, but the matter was simplified by the death of Sophia, George's mother, whom Anne detested, leaving him to be the person who would in fact succeed to the British Throne.

The passing of the Queen marked the effective end of the Stuart reign and influence in Britain; a period which by any account must be regarded as quite remarkable, starting with monarchs exercising absolute (divine) power and ending with their surrender of it in favour of a dependence on Parliament. The Stuart era having started with no overseas colonies, had ended with a dominant position at sea, a worldwide trading network and the essential foundation of the British Empire. It also coincided with a forced peace in Europe; Holland by that time having been emaciated, much like Britain after World War II, by years of war. The political climate, particularly in France, had pre-empted any immediate attempt to recall the 'Old Pretender' James III, which may have been mounted by pressure groups such as the Tories surrounding Bolingbroke, whose schemes had actually reached a very advanced stage at that point. However, most important of all so far as we are concerned, it left the Whigs in a position of great influence, with commerce and industrialisation influencing the social structure. Everything was in place to encourage the formation of social groupings, especially clubs and the like, particularly the establishment and consolidation of a structured form of Freemasonry.

References

1. Curtis, G., *Queen Anne* (George Weidenfeld and Nicolson and Book Club Associates, 1972).
2. Fielding, K.A., *History of England* (Macmillan, London, 1966), pp. 598-631.

Table 28.1 Status of family during the reign of GEORGE I (1714 – 1727)

HOUSE / CODE	1	2	3	4	5	6	7	8	9	10	11	12
Abercorn												
James Hamilton	S	E_6			c	s	b	x	d	x	x	01
James Hamilton		(see	George	II)								
Buccleuch												
Dormant (Ex Dalkieth)												
Francis Scott		(see	George	II)								
Chandos												
James Brydges	E	B_8							x	c	x	76
James Brydges	E	$(b)B_9$	$(c)D_1$				b	xsc	d	x	x	14
Coleraine												
Henry Hare	E	B_3					?	sct	g	x		08
Crawford												
John Lindsay	S	E_{20}						sct	d	x	x	14
Darnley												
John Bligh	I		$(c)V_1E_1$			s(m)	b	x	n/a	x		23/25
Inchiquin												
William O'Brien	I	B_8E_3				i	b	x	d	x	x	92
William O'Brien	I	$(b)B_9E_4$				i	b	x	d	x		19
Kingston												
John King	I	B_3			c				x	b		93
James King	I	$(b)B_4$							x	b		28
Leicester												
John Sydney	E	E_{20}						x	d	x		05
Loudoun												
Hugh Campbell	S	B_4	E_3		s			x	d	x	x	84
Montagu (Vct)												
Henry Browne	E	V_5						x	b			08
Anthony Browne	E	$(b)V_6$						x	d			17
Montagu (Bart)												
John Montagu	E	E_2D_2					b	xsc	d	x	x	09
Norfolk												
Thomas Howard	E	D_{13}				e				n	x	01
Raymond n/a												
Richmond												
Chas (Lennox) Stuart	S	D_1				e/s	b	x	i	x	x	75
Chas (Lennox) Stuart	S	$(b)D_2$				e/s	b	xsc	d	x	x	23
Strathmore												
Charles Lyon	S	E_3			ck_1		b		d	x	x	12
James Lyon	S	$(b)E_4$			ck_2		b		b	x	x	15
Weymouth												
Thomas Thynne	E	V_1					b	xsc	n/a	x	x	82
Thomas Thynne	E	$(b)V_2$					b	x	gn	x		14
Wharton												
Thomas Wharton	E	B_3E_1	$(c)M_1$				b	x	d	x	x	06/15
Philip Wharton	E	$(b)E_2M_2$	$(c)D_1$				b	x	d	x	x	15/18

For key to table see foot of Table 20.1

302

Chapter Twenty-eight: George I
(1660-1727, r. 1714-27)

It may have been noted that as the various reigns are discussed the nearer they approach the time when the Premier Grand Lodge was instigated in 1717, the amount written about them decreases rather than expands. This is for a number of reasons, but primarily two. Firstly, fate/circumstances and the contrivance of others had predetermined their succession, rather than it having to depend upon their own personalities and those around them. Hitherto if these monarchs were to survive at all, their actions had, of necessity, to be extreme, rarely pleasant, but in a perverse way much more interesting to historians and, for that matter, us, in terms of general interest. Although the early period sieved out those with the ability to survive, it was the influence of the later monarchs that created the conditions that were to affect the affairs of the families central to our study. Secondly, what these latter kings and queens lacked in statesmanship they made up for with pronounced personality traits. These they appeared to have compensated for by displaying a mixture of arrogance and total mediocrity.

If the historians are to be believed George I was to prove to be the most pronounced example of this characteristic[1], but this is further exemplified in the political and social structures that grew around him.[2] Like William III before him, it is generally believed that he was not interested in Britain or the British, except insofar as it furthered his interests abroad. It is generally believed that he refused to learn English, although there is some dispute over the extent of this claim. An example of his perverse logic was that he had his wife imprisoned for life on the suspicion, not proof, of her infidelity, whilst at the same time and quite blatantly, had many mistresses of his own. Two of whom, just as the close intimates in previous reigns, became more influential on the political scene than George himself. However, in his case some of this shortfall may be explained by the fact that he was already fifty-four years old when he came to the throne. We are told that he was a very fine and brave soldier, but it would seem that this attribute and the arrogance of the German Court environment had left its imprint. He was an indifferent churchman, but what little he practised was Protestant, which pleased the established Church well enough, since it gave them authority without interference and by the same token did not unduly trouble the dissenting groups. So saying, there were some problems in the middle of his reign, which had some repercussions within the politics of the early Premier Grand Lodge (Wharton and Stukeley for example).

Some dissident Tories, encouraged from afar by the Old Pretender, James III, were persuaded by their own publicity that there were sufficient grounds to engineer his return, which brought about some political uncertainty and one or two skirmishes in Scotland. These were soon suppressed and James III's own lame attempt was effectively over before he landed; causing him to quickly returned to France, only then to be forced further afield (*see* the bibliography of Wharton, the 6th Grand Master) by the political situation.

However it is reasonable to suppose that the real reason for the cooling of the political climate was the underlying (booming) economy. Thus the general prosperity led to a sense of wellbeing, not least that within the (moneyed class) Whigs, who were by then not only in power, but able to consolidate it further by extending Parliament for seven years on the basis of the threat posed by the Jacobites. This was later given some justification by James III's attempted uprising in Scotland and it was argued successfully that to counter such threats an extended (guaranteed) Parliament was needed for stable government. The ageing Marlborough and his venomous (not my words, but those ascribed generally) wife, were by then completely 'outgunned'. If one then looks at the group of people who formed the Premier Grand Lodge, it is reasonable to conclude that the climate was right for the lesserlings (Wharton and Montagu excepted) of these influential families to spread their wings on various business ventures and social activities, such as joining or forming clubs and societies. However, there was a bitter dispute within the Royal Family – so severe that king George took his son's children from him and such was the level of animosity that there was even talk of separating the British and Hanoverian Courts.

There was much acrimonious jostling for power within the political grouping and this came to a head when the financial gerrymandering relating to the 'South Sea Bubble' fiasco erupted. An understanding of the 'South Sea Bubble' affair is in one sense a distraction to this study, but on the other-hand it played an important role in the lives of those with whom we are concerned – *see* individual biographies. It gives a guide to the personalities involved in the formation of the Premier Grand Lodge and helps to explain the politics of those critical years in the early 1720s. The phenomenon is difficult to summarised, but is quite well explained by the following extract taken from the book by Fielding:

'British finance being still in its infancy, the method of paying for the wars since 1689 had been casual and extravagant. The 'tallies' issued on an early equivalent of Treasury bills, were at a heavy discount; much was borrowed from the Bank and other corporations. At the end of the war [Queen Anne's] the public debt of £54 millions was thought alarming, especially as a good deal of it was irredeemable, held at varying rates up to nine per cent. Walpole made a beginning by getting Parliament to accept a sinking fund and to fix five per cent as the rate for new loans, though Stanhope took additional borrowings from the Bank and the South Sea Company.

The last corporation had been founded by Harley in 1711 to clear a large unfounded debt, and was assigned a monopoly of trade with Spanish America. This trade, however, never materialized, the Company was over-capitalized from the start, and in 1719, influenced by the apparent successful speculations of Law, it put forward a scheme to retrieve its fortunes. This was nothing less than to take over £31 millions of national debt. Government was tempted by the interest offered and hopes of converting a mass of long-dated annuities, and tempted by the Company's bid of £7.5 millions, cash down – [readers may recall that it is not unlike the re-scheduling of the extraordinarily dubious insurance liability in the 'Names' scandal at Lloyds of London in the 1990s]. But bribery also played a large part, in the allotment of fictitious stocks to Craggs the elder, his son the Secretary of State, the King's mistresses, and Aislabie, Chancellor of the Exchequer.

Rejecting, against Walpole's protest, a better-assured scheme from the Bank, the Commons accepted that of the Company, the success of which would entirely depend on keeping the price of their stock high. To achieve that, the directors used every fraudulent device they could put their mind to. The stock rose from 130 in February 1720 to a maximum of 1050 in June, the nation went mad with gambling, in one week of August there were lodged 36,000 transfers. A swarm of bubble companies buzzed into life, including one for 'importing jackasses from Spain', in which millions were pledged. But the directors overplayed their hand. It was impossible for ever to 'peg' the price of stock not covered by assets, they overloaded the market, and struck the first blow at their own safety by getting Government to proclaim as illegal some eighty rival companies. A rush to realize those worthless shares spread panic to the South Sea stock also, which tumbled between July and September from 1000 to 400, and in November was back at 135.

The crash destroyed the ministry, but made Walpole. Hounded on by a secret committee, the Commons sent Aislabie to the Tower and confiscated the director's estates. Only a party vote acquitted Sunderland, the elder Craggs killed himself, the younger was fortunate to die of smallpox; early in 1721 Stanhope died of apoplexy ...'[3]

The association of the King's mistresses and his general indifference, if not antipathy, towards the British marginalised his influence and promoted that of Walpole's, desensitising and stabilising the politics of the ensuing years with which we are concerned. The importance of this was that many of those influential in the crucial early years of the Premier Grand Lodge were caught up in and several impoverished by, the South Sea Bubble affair and involved in the politics and influence of the King's appointees – *see* the individual bibliographies. Walpole, himself a freemason, held on through this turbulent period and needed to employ numerous devices, not least to exploit the fact that the King's mistress, the Duchess of Kendal, had been shown to have accepted bribes. The indifferent impact of this King, his influence on the nation and his inglorious demise and the prevailing state of the politics can be gained by once more quoting Fielding:

'His (Walpole's) moment of danger came in 1727 when the King died at Osnabruck, on his way to Hanover, for George II could not begin by liking his father's servants. But the new Queen had more sense, the transparent incompetence of the King's choice, Sir Spencer Compton, drove him back on Walpole, and a handsome increase in the Royal civil list settled the question. [Note the one exception to the almost unbroken line of royal/aristocratic antecedence, right up until the present day, of those appointed as Grand Master, was that of the 22nd Grand Master (1739): the 2nd Lord Raymond, whose father was a crucial politician in Walpole's scheme of things in the early 1720s – elevated to baron in 1732]. After six years of struggle, Walpole was seated in power for fifteen years to come.' [4]

In other words the King's parting was in effect totally incidental to the course of events; he was even buried in Hanover.

However we choose to judge his reign the consequences of it created a social climate that brought together this, some might say strange, ad-mixture of people who saw advantage in restructuring this *ad hoc* bringing together of disparate London lodges into a formally structured and socially powerful society.

References

1. Marlow, J., *George I* (George Weidenfeld and Nicolson and Book Club Associates, 1972).
2. Fielding, K., *A History of England* (Macmillan, London, 1966), pp. 643-652.
3. *Ibid.*
4. *Ibid.*

Table 29.1 Status of family during the reign of GEORGE II (1727-1760)

HOUSE / CODE	1	2	3	4	5	6	7	8	9	10	11	12
Abercorn												
James Hamilton	S	E_6			c	s	b	x	c	x	x	01
James Hamilton	S	(wl)	(c)E_7*				s	b	sc	d		34*
Buccleuch												
Francis Scott	S/E	(c)E_2D_2		r*		s/e	b	sc	ggs	x	x	32*
Chandos												
James Brydges	E	(b)B_9D_1					b	xsct	d	x	x	14
Coleraine												
Henry Hare	E	B_3					?	sct	gs	x		08
Crawford												
John Lindsay	S	E_{20}						sct	d	x	x	14
Darnley												
John Bligh	I	V_1E_1				s(m)	b	x	n/a	x		23/25
Inchiquin												
William O'Brien	I	B_9E_4				i	b	x	d	x		19
Kingston												
John King	I	B_3			c			x	b			93
James King	I	(b)B_4						x	b			28
Leicester					n							
John Sydney	E	E_{20}						x	d	x		05
Jocelyn Sydney	E	(b)E_{21}		e				x	b	x		37
Thomas Coke	E	(b)B_1	(c)E_{22}*					xsct	n/a	x		28/44*
Loudoun												
Hugh Campbell	S	B_3E_3	E_3				s	x	d	x	x	84
John Campbell	S	(b)B_2E_4					s	xsc	d	x	x	31
Montagu (Vct)												
Anthony Browne	E	(b)V_6							d	x		17
Montagu (Bart)												
John Montagu	E	E_2D_2					b	xsc	d	x	x	09
Norfolk												
Thomas Howard	E	D_{13}					e		n	x		01
Raymond												
Robert Raymond	S		(c)B_1					x	n/a			31
Robert Raymond	S	(b)B_2						sc	d	x		33
Richmond												
Chas (Lennox) Stuart	S	D_7				e/s	b	xsc	d	x	x	23
Strathmore												
Charles Lyon	S	E_4			ck_2		b		b	x	x	15
James Lyon	S	(b)E_5					b	sc	b	x	x	28
Weymouth												
Thomas Thynne	E	(b)V_2					b	x	gn	x		14
Wharton												
Philip Wharton	E	$E_2M_2D_1$		fr	ce		b	x	d	x	x	15/18

For key to table *see* foot of Table 20.1

Chapter Twenty-nine: George II
(1683-1760, r. 1727-60)

umerous authors have chosen to write about the Tudors and the Stuarts, but substantially fewer have chosen the Hanoverians and when they have, the text quickly lapses into the politics of the times rather than some detailed analysis of their personalities.[1,2] Because we are concerned with this period in particular and the closeness or otherwise within the Court circles of those with whom we are interested, it is necessary to at least gain some understanding of their relationship to it. George II was already in his forty-fourth year when he became king. In 1706 he had married Caroline of Anspach. She was an intelligent and vivacious woman and proved to be an extremely valuable asset to her husband and incidentally, to Walpole,

who she is reported (depending on historians) to have disliked, but whose basic views on politics and *modus operandi* she shared – *see also* the very last few lines of Desaguliers' poem in Appendix 1. This synergetic relationship, but mutual dislike is illustrated well by Walpole's ugly remark (especially since he weighed over twenty stone and was not handsome by the standards we have now come to expect, whereas she was by all accounts an attractive woman) when addressing the problem of whether to court the King's mistresses or the Queen herself: 'I have the right sow by the ear'. Like many, if not most, queens both before and since she had to endure blatant infidelity, which she appeared to do without retaliation. Prior to the death of George I, the future George II's private court, probably due to his wife, had been much more light-hearted and was reminiscent of the activities that surrounded Charles II. But once George II actually ascended the Throne a Germanic authoritarianism set in and gloom seemed to descend, centred on the King's introversion. The other factor was that there seemed to be a family gene that predetermined a violent aversion to their first-born, but in this case it seemed that neither the Queen nor the King liked their son, which led to a level of disaffection that is difficult to conceive. The extent of this dislike is illustrated by a comment the King was said to have made when preventing the marriage of his son to the person he was most disposed to marry:

George II

'... "I do not think that engrafting my half-witted coxcomb upon a mad woman would improve the breed." Later the King exclaimed "... our first-born is the greatest ass, the greatest liar, the greatest *canaille* and the biggest beast in the whole world and we heartily wish he were out of it ..." [Surely even George I would not have said this about his son?][3]

This animosity was to prove of great political disadvantage to the King particularly after the Queen died in 1737. Of course her death and the subsequent further deterioration of relationships are in effect outside our period of interest, but the climate leading up to it is not. It impacted upon the social climate generally, not least the strata of society in which the Premier Grand Lodge was operating and if Masonic historians are right (this aspect of their basic premise is accepted with respect to this study) there was a marked decline from the euphoric interest in the Freemasonry of the early to mid 1720s and in consequence its social impact also. For instance, other than his constant philandering, the only real interest of the King was his military activities and he was behind the politics that led Britain into the various wars during his reign, even with erstwhile friendly nations. Its importance in the context of this study was that coincidently there was a shift away from science and philosophy in the upper echelons of Freemasonry towards those having high military rank, but not accompanied by an equally high enthusiasm towards Premier Grand Lodge Masonry. This shift of emphasis and personalities occurred towards the very end of the 1720s – *see* bibliographies of several of the Grand Masters who were shown to have distinguished themselves greatly in these same skirmishes.

After the Queen's death in 1737, George went on to reign in a deteriorating climate for a further twenty-three years, which was also the period when Freemasonry, after the formation of the Premier Grand Lodge was perhaps at its most divided. Even his death turned out to be inglorious in that he died on the toilet.

This concludes this brief résumé of those who held supreme power prior to and during the time of interest, since George III's reign extended well beyond the first twenty-one years of the Premier Grand Lodge (as defined here). We can disregard the time from 1740 onwards and as has already been premised, there is reasonable contemporary corroboration to the notion of there being Royal Arch Chapters by 1742, thus conveying the clear implication that it was referring to something that had by that time been established for some years. The text but especially the Tables show the close social and political interrelationship of the Founders of the Premier Grand Lodge and their predecessors with the successive royal courts as well as Cromwell's Commonwealth. The relationship was quite profound, especially that of the progeny of Charles II; greatly influencing if not determining the eventual hierarchical structure of the Premier Grand Lodge. It can now be seen that whilst not all the rows of the Tables preceding each of the last few Chapters were filled, that during George II's reign the last empty row was filled and much can be gained by studying the respective status etc. of each of those within it. However, if the complex interrelationship of the various factors that affected the formation of the Premier Grand Lodge is to be substantiated then a number of the broader sociological factors will now have to be considered.

References

1. *George II* (George Weidenfeld and Nicolson and Book Club Associates, 1972).
2. Fielding, K., *A History of England* (Macmillan, London, 1966), pp. 653-680.
3. Clare, J., *Kings and Queens of England* (Futura Publications Ltd., 1985), p. 225.

Chapter Thirty:
Social factors and their influence on Masonry

haptters fourteen to nineteen dealt with those men most likely to have some, if not most, influence in the formation of the Premier Grand Lodge; sufficient it is hoped to give an insight into the personalities involved and the nature of their likely motivation. The potted history given in Chapters twenty to twenty-nine of the absolute authorities (kings, queens and the Lord Protector – the favoured topic of numerous historians) was merely intended to convey a flavour of the times during which the families of those of interest here had managed to survive or needed to be re-invented. However, just as the sailor returning from the traumas of the Falklands War (or indeed any far distant localised conflict), who on seeing those holidaying on the beach, was dismayed by the seeming indifference of the Nation at large; appearing to pursue its life in this untroubled fashion, it is necessary to look for factors outside the fractious world of power politics, that may have influenced events and allowed this imperceptible and yet unprecedented prosperity. For instance, it is patently obvious that by the early 1700s it was quite common to navigate over large regions of the Globe. This factor had created a different perspective on trading, such as a desire for the exotic in the upper (now changing) echelons of society and which led to the establishment of institutions and social behaviour such as clubs and the social intercourse of coffee-houses. Equally important was the fact that science was cutting itself free from religious constraint and it was offering the glittering prize of wealth to those who were able to exploit it. Ingenuity, that which we would now regard as technology, was becoming important in the shift of emphasis from an agricultural, cottage industry based society to an urban one, especially in London - a factor of extreme importance to this study. So saying, agriculture was not immune from scientific development, the extent and subtlety which became clear whilst attempting to research a Dr Beal reportedly of Masonic association in the early years of the Premier Grand Lodge. There was indeed a certain Dr Beal who had been a member of the Royal Society, but on further investigation he was found to be completely unrelated to the Masonic 'Dr Beal'. However the exercise was of considerable scientific interest, revealing that there was considerable biological sophistication at a very early date (c. 1640). It is an important factor when attempting to determine why Biology had not been included in the 'Nature' of Masonic ritual. It transpires that Beal was in fact a man who had made his impact in the first half of the 1600s, that his research was quite (scientifically) brilliant and primarily based on crop selection and management; to such an extent that if he had conducted the work in the twenty-first century, there is little doubt environmentalists would have seen the need to trample down his trial crops. Indeed, we shall see that the absence of biological input in the science of Freemasonry could not be discounted due to a lack of the interest by the Founders, since they showed interest in all science, but rather that it was outside their primary field of activity – *see* Chapters thirty-six and thirty-seven.

It is not surprising therefore that there was a considerable public interest and motivation in understanding science and technology, both for its own sake and potential financial gain. Similarly, with the expansion of commerce there was great desire to be in association with those men of influence; exemplified by the determined fight and bizarre reorganisation of some of the guilds and livery companies in an effort to retain the monopoly they had long enjoyed hitherto. These several aspects alone were strong social factors that were likely to determine the eventual success of any one of the many societies and clubs etc. floated during that period, not least the Premier Grand Lodge. However, in this particular case, quite apart from the innately laudable and potentially lasting qualities of speculative Freemasonry, which would have commended it as a socially desirable concept in any age, its outstanding success at that precise moment was that it chanced to be the right product, at the right time and in the right place. This contention will now be expanded upon by considering a number of social factors, the first being the way in which sociological changes appeared to affect 'operative' masons and proposes a scenario that would explain the development of 'speculative Freemasonry'. The most obvious place to begin was the concept of guilds or a similarly close-knit (lodge) society.

It is therefore useful to consider the likely evolution of what was essentially a craft based society into one that to all intent and purpose was that of a social club whose declared *raison d'être* was predicated upon purely philosophical concepts. There is little dispute that of all the trade associations or guilds prior to the dissolution of the monasteries, masons were by far the most prestigious and secure. Indeed they were so respected that they were able to traverse borders that were otherwise blocked by feuds and wars. They could, within reason, command their own price and terms. They were able to protect their interest by the formation of close-knit groups of highly skilled workmen in a formalised hierarchy called a lodge. They reinforced this structure further by a strict regime of internal hierarchical gradation. Perhaps the most obvious manifestation of their craftsmanship and influence were the cathedrals and abbeys they built following the Norman Conquest. The very scale of these truly awe-inspiring structures and their deep religious connotations would have been sufficient to intimidate the masses and engender a desire within the influential members of society to be associated in some way with such work. In the centuries preceding Henry VIII and in the early years of his reign, the ecclesiastics who commissioned the work encouraged this reverence of the building and its craftsmen.

Social factors and their influence on Masonry

The influential members of the Church and society were anxious to be associated with the master builders, since these awesome structures appeared to emphasise the omnipotence of God, but more practically, it perpetuated the subjugation of the populous to the power of the church and its right to impose tithes. However, just as much else when Elizabeth ascended the throne, the next hundred and fifty years were to see the Church's influence (and buying power) decline even further. The need for operative masons and their exquisite craft skills declined in equal measure and in consequence their perceived importance within the wider community was emaciated to such a state, that their hitherto tight-knit socially powerful lodge structure was prey to a 'take-over' by those who previously would have considered themselves privileged to be associated with them. That the psychological and hence sociological imposing nature of these massive stone structures was a factor is well illustrated by the comparative size and beauty of parish churches; their size appearing to bear absolutely no relation to the number of intended worshippers or their capacity to fund their local building without severe financial penalty.

By the time the sixteenth Century had opened in England, Scotland and Ireland the era of the great gothic cathedrals commissioned by individual bishops was already in serious decline, but Henry VIII in particular, was in one fell swoop, to decimate the power and wealth of the Church. Building on a grand scale still took place, but it was now in the form of houses and palaces. However, these were commissioned and used for a quite different and secular purpose, but more importantly, owned by intrinsically different people. No longer were the conditions such that a great cathedral could be conceived and funded from within a small segment of the church. Neither did there seem to be the patience for a building to be commissioned and begun by the master builder, in the certain knowledge that it would almost certainly take the rest of his life and that of his patron as well as many more years besides to see it completed. This long term approach had meant that in order to undertake this work, the masons would have had to live on the site in question, set up their lodges, lived as a close-knit society and employed a 'hands on' approach. Now if buildings of this magnitude were to be built and occupied in a relatively short space of time then the flexible materials of brick and timber would once again replace stone, which meant that stone was then relegated to that of mere decoration rather than structural integrity, with only token architectural use in the form of mullions, stone facing etc.

The glorious manifestation of this change of technique and use of materials can be seen in the commissioning and erection of major structures as the rebuilding of St Paul's Cathedral and also other civic buildings after the Great Fire of London. Whereas in outward appearance St Paul's was equal in every respect to these magnificent earlier structures, its design and construction employed a fundamentally different approach and was now part of a corporate plan and in this instance paid for through a civic taxation on coal. The principal architect was not only a (mathematical) scholar, but a member of the laity, ably partnered by the outstanding (applied scientific) scholar Robert Hooke. They were employed to supervise the construction of many churches and buildings in a grand plan, relegating the mason to that of a highly skilled artisan; an employed assistant and not in any real sense the 'architect' or supreme 'master' mason. Although this trend was perhaps most apparent in London, virtually all other large houses and palaces were being commissioned and built in this same way and so the influence of the operative mason declined rapidly from a position of the most privileged of all professions, to one of comparative irrelevance. Hitherto, many of the wealthy and powerful had sought to be associated with this privileged group where it suited their purpose or enhanced their social standing. For much the same reason the masons had selectively encouraged an affiliation between themselves and these very influential members of society. Since these people were in no way operative masons, some artefact of association had to be devised and the concept of 'speculative' Freemasonry came about. Masonic historians have waxed long about the nature of this association and whilst it is most interesting there is little hard evidence of precisely what it amounted to. It is certain that it varied greatly from place to place and lodge to lodge. More interestingly this affiliation was also taking place from country to country and since the more modern communication networks that encourage what is now termed as 'hype' did not exist, it could be argued that there must have been some innate quality and virtue within the concept for it to happen at all. Whatever the reasons or their precise form, the reality is that such lodges existed and others were being formed, they consisted of men of considerable influence and the device of ceremony was used to effect the tenuous link necessary to associate Freemasonry with operative masonry. Thus by the late 1600s there existed a strange and in terms of its controlling caucus, an inverted admix of the now totally dominant 'speculative' partner, with only a very few, by this time ineffectual, operative masons.

It is perhaps convenient here to refer to the comparatively recent book in terms of popular Masonic writing, the *The Hiram Key* by Knight and Lomas, which purports to explain much of the history of Freemasonry, but in particular claims that Freemasonry, essentially in the form that we know it today, had in effect existed from time immemorial. The book makes a number of interesting observations on Freemasonry, but in terms of proving its antiquity it is far from convincing, which is disappointing, since its great antiquity is what most freemasons are encouraged, indeed in places told, to believe and some proof would have been most welcome. Unfortunately in the whole of the research done here nothing has been discovered that suggests anything other than the simple evolutionary model suggested above and unless there is some really strong evidence one way or the other, debate will

Social factors and their influence on Masonry

continue undiminished.

If attempting to define the nature of these lodges has occupied the attention of many Masonic historians over the years, then the nature of the rituals enacted within them has by comparison become an obsession and this part of the study may be considered as adding to that list. However, it will serve no purpose to even attempt to improve on the dedicated work and scholarship of these people by re-entering their lines of enquiry. To gain some understanding of how historians have approached this topic the reader is encouraged to refer to a commendable example in the chapters dedicated to this subject in Jones' book.[5]

It will be necessary to return to this matter later, but before doing so consideration will be given to several sociological factors outside of Freemasonry. For the moment some factors are left to be inferred, but three, the political, social and scientific/technological changes will be given specific attention.

In summary: by the time that the Premier Grand Lodge was founded the relationship between a Freemasons' lodge and operative masonry, would have been purely coincidental, such as in the case of Anderson's father earlier in the 1680s, (although less so in Scotland at this time) who just happened to be a specialised glazier in stained-glass. Further discussion on this subject and in particular the influence of construction methodology is discussed in a paper by Lawrence.[7]

References

1. Knight, C. and Lomas, R., *The Hiram Key* (Barnes and Noble, New York, 1998).
2. Jones, B.E., *Freemasons' Guide and Companion* (George Harrap and Co. Ltd., London, 1950).
3. Lawrence, C.C., 'A Brick-by-Brick Account of the Metamorphosis of Operative to Speculative Masonry', *AQC* 122 (2009), pp. 121-184.
4. *Ibid.*
5. Knight, C., & Lomas, R., *The Hiram Key* (Barnes & Noble, NY, 1996).
6. Jones, B.E., *op. cit.*
7. Lawrence, *op. cit.*

Chapter Thirty-one:
Political Changes prior to and during the founding of the Premier Grand Lodge

iven that the chosen model for this Study is English Freemasonry and that presently one of its strongest ritualistic and ethical claims is that it is stridently apolitical, it raises the question as to whether that has always been the case? Clearly to address that question it is necessary to consider the political situation prior to and during its early history. However this laudable intent is thwarted by the fact that virtually all information (specific literature) related to Masonic affairs stems from that same two distinctly polarised groups of people that have been used in other aspects of this Study; namely those compelled to denounce Freemasonry, the inevitable outcome of which is a need to replace their lack of knowledge and hence objectivity, with venom or cynicism and the second group are those who approach the subject because they have some connection with it and/or have developed a deep interest, usually an affiliation, in one form or another but who could be equally prejudiced. The predilection, pseudo reverence and determination of the second grouping in attempting to avoid any sense of impropriety results in their writing and speaking of Freemasonry in an idealised way. They expressly distance themselves from contentious matters such as religion and politics, avoiding any adverse connotations that may be interpreted unfavourably, or that appear to detract from the laudable precepts of the Order and in consequence both sources are unreliable with respect to teasing out the true level of any possible political involvement of those of interest here.

Whilst it is the intention here to strenuously avoid painting either an unfair or sycophantic picture we are nonetheless concerned with the charged atmosphere of the early years of the Premier Grand Lodge, the individual personalities, aspirations and consequential actions of those involved and as such must be prepared to accept the outcome, whatever that may turn out to be. Firstly: because of the exaggerated manner in which social intercourse took place (*see* the exchange letters in Martyn Folkes' short biography) it is likely that they would have paid 'lip service', rather than feel obliged to conform to the laudable expectations that would in due time become especially synonymous with the Order. Neither should they have been expected to do so since they had arrived in their present position because they were most decidedly political animals. If within the Ritual of that time there was already a stated ethic of political restraint and moral rectitude (for example something similar to the edicts contained in modern ritual), they would have almost certainly not felt bound by them and after all they were in the habit of delivering sermons not receiving them. In any case they could point to the Court of King George I where there was blatant infidelity and corruption and the ethos was clearly one of 'Don't do as I do, do as I say'. Although we may assume that the stated principles within the adopted Ritual may have been most laudable and suitable for public consumption, in practice the social behaviour within that strata of society was more likely to have been one where such strictures were not even contemplated, let alone expected. It would be many years later before such high expectations of its members would coincide with the concepts within the ritual of Freemasonry; certainly not with the emphasis and rigour that is propounded today, by those who, outwardly at least, are more idealistic in their concept of Freemasonry. Indeed it was this lack of direction and moral rectitude that was aimed at the 'Moderns' by the 'Antients' in the 1730s. It is left to the reader to decide whether and to what degree, politics still play a significant part in the politics and hierarchical affairs of modern Freemasonry. 'Societies' are 'people' and whilst the rules of a society may act as a constraint, their interpretation will differ from person to person and from group to group, depending upon the intent and aspirations of a dominant (not necessarily gifted or inspired) few.

Much of the following is based upon the assumption that the underlying drive of all political action is power and that it is merely fortuitous if it happens to coincide with the public good, in terms of such things as service towards and the wellbeing of others. Power certainly appears to describe the politics of the early 1700s, both within and outside of Freemasonry. Whilst this cynical view of the managerial structure of societies may be less true in, say, the local tennis club, as societies get larger, so this basic altruism appears to get lost in its upper echelons and is replaced by an unseemly jockeying for position, such as in the choice of chairman, president etc. A further important factor is that although the personality traits behind these actions are without doubt extremely complex and vary from individual to individual, it does not stop historians from gainsaying their thoughts, or concluding with certainty the precise reasons for their actions and although this study is not necessarily immune from this tendency it is at least aware of it

It has already been noted that there is a progressive decline in the number and extent of books on the kings and queens in the period leading up to George III, namely for that period with which we are primarily concerned, but there are fewer still devoted to the politics. Although it is perhaps apposite to reiterate the point that one should not rely too heavily upon the views of any particular historian. Even so when one is faced with the task of actually researching the subject there still remains a goodly number. Since we are concerned with the political impact on the formation of the Premier Grand Lodge and consequentially Royal Arch Masonry, there is a need to 'cherry pick' from these studies; to give an insight into the climate that surrounded those of interest here. Specific consideration will be given to the political/commercial 'wheeling and dealing' of ambitious (in modern parlance 'upwardly mobile') men such as James Brydges – the Duke of Chandos, since they epitomise the ambitious man of that strata of society and their actions are typical of such behaviour. The first Section relies heavily upon a book by Plumb,[1] which fortuitously is devoted specifically to this aspect of our study, it is hoped that this one track approach may be excused to some extent by the absolute necessity to condense this hugely complex topic into a few pages. His book appears well researched, seems cognizant of other people's views, even if we allow that in the end, he appears to have chosen to ignore or misrepresent them. His task in writing the book is much like that encountered in this study, in that it relies upon bringing numerous strands together, showing that they are in fact all interrelated, that none of them are 'cut and dried', but when viewed collectively are convincing. Clearly politics cannot exist in a vacuum, but it is convenient here to consider it in comparative isolation. The second half of this sub-section is based primarily on the work of Larry Stewart, whose *The Rise of Public Science*[2] singles out several individuals quite specific to our study, but in particular the Duke of Chandos and his relationship with John Desaguliers.

Almost imperceptibly at first, but much more apparent by the time Elizabeth had died, Parliament was beginning to assert noticeable influence. This was of course in direct conflict with the concept of the 'exclusive and divine right to rule' that monarchs had enjoyed hitherto. The story from then onwards was the relentless (and generally ending in inglorious defeat) battles of each respective monarch to retain as much of that 'divine right' as was possible under the circumstances. But the nature of their actions, far from slowing the trend, simply antagonised it further and added to the rapid sociological changes that were taking place otherwise, both at home and abroad. Some understanding of the various devices employed may have been gained from the earlier sections that dealt with their lives and the families of those with whom we are concerned. Over the period from James I, the execution of Charles I and immediately after the Civil War there was a rapid decline of kingly power, which superficially at least should have become complete with the ascendance of Parliamentarians, but because of political feuding and the way in which Cromwell intervened, it was more apparent than real. There was some restoration of the kingly powers at the expense of Parliament after the return of Charles II. But this too was superficial, principally because of his unfortunate behaviour, which put him and the monarchy back on the slippery slope of disaffection and consequentially steadily declining power. This erosion of kingly power was set to continue up until the present day, but was most especially true of his brother James II who Charles II had carefully engineered to succeed him. All attempts to sustain the inherited mystical 'divine right' of kings, disappeared when 'the country', essentially those few who had real influence, feeling threatened by the continuance of James II's style of leadership, were galvanized into action when his son was born. In order to counteract any possible chance succession, it became necessary through the auspices of invoking an essentially (non-) parliamentary device, to ensure that William III was placed on the throne. Thus by an 'earthly' contriving of an act of parliament which legitimised their action of allowing kingly status to be transferred to William III, they had removed any future claim by a sovereign to rule by 'divine right'.

Many causal factors may be ascribed to justify why successive monarchs steadily relinquished their kingly powers. But there is little doubt that a predominant factor was their perpetual need for money. The expenditure of each successive king/queen always exceeded income by a large amount, with the only action left open to them being recourse to Parliament, but always at the expense of their absolute power. However, historians are quick to caution their readers not to assume that the parliaments in question were anything like those we would recognise today, since their members were there by numerous devices such as patronage, nepotism, placement, bribery etc. (however the more cynical reader may challenge the claimed distinction.)

Whilst there are many factors that led to the demise of operative masonry as a powerful section of society, it is necessary to make a brief study of the sociological events of this period in order to come to a view on the part that it played in this seemingly inevitable process. Certainly a most influential factor was the political/socio-economic evolution that was taking place during that time (early 1720s), which created the situation where there was a desire, if not an imperative, for men of influence to associate with men of money, thus establishing powerful social liaisons; which in this instance provided the motivation to usurp the original purpose and intent of the Premier Grand Lodge formed in 1717.

The essence of this latter strategy may be best illustrated by quoting Plumb in a section where he is discussing an analogous situation when Charles II needed to gain some control over the membership of Parliament

'... Over the long term the control of Parliament could be achieved in three ways: by building up a Court party powerful enough to dominate the Commons among those elected; by making certain of obtaining a Court-tied majority through electoral management; or a mixture of both.

A great deal of attention has been paid to the organization of the Court party; less to that of opposition [here he refers elsewhere]. Naturally, places, pensions and honours were used by the Court, but so was skilful persuasion and management. The latter was probably on a geographical basis. A reliable county leader, usually a dependable place-holder, would have his list of sympathizers. Often Members of Parliament for a particular county had a favourite tavern, for instance the Herefordshire Members met at the Blue Post in Chancery Lane, the Cornishmen at the Fountain in the Strand, the men of Lancashire at the Swan, Billingsgate [again he refers elsewhere]. Doubtless there were professional groups, too, of lawyers and merchants. [...]'[3]

It is difficult to understand why he chose to use the cautionary word 'doubtless' since there is no doubt expressed by virtually every other historian that this type of association was everywhere, particularly in the professional guilds and commerce and that their meeting places were commonly in taverns and coffee houses. Especially well skilled in this art of 'wheeling and dealing' were those of interest here.

Stately homes, or at least those now open to the public, create an impression of ownership and power from time immemorial and that the privileged few were there due to some innate right, but that this separation within society is now a characteristic of the past. However, closer inspection shows that this is in fact an illusion and that this was not the situation then, or indeed now. We have seen from the biographies and associated charts (*see* Chapters 20-29) that there were very few ancient families that had managed to come all the way through the system and virtually none, because of the political hazards and lines dying out that were not altered radically or reallocated in the process. Thus, the enhanced social status of most of those with whom we are concerned in the early 1720's was of comparatively recent origin (*circa* fifty years). This is especially true of those who were related to the natural children of Charles II and whilst in consequence their claim to such inheritance, might be considered highly dubious their influence was real enough, especially with respect to its effects on those of interest here. Because of the destabilised nature of events over this period the Court, aristocracy, landed gentry, 'squirearchy', merchants, landowners and industrialists shared a complex relationship with each other – where, if it suited their purpose, there appeared to be far fewer social 'hang ups' with respect to intermixing than would be the case today. To appreciate fully the degree to which this social engineering occurred and its attendant corruption it is necessary to listen to historians such as Plumb and then to take a balanced view, but whatever the source, there is little escaping the fact that it was rife. In order to place some of our characters in context the following is based upon a selection of quotes from Plumb's book where specific reference is made to our central characters.

As a further indication of the authority of Plumb's work, it is important to realise that it resulted from a commissioned study undertaken for one of the Oxford colleges and it was rigorously reviewed (effectively refereed). He would have needed to be extremely precise, since like those in this study, his conclusions turned out to be other than those imagined when he commenced the work and likely to offend those holding the consensus view, including those who had commissioned the study. He showed that political stability was not a long drawn out affair in the form of a distinct set of established individuals, but could in practice come about in a very few years, especially if, as in this instance, it is engineered so determinedly. Whilst many of the social tools with which the Premier Grand Lodge was crafted were highly suspect, it had succeeded because the conditions for its manufacture were perfect.

Political Changes prior to and during the founding of Premier Grand Lodge

Whilst it could be argued that at virtually every stage the means employed were doubtful, if not downright dishonourable, they were used to great effect by a few highly skilled politicians. Its importance here is that all of the leading characters in our story of the early years of the Premier Grand Lodge were either those very same people or were closely allied to them. Because so many others societies failed during this period, it is testimony of their initiative that it not only survived, but flourished, even if at the same time one is far from certain of the basic morality of their actions in achieving that goal.

Not because Plumb's book is badly written, but because of the complexity of his argument, whole sections have to be re-read to get an understanding of the subtleties of the various political systems. However, in essence, it concerns a system where those involved gained influence by whatever means available, guided by the principle that only if all else failed would there be any concession to those entitled to vote or the community at large. Even though the electoral franchise was greatly restricted, so far as these manipulators were concerned it was already too large, due mostly to the fact that inflation had rendered the financial qualification required of those entitled to vote to such a relatively low level that even ordinary folk, e.g. 'mere tradesmen' were enfranchised. Thus because such people's votes needed to be bought, 'fixing' the outcome of an election was becoming an increasingly expensive business. Indeed as we shall see in the hectic political period leading up to the formation of the Premier Grand Lodge, there were so many (fourteen from James II to George I) general elections that many of the would-be players were driven out, simply on cost grounds alone. The level of investment required in these various dealings is well illustrated in the following extract from Plumb's book:

'This at first did not lead to great political homogeneity among the courtiers, but the potential was there. Offices, great and small, were open to purchase, both in William III's and in Anne's reigns; again, neither William III nor Anne were committed to any set of ministers for long, so patronage in the household eddied with the tide, sucking in and casting out Whig and Tory in all complicated varieties. In George I's reign, however, direct purchase of important Court appointments had virtually ceased, even if bribery had not, [here he adds a subscript: There was but one attempt, by the Duke of Chandos to buy the Duke of Montagu's office – the Great Wardrobe]. Competition for patronage remained intense, the Duke of Chandos spent over £40,000 in bribes in less than four years; these were given to George I's German ministers and one of his mistresses [again subscript: C. and M. Baker, *The Life and Circumstances of James Brydges, First Duke of Chandos*, 112 n.]. 'He obtained a peerage for his father, the deanship of Carlisle for his brother, and the reversion of a Court post for his son.'

This passage will be referred to elsewhere in reference to the extraordinary circumstances surrounding the election of second Duke of Richmond as Grand Master in 1724.

A crude assessment of Plumb's book and hence of the political development of the period is that there was a clash between the Tories (broadly the landed gentry – supporters of the crown rule and their influence upon it – essentially Stuart) and the Whigs (largely men of property, wealth etc., ostensibly supporters of Parliamentary Government – provided it was their version of it). The categories of the two factions are not distinct and analysis is made the more difficult because the main players were given to opportunistic switching of allegiances according the needs of the moment.

There was, however, a fundamental difference between the Tories and the Whigs, namely that the Tories could not remain sufficiently united to become as effective as the more cohesive Whigs, especially when compared to the tight bond within the Junto that first seized the opportunity to gain influence during the reign of William III. The Tories had started badly after the Revolution of 1688/9, some even seeking the restoration of James II and although the Tories held sway in the House of Commons, they failed to do so in the Lords. During much of Anne's reign her favourable disposition towards the Tories was due more to a combination of her dislike of the Whigs and her over reliance on the counsel of her close companions, than any real liking for the Tories as such. Plumb spends a considerable amount of time establishing this claim and the following three short extracts that relate directly to our purpose are given below:

> 1) When it was necessary to manage the affairs of Parliament; 'When it suited him Wharton [the elder] could rouse his squires to action with the skill of Harley'.

> 2) To illustrate the cohesiveness of the Whigs when in a minority position: 'From 1694 onwards the Junto began to take a much more practical attitude to placeholders. Henry Guy, the Secretary of the Treasury, was broken by Wharton; expelled from the Commons for peculation, his management of the Commons was taken over by the Junto and place-holders taught to learn the duties of their place, a system that was intensified in the next Parliament..

> 3) When managing the political scene elsewhere: '...Wharton conducted a more complex and vigorous campaign in his territories of Wiltshire, Buckinghamshire, Cumberland, Westmorland, and Yorkshire than they had witness since the days of exclusion. [...].'

Plumb, without stating why, expresses a positive dislike of Montagu's three major reforms: first; re-coinage (some historians suggest the mechanical reason for the shortage was due to the illegal trade of re-melted coin into bullion). Second; the creation of a central Bank ('of England' effectively) and the creation of the concept of the 'sinking fund', which was in all essentials the concept of what is now referred to

Political Changes prior to and during the founding of Premier Grand Lodge

as the National Debt. Third the imposition of a 'creative' fund raising type of taxation; principally 'the window tax' to recoup short-falls. Plumb proposes that this brought about great hardship, but fails to explain how, given the state of the economy at the time, some alternative solution would have been better. However, he emphasises the fact that the Montagus played an important part in the politics of the time leading up to and during the period with which we are concerned. He writes when discussing the financial differences of approach of the two parties: 'And for that, the bitter opposition of the Tory Party to taxation was as contributory as the inventiveness of Montagu or the administrative efficiency of Godolphin'. If there was indeed hardship, then its effect upon Montagu and those with whom we are concerned was minimal.

When addressing the need to include biographies of the main characters in our analysis an obvious choice was that of the first (Grand) Secretary, the pivotal office in most Masonic initiatives. Despite much effort, not least that of the excellent staff of the Library at Freemasons' Hall, Great Queen Street, London, the William Cowper Museum and the House of Lords library, nothing of any significant import could be found, leaving the impression that he was a 'cardboard' character and that his position as Clerk of the House of Lords was simply another example of nepotism on the part of his uncle. However, he was a barrister and clearly a man of some learning and the more one reflects, the more likely it seems that he was an effective 'back room' operator. After all, even if someone else 'was pulling the strings' the events that took place on the day of the election of Grand Master in 1724 had to be orchestrated and co-ordinated by someone. The machinations of both the internal and external politics of the early years of the Premier Grand Lodge were effectively inevitable when one considers the people involved and he (Cowper) was certainly used to operating in this type of environment – *see* his short biography and his handling of the fiasco relating to the organisation of a Grand Gala. Because of his lack of family seniority he was not 'ennobled' and in any case, by that time there was already a surfeit of 'nobles' competing for the top job in Freemasonry. Desaguliers the one powerful non-titled personality likely to make an impact had already had his turn during the time when the top positions were in some way related to the original and simple concept of the 'Quarterly Meetings' and he was, almost certainly, the behind the scenes force, driving the new agenda.

Before the final attempt is made to bring all the strings together there is a need to consider several characters, Cowper's uncle for example, who greatly influenced the formation of the Premier Grand Lodge. There is no evidence that he or the other people in this select band were involved directly in Freemasonry, merely hovering in the background and because of this they have not attracted the attention of many Masonic historians, but now is a good opportunity to deal with one of these – Charles (Spencer), Earl of Sunderland. He was of vital importance in Plumb's assessment of the politics of the time and to what extent may be inferred from the following extract:

'Owing to the intransigence of the Tories, Marlborough became in effect a Whig and so did Godolphin, and it is interesting to note that Godolphin did his best to prevent the free operation of the spoils system in the interest either of the Whigs or Tories. Neither in power worked with the single-mindedness of a Wharton or young Sunderland to extend the influence of their party colleagues; so long as their families were looked after, they were content'

Because Philip, Duke of Wharton, had been levered into high office, both outside and inside Freemasonry and was certainly was not a man to be content with being a mere figurehead, we can assume he would have been heavily involved in the early critical years of the Premier Grand Lodge, but Sunderland's importance in our analysis is less obvious. On closer examination however, his importance emerges in two ways. First, he was the First Lord of the Treasury (the post that is now held by the Prime Minister) in the period leading up to the South Sea Bubble affair, where because of his perceived involvement in it, he became the 'fall guy' and resigned. By so doing he let in the 'untarnished' Walpole as well as distracting attention from some of our characters who were, as a result of the South Sea Bubble bursting, politically vulnerable. It must be remembered that Walpole, for essentially political reasons, resurrected the Kingston dynasty and created the Raymond title in 1728, and whose son became Grand Master in 1739. Once again its real significance is that Raymond was the only person not related in some way to the established aristocracy to become Grand Master, other than the three originals, right up to the present day. Because the aristocratic element of the upper echelons of Freemasonry is such an important element of its sustained appeal, it is fortunate that this political nepotism was very brief indeed and patronisation by the nobility was reinstated. The second and most important factor is the many faceted and somewhat complex interrelationships Walpole had with many of the others with whom we are concerned.

Sunderland's title, like most others, was comparatively new. It had belonged originally to the Scrope family, but lacking a suitable heir became vacant in 1630. It was given to the Henry Spencer in 1643 following outstanding military service at Edgehill and the siege of Gloucester. Due to the early death of his elder brother in 1688 he became Lord Spencer. He then began a series of extremely important (fortuitous) marriages, not least of which being the links forged between him and the families of those important to this study. The first of these marriages was to Dorothy daughter of Earl of Leicester (father – Sydney) and Earl of Northumberland (mother – Percy). His military prowess was to prove his downfall since he was killed in battle later that year. He was succeeded by his son Robert, who was then only two years old and so it was to be some time before he had any impact upon the scene, but when it happened, it was truly remarkable by any standards, most especially for its opportunistic dexterity. There is insufficient space to list the various important offices and various activities with which he became involved during successive reigns. His meteoric rise appeared to have come to an end in 1688 (the Glorious Revolution) when he declared himself a Papist and elected to flee to Holland. That however, fails to recognise his political genius, for he engineered a pardon from William III and took the oath in Parliament (although he never took office.) Having 'kissed the King's hand', he then went on to become a trusted advisor. He was created a Lord Justice of the Realm (forming a link with the Cowpers). We now add two more families through his marriage to Anne, the only surviving sister of John Digby, the Earl of Bristol and daughter of George, the Earl of Bristol and Francis Russel, the Earl of Bedford. Thus the families were intertwined, even before Charles inherited the title in 1702 – *see* family trees.

Whilst he was exceptionally active politically throughout, Sunderland gained real prominence after George I ascended the Throne, rising to the ultimate position of First Lord of the Treasury in 1717. However, although his political career influenced those with whom we are concerned, the real catalyst was through his three marriages. First: was that in 1694 to Arabella, daughter of Henry Cavendish, Duke of Newcastle and Frances (mother), daughter of Hon William Pierrepont. Second: Anne, daughter of John Churchill, Duke of Marlborough and Sarah (mother), daughter of Richard Jennings. Third: Judith, daughter of Benjamin Tichbourne daughter of Henry Ferrard, Baron of Beaulieu and Elizabeth (mother), daughter of Edward Gibbs. How strong all these links were is of course a matter of conjecture, but the fact that they existed is significant and in the absence of any knowledge to the contrary it is reasonable to assume that they were likely to have considerable influence – again *see* family trees.

It is perhaps appropriate to conclude this Section with an extract from the last paragraph of Plumb's book:

'… What Sir Robert Walpole and the Whigs did was to make certain that the political and social authority should devolve by inheritance; the methods have been purified, and tortuous by-ways evolved for talent, but birth still remains a broad highway to power. And power by inheritance must mean a world run by patronage; this must be so, for the political notion is always greater than the availability of place, and this was true even at the greatest extension of our Empire. It should also be remembered that patronage can, as it did in the nineteenth century, operate through seemingly disinterested boards as well as directly from patron to the patronized; indeed, it is often forced to do so by the growth of the political nation. But patronage has been, and is, an essential feature of the British structure of power, no matter how varied the costume it may wear. In the eighteenth century it scarcely bothered to wear a fig-leaf. It was

The Key to Modern Freemasonry

naked and quite unashamed. 'He thought', scribbled the Duke of Newcastle of himself, 'Neddy Townsend (and he always thought so) must have the Deanery (of Norwich) when thus pressed by all the Townshend and Walpole families.

Of course he must, and did. Such sentiments have echoed down the centuries to our own time. It was patronage that cemented the political system, held it together, and made it an almost impregnable citadel, impervious to defeat, indifferent to social change. And yet there are historians who dismiss eighteenth-century patronage as little more than private charity. This is absurd, and arises from considering the pecuniary rewards of place only. Place was power; patronage was power and power is what men in politics [and likely the upper echelons of Freemasonry] are after.'

There has been a great deal written about this most interesting person (typically Spencer),[4] but before leaving the brief appraisal and to show that these complex links were at all levels the following quote is given:

'... Defoe and Steele were at different times his protégés, and he gave preferment to Desaguliers, the natural philosopher.'

It is clear that politics were an important facet in the jockeying for power in the early Premier Grand Lodge. It consisted of two strands; those at national level and those in local skirmishing. Indeed it was the central preoccupation of those with whom we are concerned. It is certain to have affected their behaviour and disposition towards this new activity which they were fostering, but which ironically required them to act as a (brotherly) group. As can be seen from the bibliographies of the individuals, whatever cohesion and central purpose had been there in the beginning, by the middle of the 1720s schisms had formed and the nature of the organisation was experiencing change. How this may have affected the basic culture and ethical nature of the ritual and hence its preferred content is the focus of the final conclusion to be drawn from this study.

By studying the politics at a national level it is possible to show how the intense political activity of individuals outside of Freemasonry had a marked effect on the way in which the Premier Grand Lodge developed. This is especially well illustrated by considering the complex political character of James Brydges – the Duke of Chandos. Larry Stewart's book, *The Rise of Public Science*,[5] is primarily a scholarly appraisal of how science and technology developed during the period and as such has been referred to elsewhere in that context. Nonetheless, he considers James Brydges' political chicanery during this period so important that he devotes a whole Chapter, entitled: '*The Chandos Connection*', to its ramifications.

Whilst it was left for a (lesser) Chandos to become Grand Master in 1738, by which time Freemasonry had begun to lose, if not already lost, its way, the Chandos dynasty clearly had very strong connections with all those central to its inception and early development. However there is little doubt that the two men of greatest importance to this study were those of Desaguliers and Montagu and to a lesser extent those of Cowper, Folkes, Stukeley etc., via the Royal Society and other social and commercial connections. The First Duke of Chandos was also related by marriage to the Earl of De Loraine and thereby indirectly to the Montagus. Because they were so clearly involved in many other activities a degree of intimacy is assumed. The most important socio-political aspect of the First Duke of Chandos' background is that he represents a classic example of the marriage of 'property' and 'title' with commercial 'wealth'. His father was the Eighth Baron, but equally important his mother was the daughter of Sir Henry Barnard a wealthy (Turkish Company) merchant, with significant property in London and elsewhere.

Chandos' political career started very young and he was 'elected' the Member of Parliament for Hereford when he was just twenty-four years old. His problem, as with all the others with ambition during this turbulent period, was staying on the right side, which required great dexterity and he proved to be up to the task. To a very large degree this has to be true of all those with whom we are concerned, otherwise they would not have had sufficient status to be in the group that muscled in on those who had conceived the original idea of a premier Masonic conglomerate. It would seem that he sought influence rather than power, using the advantages so gained to improve his social and financial state. Stewart describes his early strategy as follows:

'After a tour of the continent, having met Leibniz in Hanover, he was in London in 1694, where he began his siege of the influential to secure himself a place in the Excise. In 1694, he was also elected a Fellow of the Royal Society [remember he was then just twenty] in which he took great interest perhaps as much for the possibilities of preferment offered by such prestigious company as for natural philosophy [and we are led to believe that a more likely reason lay in the possibilities of the potential commercial exploitation of science]. He was in the sight of influential men like Sir John Hoskins, former President of the Society and M.P. for Herefordshire, Sir Robert Southwell, the diplomat and President of the Society from 1690-5, and Newton's benefactor Charles Montagu, the Chancellor of the Exchequer, who succeeded Southwell as President [Stewart does not mention the family or the possible Masonic connection suggested above]. But as the young Brydges was to discover, seeking preferment is one thing and finding it was quite another – especially for a young man without strong connections and a father who had no use for the ascendant Whigs.'

Stewart goes on to list the various ways in which Chandos attempted to ingratiate himself, but repeats his difficulty in attempting to do so because of the ever shifting political wind. He begins the entry into one section with the sentence: 'This is

The Key to Modern Freemasonry

not to say that Brydges was entirely without principles.' but then by virtue of its content proceeds to challenge that reflection. He cites a number of instances such as his relationship with Godolphin and the Duke of Marlborough. During the later period of Queen Anne (*c.*1706) when they were at their most influential he was very keen to solicit their company, but when the political tide turned and he wished to become an influential figure in the South Sea Company he was equally keen to be disassociated from them. Stewart explains that in order to distance himself 'in 1712 he paid his respects to the Earl of Oxford's Administration having explained that "The obligations I had to My Ld Godolphin & Duke of Marlborough were wholly personal, & as the death of ye one & retreat of ye other from Publick affairs have left me perfectly at liberty So nothing shall hinder me from following ye dictates of my own mind" '. When it became apparent that Anne's death was imminent he ingratiated himself into the Hanoverian Court to such a degree that the new King created him the Earl of Carnarvon, but this in the short term proved to be a political hindrance. He ruminated to Philpot, one of the potential, but unsuccessful MPs he had sponsored: '… he [Brydges] had retired from politics because it was futile "to engage afresh in a life of hurry & envy & in a Nation so divided into parties, that no one is allow'd any good quality, by ye opposite side" ' – it would seem that in the realm of politics nothing seems to change.

In one instance Stewart refers to him as an entrepreneur, but perhaps a better description would be that he was a 'wheeler and dealer' of the first magnitude and would use any device available to him. Because of his 'enterprising' nature he was a most interesting man and many of his schemes involving Desaguliers and others with whom we are interested were quite remarkable. For instance he introduced inoculation (one might be surprised that this technique was applied 300 years ago) for those in his African ventures for gold and other minerals and to lessen the death of slaves in transit. He was involved in the politics surrounding the South Sea Bubble affair, the York Buildings company dealings in the infra-structural supply of water to London etc. He and all the early Grand Masters, other than perhaps the first two were heavily involved in the politics of the period.

References

1. Plumb, J.H., *The Growth of Political Stability in England 1675-1725* (The History Book Club, London 1968).
2. Stewart, L., *The Rise of Public Science* (CUP, 1992), pp. 311-335.
3. Plumb, J.H., *op cit.*
4. Anon. Spencer, C., in *Dictionary of National Biography* (OUP, Vol. XVIII, 1916), pp. 750-757.
5. Stewart, L., *op cit.*

Chapter Thirty-two:

Sociological Changes from Elizabeth I to the foundation of the Premier Grand Lodge

ike the political changes discussed in the preceding Chapter the sociological changes were equally exceptional during this period and they too have attracted the attention of many historical scholars. It is of course an essential requirement of this study that each (ideally every) factor that contributed to the founding of the Premier Grand Lodge be considered in some detail and that some ascribed value be placed upon it. However in this instance the nature of the prevailing sociological climate was the very author of the Premier Grand Lodge's inception and the major reason why it succeeded and subsequently flourished and so it is especially important to gain some further insight into the particular social circumstances enjoyed by those who are of interest here. The following is an interpretation of the intrinsic attitudes of a number of historians who have written on this topic, but for convenience three are taken as the basis of the following analysis, since their dispositions range from the romantic to the cynical. However, having defined those extremes it would still seem that there are some aspects of their analysis that even stray beyond the bounds of those two strong adjectives.

In every age the constitution of all Society ranges from the affluent to the pauper, from the influential to the plebeian. These extremes are divided by a socio-economic ridge, which does vary according to the prevailing climate and as such may be sharply defined or somewhat rounded and blurred, but nevertheless it will always be there. Given that it divides the affluent and powerful from the poorer and disadvantaged of society, the degree by which it does so depends upon the prevailing level of prosperity at the time. It becomes less marked when the general level of prosperity is high, at which times it is possible for certain sectors of society to maintain a social position which may even be considered to effectively straddle the divide. However, when there is a downturn in the economy, people slide down either side of it. The position of this ridge lies adjacent to the upper levels of society, its precise location and severity being a function of the percentage of the economic cake left after sufficient has been taken out to maintain the affluent sector, the remainder being distributed in relation to the political climate. In simple terms if the cake is large, the bulk of the population, or at least the most influential sector, will enjoy sufficient prosperity to depress any driving force for change, with the extreme poor having very little impact at any time. Further, that prosperity can be measured crudely by considering the extent to which an individual's finances exceed those required to simply survive. An unfortunate corollary of such situations, is that where such affluence and/or power flourishes it depends, of necessity, upon the buoyancy of the overall economy, but to judge from history, the success of every major civilisation, seemingly without exception, depends upon the excessive exploitation of others or the over exploitation of natural resources or more likely both.

By the start of the Stuart period, the pioneering global navigation of the fifteenth and sixteenth centuries had become effectively commonplace and the potential wealth from such ventures was clearly enormous. It was just a matter of time before this seemingly boundless source of wealth from the wider world was exploited to the extent where it had a major impact on the economies of the European states. Of course it was not the sole contributor, but given the above scenario, because the total wealth flowing into the respective economies was appreciably greater than that which would have been generated otherwise within the economies of the European states it was bound to affect the then known world. This explosion in maritime activity simply added further reasons for conflict between European states and since war or the threat of it also distorts economies, considerable economic impact and social change was inevitable. Whilst financing of the various wars and self indulgence was the ball and chain of the various (British in this instance) monarchs throughout most of this period, it appeared to have only a limited effect on this underlying trend within society at large. Although effectively imperceptible this economic growth was the catalyst of the massive social changes, because whilst these wars were raging, kings and queens, were coming and going and the politicians were coming and going in sympathy, often associated with frenetic activity, a new class of entrepreneur and strata of society was emerging. This sociological change was occurring at two levels, the opulent *nouveau riche* and at the small business (middle-class) level of society. This almost incipient opportunity was providing the climate for a whole raft of otherwise unlikely people to amass wealth, of sufficient magnitude to have a profound effect upon the hitherto indisputably influential upper echelons of society. The impact of religion, culture and science is yet to be considered and whilst these important aspects of society were to play an important part in our story, it was the basic economic prosperity that allowed it to happen. Indeed it was primarily because the characters with whom we are concerned were caught up in the most intensive aspects of this 'acquisitive' stratum of society that created the circumstances which brought them together to form the revised (usurped) Premier Grand Lodge.

Whilst there may be much debate over the causes of the changes of society after the death of Henry VIII up until the demise of Elizabeth I, the reality was that the old power structures of the Royal Court, established aristocracy and the Church had drastically declined. Under James I it was being replaced by an effectively new aristocratic structure and a subtly different, seemingly *ad hoc* upper class. This new essentially entrepreneurial based section of the society, somehow managed to sufficiently divorce itself from the chicanery of the upper echelon of the Royal Court to remain independent of it. It was able to do so because it was not overly predicated upon the earlier forms of the acquisition of wealth that had relied heavily, if not exclusively, on royal patronage and/or associated political conniving of whatever type, but rather by acquiring their wealth through trading and the like, which avoided the inherent disadvantages and almost inevitable dire consequences associated with Court intrigue and patronage. This resulted in this wealthier sector getting even wealthier, to the extent where it could engineer the establishment of massive and monopolistic trading ventures (such as the East India Company) and make massive loans to the king and other notables, which in turn were to lead to agreements that even impacted upon the national debt. In the end this system produced one too many of such schemes, when some 115 years later, based upon the premise that nothing could possibly go wrong, it brought about the formation of the South Sea venture, whose subsequent collapse was to have a profound effect on many of those with whom we are concerned. However, it is interesting to note that when these noteworthy people fell on hard times, even then there were those about who were able to 'buy them out' of their predicament.

The thesis here is that once this massive readjustment in society had been set in train the *modus operandi* of this admix of operative and speculative mason was predestined to change into a complete reversal of roles and effective extinction of the 'operatives' in England, but to a lesser degree in Scotland. Prior to the time that Henry VIII dissolved the monasteries, the Church, however defined, had been an extremely powerful and rich organisation, well able to commission great structural works. It is perhaps helpful here to reiterate the changing status of the operative masons by reconsidering their demise and indeed that of many other guild type fraternities. As stated earlier because the erection of these awesome structures required the skills of very accomplished men, they had enjoyed a very exalted status in society, were comparatively well paid and able to preserve their position by an elaborate regime of trade restrictions, centred on the exclusivity of a 'lodge' type structure. They were of course itinerant workers, since they had of necessity to move from one construction site to another, but this was a slow process and wherever they were based they enjoyed very high status. There had been guilds of one sort or another from early times, but the intrinsic structure of operative masons' lodges was by far the most sophisticated. They were highly effective in the management of their affairs and were able to maintain a very high public standing. It must have represented the perfect model and been the envy of the other lesser trading (guilds) groups that were essentially cooperatives of like minded individuals with a common (commercial) interest. However, by the time James I had come to the throne the traditional way of commissioning and building of cathedrals had already come to its end. The building of beautifully crafted stone cathedrals had been replaced by the need for other buildings. The building strategies used in many of these houses and public buildings were now quite different, especially in their use of brickwork, which did not require the sophisticated organisation, exquisite skills and sourcing of materials necessary when contemplating the erection of a building that would likely take generations to complete. Thus the hitherto powerful lodges of the operative masons were now emaciated down to a comparatively low status. This decline was by then equally true of other similarly restricted interest groups such as the craft guilds, whose previous underlying purpose was to bolster their position by restricting activity to a selective group and/or skilled type endeavour. In the case of the craft guilds their threat came from industrial (factory) type developments, but again it was the speed and economy of manufacture. Thomas in his book *English Economic History*[1] illustrates this point by referring to the necessity for guilds to merge and quotes some quite bizarre cases, for instance the merger between the London Tobacco-Pipe Workers and the Wheelwrights. Thus it is reasonable to conclude that operative masons were, if they were to retain that 'selective' aura, obliged to broaden their membership, by now encouraging/enhancing their existing (historical) affiliation with selective persons of considerable public standing, but who were otherwise completely outside the mechanics of operative masonry by inviting them to become 'speculative' members and certainly towards the time that the Premier Grand Lodge came into being, more and more likely to be entitled Masons.

This halfway stage was well illustrated, when during the course of researching the bibliography of the Reverend Dr James Anderson, in recognition of his early involvement with the Premier Grand Lodge, a paper entitled 'Founder of Constitutions'[2] was suggested as a possible source of information. It did provide some help, but like Anderson's own writings, in the absence of hard fact it wandered into the realms of speculation. However, it was of interest in two other ways. First it emphasised the Scottish involvement in the early years of English Grand Lodge Freemasonry, but second it provided evidence of the increasing admix of operative and speculative masons. Figure 32.1 below is extracted from this paper, which itself is a copy of two pages of the actual *Mark Book*.[3] The point of interest is that with in this book there is a list of marks was compiled by Anderson's father, who was an operative (glazier – stained glass) mason, but whom by that time had been obliged to accept the admission of speculative Masons into his 'however defined' lodge. It would seem that in order to maintain the traditional linkage the lodge had encouraged them to adopt certain 'traditional' type mason's marks. He was clearly literate and was entrusted with the affairs of his lodge, but did not possess the same level of literacy as his son. Consequently the function of guilds was changing and for the most part their power declining and being replaced by subtle association with industrial and commercial groupings.

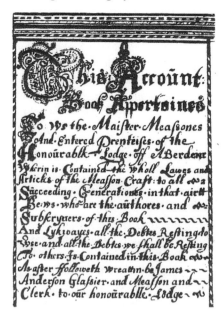

Figure 32.1 Copy of the speculative Masons' marks devised to give some symbolic connection between operative and speculative Masonry. There were forty-nine Fellowcrafts and Masters in addition to the eleven listed.[4]

In such a scenario it is not easy to understand fully why Freemasonry and the concept of lodges *per se*, should have retained/attracted the more influential of society, except for the two reasons ventured earlier, namely secrecy and whilst it had by then ceased to be a powerful trading entity it still retained an affiliation with the most influential in society. Whatever the true reason(s) may have been, by the time of Queen Anne, the ethos of their *raison d'être* have shifted from any pretence of the preservation of profound craft skills, to one of philosophical ('speculative') correctness of life and actions. Lodges of this form could be found in various centres throughout Western Europe, England, Scotland, Ireland, but especially in London wherein the centre of our analysis revolves. However, before doing so, it is helpful to first consider the concept of these small groupings and several factors that relate to the Country at large.

Masonic historians all agree that by the time the influential members of the four lodges that came together to form the Premier Grand Lodge there were already many other lodges in existence. Indeed as has been pointed out already, by the middle of the 1720s twenty-seven of them had been persuaded to become affiliated to the Premier Grand Lodge. However, few would venture to say with any certainty what precisely they practised within them. We can be reasonably confident that whatever the differences between them may have been, they had three things in common: secrecy, a ritualistic protocol for admitting a new member, and a socially elitist membership. Further that irrespective of the reported or implied amoral behaviour of many of its individual members, its ritual was founded, ostensibly at least, upon moralistic and religious precepts and that following the earlier presumption that this ritual was expressed in symbolic terms, its intrinsic morality was related to the perfection of the buildings themselves – in short; 'a peculiar system of morality, veiled in allegory and illustrated by symbols'. Although there may have been differences in detail between the individual lodges, it is reasonable to suppose that the basic content of the ritual was intrinsically the same. From a social perspective it is virtually certain that to any aspiring socialite, it would be most desirable to be seen to be a member of one of these exclusive, ostensibly highly moralistic and altruistic freemasons' lodges.

The second factor is to reflect for a moment on how these people, desirous of becoming a member of a 'lodge', came to be in a position to do so. Whatever the current pretext may have been, the 'enclosure' of land had been growing insidiously from Elizabethan times. The reasons ascribed for it being allowed to happen, such as 'improved husbandry', varied from year to year, but the process continued unabated and whilst the reasons proffered for these changes may have been specious, the move towards bigger and bigger estates continued at the expense of the small landowner and common land. The recipients of this bounteous process were the more influential (surviving) families who represented one half of this elite group, the more successful industrialist and commercial traders comprised the other half, in essence those of concern to us. Indeed the acquisition of property was so strong that some historians believe that the desire to 'look out of one's estate and only look upon one's own domain' became such an imperative that in some instances it led to complete indiscretion by certain individuals. Indeed this obsession was so overriding that it led some people into severe financial difficulties or denied them an opportunity of becoming involved in other more lucrative ventures. However, if perchance there happened to be an exploitable mineral or say coal, the aesthetics of preserving the countryside did not prevent their extraction, for instance those on the Montagu's estates. It also encouraged them to have a town house, more especially in or close to London, where they were able to conduct business and join in the social life and it would seem, if appropriate, join a lodge. It may have been due to the aristocracy's comparative newness, but there was at that level a decided hobnobbing between these upper social groupings, unlike the fingertip relationship that exists in more recent times, between the famous (sports stars, pop stars, actors, business leaders etc.) and the establishment.

Thus it would seem that by the time the Premier Grand Lodge was formed any physical association with actual craft masonry was contrived or accidental. Speculative Freemasonry was an umbrella term for groups of influential people to meet in selective groups, the formal structure of which was described in terms used by operative masons in the preceding centuries. Because ritual is an innate constituent of mans social behaviour, the ritual of Freemasonry proved to be perfect for this particular social grouping. Clearly this particular activity was meant to be identified with those earlier master masons that had been responsible for the building of the truly awe-inspiring buildings, their close affinity with religious belief, pride of profession and inordinate skills. This cocktail of qualities would have been sufficient in itself, even though by this time Freemasonry ceased to have any physical justification it nonetheless had all the essential ingredients of a tight elitist conclave, with secrecy as part of its ethos and as such it was ideally suited for the Founders' purpose.

The sociology of this period is a study in its own right and so it would not be possible to embrace it in any comprehensive way and therefore only such matters that affected those with whom we are concerned will be considered. Of the many other factors that were having an impact on the way that society was evolving, two; shipbuilding and the refining and manufacture of iron and other ores, minerals and chemicals, were exacerbating the already dramatic process of deforestation which was bringing about an increased reliance on coal. As in most cases, this process had affected society in a number of ways: the obvious one of satisfying the almost insatiable need for the timber used in shipbuilding and the thirst for materials in the other industries, not least the reliance on charcoal for smelting iron and glass-making, but the corollary provided the opportunity of those well placed, to take and exploit the ground left vacant for extensive (large single tenant holdings) farming. The large landowners could, because of their powerful position, impose all kinds of constraints on the population at large and in particular those still living on what had hitherto been their land. They were able to sponsor protectionist laws, some as perverse as the one which insisted and that was indeed enforced, that a person could only be buried in a gown manufactured from English wool. This not only had the effect of changing the very nature of land ownership and farming practice, but changing the structure of the various communities. This pattern was mirrored in other forms of commerce with large monopolistic trading companies coming into being, which in turn changed completely both the internal and external markets, with a particularly adverse impact on guilds.

The roads were far from satisfactory and because of the inefficient ways in which they operated and the tolls that were levied were making very little difference to their quality. Although the roads may have been in very poor condition, the urgency to transfer commodities etc. was great and this increased the emphasis on navigation, especially the development of canals and rivers. The transportation of goods by this method encouraged, but at the same time skewed the development of towns and cities, whose needs like all others, were ever increasing, but were clearly at an advantage if they could be supplied in this way. Indeed St Paul's Cathedral was built on the revenue raised from a coal tax (transported by sea). These factors, exacerbated by the exponential increase in population discussed below, increased further the need for coal, which in turn led to an increase in deep mining, which necessitated the removal of groundwater from them. This eventually led to the use of steam pumping, leading on to the various possibilities of transporting (lifting) water, which led to the need to employ applied scientists such as Desaguliers; who for instance was not only involved in the removal of ground water, but also proposed a type of centrifugal bellows (firedamp – clearly Royal Arch Ritual's 'a noxious vapour'). Lords Cowper and Montagu were typical of those in the influential classes who were required to seek the services of scientists and technologists for their various enterprises and so links were being formed between widely differing sections of society; their respective needs obliging them to seek each others company, including becoming members of speculative freemasons' lodges. It is interesting to note that the environmental smoke and dust pollution in London became a major problem at that time.[5] Unfortunately the various nuances of the social history of this period are manifold and for a rigorous analysis no part should be ignored, especially if one is to acquire sufficient understanding to speculate on how this most complex social climate was likely to have influenced the people with whom we are concerned.

Before continuing on to the other areas of this Study, it is useful to consider the expansion of the population and despite three visitations of the plague, in particular the case of London – *see* Chart 32.1. Because of time and space, the assertion that the overall socio-economic changes were many and significant has for the purposes of this study to be taken on trust. Whether the extraordinarily rapid growth in the population that was occurring over this period was the cause or the effect is arguable. Similarly it is not possible to debate at length which of these factors; such as survival rates, migration from towns to cities, cultural habits, immigration etc. played a part and if they did to what extent, but what is certain, is that with such an increase in the population the sociological climate was bound to change profoundly.

This rapid increase in population is perhaps best illustrated by the widely quoted (typically by, say, Thomas[6]) contemporary writings of Gregory King in 1688 – *see* Table 32.1 and Chart 32.1 below which are in fact are a representation of King's analysis. Although these figures are only his approximations, because there were no official censuses of the population taken at that time, they are considered by most historians to be quite accurate. At the beginning of the 1500s there was an estimated population of 3 million, by the time King made his assessment it had risen to an amazing 5.5 million. However, our main concern is with London and the expansion

Sociological Changes from Elizabeth I to the foundation of the Premier Grand Lodge

here was even more spectacular, approximately more than doubling every hundred years, which, given the Great Fire and the several visitations of the plague, was in actuality even more dramatic. It was attracting all sections of society and all classes of immigrants, including the highly skilled Huguenots. It was by far the greatest centre of trading anywhere, bolstered by the outstanding success of its port. It traded in many exotic goods, included among which were tea and coffee. The drinking of tea and coffee had become fashionable and had led to establishment in London of coffee houses as the centres of social intercourse.

Table 32.2. Extracted data from King's Table' *see* **Figure 32.2**

No. of families	Rank, Degrees, Titles & Qualifications	Heads/ family	No. of Persons	Yearly income (£)
160	Temporal Lords	40	6400	3200
26	Spiritual Lords	20	520	1300
800	Baronets	16	12800	880
600	Knights	13	7800	650
3000	Esquires	10	30000	450
12000	Gentlemen	8	96000	280
5000	Persons of greater Offices and places	8	40000	240
5000	Persons of lesser Offices and places	6	30000	120
2000	Eminent merchants and traders by sea	8	16000	400
8000	Lesser merchants and traders by land	6	48000	198
10000	Persons in Law	7	70000	154
2000	Eminent clergymen	6	12000	72
8000	Lesser clergymen	5	40000	50
40000	Freeholders	7	280000	91
120000	Freeholders of a lesser sort	5.5	660000	55
150000	Farmers	5	750000	42.5
15000	Persons in the liberal arts and sciences	5.5	75000	60
50000	Shopkeepers and tradesmen	4.5	325000	45
60000	Artisans and handicrafts	4	240000	36
5000	Naval Officers	4	20000	80
4000	Military Officers	4	16000	60
50000	Common seamen	3	150000	20
50000	Labouring persons and out-servants	3.5	1275000	15
400000	Cottagers and paupers	3.25	1300000	6.5
35000	Common soldiers	2	70000	14
n/a	Vagrants: Gypsies, thieves, beggars etc.	30000		
		Total	5500520	

The Key to Modern Freemasonry

Table 32.2. Extracted data from King's Table' *see* **Figure 32.2**

Family income/annum (£)	Total No. of Persons	No. of families	% of population
Over 200	209520	23586	4
70 - 190	440000	65000	8
38 - 69	2026000	412000	37
14 -37	1495000	449000	27
under 14	1330000	400000	24

Table 32.3 Shows the pronounced skew of the disposable wealth of the Nation, with the titled families with 0.016% accounting for over 4% of the National income. However, nearly three-quarters of it was distributed among 60%, quieting any public anger since.

Type of Family	No. in group	Total annual income (£m)	% of National income
Titled	1586	1.6398	4.1
Upper class	45000	10.434	20.6
Middle class and professional etc.	450000	17.494	43.7
Lower class	539000	10.456	31.6
Totals*	1035586	40.0238	100

* does not include those classified as vagrants who are deemed to have no income.

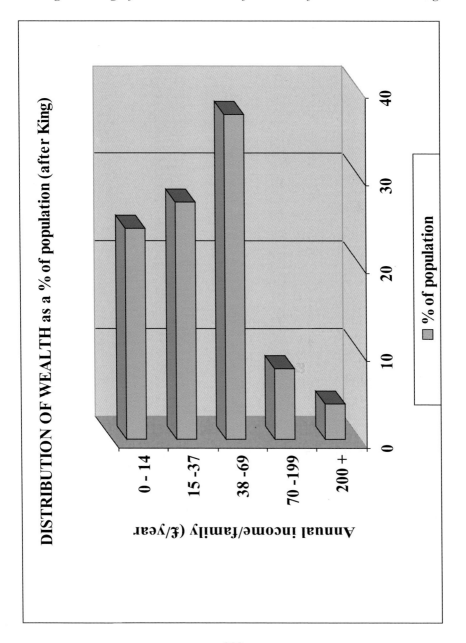

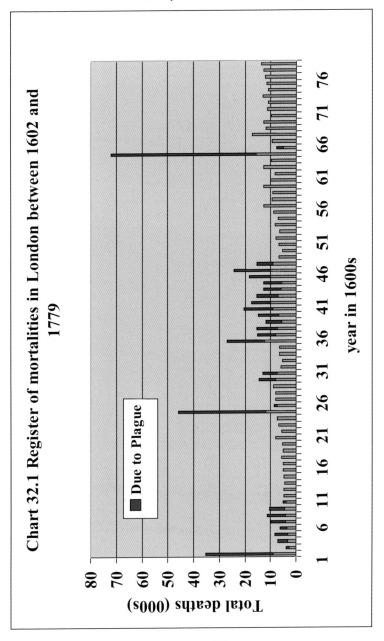

Chart 32.1 Register of mortalities in London between 1602 and 1779

Sociological Changes from Elizabeth I to the foundation of the Premier Grand Lodge

Table 32.1 is constructed from Gregory King's figures of 1688. His 'families' here represent the complete household, including servants, apprentices and other persons residing within the living area. The important factor is that whilst the two groups with which we are concerned is only the small (*c.*6%) affluent sector, there is beneath it a comparatively large and influential buffer, with sufficient wealth to be (socially) satisfied with matters as they were.

However, if one interpolates this data it still means that very nearly half the families had to survive on ten shillings (£0.50) per week, with the remaining 30% in virtual poverty. Poverty in the country was to a great extent controlled, if somewhat ineffectively, within the 'Poor Laws', but in London it created a sub-culture, which made it a dangerous place. However, it did not detract from London's attraction to the upper echelons of society, who for at least a proportion of the year, migrated there in considerable numbers, including many of those with whom we are concerned. Most cushioned themselves from the effect of this low life by residing in grand homes outside of its immediate bounds, but not necessarily from what would be deemed the more sordid aspects, since bear baiting, cock fighting, gambling, duelling, alcohol (especially gin) abuse, prostitution, muggings etc., all took place. Those who were part of the upper echelons of the social scene belonged to a range of different societies and clubs of which Freemasonry, because of its exclusivity was rather special and as suggested above was made the more so by having a formalised ritualistic structure. Again there has been endless debate as to the precise nature of these meetings, but in London these lodges were usually held in taverns and there is general agreement that an important aspect of such gatherings was 'wining (ale really) and dining', with its attendant social intercourse. However, the East India Company was now supplying tea and coffee, which had been adopted by wealthier classes as their 'socially acceptable' drink. This was reflected in the establishment of 'coffee houses', of which there were many by the time the Premier Grand Lodge was founded. This cultural phenomenon is well described by Trevelyan, including a supposed dialogue between a master and his employee:

> 'From the reign of Charles II to the early Georges, the London Coffee House was the centre of social life. It afforded a needed relaxation of the severe drinking habits of the time, for alcohol was not to be had on the premises. A list of some of the Coffee Houses in Queen Anne's time runs to nearly five hundred names. Every respectable Londoner had his favourite house, where his friends and clients could seek him at known hours.
>
> Remember, John,
> If any ask, to th' Coffee House I'm gone,
> Says the citizen to his apprentice as he leaves the shop.

The Key to Modern Freemasonry

Then at Lloyd's Coffee House he never fails
To read the letters and attend the sails. (Here he quotes – *see below*).

The beau monde assembles at White's Chocolate House in St. Jame's Street, where, as Harley bitterly complained to Swift, young noblemen were fleeced and corrupted by fashionable gamblers and profligates. Tories went to the Cocoa Tree Chocolate House, Whigs to St. James' Coffee House. Will's near Covent Garden, was the resort of poets, critics and their patrons: Trub's served the clergy, and the Grecian the world of scholarship; nor were there lacking houses for Dissenters, for Quakers, for Papists and for Jacobites. The 'universal liberty of speech of the English nation' uttered amid clouds of tobacco smoke, with vehemence whether against the Government and the Church, or against their enemies, had long been the wonder of foreigners; it was the quintessence of coffee house life.

The coffee house filled the place now occupied by the club, but in a more cheap and more informal manner, and with a greater admission of strangers. In the days when men stood much on their rank, it had a levelling influence: at the Coffee House 'you will see blue ribbons and the stars sitting familiarly with private gentlemen as if they had left their quality and degrees of distance at home'.

Quote: In Ned Ward's *Wealthy Shopkeeper* (1706), his day is thus apportioned: rise at 5; counting-house till 8; then breakfast on toast and Cheshire cheese; in his shop for two hours then to a neighbouring coffee house for news; shop again, till dinner at home (over the shop) at 12 on a 'thundering joint'; 1 o'clock on change; 3, Lloyd's Coffee House for business; shop again for an hour; then another coffee house (not Lloyd's) for recreation, followed by 'sack shop' to drink with acquaintances, till home for a 'light supper' and so to bed, before Bow Bells rings nine)'.[7]

He goes on to discuss the presence of Lloyds' Coffee House and then to indicate its eventual importance to shipping. He does not mention the 'entertainment' afforded by coffee houses, nor unfortunately the quasi-scientific talks, especially important to this study, since a good number were given by those with whom we are concerned, but also listened to by many others. This public thirst for the latest understanding of all matters scientific would have encouraged the more active of those trying to promote this formalised hierarchical structure of Freemasonry to 'sweeten the pill' by putting emphasis on Nature and science in any adopted ritual that was seeking to unify the people within these socially select, but otherwise independent lodges. Clearly science was not the sole *raison d'être* for ultimate configuration of the Premier Grand Lodge, but because of their shared interest and dependence upon it, it almost certainly would have a marked impact on its eventual development. Whilst the erstwhile Founders had chanced upon the ideal format, they were clearly not totally convinced, since we know that some were most active in trying to set up or become members of other forms of clubs etc, some of which (such as the Duke of Wharton's extreme case of the Hellfire Club) were quite radical in their basic structure.

Because there is so much more that could have been written about the general social history of any major city, but particularly the London of that period it is difficult to find a balance sufficient for this study. For instance Mainwaring's *Compendium*[8] discusses the numerous devices e.g. protectionism, trading pacts, the protected import/export of certain goods etc. that were employed to ensure Britain's trading dominance. These traders however defined seemed to be without constraint, since they were at ease with exporting people, not just slaves but many malcontents or offenders to the Colonies; if they may be so described at that early stage. But perversely one further item of extreme importance here; it also created the situation where they were required to accept immigrants and indeed encouraged it in the case of the Huguenots. Many nations at times of 'expansion' tolerate, indeed encourage the influx of people they would otherwise be disposed to exclude, especially where those people possessed skills otherwise lacking. In their book, *The Economic History of Britain*, Briggs and Jordan comment upon this 'skills shortage' and the fact that the Huguenots were not only a highly trained ethnic group, but were also being aggressively persecuted for their religious belief in France. It was not surprising therefore that there was an influx of them towards the end of the 1600s and amongst that group was the Desaguliers family. The educational ethic was paramount in the Huguenots' culture and Desaguliers Senior immediately set about giving his son personal as well as additional private tuition; finally sending him to Cambridge University, thereby ensuring that his subsequent education was equally sound. Because John Desaguliers had an exceptionally receptive mind and personal determination he fully justified his father's endeavours and he will feature largely in our final assessment.

For whatever reason there was a population explosion over the 120 years preceding the formation of the Premier Grand Lodge. It saw communities that had hitherto been effectively self-sufficient, become reliant on complex social interaction. There was a new class influence, one that was not necessarily related to ancient ancestry, since in any case most of those who would now be considered as belonging to the landed gentry, were then of only comparatively recent vintage, others had gained high status by means of wealth and/or business or politics. There was an expansion in trading in all forms, bringing about large changes in social interaction and methods of financing. There was a desire for exotic (those not essential for survival) goods, especially amongst the upper classes. There was a change in social structures brought about by those seeking finance being obliged to interact with the wealthy; who in turn were seeking influence and position. This led to the establishment of 'convenient' social groups of people in the guise of clubs, guilds

The Key to Modern Freemasonry

and in the present case freemasons' lodges. International and domestic trade brought a new emphasis on transport and the most convenient form was navigation by sea, inland rivers and estuaries inter-linked by canals, which increased the importance of those towns that could be served in this way. The advance of science and technology led to the upsurge of some activities at the expense of the more traditional. Skilled trades such as furniture makers were still around, but marginalised by the greater demand for everyday goods etc. The shortage of certain skills encouraged, if not enforced, the acceptance of immigrants of which the Desaguliers family was one.

However before leaving this aspect relating to the social history of the time the circumstances surrounding the formation and lasting success of parallel initiatives is of considerable interest. As such the Spalding Gentlemen's Society may be regarded as a justifiable addendum to this particular Chapter. From the very beginning of this book it was pointed out that because all the various sectors are interrelated there can be no defined start or finish. Inevitably this has led to some repetition of the basic aims and objectives of this work and these next few paragraphs may prove yet another distraction and arguably should have been included in the short biography of the Second Duke of Buccleuch. The short biographies found in Chapter Sixteen exemplify the sociological complexities that may well have influenced the format, or indeed establishment and success, of formalized Freemasonry as well as giving an indication of why it survived when others failed. Whilst the series of bibliographies that comprise Part III could only be brief an effort was made to keep them as balanced as possible given the marked imbalance of data available. However, in reality some characters have been researched by historians at great length whilst for others, even those in the aristocratic families, there is little or no data at all. The Second Duke of Buccleuch sits nicely in the middle and appears as neither a very appealing nor particularly exceptional character given the norms of the period, but there is some factual and implicit evidence of his early involvement with the Spalding Gentlemen's Society. Stukeley on the other hand is quite the reverse and there is such a plethora of data of his own and that written by others that his life and actions even now remains the subject of much research. However it is their background and activities with respect to the Spalding Society that will be dealt with here. Much of the following was either supplied or derived from the several communications with Dr Michael Honeybone a most active member of the Spalding Gentlemen's Society.

Maurice Johnson, a local barrister in Spalding in the county of Lincolnshire in the UK, had read for the bar in London in the early 1700s and he had become much taken by the 'coffee house' type conversations and ambience that he had participated in during this period. Setting aside the possibility that his motives may have been tempered by a need to demonstrate to the town an image of his being a man of wide learning, but rather taking the more likely interpretation that he was passionately interested in the acquisition and transference of knowledge within his community; he in conjunction with other notaries of Spalding, in 1710 set up the Spalding Gentlemen's Society. It is reasonable to take this favourable view since he became the workhorse (Secretary) and not the figurehead and remained its Secretary until 1748 when he did eventually became its President. He wrote the following:

> 'This Society is instituted for supporting mutual benevolence, raising and preserving and rendering of general Use the Public Lending Library pursuant to the statute of the 7th of Queen Anne chapt. 14th. And the improvement of the Members in All Arts and Sciences.' (minute book 1, fol.217a).

The Spalding Society like the four freemasons' lodges predated 1717 and those that were outside the initial grouping, consisted of the 'good and the great' of the local community and given its structure and declared intent it was a most laudable undertaking and seemingly underpinned by a high moral ethic not unlike (and likely based upon) the concept of the 'Improvement' movement coming from the middle of the previous century. Clearly its present existence proves that it too had sufficient merit to survive and in its earlier years was influential enough to have sponsored, through joint involvement with others, similar initiatives such as the Peterborough Society, but unlike Freemasonry has not flourished to the same extent. What then are the similarities and the differences, what is its importance with respect to this work and does its history support or contradict the basic thesis of this study?

Its inclusion here, as opposed to the numerous other pieces of relevant information that have been omitted, is because of its format, ethic and certain of its major personalities during the period of concern, but in particular to examine the subtle differences between it and Grand Lodge type Freemasonry. Although subjective there is yet another interesting aspect, namely that of imitation, since the Spalding Society was founded some years prior to the Premier Grand Lodge venture in 1717. The propensity to form clubs and societies during the early years of the eighteenth century is well documented and the reasons why the post 1720 version of the Premier Grand Lodge has survived are here argued throughout, but so also has the Spalding Gentlemen's Society survived the ravages of time. What then has led to one becoming a worldwide fraternity and the other remaining a most laudable and delightful Society performing much the same function as it did some three hundred years ago.

Some indication may be gained by considering their respective similarities and differences. Their principal commonly declared aims were:

1. the furtherance of 'enlightenment' or 'improvement' to society in general against a backcloth of humanitarian morality and through the dissemination of knowledge; especially that of the Arts and (and rapidly emerging) Sciences,

2. once formed the perceived need to encourage the patronage if not participation of the aristocracy,

3. the avoidance of all political and religious (intrusion) discussion,

4. the innate academy of their work,

5. the joint membership (patronage) of certain notable people.

However, they differed in several important ways:

1. the Premier Grand Lodge operated in the hotbed of London as opposed to the relative tranquility of rural Spalding,

2. their available feedstock; the one having the many unaffiliated freemasons' lodges and a host of people anxious to participate, the other the local community and the few who were prepared to commute.

3. the social, commercial, political and religious proclivities of those who became members or were anxious to join, as opposed to those of the Spalding Gentlemen's Society members whose only social comfort was that of being seen to be a member of a society whose aims were clearly those of benefit to the local community,

4. the one was based upon an established complex, ritualistic, already (claimed) traditional, secretive form of acceptance for its members and *modus operandi*; with its aims and objectives ill-defined, but with implicit laudability. Whereas the other was effectively open to all men of good standing, its aims and objectives the open transfer of knowledge to the declared benefit of all,

5. the large pool of aristocratic families, many already part of the disparate Masonic lodges or who could well be attracted into this now formalized fraternity. As indicated below although the Spalding Gentlemen's Society did realize the benefit of such association, it was restricted to those who were otherwise affiliated or had interest in the locality.

Thus it would seem that both the Spalding Gentlemen's Society and the Premier Grand Lodge started with many of the right ingredients, but with a slightly different recipe.

Both were successful from the start and both were to exchange ideas. The Premier Grand Lodge was to metamorphose into a fraternity based upon morality through a greater understanding of the Arts and Sciences, a strong allusion to traditional affiliation with ancient operative masonry, but above all headed by those recruited from the highest echelons of society. The Spalding Gentlemen's Society recognized the kudos that comes from such prestigious association and in due course did encourage some persons of high academic accomplishment and/or society to become part of their Society; a notable example being the appointment of the Second Duke of Buccleuch as their President. They were clearly successful in this and an extraordinarily high proportion of their members were Fellows of the Royal Society. The Second Duke of Buccleuch and Dr Stukeley were from the vicinity, but other notable freemasons joined, for instance Desaguliers. But again and perhaps unfairly, that could have been due to the fact that the Spalding Gentlemen's Society had within its membership in the middle 1720s a number of eminent drainage engineers, who were concerned with the huge (would now be termed 'civil') engineering project of draining the Fens.

Virtually all of this type of initiative set up during this time failed, but Grand Lodge type Freemasonry and similar types such as the Spalding Gentlemen's Society have survived; the reasons why the one should have remained much as it started and the other develop into an international fraternity may be inferred from the above list. Namely: the similarities were the ingredients necessary for longevity, but it was their differences that determined the nature of their subsequent growth. Equally important it demonstrates further the complex social interrelationship of that group of people who were influential in the eventual format of the Premier Grand Lodge.

The fact that the above discusses the Spalding Gentlemen's Society without regard to the other societies extant at the time, may be regarded as another example of a historian's discrete partiality of which the reader has been warned already. This assertion is to a degree true and is excused here on the basis that the Spalding Gentlemen's Society was selected for two reasons: its emphasis on science and learning and the joint significance of some of its members. However there were many affiliations of a similar structure and it is appropriate to recognize their presence and likely influence. Typically that of the Odd Fellows Society, who associated in a similar way to the Premier Grand Lodge in the 1730s (more significantly so in the early ninteenth century) and again was initially centred on London. But prior to the 1730s initiative were in many respects analogous to the disparate groups of freemasons' lodges and these too considerably predated 1717.

Such consideration assists in putting into context the Premier Grand Lodge of 1717. For instance the apparently pretentious concept of having the 'Grand Master' for the chairman of an *ad hoc* meeting of just four lodges, implying equally grand status within the community, but a long time before this the Odd Fellows, as with

The Key to Modern Freemasonry

several similar guild type organizations, had been using that form of address for the most senior of their particular body. Thus it was not at all surprising that the group who had organized the meeting of these four lodges should adopt this form of labeling. It is of particular interest to compare the scale and ambition of this 'get together' of the four lodges with the somewhat similar initiatives of these other groups, since it shows that in the first instance it was not an original concept and by comparison it was quite modest and without the serious intervention several years later would likely have remained so or even disappeared altogether.

Clearly this aspect of the sociology of that time deserves much greater consideration than this book will allow, since it is interesting if not imperative to research within their literature to understand the public's thirst for such societies. However, for those who are concerned with matters related to Freemasonry there is a quite remarkable paper by Durr[9] wherein he ranges widely over the similarities and interaction between such organizations and the burgeoning and subsequent history of the Premier Grand Lodge and formalized Freemasonry – the connection is anything but insignificant or incidental, but on the contrary is quite fundamental.

References

1. Trevelyan, G.M., *English Social History* (Longmans, Green and Co., London, 1958), pp. 323.

2. Thomas, M.W., *A Survey of English Economic History* (Blackie & Son Ltd., London, 1964). pp 217.

3. Anon. 'Founders of the Constitution', *Masonic Square* (Masonic Pubs. Ltd., London, 1975), pp. 56-57.

4. *Ibid.*

5. Lawrence, C., 'Within and Without: the Hidden Mysteries of Nature and Science as a Key to Modern Freemasonry', *AQC* 118 (2006), p. 129 (QCCC Ltd., London, 2007).

6. Thomas, M.W., *op. cit.*

7. Trevelyan, *op. cit.*

8. Mainwaring, J., *British Social History* (Odhams Press, London, unknown – circa 1960).

9. Durr, A., 'Chicken and Egg – the Emblem Book and Freemasonry: the Visual and Material Culture of Associated Life'. *AQC* 118 (2006), pp. 20-35.

Chapter Thirty-three:
Religion

Because religion affects each individual in a very personal way and for most declares a specific social disposition, it is without doubt, the most difficult area to comment upon and ideally it would have been better avoided altogether if unintentional offence was to be avoided. However despite the disclaimer in Masonic ritual that freemasons should (must) refrain from all topics of religious and political conversation, it then for purpose of 'regularity' demands that each member declares a belief in a supreme being. Given that every member is so persuaded it is difficult to imagine that they then would have no interest in its ramifications with respect to Freemasonry or not wish to moot the subject. Whilst changes in society have resulted in religion being somewhat less pronounced in contemporary Freemasonry, this was certainly not the case in the early 1700s, but on the contrary appears to have been an essential, if not predominant component; implicit in all its precepts and not least because of the background of those involved, who were almost certain to make it a major determinant of its structure. Thus whilst in an ideal world these divisive topics should be excluded from any altruistic society, in reality there never seems to have been a time when there was not a close relationship between the Church and the political affairs of nations, or indeed within discrete communities, or where personal aggrandisement has not played a part, thereby confusing belief with expediency and true motives with outward manifestations (whole PhD theses have been written on very narrow aspects of this behaviour – *see* Section on Universities).[1] For instance: did Puritanism evolve from some deep philosophical reasoning that engendered the evolution of that rather extreme (Civil War of 1649) schism in society; or did the nature of the society at large, create such disenchantment within and around that small section of society that they felt obliged or forced to go their own way? Would such temporal disaffection cause them to unite behind a banner of a controversial religious philosophy, well knowing that that would almost certainly bring them into conflict with the powers that were, if not society in general? The chances are that in reality it was a complex evolution with its share of zealots, blinkered devotees and/or convenient conformists. It is certainly the view of most historians that the events of the seventeenth and early eighteenth centuries either had or were seriously affected by a succession of underlying religious imperatives and that the individuals concerned were pursuing their own agenda, outwardly justifying their actions and secular objectives with religious labels and connotations. The problem here is that the subject is so large and convoluted and the space to comment upon it so small that there is a severe danger that brevity will be construed as unimportance. Indeed, the necessary brevity adopted here must not be allowed to detract from the immense gravity of the religious implications on society and hence the Premier Grand Lodge in the 1720s.

Whatever the motivation of such individuals or groups might have been, the net result was that many profound religious changes took place between 1600 and the foundation of the Premier Grand Lodge. Throughout this period there was a progressive and significant increase in religious tolerance, radical philosophical thinking and freedom of expression, especially with respect to the rationalisation (or imposition) of scientific discovery and it poses the question – to what extent was this process inevitable? It is here argued to be so on the premise that just as the Nation's prosperity was exploding during this period, so was the opportunity for irreligious thought; poverty could not in this instance be cited as an expression of God's admonition or for that matter a warning against excess. Science (especially that expressed in the form of physical demonstration) was being construed by some philosophers as an indication that there existed a mechanistic explanation of all things and in the extreme, that there was no need to define creation in terms of a divine creator. Thus by the time the Premier Grand Lodge was being mooted there existed an unprecedented audacity in the freedom of expression allowed. These religious deviations took various forms, from subtle changes within the established faith, or at the other extreme the establishment of new sects. Worse still so far as the Church was concerned were those individuals or small groups pronouncing total scepticism. Whilst it may have been socially inopportune or not politically expedient to profess one of these more extreme routes by 1717, in England at least, it no longer carried the same level of risk to a person's life or property as was the case elsewhere. For instance in Scotland, executions for heresy were carried out as late as 1697.

Historically the emergence of a philosophy based upon scientific precepts rather than blind faith had a profound effect on the doctrine and hence stance taken by the Church. The conflict between the two schisms within the Christian faith had hinged upon the outwardly professed faith of the reigning monarch, which in turn affected the political climate and vice versa. Whatever the underlying reasons for the unrest, religious dogma swayed to and fro, culminating in 1649 in the Civil War. In the event, the Civil war was a mere punctuation, since the Protestant/Catholic religious divide resumed with the Restoration. However, by this time religious scepticism within elements of the Church and society with respect to the omnipotence of God (however defined) was now being challenged openly. An essentially mechanical explanation of Nature, such as that proffered by philosophers such as Descartes and Hobbs, was gaining prominence. For although most accepted the need of a God to create the basic elements of their Universe, they could not accept that there was a need for him to intervene on a personal basis in the day to day fashion implicit in most major religions. However, the cork was being kept in the religious yet political

Religion

bottle by the proclaimed belief in the divine right of accession by monarchs. But this was jeopardised when James II attempted to exceed the political (proscribed) bounds apportioned to this inalienable God given right: to rule as he saw fit, which ultimately resulting in the 'Glorious Revolution' of 1688. Even so, for the powers that were, if this Protestant dynasty was to continue the only acceptable way was through James' eldest daughter, Mary. Unfortunately, Mary insisted that she would only agree if her husband was proclaimed king and notwithstanding historical precedent this was contrived. The significance of this approach has been discussed with respect to other aspects of this study and again with respect to religion this not only replaced for all time the myth of 'divine right' to rule, but with it any convincing (absolute) argument of the continuity between the king and the Faith; which with the political expediency and somewhat contrived hereditary link (since it also required James' son to be presumed illegitimate) predetermined and legitimised the Hanoverian claim on the British Crown and incidentally the 'Defender' of that Faith.

In Chapter Thirteen the nature of that which was taught in the universities was discussed and it was here that the consequence of James II's attempt to impose Catholicism was felt so strongly and was probably the 'straw that broke the camel's back'. It is important to remember that whilst the universities were the seat of learning they were also the very fount of the clergy and that factor is of importance to this Study, since it concerns Newton and in consequence a number of our people – *see* Chapter Thirty-six on Newtonianism. Massive changes were made on the university's hierarchical structure with the introduction of James II's placemen. As the situation deteriorated James realised his mistake and tried to redress these religious excursions along with a number of the other ill conceived notions, but it was all too little too late and the 'Glorious Revolution' took place. In any case the two established universities were already a hotbed of intrigue, polarising still further with the introduction of these new philosophies which offered a major challenge to orthodoxy.[2] This latitude (indeed it was termed Latitudinarianism) in religious concepts, the extreme of which being a mechanical explanation of all things, ruffled feathers and was strongly resisted within the upper echelons of the universities and was allowed very little space to develop. Since science was bracketed within these extreme concepts of religion, it too was given little outward freedom, but by the 1720s it had nonetheless gained a significant foothold and was being considered and expressed at depth by the freethinkers within the various colleges, not least by certain high ranking ecclesiastics. Other universities such as Edinburgh were less inhibited and again by that time there were also philosophical pressures from mainland Europe. It is important to this study because of the intimate relationship of our principal characters and the two major universities, particularly Cambridge. As we shall see it goes a long way towards explaining the uncomfortable admix of

The Key to Modern Freemasonry

science and religion in early Masonic ritual and why there appear to be so many anomalies. Thus individuals so inclined were allowed to contemplate, study and privately proclaim without undue molestation, provided that they were perceived by the wider community to conform to the establishment view.

Thus there is a need to reflect on how significant these changes were and how they may have affected those with whom we are interested. Trevelyan[3] when discussing this topic in the reign of Charles II reflects upon the level of persecution meted out upon middle and lower classes, whereas those of the upper classes were in essence unaffected, including the effects on their freedom to trade and the extent of their 'expediency'. He then comments:

'Very few of those who suffered belonged to the land owning gentry: among the squires, the Roundhead spirit suffered change into the Whigs, which refused to hamper its worldly ambitions by too scrupulous an adherence to the proscribed Puritan religion. A common Whig type was that of the sceptical Shaftesbury or the blasphemous Wharton, although these attitudes were no less fashionable among Cavalier courtiers and Tory leaders of Parliament'

He goes on to say that there were of course those who were, outwardly at least, very pious and professed devotion to Anglican worship, but who at the same time would employ a Puritan as a private chaplain to tutor their children. He points out that there remained a few noble families who refused to 'conform' (or at least overtly so), but those who chose to defy the edict suffered as a consequence, but they represented only a small minority. Roman Catholicism was still around in some parts of the country, but its followers were excluded from participation in all forms of government, by the laws imposed by the King. Otherwise the upper classes conformed to the Anglican faith. Indeed it became the fashion to take over their local churches to the extent where they had their own pews, private chapels, including the provision of a living for the incumbent parson. This presumably they felt entitled to do on the premise that since they effectively owned the local population, they had an innate right to stipulate the nature of their mode of worship. Trevelyan cites the case of Sir Roger de Coverly in Addison's book, stating how he was the benefactor of the local church and had been disposed to setting the entire guidelines:

'As Sir Roger is landlord to the whole congregation, he keeps them in very good order, and suffers no body to sleep in it bar himself; for if by chance he has been surprised into a short nap at sermon, upon recovering out of it he stands up and looks about him, as if he sees anybody else nodding, either wakes them himself or sends his servants to them'

Religion

Such patronage is of course most important in our study since several of those with whom we are concerned received their living (or a significant part of it), from such patronage, whilst others within the group actually awarded the said 'livings'; both having influence as a result of their involvement in this peculiar system of worship. The other factor that had a profound influence on religious thinking was the rapid advances in science and its popularisation. This has to some extent been discussed earlier, but whilst Newton and Boyle were somehow able to reconcile the relationship between religion and science, with the omnipotence of God's creative influence remaining central to their thinking; certain philosophers like the experimentalist Bacon and empiricist such as Locke were less able to do so. This is not surprising since very nearly three hundred years later, with great leaps in understanding the same philosophical conflicts remain. Religion is of considerable importance here because these early freemasons had, in order to construct a ritual, to decide upon the precise philosophical nature of their religious stance and it is clear that they chose the more prudent path of conformity. It is of interest to note that outwardly at least, they (even the 'blasphemous' Wharton) took refuge in the existence of a God; which in essence (after 1723) was essentially the Protestant Christian concept of God of their own persuasion. It will be suggested in Chapter Thirty-six in the section dealing with Newtonian philosophy that there was in practice a dualism between what they professed to believe and that which they actually believed and it is perhaps an appropriate point to consider this factor a little further.

Since we do not know the precise nature of the ritual during this period, it is necessary to interpolate, but the case will depend on whether one chooses to accept the implications of Newtonian philosophy or not. When one studies the membership of the lodges that comprised the Premier Grand Lodge in the early 1720s, the Church was well represented. Desaguliers' biographers inform us that he was a singularly poor parish vicar, but it is equally clear, that whatever his deep down religious philosophy may have been, ten years earlier it had supplemented his income and given him access to those of considerable social influence and he was unlikely to 'rock the boat' now, but again as we shall see he was a very special case. In general religion had either been or still remained a good ally to many of the influential people of the type in the Premier Grand Lodge and its pronounced inclusion into any ritual over which they had influence would have been essential and hence expected. It had the further important feature that it clearly signalled to anyone enquiring from the outside the moral integrity, laudable intent and rectitude of its members. This appraisal is expressed in these somewhat cynical terms for several reasons, but two in particular: first these were cynical times and the people concerned were obliged, if they were to succeed and ours certainly were intent on doing so, to match and indeed enhance their public persona. Second, from the very earliest times until the present day every scrap of evidence that gives an insight into the content of the ritual, presents an arbitrary mix of predominantly Christian ethics, bolstered with intrinsic humanitarian morality and patriotic duty. However, the Ritual also contains allusion to other, some ancient, religions as well as pagan beliefs and ritualistic artefacts and practices (for example *see* Stukeley's biography – Chapter Seventeen). The greatest challenge is to reconcile the strong (assumed) religious content of the ritual with brilliant minds and otherwise profound thinking of those very men responsible for the evolution of the Premier Grand Lodge during these few formative years. One point of view could be that they were simply very astute and what at first may be considered as profound thinking was in reality a goodly portion of animal cunning, political agility, adroit and expert presentation, or maybe there was indeed an element of distorted belief – *see* Chapter Thirty-six.

By the time that the Founders of the Premier Grand Lodge had reached the point where they were required to indicate the essential religious practices and intrinsic beliefs (content) of their organisations, it along with much else, had been subjected to a bombardment of conflicting ideas. So many and varied were the changes taking place, that whatever they elected to 'believe' or how deep such belief may have been, they were by then attempting to 'square the circle'. They not only had the problem of reconciling all of these conflicting notions within their own thinking, but at the same time needed to find a consensus view that was sufficiently coherent for it to be adopted as the professed theological component of their new collective society. Indeed it is a testament to their skill that if one does not dwell too long on certain inconsistencies and ignores some allusions to paganism etc., one is left with the distinct view that they were all agreed on a belief in a divine, all-powerful creator. Which if one merely scratches beneath the surface, it is essentially the Christian perception of the God of the Old Testament. Whether or not they could find a consensus view or that there were other factors such as the need to enhance mysticism and embellish the ritual, they managed to retain a considerable number of alien concepts. For example there are many instances in present day Ritual where phrases such as: 'The Sun to rule the day, the Moon to govern the night, and the Master to rule and direct....', 'The names of gods and religious symbols had ever been enclosed in triangular figures....', 'buried in the sands of the sea at least a cables length from the shore etc., retained for all time on the basis of inviolability, but which are a strange mixture of technological concepts with very distant paganistic overtones. These concepts were likely to have been included or something very similar, but it does not answer the question why they chose to do so in their new version of formalised Freemasonry in the 1720s during a period of such enlightenment? If one contemplates the behaviour of just two of the important characters; Desagulier's cavalier treatment of his parishioners, or Stukeley's harbouring of serious notions concerning the Druids, one is tempted to conclude that it was more a question of poetic licence or expediency, since if this initiative was to succeed; religious controversy had to be avoided. But as we shall see in the concluding Chapters there were other powerful influences that may have affected them.

It is appreciated that this topic is obscure even when a huge amount of time has been spent researching the subject, but as stated at the beginning of this Chapter, although the subject is very difficult it is nonetheless most important. It is especially important to this study because the claim is made that an understanding of science was not only important then, but is also important to the present day freemason if he is to rationalise his place in this World and his ultimate destiny, given that the basic tenets of Freemasonry are valid. To go very much further in a study such as this where many topics have to be addressed would be a great distraction, but the reader's indulgence is asked for in order to somehow reinforce this claimed importance. There are numerous papers written on this topic, but an excellent example of one such paper is that of Schaffer entitled *Godly Men and the Mechanical* [i.e. scientific/ technological] *Philosophers*.[4] To develop his argument he refers to over 100 references that relate to the interaction of religion and science and the outcome of his deliberations was to show that it was only the very extreme minority of the radical thinkers of that period who were prepared to dismiss the active interrelationship of God with Science. Schaffer is extremely erudite and it is not possible to capture the true depth of his argument in a few lines. The first part of his 'Conclusions' discusses the implication of the whole range of the spiritual World on the scientific thinking of the times. However, the last paragraphs of his 'Conclusions' are worthy of comment:

> 'Perceptive critics of this enterprise could uncover the experimenter's enthusiast ambitions. This was particularly apparent in the early eighteenth century. Leibnitz held that Newtonians had "grown weary of rational romances and are become fond again of tails of fairies" [Newtonians and Newtonianism will be discussed later – not least this aspect of it]. As usual, Johnathan Swift was an acute observer of this process. In 1704 he produced 'A Tale of the Tub', which satirized enthusiasm and pneumatics under the guise of "Aeolists" who "maintain the Original Cause of all Things to be Wind" [...] whence it is very justly observed by Naturalists, that Wind still continues of great emolument in certain Mysteries not to be named." '

This relates to an aspect of technology not mentioned in Part I it is what; that which we would now describe as vacuum technology (or, recognising the comment's origin, 'bodily functions'). However, Hooke whilst working with Boyle (*see* Chapter Twenty-four – the short biography of Charles II) had perfected a vacuum pump of sufficient efficiency to show the importance (to the extent of the very sustainability of life) of the constituents of air. Their work was very sophisticated and in a sense most prophetic since it postulated the likely importance of the 'aerial nitre' (their intuitive concept of one of air's important constituents – which we now know as Nitrogen) in the manufacture of fertilizer, but went on further to suggest that it also contained elements of the very spirit of life. Boyle was in modern terms also considered to be morally 'squeaky clean' and was offered a bishopric after the Restoration and this added to the moral status of his pronouncements; hence the next Section of Schaffer's Conclusion.

'He accompanied this attack with 'A discourse concerning the Mechanical Operations of the Spirit', which examined "the Phenomenon of Spiritual Mechanism" as manifested in the public assembly of philosophers and sectarians. In the same year he composed a brilliant pastiche of Boyle's spiritual reveries, A Meditation upon a Broom-stick. (This was in allusion to Boyle's invocation of the spiritual aspects of the physical world, which Swift felt was not too far removed from witchcraft). Swift was just as keen as some of our own (modern) intellectual antiquarians to find sources for seventeenth-century philosophies in Plato and Aristotle. [By implication Schaffer does not appear to sympathise with this view, but we know from the current form of Masonic ritual (if it has indeed remained unchanged in basic concept), that those who consolidated it were still persuaded, or at least their public version showed a disposition, towards a philosophy influenced by Aristotelian concepts intermingled with the occult]. 'But he saw very clearly that experimental pneumatics was a modern practice which, like enthusiasm, sought to make spirit "an effect of Artifice and Mechanick Operation." This was great wit and good history'.[5]

Perhaps the last word should go to Stewart when he was summing up the scepticism of those concerned at the impact of science and technology on the moral fibre of society, such as Swift and North:

'Latitude had clearly not meant lassitude in matters of religion and politics. The sympathies of Newtonian theologians as William Whiston and Samuel Clarke with the dissenting community reflected a relationship already recognized among the instrument makers, mathematical teachers, and lecturers of experimental philosophy' [and one might suggest the upper echelons of Freemasonry].[6]

References

1. Gascoigne, J., *Cambridge in the Age of Enlightenment* (CUP, Cambridge, 1989).
2. *Ibid*.
3. Trevelyan, G.M., *English Social History* (Longmans, Green and Co., London, 1958), pp. 323-325.
4. Schaffer, S., 'Godly Man and Mechanical Philosophers: Souls and Spirits in Restoration Natural Philosophy' in *Science in Context*, Vol. 1 (1989), pp. 55-85.
5. *Ibid*.
6. Stewart, L., *The Rise of Public Science* (CUP, Cambridge, 1992), pp. 211.

Chapter Thirty-four:
Further reflection on the (Masonic) sciences

learly science was not the only factor that had a profound influence on the formalised Freemasonry that is practiced today it, or ensured the success of the Premier Grand Lodge from whence it came, but it was the fertile delta that had resulted from the confluence and coincidence of a whole range of individual social streams that were affecting society during that period and it was the produce of that rich sedimentation which nurtured that bounty which is of especial importance to this study. Parts I and II showed that the social climate was such that it had allowed a rapid and peculiar development in certain of the sciences, both in practical and philosophical terms, but somewhat obscurely that there had been stalemate in some others. Since this strong interest in science was influencing virtually every aspect of society and especially that of the Founders (an appreciable number both practically and economically), it was ideally suited as a focal point for a study into a greater understanding of their personalities, motivations and especially their interest in Freemasonry. It would not only serve to shed light on what may otherwise appear disparate and ill-defined parts of our current understanding, but it would also assist greatly in fixing a date when Premier Grand Lodge Freemasonry as we understand it today came into being.

Today's members of the Royal Society have very diverse (usually highly specialised) interests, but Part I gave an indication of those broad aspects of contemporary science of which effectively all of the Founders would have had a knowledge, thereby allowing them to select those they considered to be of profound significance to man's understanding of his whole being and as such be an integral part of Craft ritual. If the thesis of this work is correct, these scientific concepts, although general throughout Masonic ritual, were specifically integrated within the Ritual and Lectures (especially the Symbolical lecture) of the ceremony that was to become the basis of one of the lectures in the Royal Arch. Although the research in this area added greatly to a general understanding of the many questions raised, such as why, where and particularly when, if the findings were to be convincing it was equally important to explain why were there certain topics extant at the time, but for some reason not included. Unfortunately, as with all else in this study, because it is such a huge subject, it meant that any attempt to condense the likely reasons into a few paragraphs presented an almost impossible task. However in this instance it was made somewhat easier because we were interested in the thinking of a specific person or at the most, a very small group of people and his/their thinking can be interpolated from a range of other indicators. Having now considered many other factors it is useful to return again to the topic of science and once again briefly touch upon the rapid evolution of scientific thought during the hundred or so years prior to and including the 1720s and comment on the then current state.

As already premised religious dogma had kept the lid on the simmering pot of scientific thought and discovery, but by the end of the seventeenth Century the dominance of the Church had waned markedly, perhaps most notably in the British Isles. Because science was perceived as intrinsically heretical in nature, both religious and the associated political pressure had delayed the Europeans' approach to the implications of purely physical aspects of science. However, by the early 1700s Europe was catching up rapidly and had reached the stage where their scientists and philosophers were beginning to have a profound influence on their society, but also through interchange a complementary impact upon the English scholars. The interaction of great minds and practitioners such as: Gilbert, Galileo, Bacon, Keplar, Tycho Brahe, Harvey, Huygens, Boyle, Hobbs etc. meant that science/technology had reached a point were it could be contained no further by religious declaration or edicts. It would have boiled over in any case, but the coincidence of great minds such as Newton, Hooke etc, merely fanned the flame under the pot. What precisely brought this change about is a much-debated subject; factors such as the printed word, patronage and the exchange of people were certainly three important factors. But there were also numerous other factors such as trade, exploitation of minerals, mechanisation etc. not least the impact of gunpowder on warfare (it has been asserted by one historian that the one person killed by a musket shot at Agincourt had a greater impact on history than the hundreds that died by the arrow and sword), All of these factors could be cited as having a far-reaching influence on subsequent events. In truth it can be summed up in the more modern parlance: that it happened because 'the time was right' and prevailing climate allowed the subject to be brought into open debate.

The task here is somehow to convey the complex array of conflicting scientific philosophies from which the Founders, if they were to accomplish their, seemingly imperative ritualistic demands; that all freemasons must constantly strive for knowledge. An absolute imperative in this process, if it was to be achieved at all, was to obtain a profound understanding of the 'Liberal Arts and Sciences'.

The first and most difficult, yet essential, task was to find the scientific common ground for each subject area on which they could have agreed sufficiently for its inclusion into the emerging ritual. This unfortunately leaves us with the task of first identifying those areas and where possible rationalise the logic of their choice. From Part I we have seen that this already near impossible task was made more difficult, because the Founders appeared to have engineered (or included unwittingly) conceptual irregularities in order to convey symbolic meaning. We must not minimise the task they faced, ideas were raining in on them, nearly every one requiring them to turn entrenched notions on their heads.

Further reflection on the (Masonic) sciences

Perhaps the best illustration of how difficult their task was, or indeed ours is now, is to read Dijksterhuis' book, *The Mechanisation of the World Picture.*[1] Even this extremely erudite study, which extends to over 500 pages, virtually every one of which is worthy of hours of study, is concerned only with science up to the middle of the 1600s. The title itself gives an indication of the profound nature of the argument enclosed; but put simply he proffers the contention that this period marks a turning point in the thinking of many philosophers, scholars and influential persons. He argues that by that time all nature could be explained in terms of physical (mechanical – not in the sense of a piece of machinery, but by resorting to a logical physical explanation) phenomena and did not require some organic or divine origin. His work is a succession of argument and counter-argument, either his own or those of the many others, some truly great, philosophers to whom he, even in a book of that length, refers to only in selected detail. Its value however is that it serves to verify the much less rigorous (nonetheless 110 page long) appraisal of the science during this period in Taton's (Editor of a multi-author tome) book and the works of Stewart and Schaffer,[2, 3, 4] to which reference has been made already in other Parts. Unfortunately, the section of Taton's book devoted to this aspect has a marked disposition toward 'pure' science, giving applied science (technology) short shrift, but Stewart, who has been referred to extensively elsewhere and Schaffer, compensate for this.

Whereas the seventeenth Century has been described by many historians as the 'Cradle of Modern Science and/or Scientific Revolution', the eighteenth Century is often referred to as the 'Age of Enlightenment,' although it may be deemed by some to have started *c.*1688 the demarcation appears very blurred and a case can be made for beginning much earlier. It is also important to remember that the later years of the seventeenth century were also the formative years of many of the characters in this study. It was found convenient when dealing with this topic to adopt the subject headings and sentiments found in Taton's book, since it concerned itself with the basic state of science during this critical period in an analogous way and in much the same order as that found in the 'Symbolical' lecture of the Royal Arch.

1) Perhaps the most critical change with the advent of Newton was the rise of (mathematical) analysis. The publication of his *Principia* in 1687 marked the change from a philosophical and modelled (Descartes' say) view of Nature, to one of experimentation, backed by mathematical analysis. However, whilst social changes only spread slowly (some seventy years out of phase) in Europe, scientific thought was not so disadvantaged and this was conspicuously so in mathematics ('Arithmetic', essentially 'mathematics' to their way of thinking, being a constituent of the 'Liberal Arts and Sciences' alluded to in Craft Freemasonry). In Britain Newton's complex mathematics was discussed, if not actually taught, in all the major seats of learning from Oxford to Edinburgh, but to a large degree it was

hampered by its over emphasis on 'Geometry', again one of the 'Liberal Arts and Sciences'. Newton's arch rival Leibniz had developed in parallel his own version of 'differential' and 'integral' calculus, using notation that would be recognised immediately by any present day student. The uncompromising adherence to the Newtonian method hampered mathematical development in the British Isles, but provided those public lecturers, such as Desaguliers, with an opportunity of simplifying Newton's obscure geometric approach for public consumption. To those who have been required to study mathematics as a topic, it is quite amazing how scholarly these early mathematicians were, to realise that much of their mathematics is still found in modern day syllabuses and to realise that it was developed during or before this short period. Perhaps the saddest thing is that algebra and indeed today's analytical (algebraic) geometry was a much earlier English invention and that Newton was both well aware of the technique and perfectly capable of working with it, but for some inexplicable reason refused to adopt it.

Although the book entitled 'Euclid' published by Burrows (head of Westminster School – at which Hooke and Wren were pupils) in 1655 was available, classical (deductive) geometry was available in the better schools, but not to any great depth or to all pupils, during the period with which we are concerned. Again analytical geometry was also in place, but it too enjoyed very little attention and/or development and so whilst early freemasons may have been exalted to make it part of their 'future studies', it did not come into fashion until much later in the eighteenth century.

Anyone who was a disciple of Newton and professed an understanding of his approach on gravitation needed to have a profound knowledge of geometry and Desaguliers was most certainly numbered amongst those. Geometry (of the triangle and conic sections) was the very essence of his method and whilst the authors of the Ritual could not reasonably expect such a level of proficiency in the average lodge member, unlike today they could reasonably expect, because of their basic schooling, a rudimentary understanding within their audience. However, if they were going to be able to have a real grasp of 'Nature and Science', to the point where it affected their thinking, they should at least begin to understand further some of the elements and rigour of geometry. This would justify the Ritual's extended reflections on the Jewel and the Regular Solids, in the Symbolical Lecture.

2) The next important division was classical mechanics. Because of the astounding capacity of Newton's brain he had not been forced to simplify the mechanism by which he conceptualised his ideas and its attendant mathematics. This made the task of those trying to employ his ideas, or convey them to others extremely difficult. It is not surprising therefore that even his students at Cambridge, who presumably were sufficiently proficient, found his lectures virtually incomprehensible and were dissuaded from studying the subject further. This also

Further reflection on the (Masonic) sciences

led to misinterpretation when others tried to expound on his work in rather more simplified terms, both in the British Isles and on the Continent.

The running feud between Newton and Leibniz brought about an almost childlike entrenchment in ideologies. Newton predicating his theories on the presumption of there being a universal gravitational attraction between bodies, but hedged his bets by attributing this to the omnipotence of 'God' however defined. Leibniz's response was to adhere, in a petulant way, to his Cartesian model and ridiculed Newton's belief that the celestial void was the 'sensorium' (brain and spinal chord) of God. Like all such petulant behaviour little profit came from it and progress within the subject was delayed needlessly. The British exponents (public lecturers in particular) were effectively all Newtonian, which meant that they too were required to explain all science in terms of God's omnipotence, which is consistent with its heavy presence in the Symbolical Lecture and the 'Platonic Solids' notion of there being a 'Sphere of the Universe'. Although the mechanics approach of Newton's was bound to prevail, its mathematical complexity was a distinct drawback and stifled its development in Britain for decades. Newton's concepts, at least in terms of influence, did not reach the Continent in any real sense until the late 1720s, but when they did they became the predominant concept. Once adopted the more classical (theoretical) aspects dominated, but whether in Britain or on the Continent, it was clearly too late to influence the teachings inculcated in the Symbolical Lecture. Although in many respects this dogmatism may have been a drawback with respect to the development of science in general, in terms of this study it is of considerable importance, since the range of topics covered in the Symbolical Lecture gives a strong indication of the interests of those who concocted the ritual; which to a large degree shows them to be primarily concerned with Newtonian principles as opposed to the wide range of topics and expertise represented elsewhere in the Royal Society of that time.

It is of interest to note that the subject known now as 'statics' was more amenable to general comprehension and a quote from Taton's book is of interest here:

'In 1690, Jacques Bernoulli, who had begun his important work on [mathematical] series in 1680, succeeded in solving the isochronous line problem which Leibniz had posed in 1686. At the same time, he made a fairly exhaustive study of the catenary problem [the curve in which a chain or rope hangs – *see* Chapter Two], which was later solved by Huygens, Leibnitz and Jean Bernoulli' [its solution was published *c.*1700].[5]

Thus there is strong evidence to believe that not only was the practical elegance of the form known, or at least available, to operative masons, but that its classical mathematical elegance was most likely known to speculative Freemasons such as Desaguliers and Stukeley. Its further advantage in terms of the Ritual was that it had a

The Key to Modern Freemasonry

high esoteric connotation and the concept was generally accepted to the extent where the Companions were informed that the Catenarian Arch was 'the strongest of all architectural forms', without expounding on the basis of that claim. There is little doubt that they would have appreciated the concept of forces acting on a body and that such forces could be represented analytically using 'statics'. However, as we saw in Part I, their ambition to demonstrate the cohesive ('compressing and binding') nature of the structure led them to modify reality somewhat. But if one looks at the sophistication of Desaguliers' writings on beam engines, pumping systems etc., it is more reasonable to presume that this digression was not due to ignorance, but convenient poetic licence.

3) We come next to optics, the last element of Taton's 'science' that is specifically alluded to in the Symbolical Lecture. This has been dealt with in the applied sense as light in Part I, but there are two things, which remain, that are of some importance to this work. We know from Part I that there were numerous theories and so it is useful to reflect upon why they adopted the particular explanation they did and what level of justification there is to assume that this was indeed the case and that the explanation given in present day ritual is much later interpretation. If such a process can be done with satisfaction, then the corollary of that would be that it would allow a comparatively accurate assessment to be made of when that explanation was adopted.

Given that an outline explanation of the various concepts of light was attempted in Part I was a fair assessment there seems little gain in reiterating the various concepts of colour during this period, except to say that there was no consensus. However, given the Founders' utter devotion to Newtonianism, the question remains as to why the ritualists of the Royal Arch chose to adopt the essentially Hookean, as opposed to the Newtonian, version? Without actual documentation that question has to remain unanswered, but we may deduce from the Ritual that for whatever reason they chose the former. They adopted the concept that there were '**two principal colours**' and not that found in modern ritual, where it is stated that they were merely '**two of the principal colours**'. As we shall see the words '**of the**' were added to the Aldersgate version of the Royal Arch ritual in 1953, when the 'Explanation of the Jewel' became another casualty and deleted. The reason for these changes is not known, but the most likely explanation was that those responsible for the general revision of the book of ritual were almost certainly unaware of the subtleties of the science of the early 1700s. It is reasonable to assume they would, as a result of their more modern education and perceptions, have been fully aware that there were numerous colours, certainly more than the two basic colours suggested in the Ritual. Since they were now in the process of re-editng the Ritual and given the evidence of their own eyes it would clearly be more accurate to interpose the phraseology '**of the**'. However, by so doing they had changed the significance of the scientific concept and the complexity of the Founders' intent. This apparent misinterpretation by intelligent people over 200 years later might serve to explain why in the early 1700s there was no established definitive view either, even though our people were otherwise devotees of Newton. Indeed, the theory of colour had been untidy from the start and by the middle of the 1720s Father Pardies, Hooke, Huygens and Malebranche had already published their own, quite distinct, theories. Whilst Newton, because of his strong position in the scientific community, had been able to impose his concepts, he had nonetheless changed his stance from time to time and was expressing some uncertainty even at the end (1728) of his life. Given that the Founders responsible for the ritual would not have possessed the much greater degree of certainty with respect to the nature of colour that we enjoy today, it would not have been unreasonable for them to proffer for general consumption a system that gave especial significance to the two colours at the extremes of visible spectrum. Thus whatever their physical understanding of the nature of colour might have been they realised that these two colours had, for religious reasons, an important role in earlier ritualistic ceremonies and it is therefore easy to see why they would wish to integrate them into the Royal Arch ritual.

Thus after these changes had been made in 1938, to the quasi-official and definitive version of the ritual, all future Royal Arch Masons would accept the modified (Aldersgate) words as fact. The conceptual inference would be lost which would most likely mean that future Companions would almost certainly never appreciate the intrinsic reasons why these two colours were considered so important by the Founders and hence the underlying reason why they were chosen for 'veils of the Temple'.

We have considered already on a number of occasions how the transfer of knowledge by the written word can be corrupted by the current thinking of the actual writer. To understand how subtle changes that appear quite innocuous, or simply cosmetic, in practice may have far reaching effects is well illustrated above. The earliest, for want of a better word, official Royal Arch Book of Ritual was written and published in 1845, *circa* one hundred and twenty years after its inception. If comparison is made with a similar version some eighty years later this sentence and we must presume meaning, has remained unaltered. However, as discussed above in the revised edition some seven years after this shows that the sentence had been altered. Figure 34.1 below shows facsimiles of the three respective portions of the ritual books of 1845, 1931 and 1953.[6, 7, 8]

Clearly, the effect of making this apparently quite trivial alteration was to profoundly change the fundamental meaning of the concept, from one of specific intent and meaning to that of arbitrary choice. But far more important so far as this study is concerned it blurs the date at which the concept was decided upon, since the later the date in the 1720s, the less likely it would have been for them to embrace this particular concept of light. This for two main reasons: first this concept would have

THE

CEREMONIES ETC..

.OF

THE HOLY ROYAL ARCH.

ALSO

OF PASSING THE VAILS.

BY

COMPANION, G. CLARET.

P. M. OF LODGES 12 AND 228.

AND

P. H. OF CHAPTER 12.

London.

1845.

Claret Printer, Upper Clifton Street, Finsbury.

THE

Perfect Ceremonies

OF THE SUPREME ORDER OF

The Holy Royal Arch

COMPRISING

CEREMONIES OF OPENING AND CLOSING
A CHAPTER

CEREMONY OF EXALTATION

LECTURES FROM THE CHAIRS

CHARGE AND EXPLANATION OF THE JEWEL

PASSING THE VEILS

CEREMONY OF INSTALLING THE PRINCIPALS

*With the Investiture of the Officers and the Addresses
&c. &c.*

WITH WOODCUT ILLUSTRATION OF THE ROYAL ARCH
TRACING BOARD

AND THE SCRIPTURE READINGS IN FULL

Copyright. All Rights Reserved

PRIVATELY PRINTED FOR A. LEWIS

13 PATERNOSTER ROW
LONDON

1931

THE RITUAL

OF THE

HOLY ROYAL ARCH

AS TAUGHT IN THE

ALDERSGATE

CHAPTER OF IMPROVEMENT

No. 1657

ORIGINALLY EXTENDED AND ANNOTATED
FOR THE USE OF THE COMPANIONS
IN THE DISTRICT OF NIGERIA

BY E. COMP. G. M. GRAY, M.D., F.R.C.S.
LATE GRAND SUPERINTENDENT

BY THE KIND PERMISSION OF
THE COMMITTEE OF THE
ALDERSGATE
CHAPTER OF IMPROVEMENT
AND
A. LEWIS (MASONIC PUBLISHERS) LTD.

PRIVATELY PRINTED AND PUBLISHED BY
A. LEWIS (MASONIC PUBLISHERS) LTD.
30-32 FLEET STREET, LONDON, E.C. 4
Copyright. 1953

40

denoting light, being composed of its two principal colours, with which the veil of the Temple was also interwoven, the same is further signified by its irradiated form, and in both these respects it has ever been considered as an emblem of royal power and dignity. The ensigns which the Companions bear on their staves, were the distinguished bearings of the twelve tribes of Israel, and figuratively of the peculiar blessing bequeathed to each by the patriarch Jacob, who before his death assembled them together for that purpose, as we find recorded in the 49th Chap. of Genesis. The principal Banners, are the standards of the leading tri-

---

Symbolical Lecture. 43

platonic bodies, which represent the four elements and the sphere of the universe.

The ribbon worn by the Comps. of the Order is a sacred emblem, denoting light, being composed of the two principal colours with which the veil of the temple was interwoven; it is further signified by its irradiated form, and in both these respects it has ever been considered as an emblem of regal power and dignity. The ensigns which the Comps. bear on their staves were the distinctive bearings of the twelve tribes of Israel, and figuratively of a peculiar blessing bequeathed to each by the patriarch Jacob, who, before his death, assembled them together for that purpose, as we find in the 49th chap. of Genesis. The leading tribes are pointed out in the 2d chap. of Numbers. The four principal banners represent the leading standards of the four divisions of the army of Israel, as described in the Book of Genesis. They unitedly bear a device of an angelic nature, under the figures of a man, a lion, an ox, and an eagle: a man, to personify intelligence and understanding; a lion, to represent strength and power; an ox, to denote the ministration of patience and assiduity; and an eagle, to display the promptness and celerity with which the

---

90 *Ritual of the Holy R. A.*

(*points to his own*) is a sacred emblem, denoting light, being composed of two of the principal colours with which the veils of the Temple and Tabernacle were interwoven. Its sacredness is further signified by its irradiated form. It has ever been considered an emblem of regal dignity and power.

The ensigns on the staves borne by the Comps. are the distinctive bearings of the twelve tribes of Israel, and are figurative of a peculiar blessing bequeathed to each by the patriarch Jacob, who, shortly before his death, assembled his sons together for that purpose, as we find recorded in the 49th. chap. of Genesis; the tribes are further pointed out in the 2nd. chap. of the Book of Numbers.

The four principal banners represent the leading standards of the four divisions of the army of

---

Figure 34. 1 Facsimiles of the three relevant pages (Symbolical Lecture) from the ritual cited in the text

been under increasing scientific challenge. Towards the end of Hooke's life he was obliged to pull away from his vehement defence of the concept of there being just two principal colours, to one of colour being determined by wave intensity. Newton by this time had accepted the concept of wave theory, but unfortunately the wrong type. It was only Malebranche who seized upon the notion (*c.*mid 1720s) that it was really the frequency of the waves that determined their colours. We know from other writings that leading academics such as Desaguliers, were in communications with European academics. But most of this fundamental thinking had already been discussed either during or before the early 1720s, which indicates that their ultimate choice was quite deliberate. The second reason was that the band of people who were most likely to have been responsible for preparing the Symbolical Lecture were disbanding (in some instances acrimoniously) and becoming otherwise engaged. Thus by the late 1720s several of the key players such as Desaguliers, Stukeley and Folkes were also troubled by a cocktail of debilitating factors such as illness, advancing years, financial etc. It has been asserted already that at first sight the retention of Platonism by these most informed of individuals was surprising, but somewhat less so once the connotations of Newtonianism are put into the equation. Even so their adoption of this concept of light and colours is still to a large degree inexplicable, but it would be even more so if it had occurred outside of this very narrow time slot.

The above is yet another set of examples that reiterate the theme of this work: namely that the nature of the notions of the science within the ritual adopted by the Premier Grand Lodge does by its very nature mean that it is constrained to a very narrow period in the 1720s. It was within this general train of thought that the Venn diagram approach was introduced in Chapter Ten. Having defined the approach only the broadest indication of how it would be applied in this instance was given, with some further explanation in Appendix 3. If, as is claimed here, this method is so powerful, why then is it not used in the final conclusions of this book? There are a number of reasons, but principally two: firstly there is a large number of elements that would constitute 'sets' or 'cells', the importance of any one of which, on balance is perhaps better left for assessment by the reader. Second that the reader be left to prioritize the nature and extent of any chosen set or cell and not be bludgeoned into accepting some prescribed format. However, some basic sets are effectively self evident and this is well demonstrated, when science is selected as a factor in the constitution of the inner caucus of the Premier Grand Lodge in the early 1720s. But equally illuminating is the realisation that any later version representing those aspects and affiliations would show the rapidly declining significance of science, both in terms of disposition and scale, and its almost non-existence in the 1730s – *see* Figure 34.2.

In Chapter Ten the age old questions of who, why, where, etc were mooted

The Key to Modern Freemasonry

and it is quite clear from within the various sources of Masonic research that this is a commonly visited area; as is well illustrated by Richard Sandbach in his paper to the *Quatuor Coronati* Lodge in 1995[9] in which he reflects on many of these questions. His paper clearly 'touched a nerve' since there were many responses to it and they proved to be as interesting as the paper itself. Pertinent here is that both he and the respondents considered the questions 'who and 'why' as well as a number of other matters, each assigning their understanding of the importance of the respective items and the reader may reasonably ask why has science been singled out in this instance? Throughout this study many of the complex threads such as: family, friends, trade, profession, social intercourse, financial, religious, political etc. have been discussed and not unexpectedly both Sandbach and his correspondents mused over the implications of these and their possible (in some cases claimed with certainty) importance. Indeed because there are so many factors it was the thesis of Chapter Ten that in order to keep them all in focus and where possible indicate their significance/dimension a systematic (in this instance diagrammatical) Venn diagram method was proposed.

It is clearly extremely difficult to find common ground within the reasoning of those researching the period up to and during those critical years when the Premier Grand Lodge was founded, but most would agree that there were a goodly number of freemasons' lodges in the London area and that by the early 1720s, many had joined a collective society now referred to as the Premier Grand Lodge. Clearly over the time period under consideration all the factors cited in the paragraph above were present.

Within the typical freemasons' lodges of that era the local squire, physician, tradesmen, would be significant members in their respective lodge, whereas where there was county, or say profession or trade affiliations etc. other imperatives and structures would predominate; each would have their champions who would become or aspire to be leaders and each lodge would have its own characteristics. These individual lodges may be considered a microcosm of the components of the Premier Grand Lodge; except that its ambition and the status of the people involved were in terms of the then society at least a whole order of magnitude greater.

For instance whereas the local doctor was a most important local citizen, Arbuthnot was physician to the king, whereas the scientist and engineers of Spalding were eminent in their local community, the scientist and engineers of the Premier Grand Lodge were all *FRS*s; in like vein the 'local squire' was in Montagu's case, a Duke, the son of a former Chancellor of the Exchequer, held the rank of general, holder of many royal appointments etc. Again Wharton, was a Duke, a strident member of the House of Lords and the Social Set etc. Although as elsewhere in this work no actual precision is claimed, the two Venn diagrams offered in Figure 34.2 are included to indicate the two scenarios cited above. In Figure 34.2a the diagram

Further reflection on the (Masonic) sciences

is intended to represent that of a local lodge and to reflect how the various sectors of society were likely to have interacted with each other and that certain member of that community would have aspired to become members of the 'set' representing their local lodge. Clearly the status of some would have effectively excluded them, whereas some, such as the undertaker or apothecary, although in most respects 'qualified' may have elected not to seek membership, or alternately may have been 'discouraged' from doing so. Figure 34.2b is intended to represent that specific period in the early 1720s when science and technology was predominant in the ruling sector of the Premier Grand Lodge and the records show clearly that unique situation was to rapidly decline as the decade concluded and in effect never to return.

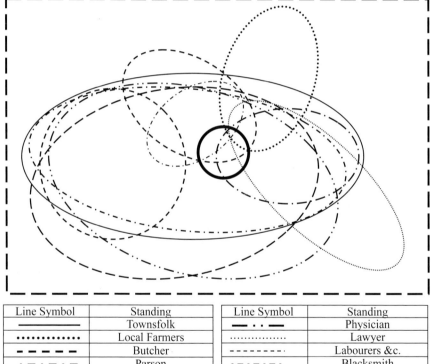

Line Symbol	Standing	Line Symbol	Standing
————	Townsfolk	— ·· —	Physician
•••••••••••••	Local Farmers	················	Lawyer
– – – – –	Butcher	– – – – – – – – ·	Labourers &c.
· — · — · —	Parson	· – · – · – ·	Blacksmith
—— —— ——	Squire	———————	Local Lodge
—— · —— ·	Schoolmaster		

Figure 34. 2a Venn diagram representing the various 'sets' and their distribution in an imagined local Freemasons' lodge around the time of the creation of the Premier Grand Lodge

The Key to Modern Freemasonry

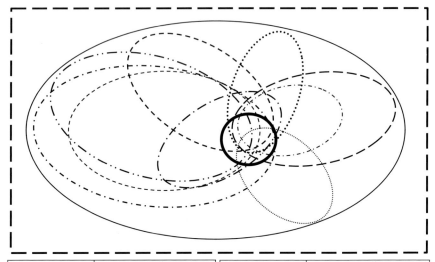

Line Symbol	Standing	Line Symbol	Standing
——————	All Members	— ·· —	Physicians
··············	Science & Maths	················	Law
— — — —	Technology	- - - - - - - ·	Merchants &c.
· — · — · —	Religion	· — · · — · · ·	Artisans
— — —	Aristocracy	——————	Local Lodge
— · — ·	Family		

Figure 34. 2b Venn diagram indicating the relative importance of the hierarchal structure of the Premier Grand Lodge

References:

1. Dijksterhuis, E., *The Mechanisation of the World Picture* (OUP, Oxford, 1992).

2. Taton, R., *A General History of Science, the Beginning of Modern Science from 1450-1800* (Thames and Hudson, London, 1958).

3. Stewart, L., *The Rise of Public Science* (CUP, Cambridge, 1992).

4. Schaffer, S., 'Natural Philosophy and Public Spectacle in of the Eighteenth Century' in *History of Science*, Vol. XXI, (1983), pp. 1-36.

5. Taton, R., *op. cit.* p. 399.

6. Claret, G., *The Ceremonies etc. of the Holy Royal Arch* (Claret Printers, London,1845), p. 40.

7. Anon. *The Perfect Ceremonies of the Holy Royal Arch* (Privately Printed for A Lewis, London 1931).

8. *Op. cit.* (1938).

9. Sandbach, R., 'The Origin of the Species – The Freemason', *AQC* 108 (1995), pp. 48-80.

Chapter Thirty-five:
The Science not embraced in the Ritual

he more essentially physical aspects of some of those topics that fall within this category were dealt with in Part I, but having now introduced other facets to this study they will be discussed more broadly: first in their own right, but then touching on matters that are of importance because of their relevance to significant elements that will be discussed further in Chapter Thirty-seven: namely 'The Liberal Arts and Sciences' and aspects that relate to certain rituals. It may be pure coincidence, but in the many books that have been referred to in this Study that relate to the science of this period, the order in which the respective scientific topics have been considered was effectively the same as that used by those constructing the (Founders') ritual. We now come to the remaining topics, namely those aspects of science with which the Founders, on a personal level were known to be concerned with and clearly considered to be of importance, but for whatever reason chose to omit from the ritual. A simple explanation could be that the subject matter was sufficiently distant from classical operative masonry for it to not warrant inclusion. However, on closer consideration the converse appears true and for a number of very good reasons, not least their desire to convey the mysticism of 'Nature'; leaving one to wonder even more why at least certain of these areas were omitted.

When, as in this case, it is necessary to assemble the salient factors prior to formulating an argument, it is often the case that elements (in this instance the unspecified sciences) that have been omitted appear to be of as much importance as those that are included. In this instance four main areas are immediately obvious, namely: magnetism and electricity (including gravity), chemistry, biology (both vegetable and animal, including human) and geology. There are several reasons why each in turn would have been of importance to those associated with freemasonry in the 1720s, but the overriding factors so far as this work is concerned are four. The first is the repeated injunction that is the duty of all Freemasons to seek knowledge. Second, is the Founders' concern with all matters scientific (Royal Society and public lectures). Third are the religious implications. Fourth are the commercial connotations, such as navigation and exploitation of mineral reserves.

Indeed, so important were some of these aspects within the science of the early 1700s that their omission from a Ritual is quite paradoxical, given the repeated stress on the importance of science expressed by the Ritualist and this factor needs to be addressed. This anomalous behaviour is the stranger still given that a number of the most influential Founders were particularly concerned with these matters. As we shall see there was (and still remains) a diversity of view on the phenomenology of ethereal forces such as the nature of gravity and associated speculation as to whether there is a relationship between it and the analogous forces of magnetism and electricity; with the even more intriguing likelihood of their association with the spiritual forces of God himself. These matters became more and more prosaic as the century evolved, but those who proffered a physical explanation struggled to replace mysticism with physical reality. This process was most pronounced during the 1720s as the political climate stabilised and there was an increasing interchange with Continental scientists and philosophers. That this pragmatism came just too late for it to have influenced the content of the earliest Ritual will be considered in the final summing up, but for the moment this brief résumé of the omitted science is continued below.

Robert Lenoble was responsible for the Chapter on magnetism, electricity and gravity in Taton's Book[1] and he chose, with the benefit of hindsight, to consider their joint interrelationship within a modern concept of the subject. However, during the period with which we are concerned there was no such definitive (or at least claimed by some eminently regarded experts) link. For instance there was a strong body of opinion that gravity and magnetism were subtly different manifestations of the same force. Others were equally convinced that this force was an expression of God's divine spirit. The remainder proffered a whole gamut of physical explanations. For consistency sake Taton's book will be used here, but the particular subject of magnetism is dealt with much better in Patricia Fara's remarkable book *Sympathetic attractions*,[2] and because she comments directly on some matters with which we are concerned it will be referred to extensively.

Popular belief is that the Chinese were the first to use the magnetic characteristic of the loadstone for navigation, but in the order of things this factor is of little concern since this characteristic had been known in the European sphere of influence since well before Christ. Indeed since we have needed to refer to Plato's *Timaeus* and *Critias* in direct reference to other aspects of the Symbolical Lecture, it is certain that those who compiled the Ritual had also read the following extract chosen by Lenoble by way of illustration:

'Timaeus states: As [...] the marvels concerning the attraction (electrostatic) of amber and of the Herculean stone [loadstone or magnet] (magnetism) – no one of all these ever possesses any real power of attraction; but the fact that there is no void, and that these bodies exert a circular [global] force on one another and, according as they separate or unite, exchange places and proceed severally each to its own region [...] will be evident to him who investigates them properly.'[3]

It would seem that Greek Atomists (essentially the philosophy that all things are composed of minute indivisibly small particles) believed objects had effluvia, a kind of innate substance that flowed into and out of the pores of the respective objects. This was the philosophy quoted by Huygens when he published his work on the subject and in one guise or another, this concept was an accepted theory adopted by

The Science not Embraced in the Ritual

many throughout the hundred years or more preceding the Premier Grand Lodge. For instance when attempting to explain why, when certain materials such as amber when rubbed lightly attracted certain light (dry) articles they did so by assuming that they exuded a sticky effluvia. Whereas to explain why only iron was attracted by a magnet it was postulated that the effluvia emitted by the loadstone was dry and only iron had the matching pore structure to accord with it, implying the converse to be true of these other (attracted by electrostatic) materials.

Following the religious suppression of science during the medieval period little attempt was made to understand the physical nature of magnetic phenomena. The combined effect of the pragmatic (primitive) use by sailors of the magnetic needle and the incisive mind of Peter Peregrine brought about a change in the middle of the 1200s. He conducted a series of experiments, which included the relationship of a magnetic compass to the heavens; he broke a lodestone in two and showed that there were now two magnets, but that on rejoining they reverted to one etc. He went on to publish a book, which even postulated perpetual motion. However, history repeated itself and no regard was paid to his work and it lay dormant until Gilbert took up the challenge some hundred years later. Mariners however did not wait for some smart scientific explanation, but continued to develop the technique for navigational purposes. During this period there was a strong revival of the animalistic and vitalistic philosophy. As good Neo-Platonists, most scientists of the time believed that the world had a soul and that magnetism was a manifestation of it. This conception will be returned to, but it is appropriate here to cite the view of those constructing (or adapting) the ritual that was to be adopted for the now unified Freemasonry of the Premier Grand Lodge by making reference to the injunction now given to the Candidate during the Second Degree ceremony. 'You are now expected to make the Liberal Arts and Sciences your future study, that you may the better be able to discharge your duties as a Mason and (thereby) 'estimate the wonderful works of the Almighty' – clearly it was in their interest to convey concepts confirming that the arts and sciences were a manifestation of God's creation and these mysterious, quite unexplained forces would have served well in this respect.

William Gilbert was responsible for reviving interest in magnetism and in so doing the whole debate of mutual attraction, electrical (electrostatic type), magnetic and gravity. Just as Gilbert was unable to distinguish between gravity and magnetism the same dichotomy was true in varying degrees of all others during this period. Although Gilbert's concepts were flawed they had a profound influence on the great scientists of the time such as Galileo, Kepler, but many others besides. Indeed Lenoble writes:

> 'The contribution of Gilbert and Kepler was so great that we might have kept silent about their minor lapses were it not that these lapses helped to explain the Cartesian reaction. Gilbert's idea of a magnetic soul, Kepler's love of animalistic

notions, Cabeo's and Kircher's use of the non-material magnetic field to bolster up qualitative physics, and finally Campanella's magic views of magnetism called for a decisive attack, and Descartes was quick to launch it.'

If Descartes' attack was to succeed he had to provide a cohesive magnetic theory of his own. Above all he wished to destroy the concept of there being some occult (religious) virtues attached to the phenomenon, which resulted in him abandoning objectivity in the process, since it required him to deny the concept of attractive forces. Again Lenoble writes:

He also wanted to destroy once and for all – and this was to prove a dangerous step – belief in attractive forces, which were to him so many occult virtues. 'In truth, there is no attraction in this [magnetism]; for the moment iron enters a magnet's sphere of virtue, that virtue is communicated to it by grooved particles [which] expel the air between them and hence draw them together' In other words, Descartes, like Plato and Lucretius, believe that magnets and iron are thrust together as the surrounding air rushes into what would otherwise be a vacuum.

In order to support his theories Descartes constructed an elaborate scheme of interconnecting hooks and screws; (he did model the magnetic environment in a form of quasi magnetic flux). Not surprisingly these concepts were challenged by others such as Gassendi, who proposed that electrical bodies 'lick up' substances with invisible tongues etc. As usual Boyle added a note of caution to this raft of ideas and by experiment with evacuated vessels showed that these effects existed without the presence of air. He also postulated that magnetism was due to the alignment of particles within the body of the artefact, which is the basis of modern thought and is now used in geology to date rocks. Huygens, as early as 1680, distinguished between electricity and magnetism and proposed that magnetism was the manifestation of some force within the æther and not air, but then spoilt it by proceeding to invoke his theory of vortices. Finally, there was the reluctance of Newton to make any definitive pronouncement with respect to magnetism.

Lenoble expresses surprise that although Newton had discovered, or rather quantified, the 'inverse square' law he did not associate it with magnetism. As part of his ongoing polemics with the Cartesians he wrote:

'The attractions of Gravity, Magnetism and electricity reach to very sensible Distances, and so have been observed by vulgar Eyes, and there may be others which reach to so small Distances as hitherto escape Observation; and perhaps electrical Attraction may reach to such small Distances, even without being excited by friction (Optics, Query 31)'.

In other words Newton believed that all artefacts had electrical properties, albeit very small in some cases, but he gave no real lead to his disciples. The result was

The Science not Embraced in the Ritual

that although Desaguliers incorporated electrical experiments in his lectures during the 1720s, he was like a magician demonstrating a trick that he did not himself understand, but realised that it would induce even greater wonderment and interest in his audience. Nonetheless it would seem that he had the integrity to acknowledge his lack of fundamental understanding and it is argued here that this would explain why despite their otherwise potent mystical and religious connotations and wonderment that could be attached to magnetism, electricity and gravity they were not woven into the Ritual of the Symbolical Lecture.

Before we leave the general area of magnetism, it is of interest to return to the very fine work of the Cambridge scholar Patricia Fara. In her book she makes direct reference to several possible links with Freemasonry, but also indirectly because she refers to a number of the principal characters of interest to us. In a passage where she is reflecting on the various devices to measure the power of magnets in the early 1700s, she writes as follows:

> ' […]. Canton explained that the first step in making artificial magnets involved hanging an iron bar from a poker with a silk thread and stroking it twenty times with the tongs until it could lift a small key.
>
> Encyclopaedias and journals included information about magnetic experiments with such readily available objects. They repeated the anecdote recounting how Canton had been inspired by noticing that his fireside poker leant at the same angle as a dip needle. Secrecy, pokers and stroking came together in a skit on Freemasonry:
>
>> Next to the SECRETS of their own wise making,
>> HIRAM and BOAZ, and Grand-Master JACHIN!
>> Poker and tongs! The signs! The word! The strokes!
>> 'Tis all a nothing and 'tis all a joke.
>
> But it was keys rather than pokers which emblamatizised the knowledge to be gained from magnetic experimentation. In his London lectures, Desaguliers demonstrated how a loadstone could "give power to a great key, to draw away a little key from the Stone it self" an attractive feat undoubtedly replicated by other performers. [...]'[4]

She cites the work of Margaret Jacob: *Freemasonry, Women, and the Paradox of the Enlightenment*,[5] but of equal or even greater importance is her reference to the religious connotations attached to this mystic force and other important workers such as Brooke Taylor with whom we are concerned. Indeed she devotes a great deal of attention to the work and book of arithmetical tables on magnetism by the eighth Grand Master the Earl of Abercorn (1726). She also includes interesting asides such as the remarks by Mary Montagu, who marvelled at the power of a particular magnet she had seen. Perhaps the most important part of Fara's work so far as this work is concerned is her many references to Desaguliers, during which she demonstrates that

Desaguliers was in touch with fellow scientists from the Continent and the difficulty of ignoring them (implying that as a devout Newtonian he was bound to do) as time (the 1720s) passed during this dynamic period.

To dwell briefly on electricity in particular we once again turn to Cambridge and the important work of Simon Schaffer and in particular his paper entitled *Natural philosophy and public science.*[6] Schaffer develops various aspects of the understanding of electricity during this period, emphasising the comparative lack of true understanding that is replaced by the device of assigning much of its obscure power to a higher authority. We will 'cherry pick' a few extracts from his paper that are of concern to this aspect of the study and/or are directly connected with those with whom we are concerned. The first demonstrates that Desaguliers' interest with electricity came somewhat later in his career and that even to the very last he was not completely at ease with it. This perhaps is not surprising since Schaffer goes on to demonstrate that real progress only took place much later in the century.

> Desaguliers, the leading public lecturer and demonstrator at the Royal Society in the 1720s and 1730s, wrote of the Newtonian system of the world as "the Best Model of Government" (1728) [*see* Figure 35.1 and Appendix 1], arguing that restrained liberty and the rule through intellectual control ought to be the basis of authority. In the same year, Voltaire altered the text of his epic Henriarde to make this point by connecting wise administration with "the Æthereal Orbs" and the "the wond'ring Universe". The emergent system of social control which persistently infested the crisis of the eighteenth century was based upon these claims. [That this moralistic imputation abounded he later goes on to demonstrate]. In 1753, Henry Fielding, then magistrate, quoted with approval works of natural philosophers and sermons which argued that "conscience will hold a man fast when all other obligations break". This system of control explicitly involved this kind of moralization of natural experience. Typical of the integration of public lectures into polite society was the response of John Wesley. Wesley preached sermons on discipline at Bedford Assizes, and also composed his 'Desideratum, or electricity made plain and useful' (1760). He reported on his own experience at a public lecture on electricity:
>
> "I went with two or three friends to see what are called the electrical experiments. How must these also confound those poor who will believe nothing but what they comprehend. Who can comprehend how fire lives in water, and passes through it more freely than air? How came issues (Static electricity) out of my finger, real flame, such as sets fire to spirits (distilled) of wine? How these and many more strange phenomena arise from the turning of a glass globe? It is all a mystery, if haply by any means God may hide pride from man." '

For the sake of convenience another digression (from the main topic electricity in this instance) is made, namely to consider Schaffer's reference to Desaguliers.

THE
NEWTONIAN SYSTEM *of the* World
THE BEST
MO DEL of Government.
A N
Allegorical P O E M.

N Ancient Times, ere Bribery began
To taint the Heart of undesigning Man,
Ere Justice yielded to be bought and fold,
When Senators were made by Choice, not Gold,
B   Ere

(b)

THE
NEWTONIAN SYSTEM
OF THE
W O R L D,
T H E B E S T
Model of Government:
An *Allegorical* POEM.

With a plain and intelligible Account of the System of the World by Way of *Annotations*:

With COPPER PLATES.

To which is added,

C A M B R I A's Complaint

Against the Intercalary Day in the Leap-Year.

By J. T. DESAGULIERS, LL.D. Chaplain to His Grace the Duke of CHANDOS, and F. R. S.

W E S T M I N S T E R,
Printed by A. CAMPBELL, for J. ROBERTS in *Warwick Lane*, and Sold by the Booksellers of *London* and *Westminster*, 1728.
(Price 1s. 6d.)

(a)

Advertisement.

COURSES of EXPERIMENTAL PHILOSOPHY, and Courses of EXPERIMENTAL ASTRONOMY, *publick or private*, in *Latin, French*, or *English*, are perform'd at any Time of the Year, and likewise all Parts of *pure or mix'd Mathematicks* taught, by the *Author*, at his House in *Channel-Row, Westminster*; where Gentlemen, who have a Mind to apply close to these Studies, may be boarded.

The Author here thinks proper to acquaint those Persons, who have subscribed some Time ago for his Course of Experimental Philosophy, in Two Volumes in Quarto, &c. that he has been for Two Years last past prevented from going on with the Work by unavoidable Disappointments; not proper to be mention'd here; but that he has now resumed the Work, and will finish it with all Expedition.

(d)

---

vi   *DEDICATION.*

YOUR Lordship can best judge, whether the *Allegory* be just; and it is by Your Lordship's Approbation that I desire to stand or fall : Only begging, that the Truth of the Philosophy may excuse the Badness of the Poetry.

INSTEAD of attempting Your Lordship's Character, which wou'd require an abler Pen than mine, and even then offend Your Lordship, by doing Justice to Your Merits; I shall only beg Leave to return my humble Thanks for the Freedom and Goodness with which Your Lordship has always receiv'd me ; and tho' Your Lordship is pleas'd to lay aside Your Quality in Condescension to me, I shall always be sensible how great an Honour is confer'd on,

MY LORD,

Your Lordship's

most oblig'd, and

most humble Servant,

J. T. D.

(c)

Figure 35.1 Reduced facsimiles of Desagulier's dedicated poem. (a) Title page (both copies seen were in very poor condition). (b) Opening stanzas of his poem. (c) Indication of his sycophantic disposition towards his employer. (d) Indicates that he was required to obtain a living from wherever he could.

The Science not Embraced in the Ritual

In reality this is a most important document to this study for a number of reasons, both in terms of his social persona and as an indication of his perception of science and outward morality at the time of writing. Figure 35.1 shows two reduced facsimiles of the title page and introductory pages of his book containing his dedicated poem – this is reproduced in more readable form, to modern eyes that is, in Appendix 1. Desaguliers is at pains to point out that he is not seeking to curry favour, ingratiate himself or impress in any way, but in practice the book is cringingly sycophantic, even by the standards of those days. His dedicated booklet is about fifty pages long, with sometimes only two or three lines of actual poetry, with the rest of the page filled with explanatory detail of the underlying science, morality, history etc., with actual diagrams illustrating the various interpretations (heavenly systems) of Ptolemy, Copernicus and Newton etc. It is important because it gives a clear indication of his thinking at that time, his reluctance to pontificate on matters electrical, which became of particular interest to him in the late 1720s and during the 1730s. Equally important is the fact that its very title *The Newtonian System of the World – The best MODEL of Government.* is conceptually consistent with the morality found throughout speculative Freemasonry. However this is particular so in relation to the Symbolical Lecture; in which it first attempts to correlate science with morality and religion, then goes on to support the physical defence of those values: '… who with trowel in hand and sword by their side they were ever ready to defend the City and Holy Sanctuary against the unprovoked attacks of their enemies, thereby leaving an impressive lesson to future ages: that next to implicit obedience to all lawfully constituted [government – 'the State'] authority, a manly and determined resistance to lawless violence is the first of social virtues'.

As the magician is aware that however mystical his performance may appear to his audience, it is nonetheless still a series of tricks and whilst Desaguliers incorporated electricity into his (lectures) act, certainly by the middle 1720s, he too would have been fully aware of his limited understanding of its true nature. This lack of understanding was not addressed until the 1730s and as such might explain why electricity, magnetism and gravity, despite all their mystical power were not integrated into the Ritual. Although it could mean that that he did not wish to share those more esoteric concepts with the uninitiated. However his lack of basic scientific understanding of these matters at the time is clear from his later writings etc., where he has attempted to address his deficiencies, indicating that he understood this behaviour in terms of 'natural' magic – a classical Newtonian artefact.

Although we now fail to be amazed when we turn on the light, watch television or communicate through computer systems, dismissing it all in terms of the flow of electrons and the transmission of electromagnetic waves etc., we have still not demystified its intrinsic nature and cannot begin to understand the nature of gravitational attraction, although theories abound. Our people in the early 1700s entertained great difficulty and Simon Schaffer gives many examples of this, with only a resemblance of order beginning to emerge from about 1750 onwards, far too late to have any influence upon the period with which we are concerned. His explanation covers many pages of closely researched data and so no attempt will be made to précis it, but for those interested in the subject his work makes absorbing reading.[7]

Whilst these facets of electricity, magnetism and gravity were of profound interest to those with whom we are concerned, it would appear that none of them felt sufficiently confident in the limited understanding they possessed of the subject to integrate their interpretation of it into the body of Masonic ritual. The decision to omit this important manifestation of natural, or if one so wished supernatural, forces from the ritual is not explained easily for there appears to be a very strong case for including it given the plausible implication of the subject matter with divine power, a seeming attribute repeated many times in Fara's work on magnetism.[8]

A notable exception is Chemistry. It would appear therefore that electricity, magnetism and gravity might well have failed to find their way into the Ritual because of a fundamental gap in the Founders' knowledge, even though there was a strong case for proposing a link with a divine power. But was this very mysticism the limiting factor in terms of basic understanding of other topics such as chemistry; which had earlier prompted the remark by Hooke: 'they prefer to rely on pleasant fables rather than make the sustained effort of advancing science by experiment and precise deduction'. Which meant that whilst there had been a minor surge in chemistry in the late 1600s and early 1700s, as the subject became more intractable (a case of the more one knows the less one understands) there was a distinct lull during the period with which we are concerned primarily. It was followed by a surge later in the century; although as with electricity and magnetism its theatrical magic continued. The progress of chemistry started in earnest in the 1600s when a few exceptional workers began to pull away from alchemy, led by Boyle, with his work on gases, respiration etc., complemented by other able people, such as Hooke, probing aspects of chemistry such as combustion. By the turn of the century it had become an acknowledged topic at Cambridge, so why then this reticence with respect to the Symbolical Lecture? It could be argued that this resistance to change was due to the widespread, effectively total, adoption of the Pholgiston theory, which by its nature prohibited the development of challenging theories on combustion, especially as it was bolstered by an almost total acceptance of the concept of 'fire' as a quasi element – *see* Appendix 2. As can be seen from the Section dealing with the 'basic element' fire in Part I, from about 1690 until the late 1700s this was the predominant scientific concept and it would have had a profound influence on our people, causing them to be more comfortable with the generally held concept of fire as an element and reluctant to think in terms of a chemical explanation.

Compounds continued to be discovered in an *ad hoc* fashion, but these discoveries had little impact on the scientific community at large and unlike electricity and light (colour) where challenges were beginning to emerge in the 1720s. It was not until much later in the century that real inroads were being made towards debunking the Phlogiston concept, but in terms of outright rejection it had to wait until Lavoisier's pronouncement in 1772. However, we have seen from the short bibliography of Desaguliers and Montagu that mineral extraction, smelting etc., was of direct interest to some members of the Premier Grand Lodge. Indeed it was included within the ritual; 'They were made from molten brass, and cast in the plain of Jordan in the clay ground between Succoth and Zaradatha, …', but with no explanation of how such a process was possible and the alloy brass not considered in any chemical sense, but rather one of the unusual forms of Platonic 'water'. We can only conclude that at least for those who constructed the Symbolical Lecture, it was still reasonable to let Fire and Water remain as a fundamental element.

Again the importance of biology to this study is in its absence, given the repeated allusion to 'Nature' in the ritual, but equally the suggestion by some Masonic historians that the foundling Premier Grand Lodge (and by implication its adopted ritual) was greatly influenced by the presence of many 'barber surgeons' (physicians). The fact that selective breeding within agriculture, both of flora and fauna, was already established by the middle of the 1600s has been mentioned already and that surgical (public) operations performed on poor unfortunate patients were common practice, some explanation has to be advanced to explain why this wondrous manifestation of Nature is not woven into the Symbolical Lecture. It is perhaps pertinent to remind ourselves of Montagu's use of inoculations in the middle 1720s, from the intended effects of which he must have conjured up some physical model of how it worked. If this riddle could be solved it might help to provide an understanding of two important factors that need to be addressed when considering a possible date when Craft ritual was consolidated and the Royal Arch came into being and their content. The first factor is that none of those involved in the hierarchy of the early Premier Grand Lodge had their expertise centred on biology. People like Montagu who were supposedly qualified as Doctors of Medicine, had in reality 'engineered' their medical qualification and could profess no profound learning in the subject. On the other hand Arbothnot was a qualified physician, but was also extremely active in other areas outside his basic discipline, not least politics. The second comes from a study of W Bro. Clarke's two papers: 'The Medical Profession and Early Freemasonry'[9] and 'The Royal Society and Early Grand Lodge Freemasonry'.[10] Setting aside the slight discrepancies found in those he listed or rather failed to list in the second paper, it shows that it was the early members who were most likely to have been *au fait* with the science of the Symbolical Lecture. Many were intimately connected with the Royal Society and gained much of their living and/or kudos from public lectures. Whilst there were medical men in those early constituent lodges they were comparatively inconspicuous. Clarke showed that those freemasons who were both medics and members of the Royal Society came much later in the 1730s, when the military faction was beginning to take precedence in the extreme hierarchy of the Premier Grand Lodge and hence its affairs and the original impetus in Grand Lodge type Freemasonry had begun to wane.

Since clearly this subject (life sciences) did not lack wonderment or fail to epitomise a natural affinity with God it would appear that its exclusion must be attributable to a lack of direct involvement by those concerned with the construction of the Lectures. This is borne out by the fact that most of the published work using the microscope had been on biological specimens; notably those sparked by Hooke's best seller the *Micrographia* in the late 1600s. It is reasonable to suppose that if those in the medical profession had indeed taken an active role in the formulation of the ritual, some allusion to this mysterious and wondrous aspect of Nature would have been made. This section on biology has relied extensively on Taton's Book,[11] which deals extensively with the various aspects of biology, listing numerous workers in the various fields, including medicine, but none within the group with which we are concerned were cited. Thus whilst it is true that no exhaustive enquiry was made, unlike the subjects associated with the Symbolical Lecture, there was clearly an absence of eminent workers in the biological sciences who were capable or in a position to exert sufficient influence amongst the more prominent people concerned with the founding of the Premier Grand Lodge.

When considering the 'earth' sciences we once again have to grapple with the problem of trying to understand how they 'squared the circle', since Masonic ritual is very much related to the Old Testament and more specifically the concept of the creation of 'the world' some 6,000 years previously. However, that becomes less of a problem when one accepts that today there are millions of people (including their many respective and acclaimed scholars) who are required to do exactly the same in many major present day religions. Its importance to this Study is that many of our people were actually noted antiquarians, or if not, they were certainly *au fait* with the underlying concepts. The presence of fossils in rock had already led to publications which showed that fossils were not only infinitely older than 6,000 years, but that similar forms were found whole continents apart and at such high elevations that the theory of the great flood, as recorded in its several guises, was untenable.[12] This is especially relevant since the ritual of the Royal Arch rests heavily on the Old Testament and a set of somewhat imaginative stories woven around it.

The other complexity is that by this time there was a sufficiently sophisticated

The Science not Embraced in the Ritual

understanding of the earth's geology for them to realise that the use of the term 'earth' in the four elements without explanation assumed some larger and existing understanding within the brethren, but on the other hand perhaps not, since the same question could be asked of anyone listening to that same Lecture today. Indeed, we know from Montagu's bibliography that he and Desaguliers were active in the exploitation of mineral resources based on elementary chemical (principles) reactions. However, as we have discussed already, the originators of the Lecture persisted with this antiquated concept, our problem is to reflect on why and because this question is important it is considered further in the remaining chapters.

Thus there is little doubt that they had sufficient understanding of the sheer complexity of the earth's geology to know that there was no simple explanation for what they observed. The evidence suggests that rather than confronting the difficulty (facts); they took the pragmatic non-divisive (in terms of sociological, religious and scientific antipathy) approach of retaining the biblical account.

References

1. Taton, R., *A General History of Science (1450-1800)* (Thames & Hudson, London, 1958), pp. 307-321.

2. Fara, P., *Sympathetic Attractions* (Princetown University Press, New Jersey, 1996).

3. Taton, R., *op cit.*

4. Fara, P., *op cit.*

5. Jacobs, M., *Women and the Enlightenment* (The Haworth Press Inc., NY, 1984), pp. 69-91

6. Schaffer, S. 'Natural Philosophy and Public Spectacle in the Eighteenth Century', in *History of Science*, Vol. XXI (1983), pp. 1-36.

7. *Ibid.*

8. Fara, P., *op cit.*

9. Clarke, J.R., 'The Medical Profession and Early Freemasonry', *AQC* 85 (1975), pp. 298-311.

10. Clarke, J.R., 'The Royal Society and Early Grand Lodge Freemasonry' *AQC* 80 (1967), pp. 110-117.

11. (Various) in Taton, R., *op. cit.*, pp. 511-564.

12. Furon, R., in Taton, R., *op.cit.,* pp. 565-577.

Chapter Thirty-six:
Newton, Newtonians and Newtonianism

To those interested in the emergence of cults and factions within Masonry Newtonianism must be considered of considerable interest, but its inclusion within this study can only be justified because of its great importance to those immediately responsible for the establishment of the eventual Premier Grand Lodge which is of course the very basis of modern Freemasonry. In his book, *Art and Architecture of Freemasonry*,[1] James Curl states, almost in passing, that Freemasonry is littered with allusions to Newtonian symbolism, but without further elaboration then moves on to other matters. However, any reader who has persisted to this point will now be aware that science was not only inexorably linked with Freemasonry, but was exceptionally so during the period under consideration and consequently these factors must be given serious consideration in any study that purports to shed light on the early years of its formalisation. When this interrelationship between Freemasonry and science is coupled with the fact that some 300 years later every educated person, whether particularly interested in science or not, is well aware of Newton and the impact he made on the understanding of science, it is not surprising that as a contemporary figure in the early 1700s he was considered a colossus by many. Volume upon volume have been written about him and his science, philosophy, theology etc., and so no attempt to add to that data will be made here, except to give some condensed indication of why he had such a profound influence on Freemasonry in particular. A further matter of importance is that whilst most people will acknowledge his contribution to astronomy and applied mechanics, far fewer will have realised that this exceedingly complex person, of prodigious brainpower, industry and perseverance was also deeply involved in alchemy, magic, theology etc. But more especially from the perspective of this study, he was actively concerned, if not possessed, with the notion of ancient cultures and their mysticisms and his (destined) direct involvement with them.

Given his intellectual capability there would be nothing particularly strange about his having healthy interests in other areas, except that in this instance he went well beyond that point and it asks the question why this, otherwise clinical, scientific mind should go to such lengths to distort history in such illogical, almost pathetic, way? He took the most probable chronology and insisted on juxtaposing the respective dates in order to make the Egyptian and some other earlier civilisations post-date biblical events in a most fanciful way. Of central concern here was not his belief that God had handed the fundamental concepts of Nature and science to the Israelites (via Moses), since many people believe that, or conceivably that these secrets had then been handed down to successive worthies until corrupted and thence lost by the action of pagans (or perhaps cowans: the analogous term used in Masonic ritual, but of dubious etymology); but the extrapolation of the concept that he had been singled out by God to rediscover them. As will be discussed in Chapter Thirty-seven, he studied to great depth every piece of information he could gather on the subject (evidenced in his writings and by the content of his Library). But in particular he believed them to be enshrined in the proportions and manner in which King Solomon had constructed his Temple and that its construction pre-dated the architecture of all the preceding civilisations, not least the Egyptians. Again it is not unreasonable for him to have believe that, for whatever reason, those secrets had been lost in a way similar to that suggested above, but what is most surprising is that he was so besotted in the belief that God had singled him out to redress this situation, that consequently he had now been chosen to be numbered amongst those illustrious Greats, that he was indeed a Magus and that very few, if indeed any, could be trusted to share those secrets with him.

At a point such as this psychologists and historians, in order to rationalise this behaviour might point to his somewhat abnormal childhood, unusual education and hyper reclusive interest in science, mathematics and alchemy and indeed a number have made reference to it; but the validity of such contentious analysis will be left to others and will not be attempted here. However, an excellent example of such writing is found in Fauvel *et al*'s book *Let Newton Be*.[2] This book, for reasons of continuity and balance has been used extensively in this Chapter; primarily because the book is a compilation that required its many authors, each a recognised authority, to reach a consensus view and as such it may be considered as having a greater authority.

They chronicle, if not explain, how this secretive, non-communicative, very poor lecturer, essentially introverted and outwardly self-effacing man, did in practice consider himself to be in direct communication with God and as such should be numbered among the ancient Magi. That he had been selected to be the one chosen to rediscover knowledge of those hidden, hitherto long lost mysteries, originally handed down, by the word of God to Moses. That he would, in a very restricted way, be permitted by God to communicate his higher understanding to others, but with the proviso that such knowledge would be confined to specific matters and only with those he felt were competent within these narrow bounds and hence worthy of such trust. For instance other like-minded alchemists of high repute such as Robert Boyle (at least Newton considered him to be so, although Boyle would almost certainly have been dismayed at the thought of his painstaking work considered to be alchemy). Indeed, Newton felt somewhat betrayed when Boyle made some of his own research findings public and rebuked him on the matter. This type of reprimand would have put a shot across the bows of any of his disciples who may have been tempted to reveal too much in a public lecture or include it as part of some ritual. During his early years he had a high regard for Robert Hooke, but as discussed earlier this relationship, as with many other eminent contemporary scientific brains, went very sour. The vitriolic attack was symptomatic of his disposition and ability to ferociously attack anyone deigning to challenge him in any way, but especially Hooke who Newton knew must, by any standards, be considered a competing genius. In terms of the development of science it was unfortunate that although they were slightly out of phase contemporaries, they were both fishing in the same pond for the same prime fish, although Hooke was not so fussy about catching just one species.

Which brings us to the later stages of his life that are so important to this study, by which time he had entered Parliament and quickly became Master of the Mint (at which he proved to be most proficient – albeit somewhat brutally harsh with respect to enforcing laws, appearing to have no qualms about imposing the death penalty for currency abuse). He acquired several other important strings to his bow, not least becoming President of the Royal Society. It is widely asserted that in his early years he had a passive disposition and indeed needed to be provoked into publishing his famous book the *Principia*. However, the publication of his works did not in themselves bring wide recognition because, as discussed earlier in the section on geometry, his mathematics (essentially geometry) were so complex that they were effectively incomprehensible to all but the most able mathematician and in most other ways he was a poor communicator. Although, just as in more recent years Einstein's theory of Relativity is incomprehensible to most people, it is nonetheless or perhaps because of it, accepted by virtually everybody as being the work of a genius. In an analogous way so was the public's perception of Newton, but because of the peculiar circumstances at that time it was especially so. This is where, by dint of association, a number of those with whom we are concerned made great capital. Such was the impact of the public's perception of Newton's findings and so great was the public's thirst for some understanding of these subjects, that they were prepared to pay substantial sums of money to attend public lectures. It only required the speakers to give a simplistic account of certain aspects of his science for them to be enthralled.

What in effect had happened was the creation of a new philosophy, here referred to as Newtonianism. Again the problem is that this subject is too complex to deal with at depth at this time, but what will become clear is that it is crucial to this Study and that at least some explanation is essential. The difficulty is that Newtonianism can be as intricate as one chooses to make it. For instance the man in the street (the 'vulgar' or 'workman' as they were prone to be called at that time), whilst not being able to appreciate to any great depth the true subtleties of Newton's work, for example the *Principia*, would, after attending a lecture or physical demonstration of some aspect of it, be able to appreciate sufficient of it to be amazed by its revelations; much as wondrous scientific subjects are conveyed currently in dramatic form in today's Media.

However, the group of people with whom we are concerned were so gifted intellectually and were sufficiently well educated to grasp a much greater understanding of Newton's arguments. The word 'argument' is used here in preference to philosophy, because as will be claimed when discussing the 'Liberal Arts and Sciences' in the next Chapter, it is difficult to know what Newton's actual opinions really were because he was a very secretive person and worked on a wide range of subjects. But as suggested above he was paranoid about the way in which his concepts were released and highly selective about what he communicated and to whom. Despite the fact that we cannot really know what they were, it has not stopped people from writing upon the subject of Newton's beliefs and thus putting their own interpretation of his 'Philosophy'; conveying the impression that it may be defined uniquely. This multi-layered 'confidentiality agreement' that Newton had with those within his circle, and there were quite a few who would have wished to claimed that distinction, must have found it very difficult to know what was for general distribution and what was not. His chosen disciples and there were far fewer in this category, were worse placed in this respect. What is of particular interest here is that among that small band there were several that were both socially prominent and especially influential in the emerging Premier Grand Lodge. Despite or perhaps because of the limitation resulting from the difference between his publicly acknowledged 'philosophy' and his inner thoughts, it is necessary to construct a quasi list of his basic precepts outside of his public persona.

To the popular world therefore Newton was an uncomplicated towering genius of a man who had enunciated the (mathematical) laws governing the Universe, of mechanics, of light and colour, of music etc. and a truly remarkable system of mathematics. On top of his scientific achievements he had then gone on to demonstrate his political and administrative acumen, for which he had understandably received a knighthood. To the ordinary person therefore the rules governing Nature and Science were to all intent and purpose an all-embracing philosophy and that unlike many other strands of philosophy, they were clinically precise. In this simplistic sense Newtonianism would have been the application of a set of rules and our group of men were well placed to apply them. But sociologically if Newtonianism had been so clinical it would have also been bland and would have had none of the supposed mysticism that was to prove to be so influential in the new brand of formalised Freemasonry. This emerging Freemasonry was appearing to be a system that was not only promising the revelation of the secrets of building construction, the inner (secret) workings of the hierarchy of operative masons and a sharing of their social status and protocols, but also a profound understanding of the whole 'purpose of being'. It could be argued that it was a major determining factor in the process of persuading a number of the as yet unaffiliated lodges to subjugate themselves under the umbrella of the Premier Grand Lodge, which was to forever, or at least right up until today, stamp its mark on Freemasonry in general and virtually all subsequent compliant or otherwise 'regularised' grand lodges throughout the World.

Despite having read numerous words on the subject and entered into conversations with those who are far better informed, it is still not clear what Newton really believed as opposed to what he proclaimed or in some other way admitted to. It was clear that he rejected the philosophy of Aristotle, because it was no longer consistent with his assessment of nature, science, religious truth etc. In essence this was because wherever and whenever the believers in Aristotelian philosophy came upon a difficulty they were disposed to explain it away by some quasi-occult device. Ironically Newton was not averse to applying this very same technique when placed in a similar difficulty (*see* his explanation of the various colours – Chapter Three and 'Logic' in Chapter Thirty-seven), although his approach was more subtly disguised.

Whilst originally having some sympathy with aspects of Descartes' mechanistic approach he grew to reject its concepts, more emphatically so with time, although the severity of his rejection was likely as much religious as scientific. This because he was strongly anti-Catholic and although he was also anti-Trinitarian he was persuaded towards Protestantism, yet opposed to church reformism – with Puritanism at its other extreme. He retained the basic concept of the Atomist, namely that matter consisted of minute and discrete particles (atoms: Descartes – corpuscles: Newton), but rejected his concept of all matter being controlled by motion or Vortices. For instance Descartes could explain by mechanical means the way in which the non-contacting influence of a magnet operated; indeed his sketch of what we might now regard as magnetic flux looks very much like diagrams found in a modern school's textbook on physics, whereas Newton relied upon some occult influence. From the point of view of this Study it was his rejection of Aristotelianism, which had been the bedrock of science for a thousand years and was consistent with the established church's view, which is of importance and has to be addressed, since it was nonetheless (prudently?) incorporated in the ritual adopted by the Premier Grand Lodge and the subsequent the Royal Arch. His interest and one must assume his belief in alchemy remained with him throughout. He believed in natural or to the mind of some historians occult magic (i.e. providential/Godly intervention not that in the modern sense of sorcery, witchcraft or demonic). This ambiguity over the definition of 'magic' is because many historians use the term, but like the word 'metaphysics', they cannot seem to universally agree on what precisely they mean by it. It is therefore difficult to know whether, or which part of, his magic was some innate inexplicable quality or that which merely described a current mystery that may some day have a physical explanation; or more dramatically in a way more akin to the mechanistic view of Hobbes or Descartes. The balance must be toward the former since, to riterate, he was of the view that he had been somehow chosen and raised by God to the stature of a magus. There seems little doubt that he believed that this divine selection required him to rediscover those ancient mysteries of Nature and science that had been handed down to Moses by God, all those years before and that he was the person chosen to unravel the mayhem left by the intervening paganism. He believed that it (Nature/Creation) had all revolved around innate divine harmony and proportion. He believed in the omnipresence, omnipotence and omniscience of God, but had great difficulty with the concept of the Holy Trinity and openly refused to accept the subordination of the Son of God to the Father, claiming that there was only one God. So strident was he in this belief that he refused to take Holy Orders in the Trinitarian Faith and was nearly expelled from his professorial chair because of it. He was prepared to communicate certain aspects of his inner thinking to his Disciples, but only on the condition that they retained its secrets and shielded them from the profane. It is believed that this, albeit quite limited level of sharing was sufficient to have had a very profound influence on those who were instrumental in founding the Premier Grand Lodge.

Thus it would seem that Newtonianism is in two distinct parts; the first a philosophy, almost a set of rules, describing the physical world, a world that can be verified by experiment in a Baconian way. The other part was a hotchpotch of various obscure quite strange notions, one might say complete fantasies, part quasi scientific, part magic, part theological, part ethereal, part mystical, based upon a deliberately distorted view of history and entered upon in great secrecy. Such odd manifestations in an otherwise brilliant academic are often regarded as interesting eccentricities, possessing their own degree of charm and thereby allowable. However, in the case of Newton such was his general position of authority, in every sense of the word, that his intellectual power, personality, fame and position of great influence, had a great impact on those about him and especially from our point of view the group of men with whom we are concerned most.

Because the nation was gripped by his scientific revelations, Newtonians and there were many who would consider themselves such, could be ranked in grades of understanding, rather like the colour of belts in Judo, but his true disciples, especially the high Dan 'black belts', very close to him were far fewer, but importantly several of our people were definitely numbered amongst those and even if in reality he had not truly admitted them, they nonetheless would have felt that they had been, or were about to be. However the penalty for being so privileged was that they were obliged to accept a (his) convoluted concept of things, which they were more or less able to understand depending upon the degree of their wit and the level of confidentiality Newton had entrusted to them. Because they held him in such high esteem, those areas where he had left them in ignorance or as yet they could not fully understand they would have likely assumed he was holding in reserve until such times as they were worthy to be entrusted with them. Of course in reality he did not and could not know such things himself, but that would not be the first instance where the self belief of those elevated to high social status has been allowed to numb reality. Indeed it would appear that his Masonic disciples conveyed the same impression to their lesserlings: with the promise of eventual reward within the ritual, since they were informed that 'patience and industry would, in due time, entitle a worthy Mason to a participation of them' – which undertaking they were encouraged to believe dated from a much earlier date and related to the Menatschim or overseers during the building of King Solomon's Temple. It is worth reiterating that there were a disproportionately high number of men who were also Fellows of the Royal Society amongst the comparatively few Members of the early Premier Grand Lodge. Given Newton's all pervading status in that Body there is little doubt that many of those freemasons who were also Fellows, as well as other members of the Premier Grand Lodge, were committed Newtonians. However, we are concerned principally with six: Desaguliers, Senex, Folkes, Stukeley, Arbuthnott and Brooke-Taylor, with a possible seventh in Hauksbee.

In the various bibliographies an attempt was made to only dwell on those aspects of their lives which related to their activities and connections with Freemasonry, which required particular care not to bias factors unduly in that direction, but because they appeared to be so active in Freemasonry this was bound to be a very important aspect of their lives and so comment was slewed in that direction and so some bias was inevitable. However at that stage no direct reference to the level of their commitment to Newtonianism was made, but without stretching credibility too far it is clear that all those men, in the period 1720 to 1726, had good reason to be so persuaded. Indeed we are led to infer from his own writings that Stukeley joined Freemasonry in the belief that by so doing he would be privileged to some of those innate secrets. It is interesting to reflect upon how many people there are who join Freemasonry today with that specific intent, a very small fraction of a percent one might be tempted to conclude. The question that needs to be addressed is why Newton and to a lesser extent his disciples held these views?

The answer to this question would appear to be at the very heart of the quest from Part II onwards of this Study; namely to speculate upon who, why, when etc. For the moment it is sufficient to address the question of whether there is good enough reason to claim, from this now distant assessment of the relevant factors, whether these really important people who were so influential in this newly emerging society were also devoted Newtonians and considered themselves to be close to the ear of Newton himself and hence his secrets. For instance Stukeley had been deeply interested in science from a child, but in some strange way this had also led him to be strongly disposed toward the mystical ancient religions such as the Druids. He would have known Newton well enough to realise that underneath Newton's public persona there was a much more complex and profound interpretation of Nature, science, theology, etc. and he would have wished to penetrate this. All these characters were, in a somewhat superficial manner, purveying their wares in the public arena. It is clear that whilst they based their personal philosophy on a wider and more profound understanding of Newton's inner thinking, for some obscure reason they conveyed a populist version of it to others. It is therefore reasonable to suppose that the impression gained by those outside of Freemasonry was that this new manifestation of Freemasonry represented a society of powerful and intelligent men, bound by the codes of the most inviolable secrecy and revelations of a more profound nature could and would be discussed within it. In any event, as in the case of Stukeley, it would be no ill store politically to be associated with such company, as is evidenced in his many communications to others outside of Freemasonry, where he makes constant reference to the illustrious company he was keeping.

The degree to which these people were wedded to Newton and hence Newtonianism is well illustrated by reading Desaguliers allegorical poem,[3] set out in full in Appendix I. The extent to which society in general was swept up in this whole affair can be gained from Stewart's remarkably fine book *The Rise of Public Science*'and especially in his Chapter Five 'The Newtonians and the English Transformation'.[4] He incidentally devotes individual chapters to the dominant influence of Chandos and in particular Desaguliers in this upsurge of interest in what was essentially Newtonian concepts. What is at the very heart of this enquiry is to ascertain the true level of the Founders' understanding and to what degree was it influenced by their close association with Newton? An indication of this may be gained from the next Chapter, which deals with the Liberal Arts and Sciences and as such does appear to provide considerable enlightenment in this respect. In the final analysis the question that has to be answered is to what extent was the Ritual adopted by the Premier Grand Lodge and by implication given official approval, influenced by Newtonianism?

References

1. Curl, J., *The Art and Architecture of Freemasonry*, (Batsford, London, 1991).

2. Fauvel, J., *et al.*, *Let Newton Be* (OUP, Oxford, 1988).

3. Desaguliers, J., *The Newtonian System of the World, the Best MODEL of Government &c.* (Roberts, J., London, 1728).

4. Stewart, L., *The Rise of Public Science* (CUP, 1992).

Chapter Thirty-seven:

The 'Seven Liberal Arts and Sciences' and the 'Hidden Mysteries of Nature and Science'

It has been a repeated claim in this work that within present day Freemasonry there is a general disposition of those rehearsing and working the various ceremonies to simply gloss over many words and phrases within the Ritual because they would, in view of their archaic form and/or remoteness from common usage, require too much research to understand them in depth. Indeed, it is helpful to reiterate that when a person is first admitted into Freemasonry they are immediately 'charged' with their obligations to society in general and to Freemasonry in particular with 'a last general (effectively an injunction) recommendation' added to this already formidable list: 'to study more especially such of the liberal Arts and Sciences as may lie within the compass of your attainment and without neglecting the ordinary duties of your station endeavour to make a daily advancement in Masonic knowledge' etc. Part I was an attempt to redress a little of this imbalance, to convey an understanding of the science that the Founders had in mind and thereby encourage, indeed insisted upon, a continued interest in the science related to Freemasonry. For the sake of brevity it was only possible to consider the physical meaning of some of these concepts in relation to modern day understanding and was not able to address the underlying (deeper) connotations that affected the lives of those living through the early 1700s. Nonetheless it is clear from the previous Chapter their outwardly professed 'Science' was bound up with a much deeper inner meaning, even to the extent of providing an insight, if not the key to understanding Creation itself and perhaps far more important their ultimate salvation. It is therefore necessary to consider that aspect in greater detail in order to give some indication of what were those elusive 'Liberal Arts and Sciences', which even today's freemasons are encouraged, if not obliged, to study at depth. However, when attempting to do so, there is a plethora of information from which to choose, the difficulty therefore is that of making appropriate choices. Numerous people have pursued a range of aspects within each of these various areas, some as pieces incidental interest to some main theme, others to great depth, many representing it as a consequence of their (often PhD theses) many years of research in a comparatively narrow field. All have their flag to wave and thus it is impossible to convey all the nuances of this vast array of work in a few paragraphs.

As with most else in this study when trying to discover what the contemporary view in the 1720s was likely to have been, it was found to be laced with the unexpected. That the surrounding circumstances were far more elaborate than anticipated and the words used often conveying a quite different meaning from those commonly

'The Seven Liberal Arts and Sciences'

understood today. It is generally agreed that the term the 'Seven Liberal Arts and Sciences' took its current meaning when the Roman philosopher Bothius (*c.*480-524 AD) referred to the four scientifically (numerically) based topics of geometry, arithmetic, astronomy and music as the *quadrivium*. However, as always it is not quite so clear-cut, since Pope Sixtus II (*c.*257 AD) was reputed to have railed against the 'Liberal Arts and Science', although it is difficult to know precisely what he understood them to be. Bothius considered the Arts to be those of grammar, rhetoric and logic (dialectic); they having at some stage been assigned the name *trivium*. In terms of this study the significance of this distinction and many respects greater awareness was that the *trivium* took centre stage and became the basis of effectively all learned establishments, notably the universities (not forgetting the influence of monasteries), from whence derived the Bachelor of Arts degree. Although the Seven Liberal Arts and Sciences proved to be the basis of scholarly activity for a thousand years, the sciences took an especially (knowingly suppressed) subordinate role, but during the seventeenth century, because of the way in which the world was changing, their roles began to reverse.

However, the Arts remained the very basis of the educational community and were then and still remain an extremely important aspect of learning and given that they were intimately connected with the churches' dominance in the educational process they were not going to be brushed aside lightly and proponents of science had to fight hard to gain a foothold. Some attempt was made to accommodate the philosophical implications, but they conveyed the wrong messages and were resisted by the Church at every turn. An example of this quasi-reverence for the 'Arts' is found on the Eastern Seaboard of North America at the time when the American Colonies were becoming established and who later that century were to become the beginning of the United States. They were not only importing people, but also a university style education and although there was an urgent and immediate need for science and technology the Arts were nonetheless dominant, Ralph Emerson said 'that a man must be a man (have studied the Arts that is) before he can become a good farmer, tradesman or engineer', echoing the exhortation made to all freemasons. There is no denying the intrinsic validity of that assumption, but in this instance, given the need, it is the priority given to them that is striking and many universities both in the United States and elsewhere have retained that view even today, specialising only in the latter years of a three or four year course. It is not surprising therefore that the Seven Liberal Arts and Sciences were considered sufficiently important to be referred to specifically in the ritual of early Freemasonry and for that reason it is necessary to first attempt to define terms that would have been acceptable to the Founders and why they were retained in its basic concepts despite the sophisticated changes in science that were beginning to supersede all else before it.

A cynical interpretation of the *trivium* would be that it defined a modern politician; namely 'grammar' – a whole arsenal of the 'right' words, 'rhetoric' – the capacity to render them in great profusion and only when that had been done is there any concession made to 'logic'. This somewhat cynical aside and attempted humour is used to illustrate that is only pertinent because of the more modern usage and understanding of those words. The same is almost certainly true of most of the unusual, but often quite commonplace words and phrases found in the various present day rituals and where most people naturally accept their modern interpretation without feeling the need to consider them further. But as will be shown below their meanings were, for the most part, quite different in the early 1700s. They will be dealt with in the order in which they appear in the Ritual, which is also the way they appear in history and in their respective groups, beginning with the *trivium*.

Scholarly learning however defined had from the earliest times been the preserve of only those (Scholastics) who because of their wealth and/or privilege had the time and money to do so, which in practice meant that it was a narrow group consisting of the wealthy, the sponsored or the religious devotee (otherwise supported). Since wealth is usually associated with political power or a dominant religious grouping it is not surprising that such study was predominately philosophical in nature and generally supportive of the establishment, with only the rare exception transgressing these bounds. Even when such transgressions occurred they were either suppressed completely or emasculated to such a degree that they made no impact. However, as has been discussed earlier, by the end of the sixteenth century the world was changing at an incredible pace, especially in terms of the written (printed and therefore more freely available) word, that it was only a question of time before men of learning, such as Copernicus, would gain sufficient force to overcome such organised suppression. By the time the seventeenth century had begun the factors that govern aspects of science and in particular astronomy were already becoming established and again it was only a question of time before the laws governing the universe (gravitation as it was to become known through Newton) were discovered. It was only because it coincided with the genius of Newton that they were discovered in such a spectacular and comprehensive way, otherwise they would have percolated their way through as a result of some iterative process, in say the form of a series of propositions, discoveries etc. Thus for the preceding millennium the *trivium* represented the essential substance of the established seats of learning, with only occasional excursions into the sciences by the more inquisitive scholars. Indeed it will be argued that it was this proclivity to retain this Scholastic format that explains, to a large degree, why the ritual adopted by the Founders took the out-of-phase, anomalistic form it did.

It would seem reasonable to assert that in modern parlance grammar is considered to be the study of one's language, in terms of its technical aspects such as syntax, phonetics etc. and its literature. However, in the late 1600s and the early 1700s grammar was the study of the classical languages and literature and we saw in Chapter Thirteen that Harrow School was a grammar school set up specifically because there was a transgression from this adherence to the classics and the teaching of the curriculum in Latin. The whole tradition of the established universities was the study of the Classics and theology and they adhered to it with great tenacity, resisting change at every turn. All the Founders in question would have been totally literate in Latin, likely more so (when writing) than in their native language. They were, despite the system, scientists and a great deal of the recorded science was described in Latin, which was in effect the common language that linked those on the Continental mainland with Britain. Thus when those joining Freemasonry in the early years were exhorted to study grammar, they were really being requested to study the Classics as well as their native tongue. It is now necessary to expand on this distinction, but unfortunately what might appear to be a straight forward exercise is in practice an absolute literary minefield, because it raises the seemingly simple question of what is meant by each of the concepts? One's first reaction is to simply look the word up in a reputable dictionary, but English is an outstanding example of a living language and there have been remarkable changes in the language since the foundation of the Premier Grand Lodge. Lexicography is a science in its own right and it would be a distraction to attempt to introduce it here, but because a clear understanding of the terms in the ritual, is central to this work. An expansion of the respective definitions of most of those words of direct importance here will be found in Appendix 2.

The following analysis is primarily extracted from sources that have been concerned with the philosophy of the times leading up to the 1720s, but restricted to the better educated portion of society. The problem is that when these definitions are compared with their modern counterpart the correlation is less than perfect. The goal of the remainder of this Chapter is to attempt to reconcile these differences. For instance the *Concise Oxford Dictionary* defines rhetoric as follows: '(Treatise on) the art of persuasive or impressive speaking or writing; language designed to persuade or impress (often w. implications of insincerity, exaggeration etc.); persuasiveness of or of looks or act'. However, time has had its impact of this definition, for this is not the interpretation that would have been recognised by the Founders, they would have been close enough in time, for them to have assumed the classical meaning, accepting it to be that which had occupied an important place in education for a thousand years. Rhetoric had seen some change during that period, but by the late 1600s and early 1700s it was heavily biased towards the basis and hence study of Law (primarily Roman law). However, it meant much more than simply possessing a knowledge of the laws of the land, it was a study of morality, fairness, but in addition because the Church was so dominant, it had a pronounced theological bias and in that sense was conditioned to a state where it was obliged to be consistent with it. Again its retention as an innate part of the Ritual, as opposed to some more sophisticated philosophy, foreign to most people, can be gauged from two short extracts:

> 'To your neighbour, by acting with him on the square, by rendering him every kind office which justice or mercy may require, by relieving his necessities and soothing his afflictions, and by doing to him as in similar cases you would wish him to do to you,' etc.

> 'As a citizen of the world, I am to enjoin you to be exemplary in the discharge of your civil duties, by never proposing or at all countenancing any act that may have a tendency to subvert the peace and good order of society, by paying due obedience to the Laws of any state which may for at time become the place of your residence or afford you its protection,' etc.

Thus in simple terms, to the lay Brethren of the 1720s, rhetoric was to possess a knowledge of the Law, morality and religion and as such they would have been comfortable with it and in addition it could be easily defended against hostile inferences of impropriety made from outside the Fraternity. Although as is shown in Appendix 2 the definition of the word in English dictionaries was already beginning to move away from its quasi-classical meaning.

It is unfortunate that 'logic' cannot be considered with the same simplicity, but the problem in this instance is that for logic in the classical sense read 'philosophy'. Thus logic cannot be defined by some convenient umbrella definition related directly to the period and this is for two main reasons: the people concerned, but especially because of their complex status within the extant Newtonian hierarchy. For as discussed in the previous Chapter, these concepts operated at various (but again principally two) levels, namely those for general consumption and those restricted to the inner, far more complex and secretive thinking of Newton himself; only parts of which were deemed appropriate for disclosure and only then to his most trusted disciples. That the subject is extremely difficult to cover is demonstrated by the work of Garber and Ayres, who required a two volume (1600 plus pages) *tour de force* to address a narrow area of the topic. Their study comprised the work of many authors as well as their own contribution and even then dealt only with those factors affecting the philosophy associated with Cambridge University in the seventeenth and early eighteenth centuries.[1] Notwithstanding this overall limitation it is necessary to cover the subject in sufficient detail to indicate the nature of the logic that the Founders were prepared to include in the ritual and with safeguards with respect to the outside world; for to go further would endanger exposing their innermost (hidden mysteries) beliefs and privileged position. As will be argued in the concluding section of this work a simple way forward was to construct the ritual on the generally accepted historical interpretation of Aristotelian logic or dialectic. From that base to suggest to the newly joining brother that he may expect from within the Body of Freemasonry the opportunity of gaining a much deeper interpretation of 'Nature and Science'. The implication being that although the acquisition of such knowledge would require patience and industry, for those with the required disposition, there were great rewards; especially the facility within Freemasonry for them to discover the innermost meaning of their Existence – 'to trace it from its development, through the paths of heavenly science, even to the throne of God Himself'.

Having decided to pursue such a policy there was an inherent danger since it was likely to lead to difficulty when it became necessary to deal with the science based subjects of the *quadrivium*. In practice the Ritual (particularly the Royal Arch) when it alludes to 'Platonism', is in reality referring to the derivative of Aristotelian philosophy that was adopted and customised in the Middles Ages. Aristotelian logic or dialectic followed the discovery of Aristotle's *Oreganon* in the twelfth century, it is convenient for the moment to précis this. Aspects of this important discovery have arisen already throughout this work when dealing with certain subject areas in the Symbolical Lecture of the Royal Arch, especially in Chapter Six. Aristotle's concept was that all things were in a sense organic and hence had spiritual purpose. Its great appeal was that at its heart it required divine (God's) intervention and in such a way that it could be construed as being consistent with the God of the Christian Church and indeed most other religions – but it is important to note that this was only after it had been 'reconciled' with the Christian faith by St. Thomas Aquinas in the thirteenth century. Aristotle's brand of logic (philosophy) was 'deductive' and is usually illustrated by employing the classical model: (given that) 'Socrates is a man, (and that) all men are mortal, (it follows that) therefore Socrates is mortal'. But as discussed elsewhere those advocating his philosophy in this rapidly changing (scientific) environment were forced onto the defensive, being required to invoke occult explanations for effectively every discovery as they occurred. The important factor for the purposes of this work is that Newton and his disciples preferred a subtly different logic coming from the French (Protestant) School, headed by the Protestant Huguenot Petrus Ramus. Using the same model, the rationality of Socrates' 'mortality' becomes an applied or inferred truth, rationalised in a rhetorical vein: Socrates is a man, is it not then true that Socrates is mortal. The difference is quite subtle, since the philosophy does not 'paint itself into corners' by insisting upon absolute truisms. Newton believed in a God, but his God was above the need of having 'substance' and as such was excluded from physical laws – but rather embraced in the magic of Nature. Thus when confronted with things that they could not explained Aristotelians adopted the stance that they 'dwelt in the province of God – to discourse of (God) from the appearance of things, does certainly belong to Natural Philosophy'.[2]

Aristotle's philosophy could not be discarded lightly without affecting the established seats of learning particularly with respect to the Church. Indeed, the fact that it complied with church doctrine was its principal merit and so it continued to be woven into the explanation of all things, not least that of man himself. But as will become apparent, by the early 1700s the established scholasticism of the universities and other seats of learning were falling foul of the increasing intrusion of the 'truisms' within the new scientific understanding of the basic elements of the *quadrivium*. In the case of those at the very centre of the affairs of the Premier Grand Lodge in the early 1720s, it is almost certain from their writings and their close affinity with Newton that they had embraced his basic concepts – for such was the personality of Newton that he would not tolerate the company of those who did not. Their acceptance of his doctrines would have needed to include his complex analysis of the nature of things, his partiality in the way he dispensed knowledge to the various strata of the privileged about him and an awareness of the need for secrecy as further revelations of the hidden mysteries were unveiled. By definition such secrecy would require a facade, which in their case was the brand of philosophy proffered by the School of Ramus cited above. This did not mean that the Founders, in view of their earlier education, would not have sought to denigrate the Arts of the *trivium* in any way, but because of their scientific background they would have wished to emphasise the fundamental truths now becoming apparent from a greater understanding of the *quadrivium* (Sciences).

'Geometry' the first of the four (geometry, arithmetic, astronomy and music) is dealt with in some measure elsewhere in terms of its mechanics, it is only necessary therefore to dwell a little upon its philosophical importance. The inherent problem when studying philosophy is that of isolating truths from concepts (often desires) and from that to then deduce laws which may be considered to hold for all cases and the subsequent realisation that there are very, very, few incidents where such rigor may be found. However, geometry, right from the earliest known accounts fulfilled this basic requirement; it is traditionally based on a series of logical premises, which if not violated are totally consistent. Because of this indisputable rigour geometry in the eyes of many philosophers took upon itself the status of divine perfection.

However, there are very few cases indeed where it is possible to define the intricacies of natural behaviour in some exact mathematical way. Effectively all 'academics' seek to find such relationships (mathematical models) in their chosen discipline, but the natural world is unsympathetic to such approaches and the vast majority fail. They overcome this by employing more and more abstruse mathematics, requiring an increasing number of caveats, but provided they abide by the protocols of their peers who are employing the same techniques (on the 'do not rock the boat' principle) and serve on the right committees etc. they will most likely gain eminence in their field. Newton however, picked the ripest plum possible and at a time when its impact was certain to be explosive, not just within his close (scientific) community, but the world in general and its was founded on the one philosophical, irrefutable, set of laws that had stood the test of time: geometry. Employing this technique he was able to explain and predict the behaviour of the very Heavens themselves; explain (really describe) phenomena such as 'attraction', the laws of motion and predict natural events such as the rise and fall of the tides and the heavenly motions of the planets etc. Not only were those with whom we are concerned persuaded, indeed intoxicated, by the power of his argument, but in addition were in a position to make social and economic gain from it. Reason enough to lay particular emphasis on the scientific and philosophical reasoning underpinning geometry.

For 'arithmetic' read 'mathematics' because the science of mathematics in the 1700s would have included not only the developing theories of number, but also every other aspect of computation other than geometry and even that was already being defined in mathematical (analytical) terms. The level of sophistication of mathematics at this time has been alluded to already, especially that associated with Brooke Taylor. However, to gain a better idea it is necessary to refer to more detailed studies. Tatons' book[3] is an excellent example in this respect, although even this is comparatively demanding in that it requires an appreciable knowledge of mathematics, which in a sense gives an indication of the level of their (the Founders) mathematical understanding. The impact of arithmetic (mathematics) on the Scholastics is illustrated by the following extract from Fuller's book. He had been discussing the fact that the acceleration of mathematics (especially geometry) in the early 1700s was replacing Aristotle's logic. In particular he made reference to a certain (contemporary of the period) Edward Law who was bemoaning the fact that mathematics had been introduced into philosophy to enliven thinking and support certain concepts, but that it had now got completely out of hand:

> '... the dull, crabbed system of Aristotle's logic [...] called in the assistance of the Mathematics, little imagining that in a short time the assistants, these comparatively meagre instruments, should, like Pharaoh's lean kine, eat up all that was good and well favoured in the sciences themselves, that they should usurp the place of those very sciences to which they were originally designed to be subservient and for which station they were sufficiently qualified.'[4]

However, our people were the very culprits of such behaviour and would have experienced no discomfort in recommending the study of arithmetic. But as will now be discussed the science of number and hence 'order' in Newton's world becomes entwined to a remarkable degree with astronomy and music and even more obscurely in colour and religion (typically magical numbers in the guise of the seven veils, seven lights etc.).

Again in Part I astronomy was considered in relation to the Sphere of the Universe referred to in the Symbolical Lecture and the explanation given was in response to the way in which it was introduced in the guise of the fifth regular solid and as such was skewed. Even so this interpretation was to a large degree consistent with the generally accepted Scholastic's interpretation of the Heavens and as such was also consistent with contemporary religious beliefs. However, if the preceding assumption of the way in which matters were developing is true then the (*quadrivium*) astronomy of the Ritual adopted by the Founders would almost certainly have been an interpretation consistent with that propounded by Newton (*see* Appendix 1). However, because of the innate duality of Newton's publicly professed views as opposed to those understood by his inner circle, any explanation needs to be separated into the two levels. The physical and philosophical concepts of the five (Platonic) regular solids have had a strange fascination for thinkers in every recorded age and so it is not surprising that it was included in the ritual in allusion to astronomy. It appears again in Bennett's book *The Mathematical Science of Christopher Wren* when he is discussing the influence of the mathematician Drigges on the development of Wren's mathematics and in particular '... the five regular Platonicall Solids':

> 'I have thought good to adioyne this Treatise of the 5 Platonicall bodies, meaninge not to discourse of their secrete of mysticall appliances to the Elemental regions and frame of the Coelestiall Spheres, as thinges remote and farre distant from the Methode, nature and certaintie of Geometricall demonstration, only heere I intende Mathematically to conferre the Superficiall and Solide capacities of these Regular bodies with their Circumscribing or inscribed spheres or solids [no mean task given that is was universally known that Kepler had already done it]'.[5]

Wren's understanding of mathematics was quite exceptional and would have been contemporary with that of Newton's. This disposition within academe to dwell upon this singularity would help to explain, if not totally justify, its inclusion in the ritual, but it is reinforced further by the allusion to the 'crystal spheres' of Scholasticism. The concept of these concentric spheres may have sufficed for the uninitiated, but for Newton and his close disciples it was an inadequate model. Indeed the concept of crystal like celestial spheres remained part of their thinking, although as we shall see when discussing astronomy they were not configured in the simplistic way assumed by Aristotle or indeed Copernicus. Thus we may assume from their close dealings with men of the stature of Newton and Wren and know from their scholarly writing that the 'arithmetic' of Desaguliers, Stukeley, Haukesbee and especially Brooke Taylor was of a very high order indeed.

All of the liberal Arts and Sciences are intertwined, but astronomy and music would, from our present day understanding of the terms not appear to be so, but as will become apparent they are closely associated with 'the hidden mysteries' alluded to at different points throughout the ritual. The outer crystal sphere of perfection that held the fixed stars according to the Aristotelian view had been replaced in the more advanced thinking of Newton by an increased number of spheres, with the outer two of much greater dimension. Indeed the outer shell was infinite although like today's philosophers he was not at all sure what that (infinity) really meant – *see* Appendix 1. Newton and hence those with whom we are concerned were as a result of his gravitational theories aware of a planetary system, albeit short of those planets that were yet to be discovered, but in every other respect very much like our present day understanding. Those who at that time adopted this basic concept of the universe were, like us today even with our huge fund of discovery, unable to explain why or how the system came to be created with its intrinsic orbital motions, although that does not mean that there is any lack of theories.

Descartes believed that all Nature depended upon such motion and as such planetary motion could be explained in terms of an ingenious system of vortices. Newton came to reject this concept and simply believed that the Creator had imposed the Motion upon the heavens, but interestingly enough realised that it could not be self-sustaining and would suffer losses (indeed Desaguliers discusses these losses – again *see* Appendix 1). He concluded that this deficiency could be made up by the appearance of comets from outside of the system coming in and replenishing the lost momentum. Thus far, as with most of his published science, everything he offers has the rigour of a mechanical explanation and has the rationale one associates, albeit unjustly so, with the scientific process. But inwardly, even making allowances for the thought processes of the time, he entertained a panoply of fanciful ideas, related to alchemy, magic, astrology, theology and ancient history, which he wrapped up in scientific or quasi-scientific clothing. This may appear to be somewhat removed from defining astronomy, but his, for want of a better description, secret science directly involved those with whom we are concerned. In order to make progress and put the topic into perspective, astronomy will be left for the moment.

When contemplating the last of the 'sciences' again it is necessary to make allowance for the changes that have taken place in the English Language over the years and for 'music' we have to read 'harmony'. Of course there was music in the conventional sense of the word and from the bibliographies of the Grand Masters it is known that freemasons were not backward in giving their own raucous renditions at table, but the music of the *quadrivium* was based upon a much deeper understanding of number or arithmetic. The subject is far too complex to deal with in depth in this short appraisal and whole treatises have been written on this topic, an especially good example of which is the book by Penelope Gouk.[6] Legend has it that Pythagoras was passing by a blacksmith's forge, when he heard the (pleasing) sounds coming from the blows of hammers on an anvil. On enquiry he found that these various notes were related to the weight (mass) of the respective hammers. That he then went on to discover that there was a direct arithmetical relationship between the respective weights of the hammers and the consonance (harmony) between them and that weights outside of this series resulted in notes that were discordant. He then went on to show a similar correspondence between a pipe's length and its diameter, weights applied to strings of a given weight to length, of bells with different masses etc., from which he was able to define the respective ratios. There is considerable scepticism over this discovery by Pythagoras, but Boethius appeared to believe it to be so and laid down the basic laws of this musical relationship. As was mentioned in the short appraisal of astronomy the heavens consisted of concentric shells, these rubbed together and produced the 'Music (harmony) of the Spheres' and Pythagoras was credited as the only human being that had ever heard them, until the arrival of Newton. Although devoid of musical (as a actual musician that is) skills much of Newton's early work was concerned with the theory of music, as were many others, such as Hooke (who was a considerably talented musician) and although much later, but of especial note, those of Brooke Taylor and the Earl of Abercorn. The importance here is that transmission of sound was associated by many with transmission of light and hence colour, the heavens, but above all, because of the divisions of the octave, the magical (the modern usage of the word) or mystical number seven (irregular or logarithmic type spacing between notes).

It is perhaps apposite at this juncture to reemphasise that we are concerned with the 'hidden mysteries of Nature and Science' of the early 1700s, since it is necessary to contemplate whether there were certain mysteries then or now, that were ever within the possible wit of man. Few would now challenge that there are many matters beyond human comprehension, ranging from unfathomable facets of the physical world about us, creation, our ultimate destiny etc. and in acknowledging that to be so there is little recourse but to rely upon simple faith. It would seem however that this was not necessarily the case in the 1720s and as discussed above with respect to Newton and presumably his disciples, they believed that God had transmitted those fundamental truths to Moses, but that now Newton and his disciples in part, if they proved sufficiently worthy, were the people chosen to decipher them under God's divine influence. At least on a superficial level it is not unreasonable to suppose that to those contemplating Freemasonry from the outside at that time, would have believed that it held the distinct prospect of being admitted amongst those who were so privileged and that once admitted they would by some means or another, within the process of advancement, have the opportunity of sharing in those mysteries.

Again it is not possible to develop the numerous ramifications here, especially as it has been extremely well done by others, for example that by Flavel *et al.*[7] However several factors directly pertinent to this study will be expanded slightly. Seven is a number that has mystical connotations and appears throughout the ritual of the various Masonic ceremonies. For instance: seven had great significance with respect to a true understanding of the world-system, from ceremonial representations, such as those in Vestal temples, the symbolic arrangement of the Planets and the Sun in the seven lamps in the Jewish temple that surround the central fire. But another factor that intrigued them was the correspondence between the ratios of the orbits separating the Planets and those of the phonic scale and the visible spectrum etc.

All the allusions are represented in Masonic ritual, but as one researches into Newtonian concepts and their relationship with those in the initial years of Freemasonry, one is struck by the degree of correlation, of ideas and significant terms. It is hoped that there has been sufficient discussion on this matter to at least establish the likelihood of an interrelationship. However, before leaving this topic it is perhaps helpful to give one more example of incidental correlation between Newton and the essentials of Freemasonry: Gouk when quoting a passage from Newton's work with respect to planetary motion explains how Newton acknowledges the wisdom of Pythagoras:[8] 'Newton explains that Pythagoras concealed such divine wisdom from the vulgar, while at the same time revealing it to initiates such as (Newton) himself, by means of allegory and symbolism'. Most freemasons will be totally familiar with the concept that Freemasonry is 'a system of morality veiled in allegory and illustrated by symbols'. Newton when writing one of his theological texts quoted Daniel 12.3: '... that they turn many to righteousness and [that they] shall shine as the stars for ever and ever'.

A comparatively minor issue raised by John Brooke in Flavel's book[9] is of extreme importance to this study and illustrates well the profound, impartial, lessons to be learnt about the workings of Freemasonry from the study of topics outside of it. An attempt has been made not to ridicule the more extreme views of Newton, but rather to explain them as rational thoughts during that period. However, in this book Brooke's task was to reflect on Newton's concept of God and as part of that process he discussed those things he (Newton) was strongly opposed to. Brooke explains that Newton had made an extensive study of human history, from which he began to realise his important place within it (the phraseology used here is meant to be objective rather than cynical, since his belief appears sincere if not justified) and this caused him to abhor the way in which Christianity had been corrupted to suit the doctrines of the Church for their own ends. In particular he disliked the concept and pre-eminence of the Trinity within the Church's teaching, which in his view had changed it into a false infernal religion. He accepted that Christ was the Son of God, but in terms of a complex integration of equals. He was against Popery and its icons, against 'monkery'; stating that they should stop bewailing their fate and to go out and earn a living the same as everyone else. Equally important was his dislike of ancient chroniclers who had wantonly distorted history to suit their ends and had endeavoured to show that pagan civilisations had preceded the Jewish one. He believed passionately that it was the other way round and that these great civilisations, such as the Egyptians and the Greeks had derived all their wisdom via the word of God, which had been first handed down through Moses and that by their aggression and lack of profound understanding of those deep truths (secrets) they had been lost, coming to realise that he was the one that had been chosen to rediscover them. In particular he believed that these truths were especially encapsulated in the Temple built by King Solomon, made manifest by its perfection and harmony. He spent prodigious amounts of time studying biblical texts from many quarters and languages and was, because of his privileged position as a Magi, finally able to draw up a precise plan *see* Figure 37.1.

Figure 37.1 is a reproduction of Newton's plan of the Jewish Temple. The illustrations are in fact copies of the first two of the three drawings he made of the Temple, the third being the Inner Sanctum. They may be found in his book *The Chronology of Ancient Kingdoms Amended* (1728). It was primarily based upon the book of Ezekiel (from a number of sources and in several languages), but also numerous other texts outside of Ezekiel. Subsequent scholars (especially Masonic) will, quite rightly, challenge his concepts, but such evidence is irrelevant, since it was the strength and conviction with which he and his disciples believed it at the time that is so important here.

Clearly, to maintain faith, his Disciples would have needed to share his belief. In the case of Desaguliers this would not have been difficult, since he was only one generation removed from those Protestant Huguenots who had been persecuted by the Catholic French State. With the demise of the Duke of Wharton and the use of his casting vote in the election of the Duke of Buccleuch, the lingering, essentially covert, faction holding Catholic persuasion, had been snuffed out and any chance of a subsequent Catholic resurgence had been dealt a severe blow. This may have been the origin of the Catholics' aversion to this ostensibly non-sectarian society. More especially it would explain why this organisation made up of lodges that were founded upon the honourable and ancient practice of architecture, should adopt the Temple of King Solomon with such prominence as their principal link with ancient culture and profound truths.

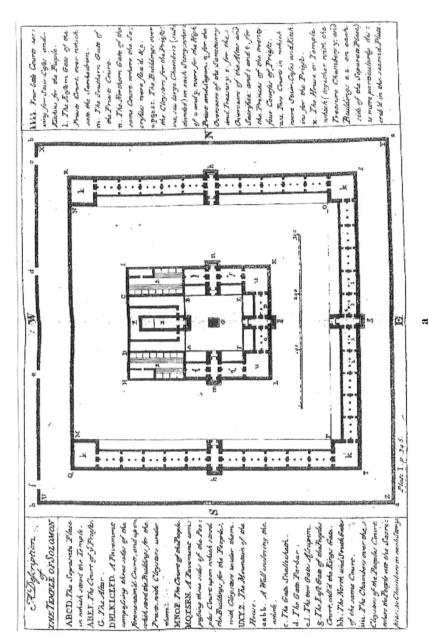

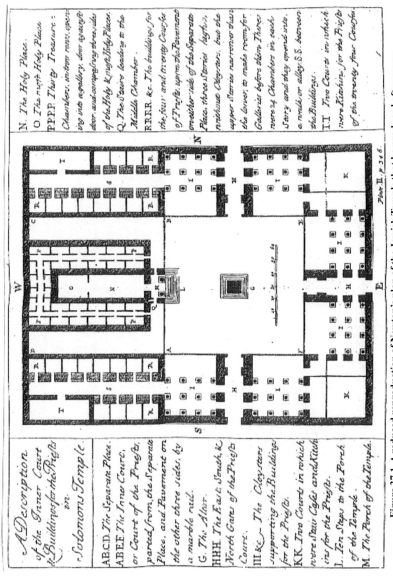

A Description
of the Inner Court
& Buildings for the Priests
viz.
Solomons Temple.

ABCD. The Separate Place.
ABEF. The Inner Court,
or Court of the Priests.
parted from the Separate
Place, and Pavement on
the other three sides, by
a marble rail.
G. The Altar.
HHH. The East, South &c.
North Gate of the Priests
Court.
III &c. — The Cloysters
supporting the Buildings
for the Priests.
KK. Two Courts in which
were Staw Cages and Kitch
ins for the Priests.
I. Ten Steps to the Porch
of the Temple.
M. The Porch of the Temple.

N. The Holy Place.
O. The most Holy Place.
PPPP. Thirty Treasure =
Chambers, intow rows, opening into a gallery, low up aloft
door and a passage in two sides
of the Holy King's Holy Place.
Q. The Stairs leading to the
Middle Chamber.
RRRR. &c. The buildings for
the four and twenty Courses
of Priests, upon the Pavement
on either side of the Separate
Place, three Stories high, in
without Cloysters, but the
upper Stories narrower than
the lower, to make room for
Galleries before them. There
were 4 Chamber in each
Story and they opened into
a walk or alley S.S. between
the Buildings.
II. Two Courts in which
were Kitchins for the Priests
of the twenty four Courses.

Plate II. p. 346.

Figure 37.1. A reduced reproduction of Newton's plan of the Jewish Temple that he produced after many
years of research. In his book there is a third of these depictions – that of the actual Inner Sanctum.[10]
(Distortion due to the restrictions necessary in the copying process from this delicate old book)

However, before leaving this particular item it is interesting to consider a more recent publication of John Neal.[11] Whilst this book merely reaffirms much of what has been written above it gives an insight into language, concepts and the complexity of the various terms used over the years. It also gives some indication of why the quasi-lecture in the Second Degree Tracing Board should have concentrated on Solomon's Temple and why it was essentially Newtonian. The following paragraph is a good illustration of this:

'His biblical studies were not entirely theological determinism. He expended much time and thought upon interpreting the dimensions of the holy temples that are given in both the old and new testaments, all of which are described by divine messengers. He was the first scholar to realise that the golden measuring reed held by the messengers who explained the temple and city to Ezekiel and is described as being six cubits and a hands breadth in length, actually means that of six cubits. Each of which are a hands breadth longer than the biblical 'cubit of a man', the 'profane' cubit, as Newton termed it. He roundly berated the earlier historian Josephus for not realizing the fact that when describing the construction of the pillars of Solomon's temple. He concluded that the temple of Ezekiel and that of Solomon were identical and the tabernacle of Moses to half scale etc., [see side note Figure 37.1]'.

This discussion on the Liberal Arts and Sciences will be left here, although it is quite clear that the subject is extremely complex and is deserving of further consideration. However, it is hoped that the above was sufficient to demonstrate that any interpretation is a function of the time under consideration and that there is considerable justification in claiming that the particular conception of the Liberal Arts and Sciences likely to have been held by those with whom we are concerned is fundamentally consistent with both that narrow slot in history and that found in the ritual of Freemasonry.

References

1. Garber & Ayres, *The Cambridge History of Seventeenth Century Philosophy* (CUP, Vols 1 & 2, 1990).
2. *Ibid*, p. 433
3. Taton, R., *The Beginnings of Modern Science (1450-1800)* (Thames & Hudson, London, 1958), p. 433.
4. Fuller, T., *The History of the University of Cambridge* (CUP, 1840), pp. 213-214.
5. Bennet, J., *The Mathematical Science of Christopher Wren* (CUP, Cambridge, 1982), p. 13.
6. Gouk, P., *Music, Science and Natural Magic in Seventeenth-Century England* (Yale University Press, New Haven, 1999).
7. Fauvel, J., *et al.*, *Let Newton Be* (OUP, Oxford, 1988), p. 253.
8. Gouk, *op. cit.*, p. 253.
9. Fauvel, J., *et al.*, *op. cit.*, p. 177.
10. Newton, I., *The Chronology of Ancient Kingdoms Amended* (1728).
11. Neal, J., *All Done with Mirrors* (The Secret Academy, UK, 2000), pp. 5-14.

Chapter Thirty-eight:
The Whys and Wherefores

uring the course of this research it has been necessary to range over many specialist areas, effectively every one of which has proved to be an academic discipline in its own right. All have contained areas of great general interest, but more importantly data that is quite specific to the narrow context of this Study and having an unambiguous relevance to Freemasonry. A major difficulty has been to assess whether, or to what extent, this information should be introduced into this presentation. Whether justified or not, it is felt that this balance has been achieved and that sufficient data has been extracted from the various parameters to construct a scenario which would explain the concept of Premier Grand Lodge Freemasonry, how the conditions were such for it to first begin and then evolve into the form we know today. Further to indicate the mechanism by which that process was possible and why shortly afterwards there was a fundamental change in its character; which resulted in a system that has lasted unto the present day. Within that same approach it was possible to show how the data also provided sufficient evidence of the precise (in historic terms) date. In Chapter Ten it was explained that although numerous Masonic historians had studied the subject of 'when', it had been largely unsuccessful and that there is still little or no definitive understanding of this, or effectively any of the other parameters. Further that whilst this Study does incorporate data from within the sphere of Masonic archives, because it concentrates mainly on interrelated factors outside of it, it is very much more versatile and verifiable. It does not seek to find irrefutable fact within a narrow study of any one topic, but works upon the probability that it would be extremely unlikely that these numerous factors could come together in this mutually supportive way by chance. That the inter-play between these factors was such as to create a unique climate for this great Institution to first form and then flourish and that there was only one narrow period when the mix of these parameters were in that optimum state. The use of a Venn diagrams and the concept of 'sets' was suggested as a suitable device to focus (also adding dimension) on the fact that it required all such sets to overlap in such a way that a common core was revealed. Since the size of the resultant core of any resultant diagram would shrink or expand according to the prevailing circumstances both within and external to each set, their overall favourability at any one time could be assessed. Although in the absence of hard facts the highlighted zone would be merely illustrative and hence be qualitative rather than quantitative it would nonetheless be possible to make a convincing assessment because it allows an appraisal of the relative vigour of each set at any particular time. Thus the task was to research the factors affecting each set for the period before and during the critical years from 1720 to 1740 and to provide sufficient (convincing) data to validate a set's presence and estimate its importance at any particular time. If this reasoning is sound then an assessment would be possible to determine the time where each of the respective sets were sufficiently strong and mutually supportive to have reached that point where a sustainable amalgamation could have taken place.

Clearly there is no doubt over the dating of the short period that the Premier Grand Lodge came into being, but would the finding of the proposed method prove robust enough to show consistency with that dating? Further, to answer the question whether at that short period the conditions were such that a common mode of working was possible, both in terms of regulation and ritual? In addition whether within that process a new concept: the Royal Arch could or indeed needed to be introduced? It was decided that whilst these factors were many they could all be embraced within the inquisitive 'W's of: why, who, which, where and what and that at the point where their compatibility was at a maximum it would answer the question when? The remaining query 'how' being left to inference whilst answering the other questions. All the previous chapters have been written with the intent that they were at once of enough interest to be read in their own right, but also meet the underlying objective of providing a sufficiently convincing argument to satisfy the above criterion. Having now considered many of these topics in some detail it is possible to return to the task of consolidating this information. The following is an attempt to condense this information into respective sets, a process much more easily done in some cases than others, which may be reflected by the extent of the text or data available, but not necessarily reflecting their importance.

As a consequence of the fact that there are no irrefutable facts relating to this immediate area of enquiry and that the only data available was qualitative and in some instances indirect, it was in consequence not amenable to a rigorous analytical/mathematical solution; it was however possible to adopt the classical approach of presenting a hypothesis and through research thereby to establish its 'validity'. An important element of such an approach involves the need to show that all the data supports that hypothesis and that there are no glaring anomalies suggesting it to be false. However, the problem is that because these findings can never be anything other than hypothetical, their level of credibility can only be judged by the authority of its argument. Thus the overall hypothesis to be tested is as follows: *That by the very early 1720s, the circumstances surrounding the Premier Grand Lodge originally formed in 1717 were such that a whole new structure and ethos emerged (herein called the Premier Grand Lodge). That a revised, commonly agreed, version of the ritual was adopted, which led to a new extension called the Holy Royal Arch.*

Although presented below as a series of seemingly independent questions they are in practice interrelated and so the discussion is somewhat contrived, but for

The Key to Modern Freemasonry

convenience they will be kept separate.

The process of summarising these various aspects will begin with the question 'why'? The science of Sociology appears to support the claim that man is a gregarious creature and has an innate disposition to form a close association with others. However, as we have seen in earlier Chapters, particularly those of ten and eleven, the reasons why there was a need in the early 1700s to form clubs, societies, public assemblies etc., are many and quite varied, but in essence they all relate to changes in the prevailing social climate. For convenience the principal factors are repeated here, although in no particular order of precedence:

1. The rapid expansion of science and technology,
2. The expansion and commercial exploitation of that science/technology, especially in terms of steam, hydraulics, mining, navigation etc.,
3. The wider distribution of wealth and (sometimes bought) social influence and the increasing influence of the entrepreneur,
4. The expansion of commerce, both at home and abroad; at home in such enterprises as share trading, insurance and the exploitation of patents etc. and abroad (colonisation and world trading) in areas such as slave trading, commodities, land acquisition, piracy, manufactured goods, etc., especially the granting of sole rights,
5. The development of the infra-structure (water transport, roads, but sadly not public health and sewage) which led to the relocation and sustainability of whole communities,
6. The public appetite for knowledge, given its perceived potential for advancement of whatever kind,
7. Other aspects of the social climate, such as profound changes in the Monarchy and political/religious expression,
8. The increased leisure time and hence socialising activity of the influential classes.

The respective justification for inclusion of each of these will not be reopened, except for the last, which in a sense is a consequence of all the factors above it. The reason for doing so is that it holds the key to content of the set 'why'. There seems to be no conflict between historians with respect to the frenetic increase in meeting places, coffee-houses, balls, afternoon tea etc., during this period and of particular interest here the desire to establish clubs and societies. They were springing up everywhere as the Nation's wealth grew. Whilst most were new, one of particular significance resulted from the amalgamation of already established *ad hoc* independent social groupings, under the generic label of speculative Masons. Despite all that was going on about them these disparate groups had somehow maintained their seemingly unique attraction for men of influence, especially so in large towns and in particular

408

The Whys and Wherefores

London and whilst they met in taverns etc. they continued to adorn their meeting rooms with the (transportable) ornamentation of erstwhile operative masons lodges; thereby retaining the concepts and relative status of their now departed symbolism and hierarchical structure. As we have seen that the Royal Society was by far the Nation's most august body, but it lacked the universality necessary to embrace the entire influential sector; for instance at least two of the original four were not *FRS*. When the masters and influential members of four of these London lodges decided to meet in a formal way (we will perhaps never know precisely quite how or why) it was likely to have been part of this general trend toward social intercourse. However, it transpired that one of the four not only had a foot in both camps, but was also a brilliant academic, was a Fellow of the Royal Society and practitioner in science and because it was his means of gaining a living, meant that he rubbed shoulders with extremely well placed members of society; who were both moneyed and/or aristocratic and this factor will be returned to when discussing the question who, what, etc?

During Queen Anne's reign and despite the political swings and roundabouts in the upper echelons of politics, the Country at large was beginning to feel the impact of the changes in wealth generation and distribution and although there were local skirmishes it was nonetheless becoming stabilised politically. There were some engagements in wars, but they were no longer having a debilitating effect on the wider economy. The Whigs were in the ascendancy by the time King George I came to the Throne, which combined with the increasing prosperity, stabilisation of society (if we disregard the claims and later efforts, or ineptitude of the Pretender James III as a mere distraction) it brought with it a change in the social behaviour of the affluent. It fostered what may be described as the new age of leisure activity and to a somewhat lesser degree galvanised into action those that did not have quite that status, but nonetheless wished to be associated with those who did. By 1720 the Premier Grand Lodge had been formed three years and had proved especially successful and was attracting others to join, but this meant that it had now become a candidate for the 'holy grail' of becoming a very influential society. Thus the answer to 'why' is that there was an almost insatiable need to find the right formula for an influential grouping that could be moulded to form a powerful association and here was an already established body, qualified in every respect and ripe for a 'take-over'.

However, before we leave this aspect it is helpful to address two further questions: when did it all take place and why did the process stop there? The answer to the second question is that it did not stop, even among the Members themselves there were those who tried to instigate clubs of their own – Wharton's 'Hellfire Club', Stukeley's 'Brassnose Society', Desaguliers' 'Spitalfields Mathematical Society', the provincial 'Spalding Gentlemen's Society' etc. are examples of similar efforts. It is argued here that certain Members and one in particular, recognised this danger and realised straight away that the ceremonies needed to have purpose, be regularised and added to, in order to increase the range of activities and the interrelationship between this central core and the affiliated lodges. The reason that effectively all of these other ventures of the type suggested above either failed or remained static was seemingly because their format, lacking certain vital ingredients, fell far short of the Masonic formula, which proved to be as near perfect for purpose as it could be. The 'when' will become more apparent after all the sets are over-laid, but in terms of answering the question 'why', it was because the concept met the unprecedented demand for such a venture, meaning that the moves for the 'take-over' had to be as soon as was possible. Thus it was that some time during the period 1718 to 1722; the imperative for the perpetrators of the *coup d'état* being 'the sooner the better', since it is much harder to modify entrenched practices.

The next set to be considered is 'where'. Of course 'where' is one of the few known facts, but why should it have been London? The reasons why operative masons, the most widely dispersed yet intrinsically close-knit, trade (guild type) of skilled based organisations had metamorphosed into these disparate groups of local dignitaries and men of influence have been discussed earlier. Clearly these, now unambiguously named freemasons', only (in England at least) connection with operative masonry was the historic link of earlier affiliations and a retained desire to model their aims and objectives on the majesty and perfection of the buildings that these worthy masons had constructed and for the most part designed. Whilst there was evidence of similar lodges throughout the land and beyond, because of the peculiar social climate in London there were a good many, but equally important they were all concentrated within a comparatively short, commutable, distance of each other. It was therefore only a question of time before links through business and social mixing would bring various members in contact with each other. All that was then required were men of the right calibre and inclination to start some process of amalgamation. Three other factors are of particular note: the social importance of the 'London Scene' to upper classes and the proximity of their 'Town Residence' and the comparative ease of their getting together given the otherwise limited means of transport generally.

The 'when' associated with the 'where' is less certain since communication became steadily better with time, although roads were particularly out of phase, principally because of their disparate ownership and the associated costs of upkeep relative to income – organised road pricing and hence building and any attempt at systematic maintenance only started in the 1730s. However, even before the turn or the century (1700), there were a considerable number of lodges within the London area, some as we have seen strongly affiliated to Provincial counties and/or even aristocratic patronage, so that London was extremely well placed to provide the necessary feed-stock for some grander concept. The 'when' can only be judged by studying the changing influence of the hierarchy within the Premier Grand Lodge and the input they were likely to have on the composition of an agreed ritual. There was a copious supply of possible aristocrats who might be persuaded to take high office and an even greater number of lay members who would wish to be associated with them and this has been retained to a pronounced degree from 1720 right through until the present day. In this respect the election of an aristocrat as Grand Master may be regarded as a constant, but with the following caveat; that each style of management tends to promote in its own image. So it is not at all surprising that there was the very strong scientific bias at its commencement, but as we have seen this was nudged off course by the political/religious connotations of the election of the Grand Master in 1724 and was never able to recover totally from it. Thereafter the Grand Masters were for the most part to become mere figureheads, which it must be assumed they seemed quite happy to accept, since the evidence suggests that they were content to have had very little involvement in the day to day running of the organisation. This emphasis on science was destined to decline due to the loss or reduced involvement of the hierarchy in the physical sciences during the middle to late 1720s and this deficit was replaced by the medical profession and others, albeit with far less commitment. From 1730 the hierarchy then tended to be selected from the military, again with either inappropriate or indifferent management styles. Given the scholarly (strongly scientific) nature of the Ritual and the pursuit of learning insisted upon within it that was adopted by the restructured Premier Grand Lodge, coupled with the proximity of the Royal Society and the dual affiliation of many of its Members, suggests that there is very strong reason to suppose that the 'when' associated with the 'where; is London in the early 1720s.

The question 'what' is a function of how strongly it may be argued that the essence of the ritual has remained unaltered over the intervening years. There can be little doubt that ceremonies have undergone change and likewise the supporting dialogue, but if the studies of historians such as Curl[1] are correct there is a surprising degree of adherence to the basic forms in the ritual practice today. The only real change of emphasis seems to be the level of importance attached to the 'Hiramic' Legend in modern Freemasonry, the inclusion and details of which to a large degree rely upon Prichard's exposé *Masonry Dissected*.[2] Whilst Prichard's prejudices make him a quite unreliable source, it is unlikely that even he would have gone to that level of perverse invention. Which means that unless there is some irrefutable evidence to the contrary it would seem that the 'Legend' gained its present (dominant) status somewhat later in the 1700s, although not necessarily that late and because of this it will continue to be the subject of contentious debate? Certainly for the purposes of the pragmatic working of both the Craft and Royal Arch, the Hiramic Legend inclusion would have been quite peripheral. It is a great pity that this assertion needed to have been introduced at this point, since it is likely to cause a great deal of huffing and puffing among some authorities and as such could prove to be an unnecessary distraction, especially as the importance of its role would not make that much difference to the overall argument. As with the story of the 'secret vault' in the Royal Arch, Hiram's stoic manner and death is a 'ripping yarn' and as such provides an opportunity to demonstrate valour, integrity, unswerving loyalty etc. the essentials of its theme are the basis of many previous allegorical tales and like those appears to have absolutely no authenticity. Even then historians have offered other reasons for the inclusion of the 'Legend' such as the allegorical return from exile of Prince Charles,[3] a further addition to this list will be added later in this Study. However, so far as can be ascertained the innate philosophy of the Ritual has remained steady throughout. Enshrined within it are the basic tenets of the church, the humility of office, loyalty to one's country and friends etc. (*see* Appendix 1) that was the laudable public expectation prevalent in the early 1700s. But more important was the need for freemasons to enhance their being by the study of Nature and Science, which was extended further by reference to the Liberal Arts and Sciences, allusions to Heavenly science etc.

Irrespective of the degree to which the Hiramic Legend may have been included in the Ritual it is clear that its primary purpose was to provide a mechanism for prospective members to first join and afterwards receive instruction on the basic codes of behaviour and lifestyle they were expected to adopt. The introduction of a person into Freemasonry being a progressive affair of enlightenment supplemented by a series of illustrative asides in the form of alleged incidences, Tracing Boards and Charges and in the case of the Royal Arch a series of Lectures. At first sight it would seem prudent for the Founders to adopt a version of the ritual that was essentially the same as that being practised in one or more of the constituent lodges. However prudence suggests that the only safe way was to conjure up a form of ritual that had only the essential ingredients of those currently practiced, thus adopting no one ritual whilst at the same time appearing to make a new start by introducing an additional piece of ritual unique to the Premier Grand Lodge.

Thus it seemed reasonable to assume that the Ritual they adopted would have been an amalgam of the existing ceremonies currently in practice in the constituent lodges. But given the strident Newtonianism adopted by this pioneering group in the early years of the Premier Grand Lodge it suggests that they would have nonetheless wished to make changes, seeking only to preserve the spirit and protocols of the existing rituals, which then allowed them to incorporate a change of (educational/ scientific) emphasis that was predominantly new to all. Following from this it is argued that although certain ceremonial protocols may have undergone changes, the essentials of the rituals practiced today have remained consistent with that early remit. Further it is reasonable to suppose that there would have been no imperative in the versions of the rituals prior to 1717 for the inclusion of science or any especial emphasis on scholasticism, but social changes had by that time brought them into prominence and so quite suddenly it was pre-eminent and confronted this most influential and active group of individuals in their daily life. Thus the ceremonies did not need to depend upon the basis of making the most out of an irretrievable loss, but rather offered the prospect of achieving unlimited enlightenment for those of merit, a philosophical attitude that was peculiarly true of the proponents of Newtonianism. The timing therefore is again associated with the reign of the influentially placed and scientifically persuaded element of the Premier Grand Lodge *c.*1720-1723.

The 'what' may be regarded as being an amalgam of the protocols and ritual that had evolved from the various sources within the British Isles (notably Scotland) and indeed beyond and which had been practiced in the late 1600s and early 1700s. It is reasonable to assume that some analogous, but rather grander, form than would have been in the minds of those four Masonic dignitaries who had agreed upon the concept of some formalised intercourse between lodges, in say *c.*1715. Again it may be supposed that from out of these initial gatherings they would have settled upon some further strategy, but that could only be after they had sold the notion to those affected. It was clearly somewhat later, once this initial structure had proven to be so effective, that the initiative was seized by certain parties, enabling the whole ethos of this *ad hoc* association of lodges to be usurped and changed into something completely different and the *coup d'état* accomplished. Bearing in mind that the newly introduced protocols and ritual would have been influenced by the 'hidden' (quasi-philosophical) concepts lurking within the minds of the Newtonian element of those involved in the early Premier Grand Lodge. This trite analysis of events is not meant to somehow minimise the difficulties of attempting to arrive at the precise nature and projected protocols of the rituals preceding, during and after the formation of the Premier Grand Lodge that has been discussed already. For this too must remain a hypothesis, the only difference being that there is a considerable amount of circumstantial evidence to support it. The scholarly work of such Masonic historians as John Hamill and Bernard Jones is difficult to fault and when this study began there was no intention of researching the matter further, but merely to understand the place of Nature and science within the system they and others describe. Whilst there is no doubting the scholarship of their work, it seemed reasonable to suggest, since there is no irrefutable evidence, that there may be some innate, even subliminal, predisposition to suggest that there was a direct correlation between the concepts of Freemasonry practiced then with those used widely today, but was this indeed the best case scenario? To address this concern the matter was discussed at some length with Dr Simon Schaffer the outstanding (quite independent of any direct Masonic connection) academic on the interrelationship between science and society leading up to and including the period of interest here.[4] This was particularly pertinent when attempting to determine the persona of the scientists involved, for it became clear that there were further sociological ramifications to this aspect of Freemasonry. The full weight of this argument will become apparent in the next Section on 'who'.

For the purpose of this Study it is necessary to reflect the other social experiments that were being explored by those attempting to involve this very influential section of society in viable (popular) societies. It would seem that numerous formats had been tried, but they lacked the vital ingredients that would take the ordinary into the exceptional and they failed to gain any significant foothold. Then almost by accident came the formalisation of a hitherto *ad hoc* meeting of the hierarchy of four lodges in the London area, which flagged up a winning formula. Indeed this too would not have worked then if its structure had not been modified, since it lacked a 'winning' hierarchal structure, but in every other respect was perfect. However, there was nothing that some judicious gerrymandering could not put right and the 'take-over' began, one may assume *c.*1718 to 1721.

The interesting question of 'who' will now be considered, but in the process of doing so one has to be accept that this set presents perhaps the most difficult to conceptualise in terms of the notional Venn diagrams 'sets' (*see* such an attempt in Appendix 3) that are necessary to describe the complete interrelationship of all these facets. Whilst it may be an oversimplification to apply the more modern cliché 'organisations are people', it does seem especially true of the circumstances surrounding the formation of the Premier Grand Lodge. In the process of discussing the original initiative that brought the four lodges together and their subsequent formal association, the comment was made that each principal player would have had his own agenda and that they were unlikely to have been the same. For three of the four there was to be the distinction of holding the office of Grand Master, a sufficient reward for most people one would imagine! Of the fourth there is little known, he certainly did not get to hold high office, but it is the thesis of this work that by the time it had reached his turn the plot had been hatched, any pretence to power he may have had or expected was now irrelevant and the whole ethos was changing and there was no place for a commoner in that high office, however deserving. Indeed, although mere conjecture, there is the possibility that his objections were so great that he would take no further part in the process, which could explain why George Payne (he did remain active within the group, albeit somewhat sidelined) occupied the Post for a second time at the last minute as a temporary expedient.

The case has already been made that there was public thirst for social initiatives of this kind over a wide spectrum of society. It is argued here that the third Grand Master, Dr John Theophilus Desaguliers, saw the basis of the Premier Grand Lodge

as a prime candidate for an organisation that had the potential to be placed among
the very top echelons of society, *see* Figure 38.1

**Figure 38.1. Portrait of John Theophilus Desaguliers. During his most active years.
Courtesy of San Marino Library California USA**

The Key to Modern Freemasonry

His basic biographical details are given in much the same way as others in Chapter Fifteen, but the salient characteristics are for convenience précised below.

1.   He was extremely well educated,
2.   He was an eminent scientist,
3.   He was an established freemason already, holding high office in his own lodge and that of the newly formed Premier Grand Lodge,
4.   He was a practising theologian,
5.   He was a committed Newtonian and was as close to Newton as anybody could get,
6.   He was an entrepreneur, well used to organising things,
7.   He was an acknowledged technologist and because of this had a close relationship with the very highest members of the aristocracy and indeed the Royal Household,
8.   He derived a sizeable portion of his income from scientific demonstrations and lectures,
9.   He was a Fellow of the Royal Society as were many of his close associates in Freemasonry,
10. He was a committed anti-papist,
11. He was a political animal as was evidenced by his involvement within Freemasonry in the election for Grand Master in 1724, but also in the wider world outside, as is evident in the controversy over various irrigation schemes, particularly the scandal surrounding the York Buildings affair.
12. Whilst he appeared to be completely orthodox, almost dilatory, in his parish duties there is little doubt that he believed in Newton's higher concepts and that there were indeed truths yet to be unveiled, but that they were only within the reach of the most worthy,
13. As was revealed in his communication to the Royal Society of the origins of the telescope, having previously believed it to be Galileo's (invention) eyes on the Universe (*see* Appendix 1) he did not have a closed mind.

Apart from Newton he had many influential acquaintances covering a whole spectrum of interests. For example there were the following: Phillip Wharton – the 'up and coming' (in modern parlance whiz-kid) who was the epitome of the aspirant of the times; the Montagu family, the Duke himself a man of great political and social influence; the Cowpers, another family of enormous political importance; Walpole an exceptional 'gifted' politician emerging unscathed out of the South Sea Bubble affair, or as one commentator remarked: 'as white as the driven snow'; to become effectively the first British Prime Minister; Dr Arbuthnot physician to the Royal Household and many more important roles besides, etc. were all known to Desaguliers at a very personal level. Virtually to a man these associates were 'wheeler-dealers' of a very high order and it is testament to his skills that somehow or other he managed to persuade them to take some part in this venture. However, the principal reason for singling out Desaguliers is that apart from his many talents he was the ideal 'inside man'. To have engineered the switch from a low-powered gathering of people with the modest objective of forming an affiliation between their respective lodges into a high-powered society attracting an array of the leading members of society and galvanising their interest was truly remarkable. His greatest asset was that the formula was effectively perfect, in that it contained something for everybody. It seems reasonable to conclude that: the famous would have enjoyed the status and adulation, without having to exert very much effort or even the need to attend. Those immediately below them would enjoy the power entrusted to them by the absence of their masters and the freedom to set policy. Those from the lodges invited to become an active part of the Premier Grand Lodge scene, would have enjoyed the opportunity of association and the homage due to their status when they returned to their own lodges. Ordinary lodge members would have either yearned and hence worked hard to become part of that scene by whatever device they could conceive, whilst the remaining members looking at the severity of the hill to climb and having abandoning any such attempt, would have remained respectfully ambivalent; indeed the whole set-up likely to have been very much like it is today.

Of course Desaguliers would have needed to create some organisational structure and almost certainly there would have been some formal governing (Masonic lodge type structure) committee and in that respect its eventual composition has proved to be most significant in that it gives an indication who the people were and when it took place. But the efficient way in which the 'take-over' was arranged suggests that it was more autocratic than democratic. Here it is perhaps appropriate to cite one of the many variants of the ancient proverb:

> For want of a nail the shoe was lost.
> For want of a shoe the horse was lost.
> For want of a horse the rider was lost.
> For want of a rider the battle was lost,
> For want of a battle the kingdom was lost.
> And all for the want of a horseshoe nail.

The outcome of the crucial meeting of 24 June 1723, convened for the election of the new Grand Master, has already been remarked upon but in reality despite all of Desaguliers' guile, his whole meticulously contrived strategy up until that point pivoted, as with the nail, upon that seemingly trivial, 'run-of-the-mill', occasion. In truth it is a study in itself and is addressed in very much greater detail in a paper by Lawrence[5] and to anyone interested in the various scenarios attached to that incident it is a very good place to start.

A further indicator is the nature of the ritual, for if one reads Desaguliers' poem, said to have been printed in 1728, it was actually deemed to have been written *c.*1715 or even much earlier, if some historians are right and it is presented in full in Appendix 1 (only letters have been changed to make it more easily assimilated by modern readers) and contains virtually every aspect of the ritual including portions or allusion to parts of the Old Testament selected by Newton for his own particular study and purposes. This in itself is an indication of when, namely the early 1720s, but a further and perhaps stronger indication of date may be gained from the fact that the close coalition formed when the take-over took place began to break up quite soon after, which was not surprising given the ambitions of those concerned. First and perhaps the most crucial result stemmed from Wharton's excesses and latent Jacobite sympathies but then other political and serious financial ramifications from 1723 onwards affected many of the others. For economic and technical reasons Desaguliers became entangled in affairs outside of Freemasonry which occupied increasing amounts of his time. We know that by 1725 he was badly afflicted by gout, which restricted him further. By 1730 much of the sparkle had gone out of the Freemasonry of those earlier euphoric years. Once again the full focus appears to be on those early years of the 1720s.

References

1. Curl, J., *The Art and Architecture of Freemasonry* (Batsford, London, 1991).
2. Prichard, S., *Masonry Dissected* (1730).
3. Jones, B., *Freemasons' Guide and Compendium* (George Harrap & Co, London, 1950), p. 189.
4. Schaffer, S., Private communication.
5. Lawrence, C.C., 'Hell-Fire or Applied Science: The Origins and Personalities of Two Men and their Impact on the Hierarchal Structure and Ethos of the Premier Grand Lodge and Its Present Day Legacy', *Transactions of The Leicester Lodge of Research No. 2429 (EC)*, (2010-11), pp. 31-64.

Chapter Thirty-nine:
General Discussion of Findings

The ultimate goal of many, if not all, Masonic historians has been to understand and hence determine the origins of the 'regularised' Freemasonry practiced today. Whether this study can be afforded such a distinctive epithet is left to the reader, but it too has ended in this way. This work did not start as a formal academic study, but from a very keen personal interest in the history of Freemasonry coupled with a lifetime spent in science and engineering, much in fundamental research, which no doubt is reflected in the manner and style of this presentation. At first glance the contrast could not be more striking, the latter supposedly based upon irrefutable proof, verified by experimentation, the former scratching around in nooks and crannies, with scarcely a verifiable fact in sight, but in practice only a tiny fraction of the findings made in science and engineering are irrefutable, most are subsequently found to be inaccurate or flawed in some way. When, as in this case, the data is coloured by human behaviour it becomes even more tenuous and so that offered here is considered to be the best effort to date; which because it is heavily reliant on the pioneering work, dedication and scholarship of others is arguably nearer the truth of the situation than that which has preceded it.

It is perhaps advisable to reflect once again on the nature of the various sources; for whilst it is true that there are effectively no irrefutable facts on which to establish a proposition it does not mean that there is no data, for there is an absolute plethora of information to choose from. Unfortunately on closer examination a large proportion of it is unreliable and one is tempted to assert that for the most part it is fiction dressed up as fact, usually because it is written by those who either passionately love or hate their concept of what constitutes Freemasonry, or perhaps even worse wish to exploit, for whatever reason, the unique aura and associated mystification that is historically attached to it. The following examples are meant to illustrate the principal categories of such work.

Knight and Lomas's widely published book *The Hiram Key*[1] is typical of those publications set out for general consumption. It presents their view on the origins of, and associated practices within, Freemasonry. However despite its commercial success it was considered by many within the 'academic' community as being shallow and lacking rigour. No extension to that debate will entered upon here, other than to say that it is very representative of that type of popularised Masonic writing, implying 'revelation' rather than profound analysis.

Then there is the contribution of those who again for whatever reason rile against Freemasonry. Of course the most outstanding example of which was that of Prichard's exposé.[2] Again numerous studies have resulted from his publication by historians attempting to gainsay his motivations. It was clearly very popular at the time and no doubt he profited by its commercial success, but it was likely not his sole motivation. Irrespective of the validity of his work, because of the absolute dearth of alternative contemporary data he is widely quoted at all levels of research and in view of that one has to assume that it is at least regarded by those workers as comparatively accurate.

Another source of data relating to Freemasonry is the desire among the great majority of its members to claim associated antiquity and this occasions an inner need to latch upon any source of data that gives credence to such claims. A classic example of this characteristic is found in works that relate to the extended Masonic order of the Knights Templar, where it would appear that every opportunity is taken by those so motivated to substantiate that claim; a classic example of which are the claims related to its interrelationship with Rosslyn Chapel in Scotland. Numerous, books, papers, articles, etc – including it would seem those responsible for the day to day running of the Chapel. have been written either claiming or implying an intimate connection between the Chapel (both the Chapel itself and the complex history that surrounds it) and Freemasonry. Perhaps it is the romanticism or mysticism of the Knights Templar that singles them out for particular attention; but it can attract great gravitas, many with solemn weight and conviction – indeed Knight and Lomas contribute to this number, also including Craft Masonry and much else besides.[3] However, this can attract the same response when used in fiction, where, despite the authors insistence that it is fictional, there are many who accept as indication their (Knights Templar, freemasons etc.) undoubted involvement and hence association.[4]

Any work such as that above which is undertaken with the intention of reinforcing an already entrenched or disposition towards a view is prone to distortion which in consequence engenders a response from those who would wish to put the matter straight and thus present a counter claim. In this instance this form of response is beautifully illustrated in Cooper's book *The Rosslyn Hoax?*,[5] where in a very scholarly and clinical fashion he sets out to show that there are serious doubts in all such claims. This is an exceedingly well written, well researched, book; indeed in his opening Chapter he points out many if the pitfalls of injudicious research or analysis and admonishes reader not to 'tilt at windmills'.

This consideration of Cooper's work appears to centre upon what may be described as an aside with respect to this study; however it illustrates perfectly the ever present problem confronting anyone attempting to distinguish reality from myth. As already pointed out there is a prodigious amount of data with respect to the physical aspects of the Chapel, Castle and their surroundings; their incumbents and the chequered accounts of their history. One merely has to consider Cooper's Bibliography to gets some understanding of how big that source of material is. Typical of such data, although not included in his book, although published two years earlier, is the book written by Oxbrow and Robertson[6] on effectively the same theme, but it would seem without their having any direct Masonic involvement. Again they are highly respected historians who like Cooper have clearly been researching this area for many years and from the tenor of their work one gains the distinct impression that it was also the outrageous nature of the claims being made by those who they refer to as 'pseudo historians' that was the main instigator of their clearly quite independent publications.

All three authors are clearly very indignant with the claims made in what they see as being: ill-researched, 'climbing on the band wagon', self-proclaimed historical accounts. Throughout Oxbrow and Robertson's book they disparagingly refer to these 'pseudo historians' and take them to task at every turn. In this instant there is effectively total agreement between the three authors and in the process come out with a number of 'facts' (*caveat emptor*?) that relate directly to this study such as the following. They produce evidence to show that (our) William Stukeley was directly involved at one time; clearly it was not only Desaguiers who visited Scotland! They make numerous references to the Knights Templar and the claimed Masonic association, but also other factors related to Craft Masonry, with specific mention of the Hiramic Legend. However, they make interesting social comment when discussing Sir William Clair's appointment as the First Grand Master of Scottish Freemasonry, wherein they stress his passion for learning and the creation of his quite remarkable Library. Indeed to emphasise the point they cite a report: that on being told that his castle suffered a fire, Sir William Clair's first concern was not that of his family, but the safety of his revered volumes. The work of all three authors cited above has great weight and it would be extremely difficult to counter the way in which they moot the various claims, but as may well be the case here, one is nonetheless a little troubled, by the sense of a crusade in such work.

Another source is where information appears to have the 'hall-mark' of authority, such as government papers or as cited in Beresiner's paper[7] a contemporary (presumably respectable) newspaper. His publication is based upon the circumstances surrounding an exposé that he found during his research into this general area in a quasi-newspaper: *The Post Boy* published in 1723 (the very period of interest here). Since it appears to have a direct bearing on the subject area of this work it carried the insistence that it must be given due consideration here. In practice it proved to be quite convoluted since its argument is centred on a reported report, which in turn had been discovered by one of the Paper's own (presumably 'in-house') journalists. It has all the appearances of authenticity, but it also has the familiar aura of opportunistic journalism, or that found in government and official missives published with the intent of encouraging compliance with some directive, or to boost confidence in some scheme, or as in this case; where a newspapers requires a good story and so whilst Beresiner's paper is of considerable interest, because of this caveat the matter remains within the category of 'quite circumspect'.

Then as with much that is contained in this work, there is the data obtained through inference. Freemasonry can only exist as part of some social structure and populated by members of that community. Each of these mutually interact and since historically these folk were for the most part of some appreciable importance within this social framework, much of their activity is reported in one way or another – as is suggested in Beresiner's paper above. Whilst these reports may ostensibly have no direct reference to Masonic activity they are nonetheless powerful indicators of motivation and social intercourse. A classic example is way in which the architectural ambitions of the wealthiest in the social fabric that evolved after the dissolution of the monasteries brought about a fundamental change in building practice, of which the humble brick proved to be a significant factor in the demise of traditional stonemasonry.[8]

It would be reasonable to presume that the most valuable source of data would be that which may be derived from established seats of learning, libraries, museums and centres of research. There are now a number of universities that formally acknowledge Masonic studies, a major part of the output of which are the dissertations leading to higher degrees. There are many Masonic research centres of high repute within the body of each Masonic constitutions throughout the world and a number of lodges who sole objective is that of furthering research, Both because of its antiquity (founded 1884) and its retained status within the Masonic community the *Quatuor Coronati* Lodge situated in London, is considered by many to be pre-eminent in this field of study. Whilst it has a very restricted full membership it has very many corresponding members/delegates throughout the world, with each country having a chosen representative. All these are backed in some way by their specific publications, lectures, libraries etc. and usually have some mechanism in place to entertain enquiry. Indeed this leads to another, increasingly important source of data the Internet. Again the data so derived (as with all else in this particular medium) must be treated with great circumspection, but once that process has been followed there is much to be found; indeed the whole of *Ars Quatuor Coronatorum* (published proceedings of the *Quatuor Coronati* Lodge) along which much else is now available.[9]

There are of course other avenues that may be consulted, but the above indicates the very wide range of data available, but all carry the caveat of great caution, since it seems that at every turn there are those who wish to find facts to fit their particular case, under which circumstances objectivity falls victim to desires or contrivance. It is for this reason much of the argument presented here is from work derived from sources outside of those directly related Masonic research. For instance one trace of Figure 39.1 is meant to reflect the (or at least those in receipt of education) public's perception of religious certainty and the remaining traces to indicate the level of informed understanding of various aspects of science at any one time during that period. Of course it too cannot be a rigorous description and is likely wrong in detail, but it holds sufficient truth to be of assistance.[10] It indicates the rapid awareness of matters scientific and the realisation of man's shrinking significance with respect to the revelations of our ever expanding Universe and the need to make the necessary (religious) accommodation resulting from it. Vague concepts were being explained in terms of physical demonstration, especially during the 1720s. A further factor was that whilst the institutions of Church and State on mainland Europe had been more successful in stifling radical thought; from 1700 onwards they too had been obliged to loosen their grip. Thus by the 1720s there was an established interchange between Britain and the Continent of philosophical, religious and scientific precepts, making it increasingly more difficult for those with such blinkered self interest to maintain their seemingly spurious arguments.

Before proceeding further with this discussion it is perhaps helpful to explain the purpose of Figure 39.1. It encapsulates the way in which at the beginning of the seventeenth century the sciences were seen to be poles apart from mainstream thinking and the stance taken by the upper echelons of the established church and hence that purveyed to the population in general. Because of the way the World was evolving the progress of science was bound in the end to impose its presence and the graph shows how scientific discovery and its associated community eventually inverted the relationship between the Church and science and hence the perceptions of the population in general. All the sciences were making progress, but some like astronomy had mind-changing significance and Figure 39.1 shows that this inversion occurred *c.*1720. In order to establish some credibility for such an interpretation this was discussed with a number of informed people, but more especially Simon Schaffer.[11]

Thus it would seem that much of that outlined above could have been used to supplement the case made for the intensity of the sets of the Venn diagram discussed earlier. Further, if the arguments made in Chapter Thirty-eight are valid then each of these elements would appear to have had an enhanced period of activity in the early 1720s and if these were then overlaid the resultant diagram would show a pronounced peak. But whereas it is possible to search the literature for say the status of Geometry or Chemistry in schools and universities etc. and construct a quasi-graphical representation, in the case of the sets seen in the Venn diagrams used in this work, we were concerned with the mind-set and/or social ambition of the particular individuals who were influential with respect to the form of Freemasonry adopted by the Premier Grand Lodge and which in some important aspects appeared to be out of step with the perceptions of the general public. Subject to that constraint it is necessary to stand back and look at the content of the perceived ritual and ask the question: *under which management structure (personalities in reality) would it have*

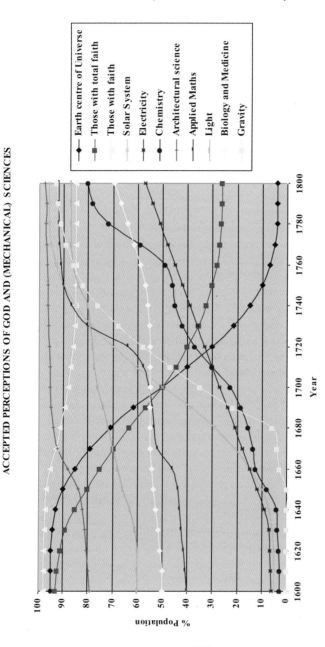

ACCEPTED PERCEPTIONS OF GOD AND (MECHANICAL) SCIENCES

Figure 39.1   The vertical axis denotes the average educated individual's perception of matters scientific and also the level his unquestioning faith in the Church's doctrinal understanding of their God

most likely evolved?

An important constraint, yet at the same time indicator, is that current Rituals are laced with reference to matters scientific and the need for learning. Desaguliers' allegorical model of government and moral ethic is based on Newtonian science (*see* Appendix 1). The greater majority of those about him shared this same messianic reverence for Newton and Newtonianism and those who did not would most likely have considered themselves insufficiently qualified to argue against it, or press for an alternative. It is therefore reasonable to assume that this new Ritual was within the spirit of the moment and would have therefore met with approval rather than criticism. This scenario is perhaps less contentious than at first imagined since it is already implied in Masonic literature: indeed no less an authority than Jones challenges whether it would be possible to enforce a completely new degree on the joining partners[12] and in consequence the degree to which the new avant-garde concepts must be addressed.

However on reflection Jones' very words hold the key, for he makes the point that these people were not 'forced', but joined of their own volition. Indeed the converse would more likely apply, since to adopt in its entirety one particular version of an existing ritual would likely offend those who were currently practicing others and so it is reasonable to suppose that it makes more sense to arrange a ceremony that retained the salient elements of the established versions, but at the same time includes the latest fetishes, thereby appearing to be starting afresh with new purpose and thereby avert or at least minimise any hostility. Jones' justification for discussing the problem was his search to understand the precise nature of the rituals being worked prior to the formation of the Premier Grand Lodge and in particular the status of the Hiramic legend. He had found (or at least chose to find) evidence of it in these earlier rituals, but had been unable to gain any real understanding of the Legend's importance. After all Prichard's exposé had provided sufficient proof of its presence, but on balance he felt that the full force of the legend did not come into effect until much later in the 1700s. It would seem that when these powerful (operative) lodges of yesteryear had allowed certain influential people to meet with them as 'house members' they adopted certain protocols (quasi-, somewhat pontifical, rituals) to, as it were, legitimise the presence of these outsiders. As circumstances changed so did the emphasis and relative roles and from what may be gleaned it would seem that by the end of the 1600s (in England at least) there were virtually no matters of operative masonry left to be discussed at these meetings and that these *ad hoc* procedures had by this time replaced completely any operational procedures of a working lodge.

If operative masons were in attendance it was merely by dint of their status within the community and the mechanics of construction and the paraphernalia associated with operative masonry simply symbolic, why then was it necessary to agonise over what appears to be the highly dubious history of Hiram Abif and why was the Hiramic legend retained or introduced into this new version of the ritual? Various writers have attempted to account for the legend's dominance in present day ritual and as we have seen from earlier discussion some quite extreme, but if the hypothesis here is correct, a much more straightforward explanation appears. If the inclusion of the legend of the vault in the then newly formed Royal Arch is taken as an indicator, it is reasonable to suppose that those responsible for deciding upon ritualistic matters enjoyed the concept of embroidering a yarn within it, in order to add a human dimension. But we learn from Desaguliers' Poem (*see* Appendix 1) and in reading serious research on matters outside of the adopted formalised Freemasonry during the period that allegory was used as a potent means of emphasis in many other forms of communications. In the opening Chapter of Gouk's detailed and well researched (44 individual references) book *Music, Science and Natural Magic*, etc.[13] she sets out to define the 'Categories, boundaries and margins' of these terms in the context of that period. In her discussion she emphasises the heavy reliance they placed upon allegory when communicating meaning, and makes special reference to this same ploy when considering the methods of Newton later in the same book. Gouk was principally concerned with the music in the widest sense of the word, but it is typical of similar specialist studies by historians of that period, who point out the blurred boundaries of science, alchemy, magic, religion, astronomy etc. and we can see from Appendix 1, it most certainly describe the style used by our leading player Desaguliers.

Although less than complete we know from the records[14] who many of these strategic players were. We know from outside sources that all but Wharton (who with others of his contemporary socialite self-styled 'intellectuals', such as Pope, were petulantly sceptical) were deeply interested in science, albeit for a variety of reasons. We know that many of the non-aristocratic members gained a large portion of their income through lecture and/or technology. We know from their writings that they were disposed to use demonstrations within their lectures based more on theatrical magic rather than real understanding. We know that they were devotees if not disciples of Newton and his basic philosophy, if when studied in the 'cold light' of retrospection it can be so described. We know that they were men in a hurry because of the indecent haste with which their chosen aristocrats figureheads were rocketed into power (Wharton socially the man of the moment went from his Initiation to become Grand Master in less than a year). We know from their activities in such organisations as the Royal Society, share dealings, sycophantic behaviour in the Royal Court etc., dubious commercial and technological schemes, that they were political animals. We know from facts such as Cowper's appointment as Clerk of the House of Lords and extraordinary interrelationships between the members of the aristocracy centred on the Premier Grand Lodge that they were likely prone to nepotism. In fact it would appear they were in modern parlance 'a few shades less than perfect'. Further it would seem that when the scientific contingent began to lose sway around 1726, although the general ethos was ostensibly the same, with the change of personalities and centres of interest were to lead to a subtle change of philosophy and a *modus operandi* which was to prove debilitating.

The problem with all the subsequent groupings that followed the original junta was that they lacked the cohesion, capability and purpose of those who had conceived it, but it is argued here that in addition they lost the most important ingredient (passionate) leadership. The intriguing question is how could such a disreputable group procreate a brotherhood that is founded on the strictest principle of moral (humanitarian) behaviour? The simple answer it would seem is that the beauty of the concept was bigger than the narrowness and shortcomings of those who instigated it and this is just as true of those few individuals within its ranks today who are seen to transgress and in consequence besmirch its name.

References

1. Knight, C. and Lomas, R., *The Hiram Key* (Barnes & Noble, New York, 1996).
2. Prichard, S., *Masonry Dissected* (1730).
3. Knight, C. and Lomas, R,. *op. cit.*
4. Brown, D., *The Da Vinci Code* (Bantam Press, 2003).
5. Cooper, R.L.D., *The Rosslyn Hoax* (Lewis Masonic, London, 2007).
6. Oxbrow, M. and Robertson, I., *Rosslyn and the Grail* (Mainstream Publishing, Edinburgh & London, 2005).
7. Beresiner, Y., 'The Sham Exposure in the *Post Boy*, December 1723', *AQC* 111 (1990).
8. Lawrence, C.C., 'A Brick-by-Brick Account of the Metamorphosis of Operative to Speculative Masonry', *AQC* 122 (2009), pp. 121-184.
9. Peabody, D.J. and Currie, P.H., *AQC Transactions* Vols 1-119 (CD ROM, QCCC Ltd., London, 2007).
10. Schaffer, S., Private communication.
11. *Ibid.*
12. Jones, B., *Freemasons' Guide and Compendium* (George Harrap & Co, London, 1950), p. 305.
13. Gouk, P., *Music, Science and Natural Magic in Seventeenth-century England* (Yale University Press, New Haven & London, 1999).
14. Anon. 'The Minutes of the Grand Lodge of Freemasons of England, 1723-1739', *QCA* X (1913).

Chapter Forty:
In the Final Analysis
Discussion

Whilst this study began as an attempt to understand the science of Freemasonry the outcome has been to provide strong additional evidence to show those who, having first usurped a modestly ambitious initiative, which first came to light in 1717, fashioned it to their own ends; part of which was to settle upon the rituals that were to be adopted in this now reorganised (Premier) Grand Lodge. That they were possessed of an almost messianic desire to inculcate within this now formalised version of Freemasonry the need for diligent learning and especially that related to Nature and science. Its inherent significance being that knowledge was the most essential ingredient if its members were going to achieve their full potential and ultimate salvation. This constant admonition made throughout Masonic ritual is well illustrated by taking two typical, albeit quite small, snippets of dialogue from within the allegory of Masonic ritual: '... demanded (that the miscreant be given) the secrets of a Master Mason ...' to which the final part of the response was that: '... he neither could nor would divulge them, but intimated that he had no doubt patience and industry would ultimately entitle a worthy Mason to a participation of them, [...]'. It has also been argued throughout that they had no doubt and left their lay members in no doubt, that these powerful yet elusive secrets were intimately bound up with and somehow dependent upon the 'Hidden mysteries of Nature and Science', hence the subtitle of this work. However the questions remain: was this seemingly imperative component of Freemasonry worthy of investigating to the depth herein and how successful has the outcome been?

Although direct comparison between the various religious faiths and Freemasonry must be strenuously avoided, in a number of respects they are remarkably similar and one is that they mostly stem from the happenings of a particular event in history. In the case of most major faiths it is the events and inherent philosophy surrounding the emergence of a prophet or saviour or a significant event at an opportune moment in history, which is then galvanised into an established belief, from which stems some marked system of faith and form of worship. In the course of time certain off-shoots may occur such as the 'Born Again' or 'Latter-day Saints' schism, ostensibly related to the Christian faith, but even then the core belief remains that of the original occurrence. Freemasonry has had its share of those who for whatever reason would wish to be 'Latter-day' or 'Born Again' freemasons, but the evidence here suggests that the vast majority of freemasons are wedded and contracted to that which was originally inculcated in the Premier Grand Lodge in

In the Final Analysis

the early 1720s. It was for this reason considered to be of particular importance and that an attempt should be made to gain an insight into the thinking of those who founded the Premier Grand Lodge in order that we may begin to understand the nature of its structure and intent. From the words contained in the ritual there can be little doubt that the Founders felt that in order to understand the purpose of life, the ultimate destiny of man and the ethos of Freemasonry there was a need to strive continually to comprehend the mysteries of Nature and Science. However, if a present day freemason is to understand the nature of that to which he subscribes then there is merit in trying to understand the basis upon which the Founders adopted their (likely) version of the ritual and Constitutions drawn up in the early 1720s and just as with a religious faith, why in the final analysis modern day freemasons in the end revert to these original teachings and innate precepts. In consequence much significance has been attached in this study to the assumed antiquity and faithful transmission of that early ritual's basic precepts. However is this assumption credible given the fetishes of the high-flyers, who over the intervening years, have been determined to leave their mark and have had sufficient authority to ensure such change? No doubt certain aspects of the rituals have suffered modifications, but fortunately this impudence usually turns out to be quite innocuous and more importantly appears to have missed altogether the two main areas of interest here, namely: 1) where there are profound and distinct injunctions on moral behavior, good practice, loyalty etc., which presumably nobody would wish to dispute and hence modify. 2) either because of indifference towards or the subject lay outside their field of interest/competence: science and technology.

However before attempting to establish a consensus view it is perhaps appropriate to define the basis upon which these conclusions are drawn. Firstly to consider whether the 'hidden mysteries of Nature and science' that are cited as the basis of this work have in fact been found? Or reflect whether it is indeed possible to find something that is both hidden and a mystery and even if then believed to be found, to know whether those findings are indeed the originals or have real substance. Thus there are several factors relating to those who founded the Premier Grand Lodge that need to be addressed before attempting to answer these rhetorical issues. One approach may be to consider the relevance of the first few words of an extract from the Bible usually quoted by the Prelate in part of the Rose Quoix ceremony: 'For faith is the substance of things hoped for, the evidence of things not seen ... , but whether there be prophesies, they shall fail; whether there be tongues, they shall cease; whether there be knowledge it shall vanish away: for we know in part, and we prophesy in part; but when that which is perfect is come then that which is in part shall be done away'. This because so much is centred around their (and the then society in general, but especially the Founders) intrinsic faith in a God, but who

429

were at the same time troubled by the scientific discoveries impinging upon them and the various (ever increasing and openly expressed tendency towards) agnostic philosophies associated with it. For their part they were:

1/ committed believers in the Christian, but inwardly not the Trinitarian Faith,

2/ attempting to reconcile the somehow contentious revelations of science, but at the same time were convinced that it held the key to the understanding of all things,

3/ dedicated Newtonians and believed that Newton would in due time reveal all to the most worthy, which to a large degree was contingent on their scholarship, especially with respect to science,

4/ largely content with the existing ritual since it had all the right ingredients, but realised that it would fail if they did not now inculcate within it the importance of learning, especially with respect to the contemporary explosion in scientific discovery and hence a new reality.

Of course we are now inured to the belief that any such mysteries when sufficiently explored invariably proved to have a straightforward physical explanation. That Newton was totally deluded in his belief that he was a Magus and whilst he may have been most persuasive in purveying that belief, in reality he never had, nor could have had any magical power or inner knowledge (revelation) of God's grand design. That their understanding of the universe, by then already greatly enlarged by recent revelations, was nonetheless one whose outer (heavenly) bounds were still somehow finite and hence physically accessible, whereas faith in our time has, in some convoluted way, to be reconciled with an infinity of Space that is totally beyond man's comprehension.

However, such a pessimistic view does not mean that their contemporary (eighteenth century) deluded view of the 'hidden mysteries of Nature and science' was to them anything other than totally consistent and as such holds the key to the riddles surrounding the founding of the Premier Grand Lodge. This because an important part of their stratagem required them to 'declared their hand' with respect to the nature and importance of science and by so doing fixed the exact time and much else besides.

Some three hundred years later because of our greater awareness we are, in terms of our self satisfaction, arguably further away from finding a plausible explanation of our existence, or the true physical nature of such forces as gravity and magnetism, or our place in an apparent infinity, but rather are left with a number of esoteric and strikingly varied hypotheses, most changing with each new revelation. Although current understanding suggests that the cells of our bodies are constantly changing and as a consequence there is no part of our frame that is original, we

In the Final Analysis

nonetheless remain essentially the same human beings and possessed of that equally mysterious entity (a soul) which makes us what we are. This lapse into introspection is made only to explain why they (or indeed we, now) were never likely to be able to achieve the ritual's promised objective however patient or industrious they or we may have been. But at least their prospects of attainment were not burdened with the fund of (confounding) knowledge we have today and so with Newton's promise of fundamental revelation, the description of the known Universe and the Shangri-La at its bounds was still within human comprehension, and as such it was not unreasonable for them to suggest to a candidate that with proper diligence all in due time (within their lifetime, that is) would be revealed. Thus the best that could be done here was to at least reflect on the knowledge that they were likely to have possessed, the preceding history leading up to the formation of the Premier Grand Lodge and the environment within which they operated.

Conclusions

Given the above limitations it is extremely difficult to reach a succinct conclusion on a study that has lasted so long, whilst at the same time being constantly reminded each day via one source or another of some subtle aspect that appears to merit further consideration before the discussion on any one matter should be closed; not counting the enormous amount of material which because of space has already been marginalised or excluded altogether. However, there comes a point where private speculation needs to be tested more widely, lest otherwise introversion yields its own set of proofs. Just as in the basic study itself these Conclusions are presented in several parts. The first factors discussed were within the context of our current understanding of the contemporary science and the technology of those times. Contingent on those findings the remaining parts reflected on the role that science played in the formation of splinter groups that hijacked the Premier Grand Lodge in the early 1720s and formed that, which for the purposes of this Study, became the Premier Grand Lodge we speak of today. Acknowledging that most freemasons still attribute the epithet to the original initiative launched in 1717 and which first assumed that grandiose title and brought about the original affiliation of local lodges, but little else.

The science and technology element was itself found to be separated into two parts: the specific elements of science incorporated in the Symbolical Lecture and the remaining science inferred in the body of Masonic ritual by their repeated allusion to the *quadrivium* (geometry, arithmetic, astronomy and music) and more generally 'Nature and science'. Because the science of the Symbolical Lecture was, on the surface at least, quite unambiguous and its basic precepts fixed in time, it was possible to contemplate the real goal of determining the level of understanding that the Founders would have expected of its average member; presumably that which, but to some lesser degree, replicated their own. In the process of attempting to do this it was possible to put that contemporary understanding in context with the science that modern day freemasons would likely receive in the normal course of their basic studies and revelations from other sources, such as the Media.

Having otherwise presented some of the scientific matter discussed here in the form of talks it seemed that today there is a general misconception of the science of that time, but which when properly understood immediately demonstrates the extraordinarily sophisticated level of some aspects of their thinking and the naivety of others. These were presented in Part I as a series of individual topics and in a formal manner, with the only concession being to place some of their concepts in relation to modern understanding. Conclusions were drawn within each and they will not be repeated here.

Fortunately this list of topics and the conclusions deriving from them when put in context with the people concerned and given that the advances made in science by that time are comparatively well documented, it was possible to be much more certain of these facts than most of the other historical data relating to the period. However at first sight much of this appeared to be a paradox, since given their known ability, it left unanswered the question why did they choose to incorporate this outmoded understanding of science in the Symbolical Lecture? When the further factor of why certain topics had been omitted was put into the equation this obvious anomaly became even more pronounced. Out of interest alone it would be most unsatisfactory if the various conclusions of Part I were left without addressing this conundrum. Conversely, if the ambiguity between their professed understanding of science as opposed to their declared position could be resolved there was a far more exciting prospect; since that appeared to hold the key to a much greater understanding of the regularisation of Freemasonry in the guise of a central body, now known as the United Grand Lodge of England and in like manner all other 'regular' grand lodges. Its real significance is that it was the first centrally regularised organisation of Freemasonry and proved to be the prototype of all subsequent organisations of this form and is commonly known today as the Premier Grand Lodge. Thus the principles of science in Part I were considered in a formalised manner and the discussion was extended to include a brief résumé of those topics that had been omitted, but some of the nuances of these scientific matters were extended in Part VI.

The research necessary in Part I had been quite extensive, but at least each subject had been addressed by the various historians in its own right, the task being to seek a logical consensus from the various sources and from this present the most likely scenario and at the same time put those findings in context with the Symbolical

Lecture. The objective of remaining Parts was to try and understand the reasons why these extremely intelligent and scholarly men chose to adopt such an archaic interpretation of the science. The early Chapters of Part II were used to provide the framework for piecing together all the various facets that related to that objective. It was presented in this form so that the arguments upon which the final assertions were to be made had sufficient foundation. This work showed that whilst the Premier Grand Lodge was a product of its time, it was only possible because the history that preceded it had made it so. It was the result of the social climate and the ambitions of a range of individuals, all with different agendas, some subtle others blatant, but each looking for a vehicle to further their ambition; which in great measure was to bring about the formalisation of the fledgling Grand Lodge to satisfy their own ends; which in this particular case and almost by accident, happened to have the ingredients that would allowed it to blossom into the great institution it is today.

The metamorphosis of operative masons' lodges into speculative Masonic lodges was the basic blueprint for its organisational structure. The aristocratic power-base was to a very large extent founded on the interrelationships centred upon the social circle that surrounded the illegitimate offspring of Charles II. The intellectual support came from within a group of scientists and/or technologist and/ or ecclesiastics, almost all of whom were affiliated with the Royal Society, but of equal importance was their subtle dependence upon and associations within this narrow branch of the nobility. Virtually to a man they had received much of their tertiary education at the established universities of Oxford, Cambridge or Edinburgh and thus had received a classical, scholastic grounding, but were by then committed Newtonians which represented another important strand of the relationship. This event took place at a time when there was basic stability within society and a considerable level of affluence within the sector that would seek to be associated with Freemasonry. This general affluence had led to a surge in social diversions in the form of clubs, coffee-houses etc. and with subtle modification this formalised form of Freemasonry could be made to satisfy this need and sit perfectly well within the upper echelons of society, as well as having great appeal to those who were desirous of mixing with them.

Thus it is claimed here that all the conditions were right for the concept of a centralised body of Freemasonry to be formed and fill the vacuum that existed previously. That after the first few euphoric years, political machinations, age, ill health, monetary problems etc. had broken the initial harmony and there was no longer the driving force necessary to sustain the momentum, or provide the inspiration for innovation of the type necessary to introduce any further fundamental changes in the ritual, or instigate a new Masonic concept such as the Royal Arch.

Indeed, it is claimed here that whilst the Premier Grand Lodge may have been the result of a collective effort, it is much more likely that the original concept, the deft social engineering and basic format, including the ceremonial was essentially the inspiration of just one man: Dr John Theophilus Desaguliers. This claim, as implied earlier, is based on the premise that without just cause the sets of the Venn diagram could not have shown such a striking coincidence. The exceptional characteristics of this man are reiterated below:

a) He was a man of great intellect,
b) He had excellent organisational skill,
c) He was well versed and held high office in the disparate Freemasonry that existed in London at that time,
d) He enjoyed a mutual respect and inter-dependence with the influential group of aristocracy who were to play such an important role in the new concept of the Premier Grand Lodge and actively promoted rather than threatened their chances of success
e) He was a very influential figure in the Royal Society,
f) He was a competent scientist/technologist, a popular lecturer and demonstrator,
g) He was a practising theologian,
h) Above all he was a confidant of Newton and was a convinced Newtonian,
i) It is possible to correlate huge chunks of his poem with the basic forms, sentiment, wording and especially science of ritual practised today and because the science was specific to that exact period, but nonetheless has survived the years, it is reasonable to suppose that essential philosophy of the ritual has be maintained likewise.
j) Because of his privileged position as a disciple of Newton, he would have been reluctant to expose the true nature of his scientific knowledge to the ears of the profane, although it is known he had a tendency to digress in this respect in his lectures, but would have retained the socially prudent scholastic *trivium* (grammar, rhetoric and logic) for the initial elements of the ritual, with the prospect of greater revelation for those who progressed through diligence.
k) As a devotee of Newton and thereby likely privy to his (innermost thoughts) claim that he had at last regained the profound secrets of Nature etc. handed down by God to Moses, but which had been subsequently lost by the brute force of paganism. It is possible that the story of similar losses found within the Hiram Legend were an allegorical representation of that belief.

Thus it is argued that the Masonic structure that governs Freemasonry in England, Wales and its Provinces overseas, results not from the widely accepted Premier Grand Lodge of 1717, but its derivative formed a few years later, *circa* 1720. That this new

In the Final Analysis

regime introduced an essentially new ritual and shortly afterwards added a supplement called the Royal Arch. Whilst the basic ritual promulgated the moralistic principles inherent in the Freemasonry practised in its constituent lodges prior to that date, those involved in forming the new consortium were driven by a whole gamut of reasons unrelated in that regard. That this took place in the years 1720 to 1724 after which this hyperactive consortium went into steep decline, for in reality the great initial surge had by that time peaked already and whilst it lasted for a few glory years it was soon to decline. No further argument will be attempted here since the only real conclusion can be gained from analysis within the full text and since there are few actual facts upon which to work and the remainder can only be gained from the pronounced coincidence of the sets of the quasi-Venn diagram and the remainder by inference.

Whether the case has been made must now be left to the reader. There still remain many avenues unexplored, such as other likely candidates; further involvement of the principal players outside of Freemasonry; other ways of establishing whether certain people were freemasons etc. It may be that sufficient interest will be aroused by this study to invite comment or criticism from which further progress may be made. This rather stark assessment made here of early Freemasonry will no doubt offend many devotees, but that was not the intention, it is simply a summary of the evidence resulting from this investigation and to any who are indeed offended, it is recommended that they read again the FRONTISPIECE which was written in anticipation of this unwelcome assessment of the Founders of the early the Premier Grand Lodge.

Reflections

On the presumption that this work will be read by a sufficient number of freemasons and perhaps others, including the surprisingly large contingent of very talented women scholars (not counting those actually practising their form of Freemasonry), who are interested in the topic, there is likely to be a range of opinion as to the merit or otherwise of these findings. Of course no adverse criticism of one's work is particularly enjoyed, but provided it is objective and constructive it is essential that it be addressed. It is certainly true that the 'exception that proves the rule' has been looked for throughout this study and the prospect of quantifying certain elements such as the demographics, conducting more thorough genealogy and greater refinement of and adding more elements to the respective 'sets' would certainly strengthen or prove otherwise the legitimacy of the claims made here. However, if in the final analysis all that this book achieves is to stimulate discussion, interest and hopefully further research, where there has otherwise been just passive acceptance then it will have been worthwhile, but equally important it will have justified to some small extent the considerable trouble caused to and patience shown by, all those other than myself who have been involved in bringing this work to publishable form.

There are a considerable number who whilst pursuing their various interests have had cause to study a wide range of topics related to Freemasonry and in turn have expounded on (some very obscure and esoteric) aspects that may, or may not, be related to its origins and subsequent development, who will almost certainly take issue with much that is written here. Again that is not a bad thing since it is hoped that the book will promote further discussion and research, however in order to, at least, deflect some such comments it is fully accepted that there existed already a great deal of symbolism and quasi-philosophy within the Freemasonry that preceded the Premier Grand Lodge and upon which subtle meaning had been placed. But in the case of the Founders, because of the pressures of their public and private avocations and the urgency of getting an acceptable ritual in place, it is reasonable to assume that other than the need to encompass the new imperatives of learning and science, with which they were totally *au fait*, there was little opportunity to introduce profound changes to the fundamental precept and practices of Freemasonry. It is also reasonable to conclude from their overarching insistence on a belief in a supreme power, required of freemasons, that it should be founded upon true understanding arrived at through learning and not as a result of unquestioned, essentially blind, faith. In short the ritual was already perfectly suited for purpose; they merely needed to supplement it a little, formalise and regularise it.

If indeed the usurped Premier Grand Lodge of the early 1720s did come from these very powerful, single minded, sometimes ruthless (some extremely talented), political, materially acquisitive and otherwise dubious individuals and one then contrasts that with the whole utterly laudable ethos and basic structure of the 'accepted' Regularised Freemasonry practiced today in whatever country, then it would be difficult to deny the claim that:

' ... Out of the strong came forth sweetness ... '.

Appendix One

Desaguliers' Poem

Note: The allegorical poem set out below is in effect a direct reproduction of that which was published by Dr John Desaguliers shortly after the accession to the throne by George II, (differing only in minor detail, namely 's' for the old style of 'f' and some minor tidying of the printing technique for ease of reading). It is not at all certain when he actually wrote it, but when he elected to publish it in book form it was clearly intended for the then King and Queen, but he was not one to miss the opportunity of including a sycophantic dedication to his sponsor and incorporate a 'commercial' and these are shown in Figure 35.1 in the main text. Originally it was intended to simply reproduce the poem, but on reflection it was realised that 'notes of explanation' also gave a very strong indication of the man. For not only did his supplementary text indicate his scientific, philosophical, moral and religious disposition, but that much else could be inferred from his peculiar phraseology and so there was considerable advantage in producing the document in its entirety. Another reason was that there appeared to be no modern publication of the poem and thus unless one was prepared to go to a 'rare book' archive, it was not readily available, but yet it is of such great importance to this Study.

The Newtonian System of the World

the best

MODEL of Government

an Allegorical POEM.

In Ancient Times, ere Bribery began
To taint the Heart of undersigning Man,
Ere Justice yielded to be bought and sold,
When Senators were made by Choice, not Gold,
Ere yet the Cunning were accounted Wise, ...(5)
And Kings began to see with other's Eyes;
Pythagoras his Precepts did rehearse,
And taught the System of the Universe;
Altho' the Observations then were few,
Just were his Reasonings, his Conjectures true: ....(10)

Verse (line) 8. And taught the System of the Universe;

The System of the Universe, as taught by Pythagoras, Philolaus, and others of the Ancients, is the same, which was since reviv'd by Copernicus, allow'd by all the unprejudic'd of the Moderns, and at last demonstrated by Sir Isaac Newton. The first Figure will give a clear Idea of it. All the Difference between the modern and ancient System, is only what is added to it since the Invention of the Telescope, viz. The four Satellites, or Moons of JUPITER discover'd by Galilæo: The ring of SATURN (a thin flat Body encompassing it without touching) and one of his Satellites discover'd by Huygens, and the other four Satellites of that Planet first seen by Cassini; The Phases of VENUS and MERCURY, like those of the Moon, these Planets appearing full, when they are beyond the Sun, halv'd when at their greatest apparent Distance (or Elongation) from the Sun, as at the point P, Q; (Fig.1.) and horned, as they pass between the Sun and the Earth, not directly in Line with the Centre of the Earth and Sun; because, then they lose all their Right in Respect of us, and appear like black Spots passing across the Sun's Face, or Disc, as VENUS is drawn in this Figure. Lastly, The Orbit of a Comet, which was first settled by Sir Isaac Newton, who has given us a Method from three Observations to determine the Path of a Comet, so as to be able to know where a Comet will pass as long as long as it is visible; how near it will go to the Sun; with what increasing Velocity it will approach towards it; and with what decreasing Velocity it will recede from it, after it has pass'd by it. Dr Halley has settled the whole Time of the Revolution of some of the Comets, so as to be able to foretel their Return, and to describe that remaining Part of their Orbit, in which they are invisible by Reason of their great Distance from the Sun which enlightens, and from us who should see them.

> Men's Minds he from their Prepossessions won,
> Taught that the Earth a double Course did run,
> Diurnal round it self, and Annu'al round the Sun,
> That the bright Globe, from his Æthereal Throne,
> With Rays diffusive on the Planets shone, ...(15)
> And, whilst they all revolv'd, was fix'd alone.
> What made the Planets in such Order move,
> He said, was Harmony and mutual Love.
> The Music of the Spheres did represent.
> That ancient Harmony of Government: ....(20)

Verse 19. The Music of the Spheres did represent.

The Harmonical Proportions, which Pythogras observ'd to obtain in the Motion of the Heavenly Bodies, was taken to be real Music by the Ignorant; who fancy'd, that the Spheres (or hollow Spherical Shells, suppos'd to carry the Planets in them) rubbing against one another, produc'd melodious Sounds, but that the Music could not be heard, by reason of the great Distance.

When Kings are not ambitious yet to gain
Other's Dominions, but their own maintain;
When, to protect, they only bore the Sway,
And Love, not Fear, taught Subjects to obey.
But when the Lust of Pow'r and Gold began   ....(25)
With Fury, to invade the Breast of Man,
Princes grew fond of arbitrary Sway,
And to each lawless Passion giving Way,
Strove not to merit Heaven but Earth possess'd'
And crush'd the People whom they should have bless'd.   ....(30)
Astronomy then took another Face,
Perplex'd with new and false Hypotheses.
Usurping Ptolemy depos'd the Sun,
And fix'd the Earth unequal to the Throne.
This Ptolemaick Scheme, his Scholars saw, ...(35)
No way agreed with the Phænomena:

Verse 33. Usurping Ptolemy depos'd the Sun, &c.

Ptolemy suppos'd the Earth to be in the Center of the World, encompass'd with many Orbs or Spheres, one within another. The first immediately encompassing the Earth, he called the Sphere of Air, the next the Sphere of Æther, then the Sphere of Fire: After followed seven other Solid Transparent Shells, which were said to carry the Planets in them, from West to East in the following order, viz. the Moon, Mercury, Venus, the Sun, Mars, Jupiter, and Saturn; then a Sphere called the Primum Mobile (or first Mover) encompassing all, and suppos'd to carry the whole Machine of the Universe round from East to West, in 24 Hours, without disturbing the particular Motions of each Sphere. But afterwards for solving some apparent Motions in the Heavens, not taken notice of before, the Followers of Ptolemy contrived three other Spheres or Heavens, between Saturn's Heaven and the Primum Mobile, which he calls the First, Second, and Third Chrystalline,

The second Figure represents the Ptolemaick System, wherein we have omitted the three Crystallines, and the Sphere of Air, Æther, and Fire, to avoid confusion.

But yet resolv'd that System should obtain,
Us'd all their Arts his Tenets to maintain;
A Revolution in the Earth to shun,
Immense Velocity they gave the Sun;   ....(40)

Verse 37. But yet resolv'd that System should obtain, Immense Velocity they gave the Sun;

The Ptolemaick System was very well receiv'd among the Vulgar, and such as were not accustom'd to consider the Difference between apparent and real Motion. If a Man, who had never seen or heard of a Ship, should be carried into the Cabin of a large Man of War with his eyes blind-folded; and whilst the Ship was sailing with a steady Motion, should have the

Bandage taken off, he would not be sensible of his being carried along; but would imagine Rocks, Buoys, and other fixed Objects, which he passed by, to be carried the contrary way; and, if he did not reflect, he would think the very Shores, with the Trees and Houses, also to move. So the unphilosophical part of Mankind, (who look upon the Sun and Moon to be but small Bodies, and the Planets and fixed Stars much smaller, whilst they believe the Earth to be immensely greater, and alone to deserve the Name of the World) cannot conceive their own Habitation to move, but look upon such as assert it to be ridiculously whimsical, or to design to impose upon Mankind with a Cant of hard Words, and out of the way Notions. But when Astronomers found the Sun's great Distance and apparent Magnitude, that he must be far greater then the Earth,; then they thought it (at least) as reasonable to solve the Appearances of Day and Night, and of the Seasons by attributing two Motions to the Earth, One about its Axis in twenty four Hours to explain the first, and another about the Sun in a Year to account for the last. But such as would always have the Holy Scriptures taken in a literal Sense (as if the Divine Revelation, which was given us to teach us Morality, and our Articles of Faith, had also been intended to instruct us in philosophy) quoting several Passages to disprove the Motion of the Earth, declared it Heresy to assert that it moved; and therefore chose rather to quit the greater Probability, and find Expedients to maintain the contrary Opinion. For the Objections against the Motion of the Earth, by Reason of Weight and Bulk, vanishes at once when we consider that the Sun is about ten Hundred Thousand times bigger, and above two Hundred Thousand times heavier; and that, to produce only the Different Seasons, it must, in the Space of one Year, run through an Orbit whose Semidiameter is above eighty Millions of Miles long; but when Day and Night comes to be considered, then the Sun must be supposed to run through that whole Orbit in twenty four Hours, which is Motion incredibly swift, being three Hundred and sixty five than the Annual Motion of the Earth, or 540666 Miles in one Minute, which is 25200 Times swifter than a Cannon Ball: Whereas a Revolution of the Earth about its Axis in 24 Hours, will as clearly explain that Phenomenon.

The System of Tycho Brahe, who supposes all the Planets except the Earth and Moon to Move round the Sun, and yet that the vast Sun with all of them revolving about him is carried round our little Globe the Earth, is so absurd, that the bare sight of the Scheme (Figure 3d) is enough to confute that Supposition. Neither have I made any mention of it in the Poem; because we can never suppose any Thing to have happened in any Government so improbable, as that a Powerful Sun should be so far influenced by a Planet as to be carried about at his Pleasure; when at the same time the other great Officers move regularly in their Orbits, especially when they have Mars amongst them.

> Then Solid Orbs with strain'd Invention found,
> To shew how Planets might be carry'd round
> But when th' Observers, who the Heav'ns survey'd,
> Perceiv'd the Planets sometimes retrograde,
> Sometimes directly mov'd with hasty Pace, ...(45)
> Sometimes more slow, then, stopping in their Race,

[Desaguliers, as ever, concerned with concurrent rather than outmoded science]

Appendix One

Verse 44. Perceiv'd the Planets sometimes retrograde, Sometimes directly mov'd with hasty Pace, Sometimes more slow, then stopping in their Race, &c.

The Planets, in reality, are always direct; that is, Move according to the Order of the Signs, running through the Constellations from Aries to Taurus, and so on through Gemini, Cancer, &c. but by reason that the Observer is carried along with the Earth on which he stands, while he is insensible of his own Motion the Planets appear to him to go sometimes backwards among the fix'd stars, and sometimes go much faster, then much slower, and also now and then to stand still, (that is to keep the same apparent Distance in respect of the fixed Stars about them) in which different Cases they are said to be either Direct, Retrograde or Stationary, as may be seen in Fig. 4 and 5.

The 4th Figure shews the apparent Irregularity of Mars's Motion, which will serve to explain the Cause of those Appearances in the other two superior Planets, viz. Jupiter and Saturn.

But for the sake of such Readers as are wholly unacquainted with Astronomy, I beg leave to begin with the Explication of some Things necessary to be known, before I consider these Stations and Retrogradations, &c.

When we look out in a clear Night, we distinguish the Planets from the fixed Stars by their not twinkling as the fixed Stars do, (or what is more certain) by the Telescope, which will magnifie them, whilst the fix'd Stars are not magnified, but rather diminished by it. The Observations of one Night or two only shew us such Planets as we then see together with the fixed Stars about them rising in the East, getting to their greatest Height in the South, and setting in the West, as we see the Sun do in the Day time, and the Moon those Nights when it shines.

This seems to be performed by a Motion of the whole Conclave of the Heavens in 24 Hours, call'd by Ptolemy the Motion of the first Mover (Primum Mobile) but that Motion is only such apparently; for it is the Revolution of the Earth about its own Center the contrary way, (viz. from West to East) in the same Time, which cause the Appearance of Rising and Setting, in the Heavenly Bodies.

Now when we come to take notice of the Moon, or any other of the Planets for several Nights successively, we find that those Bodies do not appear to Rise and Set and Move along with the same Stars, but creep on softly towards the East, so as to Rise and Set later than the Stars which they accompanied before. This is called Proper Motion of the Planets, and is owing to their revolving round the Sun, in Orbits that are nearly circular, which Revolution they always perform in a certain Period of Time, viz, Mercury in 87 Days, or near three Months; Venus in 224 Days, or a little more than seven Months; the Earth (which makes the Sun seem to move in the same Manner) in a year; Jupiter in almost twelve Years, and Saturn in almost Thirty; and the Moon moves about the Earth in twenty seven Days, and about seven Hours.

If an Observer were removed from the Earth, to the Center of the Sun, and supposed to have the Prospect of the Heavens from thence, he would see all the fix'd Stars in the same Order, and the same apparent Magnitude as we see them from the Earth; for though the distance from us to the Sun is above 80 Millions of Miles, yet all that Distance is but a Point when compared with the Distance of the fix'd Stars.

Now such an Observer would lose sight of what we call the Diurnal Motion, and only behold the Planets shifting their Places among the fix'd Stars in their regular Orbits, or Ovals nearly circular, which though different from one another, yet all of them have the Sun for their

Center (or rather, in Terms of Art, the Sun is in one of the two Foci of those Orbits) and take up but a very small Breadth in the Heavens, which Breadth or Belt is called the Zodiac.

If a Line be supposed to be drawn from the Observer's Eye, through the Center of the Planet, quite to the fix'd Stars, the Place where that Line terminates among the fix'd Stars is called the Place of the Planet ... Heliocentrick Place, if the Observer be supposed in the center of the Sun; Geocentrick Place, supposing the Observer in the Center of the Earth. If the Planets were near to the fix'd Stars, vastly distant both from the Sun and the Earth the Heliocentrick and Geocentrick Places would always be nearly the same; but as they are near to the Sun, and one another, in comparison of the Distance of the fix'd Stars (Saturn the most remote, not being 10 times further from the Sun, than the Earth) the Heliocentrick and Geocentrick Place of the Planets must differ very much sometimes, and never be precisely the same, but when the Sun, Earth and Planets, have their Centers directly in line.

Since then, as I have already said, the Planets if seen from the Sun, would appear to move perfectly regular (only appearing to be largest in their Perihelion, or when nearest the Sun; and least in their Aphelion, or when furthest from it) it is plain that as we see them from the Earth, the shifting of the Observer's Place, as well as that of the Planet, must give their regular Motion very irregular Appearances: Accordingly Astronomers, when they come more nicely to observe the proper Motion of the Planets, found that as they went Eastwards among the fix'd Stars, they moved sometimes faster, and sometimes slower; that they sometime continued in the same place, (that is rose, set, and appeared to be carried among the same Stars) for some Days; nay, that sometimes they moved towards the West among the Stars, and therefore said that the Planets were Direct, Stationary and Retrograde; while the Moon (because it does really move round the Earth) has none of those Appearances.

This gave a great Shock to those who believed the Earth to be fixed in the Center of the World; but it is easily accounted for, when once the Diurnal and Annual Motion of the Earth are allowed. For Example, Let us suppose Mars (Fig. 4.) to be at B, and to move from West to East that is from B, to D, F, K, P, &c. If seen from the Sun, Mars will appear among the fix'd Stars, to move according to the Order of the Signs, viz. from ♎ to ♏, ♐, and so on to ♑, ♒, &c. through the twelve parts of the Zodiac distinguished by the said Signs and Characters, in a very regular Manner; but the Appearances will be quite otherwise, when that Planet is seen from the Earth. The Earth being at A and Mars at B, Mars will appear at ♎ among the Fix'd Stars, the Heliocentrick and Geocentrick Place being the same; but when the Earth has moved from A, to o, as Mars moves slower than the Earth, he will only move from B to D, and (seen from the Sun) shift his Place from ♎ to ♏ through the Arc ♎ ♏, but seen from the Earth it will appear to have gone faster, viz. through the Arc ♎1: then when the Earth is got to E, Mars will only be got to F, its Heliocentrick Place being a, as it has been describ'd among the fix'd Stars the Arc ♏ a; but its Geocentrick Place is 2, and (seen from the Earth) it will appear to have moved much faster describing the Arc 1 2.

Whilst the Earth moves from E to G, Mars will move from F to H, its Heliocentrick Motion, (which is uniform) being from a to b; but seen from the Earth, it has not appeared to move at all but has been Stationary in its Geocentrick Place 2.

As the Earth moves from G, through I, to L, Mars in his Orbit moves from H, through K, to M, describing among fix'd Stars by its Heliocentrick Motion the Arc b c, but seen from the Earth, it will appear to have described the Arc 2 3. by a Retrograde Motion, or contrary to the Order of the Signs, that is from East to West.

And here it is to be observed, that in this Motion, when Mars was at K, and the Earth at I, the Heliocentrick and Geocentrick Place was the same, viz. at ♑.

As the Earth goes from L to N, and Mars from M to O; Mars (seen from the Earth) will all the while appear Stationary at 3, though its Heliocentrick Motion has been from c to d.

Lastly, as the Earth moves from N to A, while Mars goes from O to P, and its Heliocentrick Motion is from c to d, the Planet (seen from the Earth) does again become direct, and seems to move from 3 to 4, and so on.

It will not be improper to shew here, how the Sun, as it is seem from the Earth, appears to describe the same Orbit, that the Earth doth really describe, without Stations or Retrogradations.

When the Earth is at R (its Heliocentrick Place being in ≈) the Sun the Sun appears to be in v; and as the Earth goes through the points l, m, I, K, N, A, e, o, f, g, h, R, in its Orbit (its Heliocentrick Place moving according to the Order of the Signs) the Sun's Place will also go thro' the Points ♈, ♉, ♊, ♋, ♌, ♍, ♎, ♏, ♐, ♑, ♒, ♓, likewise according to the Order of the Signs, but always appearing in the Sign opposite to the that in which the Earth is.

If it be asked how we know the Sun to be in such and such Signs, since we cannot see the Fix'd Stars by Day; we answer, that, that Part of the Heavens which we see in the South at Midnight is directly opposite to that Part in which the Sun has appeared at Noon, and might have been perceiv'd if there had been a total Eclipse, or we had made use of a long Telescope in a dark room, to see the Stars that were about the Sun. As for Example, If an Observer in the enlightened part of the Earth a R, cannot (by reason of the great Light of the Sun) see the stars of Aries (v) when the Sun is in that Constellation; the same Observer will be carried to q seeing Libra (≈) in the South, hc will judge with certainty that the Sun is then in Aries (v) the opposite Sign.

Mercury and Venus the inferior Planets, (so called because they are nearer to the Sun than the Earth is) have also their Stations or Retrogradations, as seen from the Earth, which must be explained by a different Scheme, See the 5ᵗʰ Figure, where the Appearances of Mercury are exhibited; which will serve to explain those of Venus.

When the Earth is at A, and Mercury at a, that Planet appears among the Fix'd Stars at 1; and as the Earth moves from A to B, Mercury which moves faster, will go in its Orbit from a to b, and appear to have mov'd among the Fix'd Stars, from 1 to 2, according to the Order of the Signs, or from West to East, being then said to be Direct.

Whilst the Earth moves from B to C, and Mercury from b to c, Mercury is Stationary, not appearing to move out of point 2; but as the Earth moves from C to D, and Mercury from c to d, it appears to describe the Arc 2 ♉ among the fix'd Stars, by a Motion from East to West, or contrary to the Order of the Signs, and therefore it is then Retrograde.

As the Earth moves from D to E, and Mercury from d to e, it becomes Stationary at ♉. Lastly, as the Earth moves from E to F, and Mercury from e to f, Mercury does again become Direct, appearing to move in the Arc ♉3, from West to East.

The Defenders of the Ptolemaick Hypothesis were sadly put to it, to give the least probable Account of the Stations and Retrogradations of the Planets. Their Solid Transparent

Orbs, or Chrystal Shells, by way of Expedient, they supposed to be much thicker than was at first imagined (*see* Fig. 2d) and within their Thickness placed little Circles, call'd Epicycles, supposing the Planet to go round in the Epicycle, whilst the Orb call'd a Deferent (or Excentrick because the Earth was supposed not to be exactly in its Center) went round from West to East, carrying round the Epicycle, together with the Planet moving in it: Only the Sun's and Moon's Orb had no Epicycle.

Suppose Mercury's Orb (in this 2d scheme) to move from West to East, and that Mercury being in the Epicycle at A moves faster from A to B, than the Deferent carries the Epicycle, then Mercury will appear Retrograde. Whilst a Planet (*see* Venus's Orb) moves in its Epicycle from E to F, it appears Stationary; but when it moves from C to D, (*see* Mars's Orb) it will be Direct, and have its greatest Velocity: And all the Planets must appear smaller in their Apogee (or greatest Distance from the Earth) and biggest in their Perigee, or least Distance. But when the Times and Places of the Stations and Retrogradations, and the different apparent Magnitudes of the Planets came to be nicely observed; the Ptolemaicks, to make their Hypothesis or supposition agree with the Observations, were force to enlarge some of their Epicycles, so far as to make monstrous Systems, especially in regard to Mars, where the Epicycle must be larger than the Deferent in order to solve the Phenomena, or Appearances of that Planet.

These and other Absurdities, make King Alphonsus say to some Astronomers, who were explaining to him the Ptolemaick System ... that, if he had been God, he would have made the World, in a more plain and simple Manner; which he said rather to ridicule those Philosophers, than out of spirit of Prophaneness.

> For this, Expedients must invented be,
> That, with it self, their System may agree,
> And keep some shew of Probability.
> Within their thicken'd Orbs new Orbs they made, ...(50)
> Each Deferent its Epicycle had,
> So round the Earth the Planets still convey'd.
> Wheels within Wheels complex'd, they thus involve,
> And yet Appearances but falsely solve.
> Like Peter's Coat, the System burthen'd grew, ...(55)
> Keeping old Fashions, adding still the new.
> But when Philosophers explor'd the Skies,
> With Galilæo's new-invented Eyes;
> In Mercury and Venus, then were shewn
> Phases like those of the inconstant Moon: ....(60)

Verse 55. Like Peter's Coat, the System burthen'd grew, Keeping old Fashions, adding still the new.

See the Story of Lord Peter in Dr S...ts Tale of a Tub.

Verse 58. With Galilæo's new-invented Eyes;
Telescopes.

Verse 60. Phases like those of the inconstant Moon:

The Phases of Mercury and Venus, whereby they seem horned, halv'd and full, and Mercury and Venus, appearing as Spots upon the Face of the Sun, as they pass in direct Line between the Sun and Earth, and their never being in Opposition to the Sun (that is on the other Side of the Earth) Shews that those Bodies do indubitably move round the Sun, as has been explained in Annotation to Verse the 8th, and shewn in the first Figure.

And like black Patches, crossing Phæbus Face,
These two inferior Globes were seen to pass;

> Which shew'd the right of Sol to hold the central Place.
> Comets, (no longer Meteors to be fear'd,
> As threatening Vengeance with their Tail or Beard.) ....(65)
> By Telescopes, were, lasting Bodies, prov'd,
> Like Planets, in revolving Orbits mov'd,

Verse 64. Comets, no longer Meteors to be fear'd,

See Dr Halley's Verses on Sir Isaac Newton's *Principia*. The Third edition.

Jam patet, horrificis qui sit via flexa Cometis;
Jam non miramur barbati Phænomena Astri.

> Whose Course destroyed the Ptolemaick World,
> And all the Crystal Orbs in ruin hurl'd;
> Prov'd 'em ficticious, as in empty Space they whirl'd. ....(70)
> So when a Minor King the Scepter Sways,
> (Some Kings, alas! are Minor all their Days)
> How hard's the Task, how great must be the Pains
> For envi'd Regents to direct the Reins?
> While jarring Parties rend the sinking State, ...(75)
> Machines, by Art, must bear the tott'ring Weight;
> Statesmen perplex'd, with their Invention rack't
> One Day make Edicts, and the next retract;
> The Coin, to Day, shall in its Value rise,
> Tomorrow, Money sinks and Credit dies; ....(80)
> One Year the Minds are rais'd by specious Schemes,
> The next, are wak'd from all their golden Dreams:
> And now th' Expedient is a Foreign War;
> And now soft Peace can ne'er be brought too dear;
> And now the Work is done by Plots and Panick Fear. ....(85)
> But bright Urania, heavenly Virgin, say,

How th' ancient System made again its Way,
And, that Consistency might be restor'd,
The Sun became, once more, the central Lord;
What Praises to Copernicus are due, ...(90)
Who gave the Motions, and the Places, true;
But what the Causes of those Motions were,
He thought himself unable to declare.
Cartesius after, undertook in vain,
By Vortices, those Causes to explain; ....(95)
With fertile Brain contriv'd, what seem'd to be
An easy, probable, Philosophy;
No conjuring Terms or Geometrick Spells;
His gentle Readers might be Beaux and Belles.

Verse 94. Cartesius after, undertook, in vain, By Vortices, those Causes to explain.

Cartesius said, that the whole Mundane Space was full of Matter; and that our System, the Sun in revolving upon its Axis, carried the Cælestial Matter about it round in a Whirl Pool, or Vortex (Tourbillion) which Matter in its Motion carried all the Planets round the Sun; but that every Planet had at the same time a small Vortex moving about it as it turn'd on its Axis, whereby it made some of the Bodies about it fall on its Surface, and carried others round. The Earth for Example, Jupiter and Saturn (as he said) moved their Satellites by their particular Vorteses.

Not knowing that Comets returned again or revolved in Orbits, He asserted that they were only Planets flying from one System to another, when one great Vortex got ground of another; for he gave each fix'd Star a Vortex and Planets to go round it, believing with the rest of the Modern Philosophers that every fix'd Star is a Sun. But Sir Isaac Newton, and other Mathematicians and Experimental Philosophers have shewn the Motion of Planets in Vortices, to be inconsistent with Observations and Appearances, and a Plenum in Nature to be impossible.

In Plato's School none cou'd admitted be, ...(100)
Unless instructed in Geometry;
But here it might, (nay must) aside be laid,
And Calculations that distract the Head.
Thus got its Vogue the Physical Romance,
Condemn'd in England, but believ'd in France; ....(105)
For the bold Britons, who all Tyrants hate,
In Sciences as well as in the State,
Examin'd with experimental Eyes,
The Vortices of the Cartesian Skies,
Which try'd by Facts and mathematick Test, ...(110)

Appendix One

Their inconsistent Principles confess'd,
And Jarring Motions hast'ning to inactive Rest.
But Newton the unparallel'd, whose Name
No Time will wear out of the Book of Fame,
Cælestial Science has promoted more, ...(115)
Than all the Sages that have shone before.
Nature compell'd, his piercing Mind, obeys,
And gladly shews him all her secret Ways;
'Gainst Mathematicks she has no Defence,
And yields t' experimental Consequence: ....(120)
His tow'ring Genius, from its certain Cause,
Ev'ry Appearance, a priori draws,
And shews th' Almighty Architect's unalter'd Laws.
That Sol self-pois'd in Æther does reside,
And thence exerts his Virtue far and wide; ....(125)

Verse 113. But Newton the unparallel'd, whose Name No Time will wear out of the Book of Fame, ... And yields t' experimental Consequence: His towering Genius, from its certain cause, &c.

See Dr Halley's Verses before mentioned

> *Quæ toties animos veterum torsore sophorum*
> *Obvia conspicimus ....*
> *Talia monstrantem celebrate ....*
> *NEWTONUM clausi referantem scrinia veri ....*
> *Intima panduntur victi penetralia Cæli ....*
> *....... nubem pellente mathsi,*
> *Quæ Superum penetrare demos, atque ardua cæli,*
> *Scandere sublimis genii concessit acumem.*

Verse 124. That Sol self-pois'd in Æther does reside, and thence exerts his Virtue far and wide; &c.

See Dr Halley's Verses,

> *Sol solio residens ad se jubet omnia prono*
> *Tendere descensu, nec recto tramite currus*
> *Sidereos patitur vastum per inane moveri;*
> *Sed rapit immotis, se centro, singula gyris.*

Like Ministers attending e'ery Glance,
Six Worlds sweep round his Throne in Mystick Dance.
He turns their Motion from its devious Course,
And bends their Orbits by Attractive Force,

The Key to Modern Freemasonry

Verse 128. He turns their Motion from its devious Course, And bends their Orbits by Attractive, &c.

From the Laws of Attraction (or Gravity) Sir Isaac Newton has deducted effects which are found by Observation; and nothing (besides the mathematical Demonstration it self) can be more certain Proof of that Attraction, whose Laws and Manner of Acting, that incomparable Philosopher has explain'd, than to find that the Motion of the Cælestial Bodies, answer exactly to the Effects that their mutual Attractions must produce.

Thus when it had been objected by some considerable Men against Sir Isaac Newton, that it would appear by the Motion of Jupiter and Saturn in their Conjunction (that is, as they pass by one another) that Attraction was a mere supposition, Astronomers observed those Planets in and near the last Conjunction with so much more Care, and found that did so affect one another, as they came near, as to disturb each others Motion, and thereby shew their mutual Attraction; which Appearance cannot be observed in the inferior Planets, in respect to each other, because they are so small, and the Sun so large and so near to them, that the Action of the Sun on them as He causes the to describe their Orbs, makes their Action on each other so insensible as to escape Observation.

This will be better understood, by looking into the Cause of the Motion of the Planets and Comets round the Sun, which will be easily conceiv'd by any one that will be at the Pains to read what follows with some Attention.

A Body once put into Motion, endeavours to continue in the State of Motion, and would forever go on in a right Line, never coming to Rest, unless some other Force equal to the first, or several Forces (whose joint Actions are equal to the first Impulse) do, at once, or successively destroy its Motion.

A Body thus moving is said to go on with its projectile Force, from whose rectilineal Direction, it cannot be turn'd to move in a Curve, unless there be some Force continually acting to turn it out of the right Line, and the Moment that such a Force ceases to act, the Body will fly out of the Curve in a right Line, called a Tangent to that Curve.

To illustrate this, let us suppose a Stone whirl'd round in a Sling before it is thrown forward; we are sensible, by the Pull which we feel, that the Stone is endeavouring to fly out of the Curve or circle wherein we whirl it; and that that Force, with which it endeavours to get loose, is the greater, the swifter the Stone is whirld round. Such a Force is called centrifugal, and the pull on the String which retains the Stone, is called a centripetal Force.

Let us suppose, for Example, that a Stone placed at the Point A. (Fig 6.) has an Impulse given it in the Direction A B, but at the same Time is held by the String S A; instead of going to C, it will go to D in the Curve A D O B. Since the Stone is drawn from C, (the Place which the projectile Force would have carried it to) to D, D C will represent the centrifugal Force, whereby it stretches the String in that Direction, and the Force of the String, or centripetal Force, which act in the contrary Direction C D, will also be equal to the centrifugal Force.

Now let S represent the Sun, whose Attraction is instead of the Force of the String abovementioned; and A a Planet, whose Tendency is to move in a Line A B: It is evident from what has been said, that if the Attraction of the Sun, which gives the Planet a Tendency towards S, be so proportioned to the projectile Force of the Planet, as to carry it to D, it will turn it still out of its rectilineal Way, whereby it endeavours to fly off at D in the Tangent D E, and make it go on to O, and then to B, and so to A D, &c. so that it shall continually describe the Orbit A D O B.

Appendix One

If A D be an Arc of a Circle, of which S is the Center, the Curve A D O B will be a Circle, and the Planet will move with equal swiftness in every Part of the Orbit. But if the Attraction had been greater in respect to the projectile Force, so as to draw the Planet out of its rectilineal way as far as d, then the Curve would have been an Ellipse, or Oval, and the Sun would have been in one of its Foci (or Centers, as the Workmen call them) and the Planet would have described one half of the Orbit, (viz. from the Aphelion to the Perihelion) with a swiftness or Velocity, uniformly accelerated, and the other half of the Orbit, (viz. from the Perihelion to the Aphelion) with a Velocity uniformly decreasing.

But this will appear plain, by looking on the 7th Figure, where the Planet at A, endeavouring to move in the Tangent A a, is by the Attraction of the Sun S, drawn to B instead of M, at which Point being nearer the Sun, it is more strongly Attracted, and consequently accelerated; but as the centrifugal Force, is proportionable to the Swiftness of the Body carried round, the Planet endeavours to fly off in a Tangent B b, its centrifugal Force being increased in the same Proportion as the centripetal Force, or Attraction of the Sun. The Planet being more attracted as it come nearer to the Sun at C, D, and P, has also proportionably more centrifugal Force, arising from its increased Velocity; and continually increasing its Endeavour to fly off in the Tangents C c, D d, P p, does thereby escape being drawn into the Sun.

When the Planet which came from A, the Aphelion, is got to P, the Perihelion; it moves through the Points P,E,F,G, quite to A with a retarded Motion, the centripetal and centrifugal Forces, equally and gradually decreasing in the same Manner as they increased before: For in this half of the Orbit, the Direction of the Sun's attractive Force, is contrary to (or at obtuse Angles, with) the Direction of the projectile Force, as appears most plainly at the Points C, and F, S C the Direction of the Sun's Attraction, making an acute Angle with the Tangent C c, when the Planet is at C; but when the Planet is at F, S F the Direction of the Sun's Attraction makes an obtuse Angle with the Tangent F f, is less than it was in E e and P p, but greater than in G g, or A a.

N.B. S is one Focus of the Ellipse, and Z the other.

It is evident that the longer (or the more eccentrick) the Ellipse is, the greater will be the Difference of Velocity. This is not very sensible in the Planets, whose elliptick Orbits differ but little from Circles, but yet enough to fall under Observation; for it is owing to this that our Summer is eight Days longer than our Winter; but in Comets, which move in very long Ellipses, the Motion is incredibly swift in the Perihelion, and as slow proportionably in the Aphelion; the Comet which appeared in 1680 and 1681, describing in less than a year, all that part of its Orbit in which it was visible to us; though its whole Revolution is not performed in less than 575 Years.

> His Pow'r, coer'ed by Laws, still leaves them free, ...(130)
> Directs but not Destroys, their Liberty;
> Tho' fast and slow, yet regular they move,
> (Projectile Force restrain'd by mutual Love,)
> And reigning thus with limited Command,

He holds a lasting Scepter in his Hand. ....(135)
By his Example, in their endless Race,
The Primaries lead their Satellites,
Who guided, not enslav'd, their Orbits run,
Attend their Chiefs, but still respect the Sun,

Salute him as they go, and his Dominion own. ....(140)

Verse 137. The Primaries lead their Satellites,
Who guided, not enslav'd, their Orbits run,
Attend their Chiefs, but still respect the Sun,
Salute him as they go, and his Dominion own.

Saturn, Jupiter, Mars, the Earth, Venus and Mercury, are called Primaries, or Primary Planets, because they move round the Sun; but the five Moons, or Planets which move around Saturn, and the four which about Jupiter, and the Moon which goes around our Earth, as they all attend their Primaries in their Revolution about the Sun, are called secondary Planets, or Satellites.

Now these Satellites are kept in their Orbits, by the Attraction of their Primaries and hindered from flying out in a straight Line or Tangent, in the same manner as the Primaries are carried round the Sun, as has been explained in the last Note. This Motion of the Satellites would be entirely regular, were it not for the Sun's Attraction, which (though it is not near enough to hinder them from going round their Primaries) disturbs their Motions; as is very evident in the Moon, which moves with more or less Velocity, and whose Orbit becomes more or less Convex according to its Position in respect of the Sun: And that seeming Irregularity of the Moon, is so various and intricate that no Body could invent any tolerable Hypothesis to solve it, or Numbers express it, till Sir Isaac Newton demonstrated every Appearance and Motion of that variable Planet to be the Effect of the mutual Attraction of the Sun, Earth and Moon, according to the different Positions of these three Bodies. *See* Dr Halley's Verses, before Sir Isaac Newton's *Principia*.

Desimus hinc tandem, qua causa argentea Phœbe,
Passibus hand æquis graditur, cur subdita nulli
Hactenus Astronomo numerorum fræna recuset.

Comets, with swiftness, far, at distance, fly,
To seek remoter Regions in the Sky;
But tho' from Sol, with rapid haste, they roll'd
They move more slowly as they feel the cold;
Languid, forlorn, and dark, their State they moan, ...(145)
Despairing when in their Aphelion.
But Phæbus, soften'd by Penitence,

On them benignly sheds his Influence,
Recalls the Wanderers, who slowly move
At first, but hasten as they feel his Love: ....(150)

Verse 141. Comets, with swiftness, far, at distance, fly, To seek .... and dark, their State they moan, Despairing when in their Aphelion.

As Comets move from their Perihelion (or their nearest Place to the Sun in their Orbit) to the Aphelion (or greatest Distance from the Sun,) they begin their Motion with Celerity, but go on slower and slower until they get to the Aphelion, from whence the Motion continually increases till they come back to the Perihelion; just as a Cannon Ball shot upwards, being attracted by our Earth, moves slower and slower, till it got up to its utmost Height, from whence it descends with an accelerated Motion. *See* the last Note but one, where we have explain'd the Motion of a Comet.

To him for Mercy bend, sue, and prevail;
Then Atoms crowd to furnish out their Tail.
By Newton's help, 'tis evidently seen
Attraction governs all the World's Machine.
But now my cautious Must consider well ....(155)
How nice it is to draw a Parallel:

Verse 151. To him for Mercy bend, sue, and prevail; Then Atoms crowd to furnish out their Tail.

As Comets begin to come near the Sun, their Orbits which was almost at a right Line, bends very quick; and as they approach the Sun its great Heat makes the Comet throw out a Vapour, or Exhalation in great Quantity, which Vapour is always carried in a Direction opposite to the Sun, and being shin'd upon by the Sun, gives a View of what is called the Comets Tail', which Tail is of prodigious Length, just after the Comet has passed the Sun, if the Comet went very near it; as happen'd to the Comet seen in 1680, and 1681, which passed so very near the Sun's Surface as to receive a Degree of Heat 2000 times greater than our culinary Fires (or Iron when it is red hot) and to throw out a Tail as long as the Distance from the Earth to the Sun, which is above 80 Millions of Miles.
As the Comet recedes from the Sun, its apparent Magnitude decreases, till at last both Comet and Tail become invisible, when they are about as far from us as Jupiter, but still we must make allowances for the bigness of the Comet, some being nearly a big as the Earth, and others very little bigger than the Moon.

Nor dare the Actions of crown'd Heads to scan:
(At least within the Memory of Man)
If th' Errors of Copernicus may be
Apply'd to ought within this Century, ...(160)
When e'er the want of understanding Laws,
In Government, might some wrong Measures cause,

His Bodies rightly plac'd still rolling on,
Will represent our fix'd Succession,
To which alone th' united Britons owe, ...(165)
All the sure Happiness they feel below.
Nor let the Whims of the Cartesian Scheme,
In Politicks be taken for thy Theme,
Nor say that any Prince shou'd e'er be meant,
By Phæbus, in his Vortex, indolent, ...(170)
Suff'ring each Globe a Vortex of his own,
Whose jarring Motions shook their Master's Throne,
Who governing by Fear, instead of Love,
Comets, from ours, to other Systems drove.
But boldly let thy perfect Model be, ...(175)
NEWTON's (the only true) Philosophy:
Now sing of Princes deeply vers'd in Laws,

And Truth will crown thee with a just Applause;

Verse 174. Comets, from ours, to other Systems drove.

See the Note on Verse 94, concerning Cartesius's Account of Comets.

Rouse up thy Spirits, and exalt thy Voice
Loud as the Shouts, that speak the People's Joys;   ....(180)
When MAJESTY diffusive Rays imparts,
And kindles Zeal in all the British Hearts,
When all the Powers of the Throne we See
Exerted, to maintain our Liberty:
When Ministers within their Orbits move, ...(185)
Honour their King, and shew each other Love:
When all Distinctions cease, except it be
Who shall the most excel in Loyalty:
Comets from far, now gladly wou'd return,
And, pardon'd, with more faithful Ardour burn.   ....(190)
ATTRACTION now in all the Realm is seen,
To bless the Reign of GEORGE and CAROLINE.

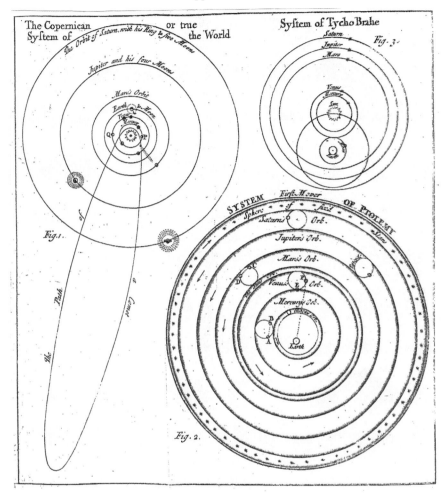

Figure Appx 1. Desaguliers' figures 1 to 3.

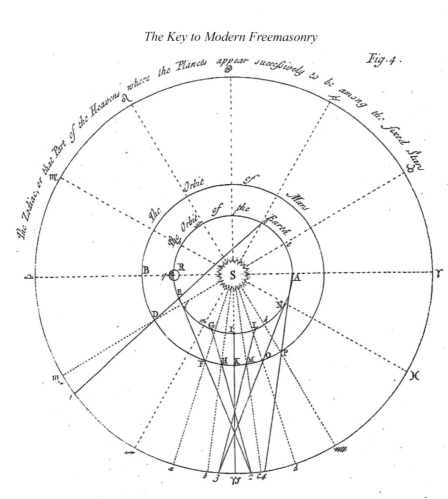

Figure Appx 2. Desaguliers' figure 4.

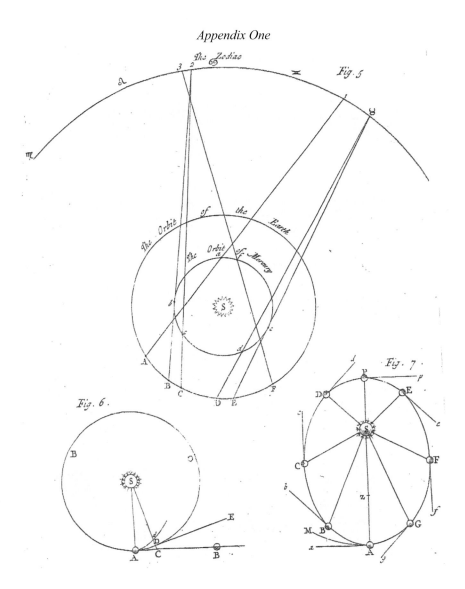

Figure Appx 3. Desaguliers' figures 5 to 7.

Appendix Two – Lexicography

Introduction

When one begins to research into a particular subject area the natural disposition is to look in a dictionary to determine its precise meaning and the derivation of any specifically associated terminology. When in this instance the various elements of the Liberal Arts and Sciences were considered each term was in present day use and their respective meaning so familiar that the temptation was to take them for granted. However, almost from the very beginning it became clear that this assumption was premature since it was realised that there was a problem of determining what precisely was meant by the different expressions; even with respect to our present understanding. The problem becomes much more difficult when an attempt is made to determine what the Founders' interpretation of these terms was likely to have been. The somewhat obscure philosophy of language has been touched upon in the main text and will not be extended here, but clearly the Founders must have derived their understanding from somewhere; for example: we know that a table is a table because as a child we were repeatedly told that objects of this form are tables and hence have a ready understanding of those features that constitute a table. The Founders and their tutors would have most likely relied upon definitions from authoritative sources such as the dictionaries available to them. At this juncture we are concerned with the problem of contrasting their understanding of the Liberal Arts and Sciences with our own and an obvious way would be to consult the dictionaries of their time.

General reading, other research and indeed the ritual itself indicates that their interpretation had remained somewhat conservative and dated and that one possible reason for this was their desire not to cause (religious) offence. Perhaps the best known and when put into context possibly the greatest, dictionary ever compiled is that of Dr Samuel Johnson and although the enormity of his task meant that it was not published in full until the 1780s, he had in practice been engaged on this work from the middle of the 1700s. This seemed a good place to start and whilst most definitions were easily recognisable as those currently accepted, others were markedly different. To those not familiar with his actual Dictionary, it is of interest to note that it is written in an apologetic style; in that having outlined his definition of the word, he then defers to the writing of others, quoting extracts of their work by way of illustration, thereby leaving in many cases a considerable degree of ambiguity, but by setting it out in this way he acknowledged the inherent dilemma facing all lexicographers. In this instance it was not quite so important since it was evident that there had been a considerable shift in the definition in a significant

456

number of these words even in the short time between 1723 and the publication of his Dictionary and so interpretation was going to be an inescapable factor.

1723 was chosen because that was the year that Ephraim Chambers' *Encyclopaedia* or perhaps more notably under its supplementary title: *Universal Dictionary of the Arts and Sciences* was published. This was a joint venture by a number of people (mostly booksellers), but an interesting factor is that one of the group was a certain John Senex (Junior Grand Warden in 1723). However, in order to determine more fully the importance of literal definition it was considered preferable to verify any assumption more thoroughly by consulting other sources. This task was assisted greatly by reference to a well researched book on lexicography by Jonathan Green.[1] The principal object of his book was to discuss lexicography both in terms of its history and its importance in framing society. The history was of particular interest since it revealed that dictionaries in the English language had existed well before the formation of the Premier Grand Lodge. It reiterated the impact of comprehension on the philosophical thought, but more importantly it showed the dependence of precise definition on the mechanics of society, such as the interpretation of laws and Acts of Parliament. Clearly it is impractical to give all the definitions of all the seven elements of the Liberal Arts and Science and significantly those subjects not included or strangely omitted and so representative examples are given.

However, before actually listing the relevant definitions it is interesting to note, that the three early dictionaries of 1676, 1702, 1721 and various editions of a fourth in 1704, 1715 and 1725 show an exponential sophistication with time, but the version of *Chambers' Dictionary* published in 1723, with which John Senex's was associated, would, if viewed in isolation, appear to be a quantum leap and so when in 1736 Nathanial Bailey revised his rather slender 1721 dictionary into a massive tome, one might be tempted by comparison to assume that he had relied heavily on that version, but yet again it acts as a warning with respect to the level of trust one can have when happening upon a contemporary document. Clearly the laws on plagiarism were different then and so it may well be that John Harris had in turn lighted upon someone else's (perhaps unknown) dictionary, but if that is not the case then it would appear that his version first published 1704 was the original masterpiece; from which others, to put it kindly, took guidance if not simply copied. Although Johnson was acclaimed for his scholarship in terms of his penmanship and scholarly referencing, it has to be tempered by these earlier versions, such as say that of Chambers, in that he had clearly made extensive use of and in essence copied them, both in content and basic format. Given the degree of knowledge at the time the substance of Harris's and Chambers's work was extremely detailed and informed and allowing that they were the first, exhibiting such scholarship, in relative terms they may be considered the more remarkable. Much credit goes to these small bands of publishers for their bold enterprise and especially people such as Senex because of their support for the Arts and Sciences in other areas of learning. Lastly; to what extent the Founders and/or those who constructed early ritual obtained aspects of their scholarship from Harris's or latterly Chambers's base material can only be estimated, but because of their comparative lateness it is likely that it would have only supplemented their earlier education which must have been derived from an understanding of contemporary dictionaries and the content of other learned texts extant at that time.

It is hoped that the subtleties of the various changes can be seen, typically Bailey's inclusion of the 'four elements' in his 1721 version and their omission in his 1730s edition (perhaps reflecting the general uncertainty at that time); but equally important their partial reappearance in *Johnson's Dictionary* some fifty years later. Or similarly Harris's definition of 'Arithmetic': 'Tis Divided into two general Branches: Common *Arithmetick*, and *Algebra – see below*. Note! Any item in the respective definitions listed below, that is not actually part of the dictionary named, is (bracketed).

Elisha Coles: *English Dictionary*: (sub-titled) 'Explaining Difficult terms that are useful in Divinity, Husbandry, Physick, Phylosophy, Law, Navigation, Mathematics and other Arts and Sciences.[2]

Grammar: The Art of speaking, reading or writing.

Rhetoric (No entry).

Logic: The art of reasoning or disputation.

Arithmetic: The art of numbering.

Geometry: The art of measuring (the earth).

Astronomy: A knowledge of the Stars and their courses.

Music: (No entry).

Electricity: (No entry),

Magnetism: (No entry)..

Gravity: (No entry).

Fire: (No entry).

Earth: (No entry).

Water: (No entry).

Air: (No entry).

John Kersey: *New English Dictionary*[3]

Grammar: The Art of right reading, writing and speaking.

Rhetoric: The Art of speaking well or eloquently.

Logic: The Art of reasoning or discoursing.

Arithmetic: The Art of numbering.

Geometry: The art of measuring all sorts of solid bodies or plain figures, distances etc.

Astronomy: The science that shows how to measure and motion of the stars and other heavenly bodies.

Music: or the Art of singing and playing upon musical instruments.
Electricity: (No entry).

Magnetism: (No entry).

Gravity: soberness or religiousness. (The others below have this connotation, but are not reported, it is included here to show that he had at least considered the word).

Fire: The element of Fire. (Defining itself!)

Earth: The earth or ground. (Again defining itself!)

Water: (No entry).

Air: an element.

John Harris: *Lexicon Technicum or The universal Dictionary of the Arts and Sciences*. London Volumes 1 and 2. 1704.[4] Editions: 1715,[5] 1725.[6] Because in his subsequent editions most entries of interest here did not change greatly, if at all, for easy reference, such definitions as there are, are kept under the one heading.

Grammar: 1704 edition: is the Art of Speaking and Writing any Language truly. It takes its Name from the Greek word *Gramma*, which signifies a letter, because it treateth primarily of the Formation of Articulated Sounds, which are represented by Letters.

1715 edition: *ibid* 1704.
1725 edition: *ibid* 1704.

Rhetoric: (There is no entry for this in any edition.)

Logic(k): 1704 edition: the art of right Thinking, or using our Rational Faculty aright: And the Power or Force of Reason, unassisted by Art, is called Natural Logick. (he then reflects on various aspects of this basic theme, but one of these is of interest here): (by Logick) we are thereby assured that we make a right Use of our Reason: for the Consideration of Rules, begets a more fervent Application and attentive Industry of the mind.
1715 edition: *ibid.* 1704.
1725 edition: *ibid.* 1704.

Arithmetic(k)1704. edition: is the art of numbering truly; or, as some define it, the science of discrete Quantity; 'Tis Divided into two general Branches: Common *Arithmetick*, and *Algebra.*
1715 edition: *ibid.* 1704.
1725 edition: *ibid.* 1704.

Geometry: 1704 edition: Originally signifies the Art of measuring the Earth, or any Distances or Dimensions on or within it; but 'tis now used for the Science of Quantity, Extension, or Magnitude, abstractedly considered without any regard to Matter. (he then goes on to discuss its origins such as the Egyptians, etc. He then gives a further definition): Geometry. Is usually divided into Speculative and Practical: the former of which contemplate and treats of the Properties of continued Quantity abstractedly: And the latter applies these Speculations and Theorems to Use and Practice, and to the benefit and Advantage of Mankind.
1715 edition: *ibid.* 1704.
1725 edition: *ibid.* 1704.

Astronomy: 1704 edition: Is a Mathematical Science, reaching the Knowledge of the stars or Heavenly Bodies, and their magnitudes, Distances, Eclipses, Order ad Motions: by some 'tis taken in so large a sense, as to contain it also the Doctrines of the mundane System, the Laws of Planetary Motions, etc. which others reckon as a part of Physicks or Natural Philosphy.
1715 edition: *ibid.* 1704.
1725 edition: *ibid.* 1704

Music(k): 1704 edition: is one of the Seven Sciences commonly called *Liberal*, and comprehended also among the *Mathematical*; as having for its Object *Discrete Quality* or *Number*, but not considering it in the Abstract. Like Arithmetick; but with relation to *Time* and *Sound*, in order to make delightful sound. This Science is also Theoretical , which examineth the Nature and Properties of Concords and Discords, explaining the Proportions between them by Numbers: and Practical, which teaches not only Composition, that is to say, the manner of Composing all sorts of Tunes and Airs; but also the Art of singing with the Voice, or playing upon Musical Instruments etc.

1715 edition: *ibid.* 1704.

1725 edition: *ibid.* 1704.

Electricity: 1704 edition: is the Quality that Amber, Jet, Sealing Wax etc. have of attracting all light Bodies to them, when the attracting Body is rubbed or chafed. And this is most probably he effect of *Material effluvium* (as the Noble Mr. Boyle expresses it in his Notes on the Quality) issuing from, and return to the *Electrical Body*, and assisted by Cases by the External Air. For solution to this Phenomenon there are several Hypotheses, and all mechanical. (he then cites various theories attributed to earlier workers, but in effects prefers that of Robert Boyle).

1715 edition: *ibid.* 1704.

1725 edition: *ibid.* 1704.

Magnetism: 1704 Edition: or *Magnetical Attraction*, or, as some are pleased to call it, *Coition*; is effected {say they} by the *Effluvia* of each Body, which drive away the Air between Iron and the stone ; so that the Union of the Stone and the Iron is occasioned by the joint Protrusion or Pulsion of the Air behind each. But this Opinion is refuted by Mr. *Boyle's* Experiment of a Loadstone being equally Vigorous and Attractive in the exhausted Receiver, as in open Air.

1715 edition: *ibid.* 1704.

1725 edition: *ibid.* 1704.

Gravity: 1704 edition: or as it may be called the *Vis Centripeta*, is that Quality by which all Heavenly Bodies tend towards the centre of the Earth, accelerating the Motion as they come nearer towards it. And this Admirable and Universal Law of Nature is that which {generally speaking} keeps all Bodies in those Places and Stations which they are designed for. (he then goes on to give an indication of the theories those illustrious people who had come before, but settles for the more up to date people, but not as yet Newton)

1715 edition: *ibid.* 1704.

1725. edition: *ibid.* 1704. (strangely he keeps the text but then includes a section on Newton, but does not effuse as one might expect)

Fire: There is no reference to fire in any of the editions

Earth: 1704 edition: The Surface of the whole Earth Mr. Keil, in his Examination of Dr. *Burnet's Theory*, makes to be 170981012 *Italian* Miles, the *Italian* Mile is a little less than the English one. (he then goes into great detail on measure and methods of doing so, but at the end provides the following definition): Which the Chymists call *Terra Damnata*, and *Caput Mortuum*, is the last of the five Chymical Principles, and is that which remains after all other Principles are extracted by Distillation, Calcination etc.
1715 edition: *ibid.* 1704.
1725 edition: *ibid.* 1704, (but minus the latter definition of Earth).

Water: 1704 edition: which the Chymists call Phlegm, is the 4th of the 5 Chymical Principles, and one of the Passive ones. 'Tis never drawn pure and unmixed, which makes it little more detersive than common Water. (he then goes on to give some understanding of how water dissolves other compounds, but does not truly explain the processes involved).
1715 edition: *ibid.* 1704.
1725 edition: *ibid.* 1704.

Air: 1704 edition: The atmospherical air in which we breath in Diaphonous, compressible and Dilatable Fluid Body, covering the Earth and the Sea to a great height above the highest mountains and differs from the Æther {among other things} in this, that it Reflects the rays of the Moon and other Remote Luminaries. This air seems to consist of 3 different Kinds of *Corpuscles*, or Small Bodies.1 Such as are carried up into it in the Form of *Exhelations* of *Vapours* from the Earth, Sea and all Animal, Vegetable and Mineral Bodies, by means of the Sun's or Subterraneal Heat. 2 There are yet more subtle sorts of Particles in the Air, which we may reckon emitted into it by Heavenly Bodies; and also the Magnetick Streams of the Globe of the Earth and Water. But: (here he goes on to list other more obscure postulations, but having done so he then spend pages on weight, compressing and evacuation air; giving very detail description of equipment for conducting such experiments).
1715 edition: *ibid.* 1704, (except the section on calculation is extended).
1725 edition: *ibid.* 1715.

Nathaniel Bailey (published first dictionary in 1721 entitled) *A Universal Etymological English Dictionary*. (He subsequently published)[7] *Dictionarium Britannicum* (in 1736).[8, 9]

(In the entries below both definitions are given in respect of date).

Grammar: The art of speaking any language truly.

(Sub): The art of speaking and writing truly, established by custom, reason, authority, also a book that contains the rules of any language.

Rhetoric: The art of speaking well and eloquently.

(Sub). The art of speaking copiously on a subject with all the advantages of beauty and force.

Logic(k): The art of thinking, reasoning or making right use of the rational Faculty.

(Sub). The art of guiding our reason in the knowledge of things, as well for our instruction as that of others. It consists in the reflection which man have made of the four principal operations of the mind.

Arithmetic(k): a science which teaches the Art of Accounting, all the powers and properties of Number.

(Sub. As above).

Geometry(ie): originally signifies the Art of measuring the Earth, or any distances, or dimensions on or within it, but now used for the science of Extension abstractedly coincided without any regard to matter.
(Sub. As above).

Astronomy: The science which teaches the knowledge of the Heavenly Bodies, showing their Magnitudes, Distances, Eclipses, Order and Motion.

(Sub. As above, but in addition): In an extension of science it is understood to signify or comprehend the doctrine of the system of the World or theory of the Universe and the primary laws of Nature. (It adds that it is one of the liberal Arts and Sciences).

Music(k): belonging to Mathematicks which considers the Number, times of sounds in order to make delightful Harmony. Art of playing, singing and making music on instruments.

(Sub. As above, but in addition: but he expands into a larger section even more esoteric in parts).

Electricity: The quality that Amber, Jet sealing wax have attracting light bodies to them when rubbed or chafed.

(Sub. As above, but adds to the list of things affected).

Magnetism: The power that a loadstone has of attracting iron.

(Sub. As above, but he now recognises that other things such as iron may be seen to have the same capacity as loadstone).

Gravity: weight or quantity by which all heavy bodies are attracted to the Centre of the Earth.

(Sub. As above, but now accepts that all things attract each other in some proportion).

Fire: One of the four elements.

(Sub). It exists in itself and which we properly call fire, of itself it is imperceptible, and only discovers itself by certain effects which it produces on bodies.

Earth: One of the four elements. Also the last of the Five Chymical Principles.

(Sub. As above, but now he drops all elusion to the four elements).

Water: (No entry).

(Sub. but elsewhere: more usually called flegm, is the fourth of the Five 'Chymical Principles' and one of the 'passive' ones).

Air: One of the four elements, wherein we breathe.

(Sub. No longer defined as one of the four (Vulgar) elements, but there are extended references to different behavioural aspects).

Ephraim Chambers (1680 – 1740) *Encyclopaedia*: or universal dictionary of Arts and Sciences 2 Vols.[10]

Grammar: The art of speaking rightly, that of expressing ones thoughts, by sign mutually agreed on for that purpose. (It goes on to consider grammar as being essentially that of the English Language).

Rhetoric: The art of copiously speaking on any subject with all beauty and force. (It goes on to point out that it may also be used in terms of persuasion and argument).

Logic: The art of thinking justly, or making right use of our rational Faculties in defining, and reasoning. (It goes on to give various instances, but also refers to 'judgement' in the sense of correct 'just' application of behaviour both personal and civic).

Arithmetic: The art of numbering; or that part of mathematicks which considers the Powers and Properties of numbers and teaches how to compute or calculate truly, and with expedition and ease. (The Section goes on to include most of the

Appendix Two

mathematics that can be assigned to numbers).

Geometry: The science, or doctrine of Extension or extended things that is lines, surfaces and solids. (The work is here expanded considerably and goes on to elaborate the philosophical aspects, including association with the Liberal Arts and Sciences).

Astronomy: is properly a mixed mathematical science, whereby we become acquainted with the Cælestial Bodies, their Magnitude, Motions, Distances, Periods, Eclipses, etc. – *see* Mathematicks. (It goes on to give some understanding of the word astronomy in a more intensified sense; included under 'the Theory of the Universe' etc).

Music: Science of sound capable of producing Melody and Harmony, or the art of disposing or conducting sound. (It is clear that by this time music had taken on some of the more modern aspects, but later the definition goes on): …..The first respecting the Order and Harmony that obtains among the Cælestial minds, the other relations and Order of everything else in the Universe, etc.

Electricity: No entry (rather surprisingly).

Magnetism: term used by some Chymists to signify a certain virtue where one thing becomes affected at the same time as another, either in the same or different manner. (It goes on to give a comparatively sophisticated concept of a magnet – *see* bibs. of Earl of Abercorn G.M.1726 and Brook Taylor).

Gravity: All the several principles of all Bodies in Nature gravitate to all Particles of all Bodies. (It goes on to describe the interpretation of other philosophers from Aristotle to Newton, but also has sections on the centre of gravity of objects and its application to hydraulics etc).

Fire: Pure or elemental Fire of itself is imperceptible; and only discovers itself by certain effects, which it produces in bodies; which effects are only learnt by observing changes that arise in those bodies. (It is an extensive entry and elsewhere): Fire makes on the vulgar or Peripetetick (from Aristotle's disposition to discuss philosophical issues as he strolled around) Elements defined as hot, dry etc. (Essentially retaining the Aristotlian device of relative qualities).

Earth: In Natural Philosophy; one of the four Vulgar or Peripatetical elements. Defined as simple, dry, and cold substances; and as such an ingredient in the composition of all Natural Bodies. (It then gives Aristotle's version implying authority). Later: Earth, in Chymistry, is the fourth of the Chymical Elements, or Principles, into which all bodies are resolvable by Fire – (this is essentially presented as the definitive definition, although the extension leaves some room for speculation).

Water: in Physicks, a simple, fluid and liquid body; reputed the third of the four Vulgar elements. (Here there are extensive references to all forms of water and there is a general scepticism towards the Aristotelian version of water).

Air: Air in Physicks, thin, fluid, transparent, compressible and dilatable Body; surrounding the terraqueous Globe to a considerable height – *see* Earth. Air was considered by some of the ancients as an element; but then by element they understood a different thing from what we do. (It goes on to say that air is not simple).

Samuel Johnson: *Dictionary of the English Language.*[11] Note: that Johnson's Dictionary gives trite definition and then goes on to give copious example of other peoples definitions in use, this will not be attempted here.

Grammar: The art of speaking correctly. The art which teaches the relations of words to each other.

Rhetoric: The art of speaking not merely with propriety, but with art and elegance.

Logic(k): The art of reasoning – one of the seven sciences.

Arithmetic: Science of number: the art of computation.

Geometry: Originally signifies the art of measuring the earth, or any distances or dimension on or within it, but is now used for the science of quantity, extension, or magnitude abstractly considered without regard to matter; usually divided into speculative and practical forms of which contemplate and treats of the properties of contained quantity abstractly, the latter applies there, to speculation and theorems to use and practice.

Astronomy: Mixed mathematical science teaching the knowledge of the celestial bodies, their magnitudes, motions, distances, periods, eclipses and order. (He then goes on to talk of the Greeks and others and their understanding of the heavens).

Music: The science of harmonical sound.

Electricity: The property in some bodies, whereby, when rubbed so as to grow warm, they draw little bits of paper, or such like substances to them. (He goes on to describe certain experiments that demonstrate the extent of this behaviour).

Magnetism: Power of the loadstone.

Gravity: Weight, heaviness, tendency to the centre. That quality by which all heavenly bodies tend towards the centre, accelerating the motion the nearer they approach towards it, true philosophy has shown to be unsolvable by any hypothesis and resolved it into the immediate will of the Creator. (This entry then goes on to give further explanation).

Fire: The igneous element.

Earth: The element distinct from air, fire and water; soil; terrene matter.

Water: (Having made a distinction in the definition of 'Earth' there is no reference whatsoever to the three elements. He then proceeds to give Newton's definition which is extremely imprecise).

Air: The element encompassing the terraqueous Globe. (Again there is no reference to the four elements).

Addendum:

From an early point in the research for this book it was realized that etymology with respect to scientific terms was likely to play an important part in the ultimate assessment and so the initial Appendix 2 above was created. However, somewhat later in the course of discussion with a respected historian the question of what would be the likely understanding of 'Nature and Science' of an informed person during the formative years of Premier Grand Lodge arose – suggesting that they were comparatively vague, non specific, terms. Since 'Nature and Science' are central planks in the structure of Masonic ritual and his comments seemed to be of sufficient force it seemed appropriate to at least see how the volumes consulted above defined them. Whether he was justified or not must be left to the reader, but at least in the case of 'Science' it would seem that by 1720 there was a pronounced shift to it being the notion of 'analytical/demonstrable'. Again note that all matter not actually in the text of the dictionaries is bracketed.

Coles, E., *English Dictionary* (1678):

Nature: (No entry).

Science: skill, knowledge.

Kersey, J., New English Dictionary (1702).

Nature: the original disposition, properties or qualities of things.

Science: knowledge or skill.

Under this heading: The seven (note none defined to be Arts) liberal Sciences:

Grammar, Logick, Rhetorick, Arithmetick, Geometry, Astronomy and Musick.

Harris, John, *Lexicon Technicum or The universal Dictionary of the Arts and Sciences.*

Nature: 1704 edition: This Word has usually these Significations: First and more strictly, it is taken for the particular disposition of *Parts* in some Particular *Body*; as we say, it is the Nature of *Fishes* to live in the *Water*. Secondly it is taken more largely for the Universal Definition of all *Bodies*; and in his sense 'tis nothing else but the *Devine Providence*, forasmuch as it Directs and Governs all things by certain *Rules* and *Laws*, accommodated to the *Natures* of things. Thirdly it is taken for the Essence of anything; not *Corporeal*, with the *Attributes* belonging to it; Thus we say, That is the *Nature of God* to be *Good*, and the Nature of the *Soul* to *Think*.
1715 edition: *ibid* 1704.
1725 edition: *ibid* 1704.

Science: 1704 edition: is the knowledge founded upon, or acquired by clear, certain, and self-evident Principles.
1715 edition: *ibid* 1704.
1725 edition: *ibid* 1704.

Bailey, N., *A universal Etymological English Dictionary* (1721).

Nature: A peculiar Disposition of Parts in some peculiar Body, also the Universal Definition of all Bodies: also the essence of any Thing with its Attributes; also Condition, Disposition, humour.

Science: Knowledge. Learning, Skill, property that which is founded upon clear certain and Self evident Principles:

Elements: among Natural Philosophers and Chymists are the simplest bodies that can be, neither made of one another, nor of anything else, but at which all things are made. Elements: among Artists signifies the Principles of any Art or Science or those Definitions, axioms and postulates, upon which any Art or Science is founded. Fifth Element of Magnitude [in geometry] are a point, a line and a surface.

Bailey, N., *Dictionarium Britannicum* (1736).

Nature (1): the system of the world, the machine of the universe, or the assemblance of all created beings; the universal definition of all bodies; also the government of divine providence, directing all things by certain rules and laws.

Nature (2): is the essence of all incorporeal things, as it is the nature of the soul to think, of God to be good, and the like.

Nature (3): is the principle of all created things.

Science (1): as opposed to art (note exclusion), is a formed system of any branch of knowledge, comprehending the doctrine or theory of things, without immediate application (abstraction) of it to any uses or offices of life.

Science (2): knowledge, learning, skill etc.

Science (3): a clear and certain knowledge of any thing found upon self-evident principles and demonstrations.

Science (4): [in God given divines] is distinguished into three kinds;
the science of mere knowledge, whereby he knows himself and all things possible. (of vision) whereby he knows all things he has resolved to do, or to permit, in the same order in which he has resolved to do and permit them. an intermediate Science whereby he knows what angels and men will do in certain cases and certain circumstances if he resolves to bring them about.

(As stated in the introduction the Chambers' *Encyclopaedia* and Johnson's *Dictionary* are formidable pieces of work and under each of the above items there are considerable entries and so these will be – fairly it is hoped – précised).

Chambers, E., *Chamber's Encyclopaedia* (1723):

Nature (1): used for a 'System of the world' – The machine of the Universe, or of Assemblage of all created Beings.

Nature (2): in a more confined sense: comprehends the several kinds of beings, Created and Increated, Spiritual and Corporeal.

Nature (3): in a still more refined sense: Essence of all things of the Soul (*à la* Johnson – quotes Robert Boyle).

Nature (4): Used to establish order; here appends a long list.

Nature (5): Power related to any Body, especially those long lived.

Nature (6): The action of Providence. (Once again *à la* Johnson – or perhaps it should be the other way round – he then quotes and to some degree explains Newton's three basic laws e.g. 'a body will continue.......' etc).

Science (1): in Philosophy, a clear and certain knowledge of anything, founded on self-evident Principles or Demonstration. (Again a much extended explanation much related to God's governance of these things).

Science (2): Particularly used for a formed system of any branch of knowledge, comprehending Doctrines, Reason and Theory of things, without immediate Application thereof to any Uses or Offices of life; in which sense the word is used in Opposition to Art.

Johnson's *Dictionary* (1784):

Nature (1): An imaginary being supposed to preside over the material and animal world.

Nature (2): the nature and properties of things, by which it is discriminated from others.

Nature (3): the constitution of an animated body.

Nature (4): disposition of the mind.

Nature (5): the regular course of things.

Nature (6): the compass of natural existence.

Nature (7): the constitution and appearance of things.

Nature (8): natural affection, reverence, native scuration (this word was not even defined in his own Dictionary – it may be just a misspelling).

Nature (9): the state of operation of the natural world.

Nature (10): sort of species.

Nature (11): sentiments or usages adapted to nature or conforming to truth or reality.

Nature (12): Physicks, the science which teaches the qualities of things.

Science (1): Knowledge.

Science (2): Certainty grounded on demonstration.

Science (3): Art attained by precepts, or built on principles.

Science (4): Any art or species of knowledge.

Science (5): one of the seven Liberal Arts and Sciences.

Appendix Two

(Note that even at this later period he listed all seven of them and it is of interest that he feels obliged to retain them or at least reluctant to omit them).

References

1. Green, J., *Chasing the Sun* (Jonathan Cape, London, 1966).

2. Coles, E., *English Dictionary* (Samual Couch, London, 1670).

3. Kersey, J., *New English Dictionary* (Publisher unknown, London, 1702) *.

4. Harris, J., *Lexicon Technicum or The universal Dictionary of the Arts and Sciences*, 2 Vols (Unspecified, London, 1704).

5. *Ibid*,1715 edition.

6. *Ibid*,1725 edition.

7. Bailey, N., *Dictionarium Britannicum* (T. Cox, London, 1736).

8. Bailey, N., *A Universal Etymological English Dictionary* (E. Bell *et al*., London, 1721).

9. Bailey, N., *op. cit.*

10. Chambers, E., *Chambers Encyclopaedia: or universal dictionary of Arts and Sciences*, 2 Vols (James and John Knapton *et al*., London, 1723).

11. Johnson, S., *Dictionary of the English Language* (W. & A. Straham, London, 1784).

* Original in Paisley Public Library 1578/3136

Appendix Three

Supplementary information of the 'Set Theory' approach

In anticipation of the publication of this work a paper was given by Lawrence[1] to the *Quatuor Coronati* Lodge in which a brief explanation of the 'Set Theory' was given and another illustrative Venn diagram of the type found in Chapter Ten was used. Since such diagrams are now quite common in many forms of communication it was intended merely to distinguish the nuances of the parameters in this particular case and not to be an explanation of the technique *per se*. However, if one is to gauge from several of those who made comment on the paper, it is clear that in certain instances this is not the case and that for some there is a need for additional explanation. An attempt was therefore made in the 'Responses' section of that paper to explain the method further by use of another, but now quasi-quantified, example. Since the model used here is not significantly different to that used in the paper cited above it is prudent to assume that there will be a percentage of readers who will experience similar difficulty and so for their benefit those sections of that paper are repeated here. For completeness both the models used in the body of the actual paper and those in the subsequent reply are given below.

'Analytical model

In terms of background research the numerous parameters listed above appear overwhelming, but as is usual with all academic research confronted with such a problem the task is made possible by the introduction of caveats. In this instance two such caveats will be invoked: that in any one sector there is sufficient data for that particular purpose and that there are no significant contradictions. This research has been conducted over many years and relied upon much enquiry and numerous references [... the fruit of which is now present in this book ...] in which the analytical model is considered in greater depth, but for the purposes of the argument proffered here, it is necessary to give a brief outline of the method. In mathematics there is sub-discipline called 'set theory' which works on the presumption that artefacts may be considered to exist in identifiable groups such as human being is defined as either a man or a woman, which in turn may be placed in sub-sets of black or white, tall or short, blonde or brunette, fat or slim, vegetarian or not, European, American, Asian etc. owns a car, has a computer, etc., etc. So that whilst human beings may be described as either men or women, as each limiting factor is introduced the probability that any one person may reside uniquely in a particular group diminishes rapidly. In, say, a town where there is good demographic data the dimensions of these sets can be quantified and actual numerical analysis is possible, but where this is not so the analysis becomes subjective, but if done with care can provide a very good model of the actual situation.

Figure 1 is given as an illustration of this approach; in which it is assumed that a person from Jamaica visiting London wishes to contact a school friend of his uncle who came to a (fictitious) London borough many years ago. He knows certain facts, such as he loved cricket, that as a boy he was tall and slim, he had been brought up in a devoutly religious family, played in the school 'steel band', he knew the district in London he went to first, he believed his name was John Anderson (or something like it), but his uncle only knew him by his nickname 'Bo'. Very few 'facts' and in only one or two of these is there any degree of certainty. However, if by enquiry within the district he can get an actual lead, other factors such as the name of the school, his age within a few years, the time that he came to the UK etc., come into play and so as each of the possibilities are put in place the probability that they will all match gets narrower and narrower, until there is a high degree of certainty that the person discussed will turn out to be the person concerned.

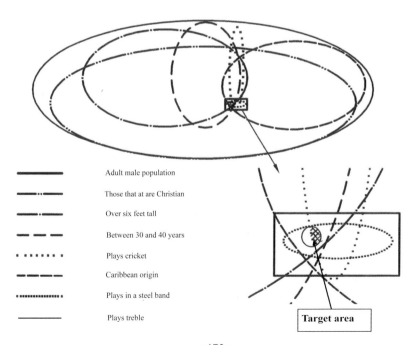

————	Adult male population
—··—··	Those that at are Christian
—·—·—	Over six feet tall
— — —	Between 30 and 40 years
· · · · · · ·	Plays cricket
—··—··	Caribbean origin
··················	Plays in a steel band
————	Plays treble

Target area

Figure 1. The supposed Venn diagram of attributes used in search of erstwhile school friend. It can be seen that as each attribute (verifiable or reasonable) is superimposed the likelihood of success becomes quasi exponential.

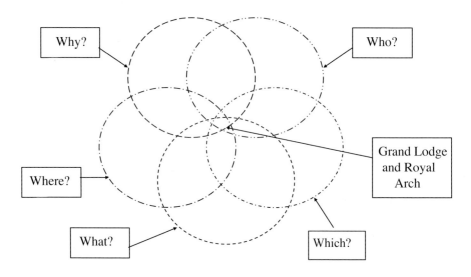

Figure 2. The symbolic representation, not to scale, of a Venn diagram used to represent the impinging factors associated with the formation of Grand Lodge and by implication the Royal Arch. Clearly when all these factors are at optimum it gives a very realistic indication of WHEN!

Of course the events surrounding the establishment of Grand Lodge are now almost three hundred years distant, but there are nonetheless many 'sets' and the same systematic argument will be utilised. Whilst in the model used in Figure 1 there are a number of demographically quantifiable facts there is little opportunity to apply such rigour to the early 1700s and it is necessary to construct an implicit model – *see* Figure 2 where the broad areas are represented. However, there are some facts, for instance there are lists of members (or at least attendees) of many lodges for that period; the principal players are known; historical documents indicate the complex and very significant interrelationship of these people outside of their Masonic activity. It is the thesis of this paper that the intense preoccupation within this community and indeed influential society in general, with nature and science provides the findings with a very large measure of confidence, if not certainty. The remaining task is to attempt by historical cross-referencing establish in a sufficiently authoritative way the content of those sets and thence by employing deductive reasoning determine the degree to which and when the common parts coincide.'

However one or two of the queries were quite strident and after some direct response to specific points the following additional explanation of the Analytical Model was attempted:

'However, since others have expressed some doubt as to the veracity of the approach I have in Figure R. (1) restated the concept by constructing three possible scenarios for the years 1723 (after the Schism), 1731 and 1738. Because these 'sets' are by nature largely subjective, in the paper I anticipated that there may be some disquiet over the apportionment of certain factors and in an attempt to avoid distraction I did not attempt to conjure up actual numbers, but rather left the relative proportions and disposition of each 'set', to the reader's understanding of the period; even so, provided this is done objectively it appears to make surprisingly little difference to the final outcome. In Figure R. (1) the major outer sets have been omitted; such as the male population in London, the number of men actually in Masonic organizations, social standing etc. and confined it to just that of any influential group that would have been needed to form Grand Lodge policy. To avoid over elaboration, other quite significant, inner sets have been omitted such as political persuasions, financial/commercial interaction, other types of social intercourse etc., all of which would add to, subtract from or leave unchanged the degree of probability of favourable conditions prevailing at any particular time.

Figure R. (1). The Venn diagram below is for illustrative purposes only since no rigorous research has been carried out to quantify the various areas. Again the levels of confidence are an estimate based upon the disposition and extent of those sets within the three sub-figures. Clearly the level of confidence increases with the number of sets or quasi-sets (such as family, social or business connections) that are introduced. Some examples of additional sets are suggested elsewhere in these responses. N.B. the need to take proper regard of each of these sets against specific criteria is far more rigorous than the usual overall (impression) assessment adopted by most historians; i.e. they were either related or not, they were either in business together or not, they were scientific members of the Royal Society or not, etc.'

A further query was how is it possible to frame any piece of data, of what ever type, into an appropriate form for inclusion into these diagrams?

'In response to his second point, it is perfectly easy to incorporate any aspect into a set, by adopting a procedure similar to that used in 'Parliamentary (U.K.) Question Time' namely to phrase the point in the form of a question e.g. would those concerned have knowledge of the early connotation of these particular words and concepts?, would they have had a more than 'passing interest' in the 7 Liberal Arts and Sciences, or would those of interest have been sympathetically disposed towards alchemic concepts etc.? Having phrased the item of interest in this way one can, after making a reasoned assessment of its validity, estimate its relative proportions and position within the general 'field' of the Venn diagram and from that gauge its influence or lack of it. For example one or two covert Roman Catholics may have remained after the schism, but would they have been in a position, or have been allowed to influence the main stream? Almost certainly not after the departure of the Duke of Wharton! That little group of Catholics would be represented within the 'set' of all members, but displaced from the zone of influence – *see* Figure R1 above (now below).'

Figure R. (1)

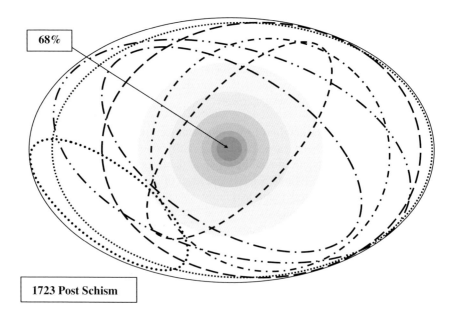

68%

1723 Post Schism

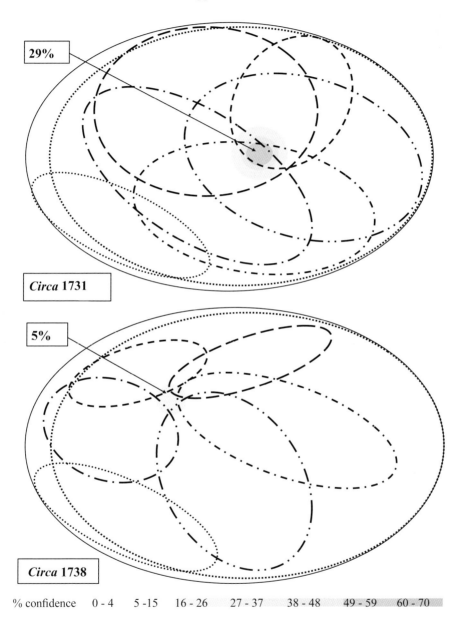

29%

Circa 1731

5%

Circa 1738

% confidence   0 - 4   5 -15   16 - 26   27 - 37   38 - 48   49 - 59   60 - 70

Line designation	Line format
Influential Group	————
Catholic disposition or sympathy towards it	·················
Protestant (declared) faith	················
Aristocrats of influence (sufficiently disposed towards action)	— — — — ·
Men with the skills to make intellectual change	— · — · — · —
Men with sufficient scientific acumen	— — — -
Theologians or extremely active authoritarians	— · — · —
Scientific/religious consistency with current thinking	— ·· — ··

References

1. Lawrence, C., 'Within and Without : the Hidden Mysteries of Nature and Science', *AQC* 118 (2005), pp. 96-98 & 122-124.

Index

Prepared by S. Brent Morris, Ph.D.